# THEORY OF FUNCTIONS

OF A

# COMPLEX VARIABLE

# THEORY OF FUNCTIONS

## OF A

# COMPLEX VARIABLE

BY

## A. R. FORSYTH
### Sc.D., LL.D., Math.D., F.R.S.

CHIEF PROFESSOR OF MATHEMATICS IN THE IMPERIAL COLLEGE OF SCIENCE
AND TECHNOLOGY, LONDON: AND SOMETIME SADLERIAN PROFESSOR OF PURE
MATHEMATICS IN THE UNIVERSITY OF CAMBRIDGE

THIRD EDITION

IN TWO VOLUMES

VOLUME I

DOVER PUBLICATIONS, INC., NEW YORK

Published in Canada by General Publishing Company, Limited, 30 Lesmill Road, Don Mills, Toronto, Ontario.

Published in the United Kingdom by Constable and Company, Limited, 10 Orange Street, London W. C. 2.

This Dover edition, first published in 1965, is an unabridged and unaltered republication of the third edition, published by Cambridge University Press in 1918.
This edition is published by special arrangement with Cambridge University Press.
This work was originally published in one volume, but is now published in two volumes.

Library of Congress Catalog Card Number: 65-17668

Manufactured in the United States of America

Dover Publications, Inc.
180 Varick Street
New York 14, N. Y.

# PREFACE.

AMONG the many advances in the progress of mathematical science during the last forty years, not the least remarkable are those in the theory of functions. The contributions that are still being made to it testify to its vitality: all the evidence points to the continuance of its growth. And, indeed, this need cause no surprise. Few subjects can boast such varied processes, based upon methods so distinct from one another as are those originated by Cauchy, by Weierstrass, and by Riemann. Each of these methods is sufficient in itself to provide a complete development; combined, they exhibit an unusual wealth of ideas and furnish unsurpassed resources in attacking new problems.

It is difficult to keep pace with the rapid growth of the literature which is due to the activity of mathematicians, especially of continental mathematicians: and there is, in consequence, sufficient reason for considering that some marshalling of the main results is at least desirable and is, perhaps, necessary. Not that there is any dearth of treatises in French and in German: but, for the most part, they either expound the processes based upon some single method or they deal with the discussion of some particular branch of the theory.

The present treatise is an attempt to give a consecutive account of what may fairly be deemed the principal branches of the whole subject. It may be that the next few years will see additions as important as those of the last few years: this account would then be insufficient for its purpose, notwithstanding the breadth of range over which it may seem at present to extend. My hope is that the book, so far as it goes, may assist mathematicians, by lessening the labour of acquiring a proper knowledge of the subject, and by indicating the main lines on which recent progress has been achieved.

No apology is offered for the size of the book. Indeed, if there were to be an apology, it would rather be on the ground of the too brief treatment of some portions and the omissions of others. The detail in the exposition of the elements of several important branches has prevented a completeness of treatment of those branches : but this fulness of initial explanations is deliberate, my opinion being that students will thereby become better qualified to read the great classical memoirs, by the study of which effective progress can best be made. And limitations of space have compelled me to exclude some branches which otherwise would have found a place. Thus the theory of functions of a real variable is left undiscussed : happily, the treatises of Dini, Stolz, Tannery, and Chrystal are sufficient to supply the omission. Again, the theory of functions of more than one complex variable receives only a passing mention ; but in this case, as in most cases, where the consideration is brief, references are given which will enable the student to follow the development to such extent as he may desire. Limitation in one other direction has been imposed : the treatise aims at dealing with the general theory of functions and it does not profess to deal with special classes of functions. I have not hesitated to use examples of special classes : but they are used merely as illustrations of the general theory, and references are given to other treatises for the detailed exposition of their properties.

The general method which is adopted is not limited so that it may conform to any single one of the three principal independent methods, due to Cauchy, to Weierstrass and to Riemann respectively : where it has been convenient to do so, I have combined ideas and processes derived from different methods.

The book may be considered as composed of five parts.

The first part, consisting of Chapters I—VII, contains the theory of uniform functions : the discussion is based upon power-series, initially connected with Cauchy's theorems in integration, and the properties established are chiefly those which are contained in the memoirs of Weierstrass and Mittag-Leffler.

The second part, consisting of Chapters VIII—XIII, contains the theory of multiform functions, and of uniform periodic functions which are derived through the inversion of integrals of algebraic functions. The method adopted in this part is Cauchy's, as used by Briot and Bouquet in their three memoirs and in their treatise on elliptic functions ; it is the method that has been followed by Hermite and others to obtain the properties of various kinds of periodic functions. A chapter has been devoted to the proof of Weierstrass's results relating to functions that possess an addition-theorem.

The third part, consisting of Chapters XIV—XVIII, contains the development of the theory of functions according to the method initiated by Riemann in his memoirs. The proof which is given of the existence-theorem is substantially due to Schwarz; in the rest of this part of the book, I have derived great assistance from Neumann's treatise on Abelian functions, from Fricke's treatise on Klein's theory of modular functions, and from many memoirs by Klein.

The fourth part, consisting of Chapters XIX and XX, treats of conformal representation. The fundamental theorem, as to the possibility of the conformal representation of surfaces upon one another, is derived from the existence-theorem: it is a curious fact that the actual solution, which has been proved to exist in general, has been obtained only for cases in which there is distinct limitation.

The fifth part, consisting of Chapters XXI and XXII, contains an introduction to the theory of Fuchsian or automorphic functions, based upon the researches of Poincaré and Klein: the discussion is restricted to the elements of this newly-developed theory.

The arrangement of the subject-matter, as indicated in this abstract of the contents, has been adopted as being the most convenient for the continuous exposition of the theory. But the arrangement does not provide an order best adapted to one who is reading the subject for the first time. I have therefore ventured to prefix to the Table of Contents a selection of Chapters that will probably form a more suitable introduction to the subject for such a reader; the remaining Chapters can then be taken in an order determined by the branch of the subject which he wishes to follow out.

In the course of the preparation of this book, I have consulted many treatises and memoirs. References to them, both general and particular, are freely made: without making precise reservations as to independent contributions of my own, I wish in this place to make a comprehensive acknowledgement of my obligations to such works. A number of examples occur in the book : most of them are extracted from memoirs, which do not lie close to the direct line of development of the general theory but contain results that provide interesting special illustrations. My intention has been to give the author's name in every case where a result has been extracted from a memoir : any omission to do so is due to inadvertence.

Substantial as has been the aid provided by the treatises and memoirs to which reference has just been made, the completion of the book in the correction of the proof-sheets has been rendered easier to me by the unstinted and untiring help rendered by two friends. To Mr William Burnside, M.A., formerly Fellow of Pembroke College, Cambridge, and now Professor of Mathematics at the Royal Naval College, Greenwich, I am under a deep debt of gratitude : he has used his great knowledge of the subject in the most generous manner, making suggestions and criticisms that have enabled me to correct errors and to improve the book in many respects. Mr H. M. Taylor, M.A., Fellow of Trinity College, Cambridge, has read the proofs with great care : the kind assistance that he has given me in this way has proved of substantial service and usefulness in correcting the sheets. I desire to recognise most gratefully my sense of the value of the work which these gentlemen have done.

It is but just on my part to state that the willing and active co-operation of the Staff of the University Press during the progress of printing has done much to lighten my labour.

It is, perhaps, too ambitious to hope that, on ground which is relatively new to English mathematics, there will be freedom from error or obscurity and that the mode of presentation in this treatise will command general approbation. In any case, my aim has been to produce a book that will assist mathematicians in acquiring a knowledge of the theory of functions : in proportion as it may prove of real service to them, will be my reward.

A. R. FORSYTH.

TRINITY COLLEGE, CAMBRIDGE,
25 *February*, 1893.

# PREFACE TO THE SECOND EDITION.

IN issuing the second edition of this treatise, I desire to express my grateful sense of the reception which has already been accorded to the book. When it was first published, I could not but fear that, if from no other reason than the breadth of range which it covers, it would contain blemishes in the way of inaccuracy and obscurity. During the preparation of the second edition, I have had the advantage of suggestions and criticisms sent to me by friends and correspondents, to whom my thanks are willingly returned for the help they thus have afforded me ; my hope is that improvement has been secured in several respects. The principal changes may be indicated briefly.

Some modifications have been made in the portion that is devoted to the theory of uniform functions : no substantial additions have been made to this part of the book, but new references are given for the sake of readers who may wish to acquaint themselves with the most recent developments.

The exposition of Schwarz's proof of the existence of various classes of functions upon a Riemann's surface has been considerably changed. The new form seems to me to be free from some of the difficulties to which exception has been taken from time to time : the general features of the proof have been retained.

Several sections have been inserted in Chapter XVIII, which are intended to serve as a simple introduction to the theory of birational transformation of algebraic equations and curves and of Riemann's surfaces. Moreover, as that part of the book is occupied with integrals of algebraic functions and with Abelian functions, it seems not unnatural that a proof of Abel's Theorem should be given, as well as some illustrations : this has been effected in some supplementary notes appended to Chapter XVIII. With minor exceptions, these additions constitute the whole of the new matter relating to algebraic functions and their integrals.

The chief omission from the contents of the former edition is caused by the transference, to the second volume of my *Theory of Differential Equations*, of the sections that discussed the properties of certain binomial differential equations of the first order. The space thus placed at my disposal has been assigned to the theory of birational transformation; and I have been enabled to keep the numbering of the paragraphs the same as in the former edition with only very few exceptions.

The increased size of the book has prevented me, even more definitely than before, from attempting to discuss some of the subjects left undiscussed in the first edition. The volume will probably be regarded as sufficiently large in its present form : I hope that it may continue to be found a useful introduction to one of the most important subjects in modern pure mathematics.

A. R. F.

TRINITY COLLEGE, CAMBRIDGE,
    31 *October*, 1900.

# PREFACE TO THE THIRD EDITION.

THE differences between the present edition and the second edition are not substantial.

The general plan of the book is unaltered; and no change has been made in the numbering of the paragraphs. Not a few detailed changes have been made in places as, for instance, in the establishment of the fundamental functions in the Weierstrass theory of elliptic functions; but some chapters remain entirely unaltered.

The theory of conformal representation is important in particular ranges of subjects such as hydrodynamics and electrostatics; so I have included a note giving some applications of that theory to some branches of mathematical physics. It is intended only as an introduction; but it may suffice to shew that many analytical results are common to these selected ranges, though they are expressed in the various vocabularies appropriate to the respective subjects.

In passing from the first edition to the second, I omitted certain sections which discussed the properties of certain differential equations of the first order. These sections are now contained in the second volume of my *Theory of Differential Equations*. Owing to their importance as illustrations of the theory of functions, I have included a note stating the results.

Here and there, throughout the book, some further examples have been added. At the end of the book, I have given a set of some two hundred miscellaneous examples, which have been collected from Cambridge examination papers. For making the collection, I am indebted to Mr C. H. Kebby, B.Sc., A.R.C.S., a demonstrator in the department of mathematics and mechanics in the Imperial College of Science and Technology, London.

The Staff of the University Press have shewn to me the same courteous consideration that I have experienced for many years;

and they have achieved the task of printing the volume within a brief period in spite of their grave depletion by the demands of this world-wide war. To all of them, who have been concerned with the book, I tender my most cordial and appreciative thanks.

A. R. F.

IMPERIAL COLLEGE OF SCIENCE AND TECHNOLOGY,
LONDON, S.W.

11 *October*, 1917.

# CONTENTS.

The following course is recommended, in the order specified, to those who are reading the subject for the first time: *The theory of uniform functions*, Chapters I—V; *Conformal representation*, Chapter XIX; *Multiform functions and uniform periodic functions*, Chapters VIII—XI; *Riemann's surfaces, and Riemann's theory of algebraic functions and their integrals*, Chapters XIV—XVI, XVIII.

## CHAPTER I.

### GENERAL INTRODUCTION.

## CHAPTER II.

### INTEGRATION OF UNIFORM FUNCTIONS.

## CHAPTER III.

### EXPANSION OF FUNCTIONS IN SERIES OF POWERS.

## CHAPTER IV.

### UNIFORM FUNCTIONS, PARTICULARLY THOSE WITHOUT ESSENTIAL
### SINGULARITIES.

# CHAPTER V.

## TRANSCENDENTAL INTEGRAL FUNCTIONS.

# CHAPTER VI.

## FUNCTIONS WITH A LIMITED NUMBER OF ESSENTIAL SINGULARITIES.

# CHAPTER VII.

### FUNCTIONS WITH UNLIMITED ESSENTIAL SINGULARITIES, AND EXPANSION IN SERIES OF FUNCTIONS.

# CHAPTER VIII.

### MULTIFORM FUNCTIONS.

## CHAPTER IX.

### PERIODS OF DEFINITE INTEGRALS, AND PERIODIC FUNCTIONS IN GENERAL.

## CHAPTER X.

### UNIFORM SIMPLY-PERIODIC AND DOUBLY-PERIODIC FUNCTIONS.

# CHAPTER XI.

## DOUBLY-PERIODIC FUNCTIONS OF THE SECOND ORDER.

# CHAPTER XII.

## PSEUDO-PERIODIC FUNCTIONS.

# CHAPTER XIII.

## FUNCTIONS POSSESSING AN ALGEBRAICAL ADDITION-THEOREM.

# CHAPTER XIV.

## CONNECTIVITY OF SURFACES.

# CHAPTER XV.

## RIEMANN'S SURFACES.

# CHAPTER XVI.

## ALGEBRAIC FUNCTIONS AND THEIR INTEGRALS.

# CHAPTER I.

## General Introduction.

**1.** Algebraical operations are either direct or inverse. Without entering into a general discussion of the nature of rational, irrational, and imaginary quantities, it will be sufficient to point out that direct algebraical operations on numbers that are positive and integral lead to numbers of the same character; and that inverse algebraical operations on numbers that are positive and integral lead to numbers, which may be negative or fractional or irrational, or to numbers which may not even fall within the class of real quantities. The simplest case of occurrence of a quantity, which is not real, is that which arises when the square root of a negative quantity is required.

Combinations of the various kinds of quantities that may occur are of the form $x + iy$, where $x$ and $y$ are real, and $i$, the non-real element of the quantity, denotes the square root of $-1$. It is found that, when quantities of this character are subjected to algebraical operations, they always lead to quantities of the same formal character; and it is therefore inferred that the most general form of algebraical quantity is $x + iy$.

Such a quantity $x + iy$, for brevity denoted by $z$, is usually called a *complex* variable*; it therefore appears that the complex variable is the most general form of algebraical quantity which obeys the fundamental laws of ordinary algebra.

**2.** The most general complex variable is that, in which the constituents $x$ and $y$ are independent of one another and (being real quantities) are separately capable of assuming all values from $-\infty$ to $+\infty$; thus a doubly-infinite variation is possible for the variable. In the case of a real variable, it is convenient to use the customary geometrical representation by measurement of distance along a straight line; so also in the case of a complex variable, it is convenient to associate a geometrical representation with the algebraical expression; and this is the well-known representation of

---

* The conjugate complex, viz. $x - iy$, is frequently denoted by $z_0$.

the variable $x + iy$ by means of a point with coordinates $x$ and $y$ referred to rectangular axes*. The complete variation of the complex variable $z$ is represented by the aggregate of all possible positions of the associated point, which is often called the point $z$; the special case of real variables being evidently included in it because, when $y = 0$, the aggregate of possible points is the line which is the range of geometrical variation of the real variable.

The variation of $z$ is said to be *continuous* when the variations of $x$ and $y$ are continuous. Continuous variation of $z$ between two given values will thus be represented by continuous variation in the position of the point $z$, that is, by a continuous curve (not necessarily of continuous curvature) between the points corresponding to the two values. But since an infinite number of curves can be drawn between two points in a plane, continuity of line is not sufficient to specify the variation of the complex variable; and, in order to indicate any special mode of variation, it is necessary to assign, either explicitly or implicitly, some determinate law connecting the variations of $x$ and $y$ or, what is the same thing, some determinate law connecting $x$ and $y$. The analytical expression of this law is the equation of the curve which represents the aggregate of values assumed by the variable between the two given values.

In such a case the variable is often said to *describe* the part of the curve between the two points. In particular, if the variable resume its initial value, the representative point must return to its initial position; and then the variable is said to describe the whole curve†.

When a given closed curve is continuously described by the variable, there are two directions in which the description can take place. From the analogy of the description of a straight line by a point representing a real variable, one of these directions is considered as positive and the other as negative. The usual convention under which one of the directions is selected as the positive direction depends upon the conception that the curve

---

* This method of geometrical representation of imaginary quantities, ordinarily assigned to Gauss, was originally developed by Argand who, in 1806, published his *Essai sur une manière de représenter les quantités imaginaires dans les constructions géométriques*. This tract was republished in 1874 as a second edition (Gauthier-Villars); an interesting preface is added to it by Hoüel, who gives an account of the earlier history of the publications associated with the theory.

Other references to the historical development are given in Chrystal's *Text-book of Algebra*, vol. i, pp. 248, 249; in Holzmüller's *Einführung in die Theorie der isogonalen Verwandschaften und der conformen Abbildungen, verbunden mit Anwendungen auf mathematische Physik*, pp. 1—10, 21—23; in Schlömilch's *Compendium der höheren Analysis*, vol. ii, p. 38 (note); and in Casorati, *Teorica delle funzioni di variabili complesse*, only one volume of which was published. In this connection, an article by Cayley (*Quart. Journ. of Math.*, vol. xxii, pp. 270—308; *Coll. Math. Papers*, t. xii, pp. 459—489) may be consulted with advantage.

† In these elementary explanations, it is unnecessary to enter into any discussion of the effects caused by the occurrence of singularities in the curve.

is the boundary, partial or complete, of some area; under it, that direction is taken to be *positive* which is such that the bounded area lies to the left of the direction of description. It is easy to see that the same direction is taken to be positive under an equivalent convention which makes it related to the normal drawn outwards from the bounded area in the same way as the positive direction of the axis of $y$ is usually related to the positive direction of the axis of $x$ in plane coordinate geometry.

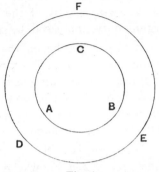

Fig. 1.

Thus in the figure (fig. 1), the positive direction of description of the outer curve for the area included by it is *DEF*; the positive direction of description of the inner curve for the area without it (say, the area excluded by it) is *ACB*; and for the area between the curves the positive direction of description of the boundary, which consists of two parts, is *DEF, ACB*.

3. Since the position of a point in a plane can be determined by means of polar coordinates, it is convenient in the discussion of complex variables to introduce two quantities corresponding to polar coordinates.

In the case of the variable $z$, one of these quantities is $(x^2 + y^2)^{\frac{1}{2}}$, the positive sign being always associated with it; it is called the *modulus** (sometimes the *absolute value*) of the variable and it is denoted, sometimes by mod. $z$, sometimes by $|z|$. The modulus of a complex variable is quite definite, and it has only one value.

The other is $\theta$, the angular coordinate of the point $z$; it is called the *argument* (and, less frequently, the *amplitude*) of the variable. It is measured in the trigonometrically positive sense, and is determined by the equations

$$x = |z| \cos \theta, \quad y = |z| \sin \theta,$$

so that $z = |z| e^{\theta i}$. The actual value depends upon the way in which the variable has acquired its value; when variation of the argument is considered, its initial value is usually taken to lie between 0 and $2\pi$ or, less frequently, between $-\pi$ and $+\pi$. The argument of a variable is not definite; it has an unlimited number of values differing from one another by integer multiples of $2\pi$. This characteristic property will be found to be of essential importance.

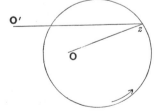

Fig. 2.

* *Der absolute Betrag* is often used by German writers.

As $z$ varies in position, the values of $|z|$ and $\theta$ vary. When $z$ has completed a positive description of a closed curve, the modulus of $z$ returns to the initial value whether the origin be without, within, or on, the curve. The argument of $z$ resumes its initial value, if the origin $O'$ (fig. 2) be without the curve; but, if the origin $O$ be within the curve, the value of the argument is increased by $2\pi$ when $z$ returns to its initial position.

If the origin be on the curve, the argument of $z$ undergoes an abrupt change by $\pi$ as $z$ passes through the origin; and the change is an increase or a decrease according as the variable approaches its limiting position on the curve from without or from within. No choice need be made between these alternatives; for care is always exercised to choose curves which do not introduce this element of doubt.

Later on, it will appear that, for the discussion of particular types of functions of $z$, a knowledge of the actual value of $z$ or the actual position of $z$ is not sufficient; account has to be taken of the fact that the argument of $z$ is not uniquely determinate.

**4.** Representation on a plane is obviously more effective for points at a finite distance from the origin than for points at a very great distance.

One method of meeting the difficulty of representing great values is to introduce a new variable $z'$ given by $z'z = 1$: the part of the new plane for $z'$ which lies quite near the origin corresponds to the part of the old plane for $z$ which is very distant. The two planes combined give a complete representation of variation of the complex variable.

Another method, in many ways more advantageous, is as follows. Draw a sphere of unit diameter, touching the $z$-plane at the origin $O$ (fig. 3) on the under side: join a point $z$ in the plane to $O'$, the other extremity of

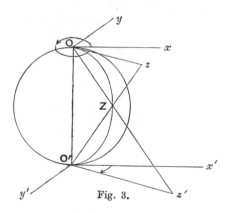

Fig. 3.

the diameter through $O$, by a straight line cutting the sphere in $Z$. Then $Z$ is a unique representative of $z$, that is, a single point on the sphere corresponds to a single point on the plane: and therefore the variable can be represented on the surface of the sphere. With this mode of representation, $O'$ evidently corresponds to an infinite value of $z$; and points at a very great distance in the $z$-plane are represented by points in the immediate vicinity of $O'$ on the sphere. The sphere thus has the advantage of putting in evidence a part of the surface on which the variations of great values of $z$ can be traced*, and of exhibiting the uniqueness of $z = \infty$ as a value of the variable, a fact that is obscured in the representation on a plane.

The former method of representation can be deduced by means of the sphere. At $O'$ draw a plane touching the sphere: and let the straight line $OZ$ cut this plane in $z'$. Then $z'$ is a point uniquely determined by $Z$ and therefore uniquely determined by $z$. In this new $z'$-plane take axes parallel to the axes in the $z$-plane.

The points $z$ and $z'$ move in the same direction in space round $OO'$ as an axis. If we make the upper side of the $z$-plane correspond to the lower side of the $z'$-plane, and take the usual positive directions in the planes, being the positive trigonometrical directions for a spectator looking at the surface of the plane in which the description takes place, we have these directions indicated by the arrows at $O$ and at $O'$ respectively, so that the senses of positive rotations in the two planes are opposite in space. Now it is evident from the geometry that $Oz$ and $O'z'$ are parallel; hence, if $\theta$ be the argument of the point $z$ and $\theta'$ that of the point $z'$, so that $\theta$ is the angle from $Ox$ to $Oz$ and $\theta'$ the angle from $O'x'$ to $O'z'$, we have

$$\theta + \theta' = 2\pi.$$

Further, by similar triangles, $\quad \dfrac{Oz}{OO'} = \dfrac{OO'}{O'z'},$

that is, $\qquad\qquad\qquad Oz \,.\, O'z' = OO'^2 = 1.$

Now, if $z$ and $z'$ be the variables, we have

$$z = Oz \,.\, e^{\theta i}, \quad z' = O'z' \,.\, e^{\theta' i},$$

so that $\qquad\qquad zz' = Oz \,.\, O'z' \,.\, e^{(\theta + \theta') i}$

$$= 1,$$

which is the former relation.

The $z'$-plane can therefore be taken as the lower side of a plane touching the sphere at $O'$ when the $z$-plane is the upper side of a plane touching it at $O$. The part of the $z$-plane at a very great distance is represented on the sphere by the part in the immediate vicinity of $O'$. Conversely, this part of the sphere is represented on the very distant part of the $z$-plane. Consequently, the portion of the sphere in the immediate vicinity of $O'$ is a space wherein the variations of infinitely great values of $z$ can be traced.

---

* This sphere is sometimes called Neumann's sphere; it is used by him for the representation of the complex variable throughout his treatise *Vorlesungen über Riemann's Theorie der Abel'schen Integrale* (Leipzig, Teubner, 2nd edition, 1884).

But it need hardly be pointed out that any special method of represent-ation of the variable is not essential to the development of the theory of functions; and, in particular, the foregoing representation of the variable, when it has very great values, merely provides a convenient method of dealing with quantities that tend to become infinite in magnitude.

**5.** The simplest propositions relating to complex variables will be assumed known. Among these are, the geometrical interpretation of opera-tions such as addition, multiplication, root-extraction; some of the relations of complex variables occurring as roots of algebraical equations with real coefficients; the elementary properties of functions of complex variables which are polynomial, or exponential, or circular, functions; and simple tests of convergence of infinite series and of infinite products*.

**6.** All ordinary operations effected on a complex variable lead, as already remarked, to other complex variables; and any definite quantity, thus obtained by operations on $z$, is necessarily a function of $z$.

But if a complex variable $w$ be given as a complex function of $x$ and $y$ without any indication of its source, the question as to whether $w$ is or is not a function of $z$ requires a consideration of the general idea of functionality.

It is convenient to postulate $u + iv$ as a form of the complex variable $w$, where $u$ and $v$ are real. Since $w$ is initially unrestricted in variation, we may so far regard the quantities $u$ and $v$ as independent and therefore as any functions of $x$ and $y$, the elements involved in $z$. But more explicit expressions for these functions are neither assigned nor supposed.

The earliest occurrence of the idea of functionality is in connection with functions of real variables; and then it is coextensive with the idea of dependence. Thus, if the value of $X$ depends on that of $x$ and on no other variable magnitude, it is customary to regard $X$ as a function of $x$; and there is usually an implication that $X$ is derived from $x$ by some series of operations†.

A detailed knowledge of $z$ determines $x$ and $y$ uniquely; hence the values of $u$ and $v$ may be considered as known and therefore also $w$. Thus the value of $w$ is dependent on that of $z$, and is independent of the values

---

* These and other introductory parts of the subject are discussed in Chrystal's *Text-book of Algebra*, Hobson's *Treatise on Plane Trigonometry*, Bromwich's *Theory of infinite series*, and Hardy's *Course of pure mathematics*.

They are also discussed at some length in the translation, by G. L. Cathcart, of Harnack's *Elements of the differential and integral calculus* (Williams and Norgate, 1891), the second and the fourth books of which contain developments that should be consulted in special relation with the first few chapters of the present treatise.

These books, together with Neumann's treatise cited in the note on p. 5, will hereafter be cited by the names of their respective authors.

† It is not important for the present purpose to keep in view such mathematical expressions as have intelligible meanings only when the independent variable is confined within limits.

of variables unconnected with $z$; therefore, with the foregoing view of functionality, $w$ is a function of $z$.

It is, however, equally consistent with that view to regard $w$ as a complex function of the two independent elements from which $z$ is constituted; and we are then led merely to the consideration of functions of two real independent variables with (possibly) imaginary coefficients.

Both of these aspects of the dependence of $w$ on $z$ require that $z$ be regarded as a composite quantity involving two independent elements which can be considered separately. Our purpose, however, is to regard $z$ as the most general form of algebraical variable and therefore as an irresoluble entity; so that, as this preliminary requirement in regard to $z$ is unsatisfied, neither of the aspects can be adopted.

**7.** Suppose that $w$ is regarded as a function of $z$ in the sense that it can be constructed by definite operations on $z$ regarded as an irresoluble magnitude, the quantities $u$ and $v$ arising subsequently to these operations by the separation of the real and the imaginary parts when $z$ is replaced by $x + iy$. It is thereby assumed that one series of operations is sufficient for the simultaneous construction of $u$ and $v$, instead of one series for $u$ and another series for $v$ as in the general case of a complex function in § 6. If this assumption be justified by the same forms resulting from the two different methods of construction, it follows that the two series of operations, which lead in the general case to $u$ and to $v$, must be equivalent to the single series and must therefore be connected by conditions; that is, $u$ and $v$ as functions of $x$ and $y$ must have their functional forms related.

We thus take

$$u + iv = w = f(z) = f(x + iy)$$

without any specification of the form of $f$. When this postulated equation is valid, we have

$$\frac{\partial w}{\partial x} = \frac{dw}{dz}\frac{\partial z}{\partial x} = f'(z) = \frac{dw}{dz},$$

$$\frac{\partial w}{\partial y} = \frac{dw}{dz}\frac{\partial z}{\partial y} = if'(z) = i\frac{dw}{dz},$$

and therefore

$$\frac{\partial w}{\partial x} = \frac{1}{i}\frac{\partial w}{\partial y} = \frac{dw}{dz} \quad\dots\dots\dots\dots\dots\dots(1),$$

equations from which the functional form has disappeared. Inserting the value of $w$, we have

$$i\frac{\partial}{\partial x}(u + iv) = \frac{\partial}{\partial y}(u + iv),$$

whence, after equating real and imaginary parts,

$$-\frac{\partial v}{\partial x} = \frac{\partial u}{\partial y}, \quad \frac{\partial u}{\partial x} = \frac{\partial v}{\partial y}\dots\dots\dots\dots\dots\dots(2).$$

These are necessary relations between the functional forms of $u$ and $v$.

These relations are easily seen to be sufficient to ensure the required functionality. For, on taking $w = u + iv$, the equations (2) at once lead to

$$\frac{\partial w}{\partial x} = \frac{1}{i} \frac{\partial w}{\partial y},$$

that is, to

$$\frac{\partial w}{\partial x} + i \frac{\partial w}{\partial y} = 0,$$

a linear partial differential equation of the first order. To obtain the most general solution, we form a subsidiary system

$$\frac{dx}{1} = \frac{dy}{i} = \frac{dw}{0}.$$

It possesses the integrals $w$, $x + iy$; then from the known theory of such equations we infer that every quantity $w$ satisfying the equation can be expressed as a function of $x + iy$, that is, of $z$. The conditions (2) are thus proved to be sufficient, as well as necessary.

**8.** The preceding determination of the necessary and sufficient conditions of functional dependence is based upon the existence of a functional form; and yet that form is not essential, for, as already remarked, it disappears from the equations of condition. Now the postulation of such a form is equivalent to an assumption that the function can be numerically calculated for each particular value of the independent variable, though the immediate expression of the assumption has disappeared in the present case. Experience of functions of real variables shews that it is often more convenient to use their properties than to possess their numerical values. This experience is confirmed by what has preceded. The essential conditions of functional dependence are the equations (1), and they express a property of the function $w$, viz., that the value of the ratio $\frac{dw}{dz}$ is the same as that of $\frac{\partial w}{\partial x}$, or, in other words, it is independent of the manner in which $dz$ ultimately vanishes by the approach of the point $z + dz$ to coincidence with the point $z$. We are thus led to an entirely different definition of functionality, viz. :—

*A complex quantity $w$ is a function of another complex quantity $z$, when they change together in such a manner that the value of $\frac{dw}{dz}$ is independent of the value of the differential element $dz$.*

This is Riemann's definition\*; we proceed to consider its significance. We have

$$\frac{dw}{dz} = \frac{du + idv}{dx + idy}$$

$$= \left( \frac{\partial u}{\partial x} + i \frac{\partial v}{\partial x} \right) \frac{dx}{dx + idy} + \left( \frac{\partial u}{\partial y} + i \frac{\partial v}{\partial y} \right) \frac{dy}{dx + idy}.$$

---

\* *Ges. Werke*, p. 5; a modified definition is adopted by him, ib., p. 81.

Let $\phi$ be the argument of $dz$; then

$$\frac{dx}{dx+idy} = \frac{\cos\phi}{\cos\phi + i\sin\phi} = \tfrac{1}{2}(1 + e^{-2\phi i}),$$

$$\frac{idy}{dx+idy} = \tfrac{1}{2}(1 - e^{-2\phi i}),$$

and therefore

$$\frac{dw}{dz} = \tfrac{1}{2}\left\{\frac{\partial u}{\partial x} + i\frac{\partial v}{\partial x} - i\frac{\partial u}{\partial y} + \frac{\partial v}{\partial y}\right\} + \tfrac{1}{2}e^{-2\phi i}\left\{\frac{\partial u}{\partial x} + i\frac{\partial v}{\partial x} + i\frac{\partial u}{\partial y} - \frac{\partial v}{\partial y}\right\}.$$

Since $\dfrac{dw}{dz}$ is to be independent of the value of the differential element $dz$, it must be independent of $\phi$ which is the argument of $dz$; hence the coefficient of $e^{-2\phi i}$ in the preceding expression must vanish, which can happen only if

$$\frac{\partial u}{\partial x} = \frac{\partial v}{\partial y}, \qquad \frac{\partial v}{\partial x} = -\frac{\partial u}{\partial y} \quad................................(2).$$

These are necessary conditions; they are evidently also sufficient to make $\dfrac{dw}{dz}$ independent of the value of $dz$ and therefore, by the definition, to secure that $w$ is a function of $z$.

By means of the conditions (2), we have

$$\frac{dw}{dz} = \frac{\partial u}{\partial x} + i\frac{\partial v}{\partial x} = \frac{\partial w}{\partial x},$$

and also

$$\frac{dw}{dz} = -i\frac{\partial u}{\partial y} + \frac{\partial v}{\partial y} = \frac{1}{i}\frac{\partial w}{\partial y},$$

agreeing with the former equations (1). They are immediately derivable from the present definition by noticing that $dx$ and $idy$ are possible forms of $dz$.

It should be remarked that equations (2) are the conditions necessary and sufficient to ensure that each of the expressions

$$udx - vdy \quad \text{and} \quad vdx + udy$$

is a perfect differential—a result of great importance in many investigations in the region of mathematical physics. Within that region, the quantities $u$ and $v$ are frequently called *conjugate functions*. Sometimes they are called *harmonic functions*; but the latter term usually has a wider significance associated with classes of functions that satisfy the equation of the potential in ordinary three-dimensional space.

When the conditions (2) are expressed, as is sometimes convenient, in terms of derivatives with regard to the modulus of $z$, say $r$, and the argument of $z$, say $\theta$, they take the new forms

$$\frac{\partial u}{\partial r} = \frac{1}{r}\frac{\partial v}{\partial \theta}, \qquad \frac{\partial v}{\partial r} = -\frac{1}{r}\frac{\partial u}{\partial \theta} \quad.........................(2)'.$$

We have so far assumed that the function has a differential coefficient—an assumption justified in the case of functions which ordinarily occur. But functions do occur which have different values in different regions of the $z$-plane, and there is then a difficulty in regard to the quantity $\frac{dw}{dz}$ at the boundaries of such regions; and functions do occur which, though themselves definite in value in a given region, do not possess a differential coefficient at all points in that region. The consideration of such functions is not of substantial importance at present: it belongs to another part of our subject.

It must not be inferred that, because $\frac{dw}{dz}$ is independent of the direction in which $dz$ vanishes when $w$ is a function of $z$, therefore $\frac{dw}{dz}$ has only one value. The number of its values is dependent on the number of values of $w$; no one of its values is dependent on $dz$.

A quantity, defined as a function by Riemann on the basis of this property, is sometimes* called an analytic function; but it seems preferable to reserve the term analytic in order that it may be associated hereafter (§ 34) with an additional quality of the functions.

**9.** In the same way as the complex variable $z$ is represented upon a plane, which is often called the $z$-plane, so the complex variable $w$ is also represented upon a plane, which is often called the $w$-plane. The two variables can obviously be represented upon different parts of the $z$-plane. The relations of the two planes to one another, or of the different parts of the same plane, when there is a functional connection between $z$ and $w$, will be the subject of later investigations; one important property will, however, be established at once.

Let $P$ and $p$ be two points in different planes, or in different parts of the same plane, representing $w$ and $z$ respectively; and suppose that $P$ and $p$ are at a finite distance from the points (if any) which cause discontinuity in the functional connection between the two variables. Let $q$ and $r$ be any two other points, $z+dz$ and $z+\delta z$, in the immediate vicinity of $p$; and let $Q$ and $R$ be the corresponding points, $w+dw$ and $w+\delta w$, in the immediate vicinity of $P$. Then

$$dw = \frac{dw}{dz}\,dz, \quad \delta w = \frac{dw}{dz}\,\delta z,$$

the value of $\frac{dw}{dz}$ being the same for both equations, because, as $w$ is a function of $z$, that quantity is independent of the differential element of $z$. Hence

$$\frac{\delta w}{dw} = \frac{\delta z}{dz},$$

on the ground that $\frac{dw}{dz}$ is neither zero nor infinite at $z$, which is assumed not

* Harnack, § 84.

to be a point of discontinuity in the functional connection. Expressing all the differential elements in terms of their moduli and arguments, let

$$dz = \sigma e^{\theta i}, \qquad dw = \eta e^{\phi i},$$
$$\delta z = \sigma' e^{\theta' i}, \qquad \delta w = \eta' e^{\phi' i},$$

and let these values be substituted in the foregoing relation; then

$$\frac{\eta'}{\eta} = \frac{\sigma'}{\sigma},$$
$$\phi' - \phi = \theta' - \theta.$$

Hence the triangles $QPR$ and $qpr$ are similar to one another, though not necessarily similarly situated. Moreover, the directions originally chosen for $pq$ and $pr$ are quite arbitrary. Thus it appears that *a functional connection between two complex variables establishes the similarity of the corresponding infinitesimal elements of those parts of two planes which are in the immediate vicinity of the points representing the two variables.*

The magnification of the $w$-plane relative to the $z$-plane at the corresponding points $P$ and $p$ is the ratio of two corresponding infinitesimal lengths, say of $QP$ and $qp$. This is the modulus of $\dfrac{dw}{dz}$; if it be denoted by $m$, we have

$$m^2 = \left| \frac{dw}{dz} \right|^2 = \left( \frac{\partial u}{\partial x} \right)^2 + \left( \frac{\partial v}{\partial x} \right)^2 = \left( \frac{\partial u}{\partial y} \right)^2 + \left( \frac{\partial v}{\partial y} \right)^2$$
$$= \frac{\partial u}{\partial x} \frac{\partial v}{\partial y} - \frac{\partial u}{\partial y} \frac{\partial v}{\partial x}.$$

Evidently the quantity $m$, in general, depends on the variables and therefore it changes from one point to another; hence a functional relation between $w$ and $z$ does not, in general, establish similarity of finite parts of the two planes corresponding to one another through the relation.

It is easy to prove that $w = az + b$, where $a$ and $b$ are constants, is the only relation which establishes similarity of finite parts; and that, with this relation, $a$ must be a real constant in order that the similar parts may be similarly situated.

If $u + iv = w = \phi(z)$, the curves $u = $ constant and $v = $ constant cut at right angles; a special case of the proposition that, if $\phi(x + iy) = u + ve^{\lambda i}$, where $\lambda$ is a real constant and $u, v$ are real, then $u = $ constant and $v = $ constant cut at an angle $\lambda$.

The process, which establishes the infinitesimal similarity of two planes by means of a functional relation between the variables of the planes, may be called the *conformal representation* of one plane on another [*].

---

[*] By Gauss (*Ges. Werke*, t. iv, p. 262) it was styled *conforme Abbildung*, the name universally adopted by German mathematicians. The French title is *représentation conforme*; and, in England, Cayley has used *orthomorphosis* and *orthomorphic transformation*.

The discussion of detailed questions connected with the conformal representation is deferred until the later part of the treatise, principally in order to group all such investigations together; but the first of the two chapters, devoted to it, need not be deferred so late, and an immediate reading of some portion of Chapter XIX. will tend to simplify many of the explanations relative to functional relations as they occur in the early chapters of this treatise.

**10.**  The analytical conditions of functionality, under either of the adopted definitions, are the equations (2).  From them it at once follows that

$$\frac{\partial^2 u}{\partial x^2} + \frac{\partial^2 u}{\partial y^2} = 0,$$

$$\frac{\partial^2 v}{\partial x^2} + \frac{\partial^2 v}{\partial y^2} = 0\,;$$

so that neither the real nor the imaginary part of a complex function can be arbitrarily assumed.

If either part be given, the other can be deduced.   For example, let $u$ be given; then we have

$$dv = \frac{\partial v}{\partial x}\,dx + \frac{\partial v}{\partial y}\,dy$$

$$= -\frac{\partial u}{\partial y}\,dx + \frac{\partial u}{\partial x}\,dy,$$

and therefore, except as to an additive constant, the value of $v$ is

$$\int\!\left(-\frac{\partial u}{\partial y}\,dx + \frac{\partial u}{\partial x}\,dy\right).$$

In particular, when $u$ is an integral function, it can be resolved into the sum of homogeneous parts

$$u_1 + u_2 + u_3 + \dots\,;$$

and then, again except as to an additive constant, $v$ can similarly be expressed as a sum of homogeneous parts

$$v_1 + v_2 + v_3 + \dots.$$

It is easy to prove that

$$mv_m = y\,\frac{\partial u_m}{\partial x} - x\,\frac{\partial u_m}{\partial y},$$

by means of which the value of $v$ can be obtained.

The case, when $u$ is homogeneous of zero dimensions, presents no difficulty; for then we have

$$u = b + a\theta,$$

$$v = c - a \log r,$$

where $a$, $b$, $c$ are constants.

Similarly for other special cases; and, in the most general case, only a quadrature is necessary.

The tests of functional dependence of one complex variable on another are of effective importance in the case when the supposed dependent variable arises in the form $u + iv$, where $u$ and $v$ are real; the tests are, of course, superfluous when $w$ is explicitly given as a function of $z$. When $w$ does arise in the form $u + iv$ and satisfies the conditions of functionality, perhaps the simplest method (other than by inspection) of obtaining the explicit expression in terms of $z$ is to substitute $z - iy$ for $x$ in $u + iv$; the simplified result must be a function of $z$ alone.

**11.** Conversely, when $w$ is explicitly given as a function of $z$ and it is divided into its real and its imaginary parts, these parts individually satisfy the foregoing conditions attaching to $u$ and $v$. Thus $\log r$, where $r$ is the distance of a point $z$ from a point $a$, is the real part of $\log(z - a)$; it therefore satisfies the equation

$$\frac{\partial^2 u}{\partial x^2} + \frac{\partial^2 u}{\partial y^2} = 0.$$

Again, $\phi$, the angular coordinate of $z$ relative to the same point $a$, is the real part of $-i\log(z - a)$ and satisfies the same equation: the more usual form of $\phi$ being $\tan^{-1}\{(y - y_0)/(x - x_0)\}$, where $a = x_0 + iy_0$. Again, if a point $z$ be distant $r$ from $a$ and $r'$ from $b$, then $\log(r/r')$, being the real part of $\log\{(z - a)/(z - b)\}$, is a solution of the same equation.

The following example, the result of which will be useful subsequently[*], uses the property that the value of the derivative is independent of the differential element.

Consider a function
$$u + iv = w = \log\frac{z - c}{z - c'},$$

where $c'$ is the inverse of $c$ with regard to a circle, centre the origin $O$ and radius $R$. Then

$$u = \log\left|\frac{z - c}{z - c'}\right|;$$

so the curves, $u = \mathrm{constant}$, are circles. Let (fig. 4) $Oc = r$, $xOc = a$, so that $c = re^{ai}$, $c' = \dfrac{R^2}{r}e^{ai}$; then if

$$\left|\frac{z - c}{z - c'}\right| = \frac{r}{R}\lambda,$$

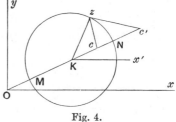

Fig. 4.

the values of $\lambda$ for points in the interior of the circle of radius $R$ vary from zero, when the circle $u = \mathrm{constant}$ is the point $c$, to unity, when the circle $u = \mathrm{constant}$ is the circle of radius $R$. Let the point $K (= \theta e^{ai})$ be the centre of the circle determined by a value of $\lambda$, and let its radius be $\rho (= \tfrac{1}{2}MN)$. Then since

$$\frac{cM}{c'M} = \frac{r}{R}\lambda = \frac{cN}{c'N},$$

we have
$$\frac{r + \rho - \theta}{\dfrac{R^2}{r} + \rho - \theta} = \frac{r}{R}\lambda = \frac{\theta + \rho - r}{\dfrac{R^2}{r} - \theta - \rho},$$

* In § 217, in connection with the investigations of Schwarz, by whom the result is stated, *Ges. Werke*, t. ii, p. 183.

whence
$$\rho=\frac{\lambda R\,(R^2-r^2)}{R^2-r^2\lambda^2},\qquad \theta=\frac{R^2 r\,(1-\lambda^2)}{R^2-r^2\lambda^2}.$$

Now if $dn$ be an element of the normal drawn inwards at $z$ to the circle $NzM$, we have
$$dz=dx+idy=-dn\,.\,\cos\psi-idn\,.\,\sin\psi$$
$$=-e^{i\psi}\,dn,$$

where $\psi\,(=zKx')$ is the argument of $z$ relative to the centre of the circle.  Hence, since
$$\frac{dw}{dz}=\frac{1}{z-c}-\frac{1}{z-c'},$$

we have
$$\frac{du}{dn}+i\frac{dv}{dn}=\frac{dw}{dn}=\left(\frac{1}{z-c'}-\frac{1}{z-c}\right)e^{\psi i}.$$

But
$$z=\theta e^{ai}+\rho e^{\psi i},$$

so that
$$z-c=\frac{\lambda\,(R^2-r^2)}{R^2-r^2\lambda^2}\,(Re^{\psi i}-\lambda re^{ai}),$$

and
$$z-c'=\frac{R}{r}\frac{R^2-r^2}{R^2-r^2\lambda^2}\,(\lambda re^{\psi i}-Re^{ai});$$

and therefore
$$\frac{du}{dn}+i\frac{dv}{dn}=\frac{R^2}{R^2-r^2}\frac{r^2\lambda^2}{}\,e^{\psi i}\left\{\frac{r}{R}\frac{1}{\lambda re^{\psi i}-Re^{ai}}-\frac{1}{\lambda}\frac{1}{Re^{\psi i}-\lambda re^{ai}}\right\}.$$

Hence, equating the real parts, it follows that
$$\frac{du}{dn}=-\frac{(R^2-r^2\lambda^2)^2}{\lambda R\,(R^2-r^2)\,\{R^2-2Rr\lambda\,\cos\,(\psi-a)+\lambda^2 r^2\}},$$

the differential element $dn$ being drawn inwards from the circumference of the circle.

The application of this method is evidently effective when the curves $u=$ constant, arising from a functional expression of $w$ in terms of $z$, are a family of non-intersecting algebraical curves.

*Ex.* 1.    Prove that, if $z_1$ and $z_2$ denote two complex variables,
$$|z_1+z_2|\leqslant|z_1|+|z_2|,\quad |z_1-z_2|\geqslant|z_1|\sim|z_2|.$$

*Ex.* 2.    Find the values of $u$ and $v$ when $w$ is defined as a function of $z$ in the following cases:—

(i)    $z=(w+i)^2$;

(ii)    $z=(1+\cos w)\,e^{wi}$;

(iii)    $\dfrac{1-(1-z)^{\frac{1}{2}}}{1+(1-z)^{\frac{1}{2}}}=e^w,\ w^2,\ \log w.$

In each case, trace the curves $u=a$, $v=c$, regarded as loci in the plane of $x,y$.

*Ex.* 3.    Shew that $x^2-y^2-2ixy$ is not a function of $z$; and that
$$x^3-3xy^2+i\,(3x^2y-y^3)+ax$$
is a function of $z$ only when $a=0$.

*Ex.* 4.    Shew that a possible value of $u$ is
$$(x-y)\,(x^2+4xy+y^2);$$
and determine the associated value of $w$ in terms of $z$.

Determine also the value of $w$ in terms of $z$ when the preceding expression is the value of $u-v$.

*Ex.* 5.    Find the value of $v$, and of $w$ in terms of $z$, when
$$u=\frac{\sin x}{\cosh y-\cos x}.$$

*Ex.* 6.  Prove that, when $x$ and $y$ are regarded as functions of $u$ and $v$ (with the foregoing notation), the relations

$$\frac{\partial x}{\partial u} = \frac{\partial y}{\partial v}, \qquad \frac{\partial x}{\partial v} = -\frac{\partial y}{\partial u},$$

$$\frac{\partial^2 x}{\partial u^2} + \frac{\partial^2 x}{\partial v^2} = 0, \qquad \frac{\partial^2 y}{\partial u^2} + \frac{\partial^2 y}{\partial v^2} = 0,$$

are satisfied.

*Ex.* 7.  Shew that, if $A$ and $B$ are any two fixed points in a plane, if $P$ is any variable point $(x, y)$, and if $\theta$ denotes the angle $APB$, then

$$\frac{\partial^2 \theta}{\partial x^2} + \frac{\partial^2 \theta}{\partial y^2} = 0.$$

Construct the function of $z$, $= x + iy$, of which $\theta$ is the real part, and also the function of $z$ of which $i\theta$ is the imaginary part.

*Ex.* 8.  Given $\lambda$, a function of $x$ and $y$; shew that $\phi(\lambda)$ can be the real part of a function of $z$ if the quantity

$$\left( \frac{\partial^2 \lambda}{\partial x^2} + \frac{\partial^2 \lambda}{\partial y^2} \right) \div \left\{ \left( \frac{\partial \lambda}{\partial x} \right)^2 + \left( \frac{\partial \lambda}{\partial y} \right)^2 \right\}$$

is expressible in terms of $\lambda$ alone.

Verify that the condition is satisfied when $\lambda = x + (x^2 + y^2)^{\frac{1}{2}}$; and obtain the function of $z$ which has $\phi(\lambda)$ for its real part.

**12.**  As the tests which are sufficient and necessary to ensure that a complex quantity is a function of $z$ have been given, we shall assume that all complex quantities dealt with are functions of the complex variable (§§ 6, 7).  Their characteristic properties, their classification, and some of the simpler applications will be considered in the succeeding chapters.

Some initial definitions and explanations will now be given.

(i).  It has been assumed that the function considered has a differential coefficient, that is, that the rate of variation of the function in any direction is independent of that direction by being independent of the mode of change of the variable.  We have already decided (§ 8) not to use the term analytic for such a function.  It is often called *monogenic*, when it is necessary to assign a specific name; but for the most part we shall omit the name, the property being tacitly assumed*.

We can at once prove from the definition that, when the derivative $w_1 \left( = \dfrac{dw}{dz} \right)$ exists, it is itself a function.  For $w_1 = \dfrac{\partial w}{\partial x} = \dfrac{1}{i} \dfrac{\partial w}{\partial y}$ are equations

---

* This is in fact done by Riemann, who calls such a dependent complex simply a *function*. Weierstrass, however, has proved (see § 85, *post*) that the idea of a monogenic function of a complex variable and the idea of dependence expressible by arithmetical operations are not coextensive. The definition is thus necessary; but the practice indicated in the text will be adopted, as non-monogenic functions will be of relatively rare occurrence.

which, when satisfied, ensure the existence of $w_1$; hence

$$\frac{1}{i}\frac{\partial w_1}{\partial y} = \frac{1}{i}\frac{\partial}{\partial y}\left(\frac{\partial w}{\partial x}\right)$$

$$= \frac{\partial}{\partial x}\left(\frac{1}{i}\frac{\partial w}{\partial y}\right)$$

$$= \frac{\partial w_1}{\partial x},$$

shewing, as in § 8, that the derivative $\dfrac{dw_1}{dz}$ is independent of the direction in which $dz$ vanishes. Hence $w_1$ is a function of $z$.

Similarly for all the derivatives in succession.

(ii). Since the functional dependence of a complex is ensured only if the value of the derivative of that complex be independent of the manner in which the point $z + dz$ approaches to coincidence with $z$, a question naturally suggests itself as to the effect on the character of the function that may be caused by the manner in which the variable itself has come to the value of $z$.

If a function has only one value for each given value of the variable, whatever be the manner in which the variable has come to that value, the function is called *uniform*\*. Hence two different paths from a point $a$ to a point $z$ give at $z$ the same value for any uniform function; and a closed curve, beginning at any point and completely described by the $z$-variable will lead to the initial value of $w$, the corresponding $w$-curve being closed, if $z$ has not passed through any point which makes $w$ infinite.

The simplest class of uniform functions is constituted by rational functions.

(iii). If a function has more than one value for any given value of the variable, or if its value can be changed by modifying the path in which the variable reaches that given value, the function is called *multiform*†. Characteristics of curves, which are graphs of multiform functions corresponding to a $z$-curve, will hereafter be discussed.

One of the simplest classes of multiform functions is constituted by algebraical irrational functions, that is, functions defined by an irresoluble algebraic equation $f(w, z) = 0$, where $f$ is a polynomial in $w$ and $z$.

The rational functions in (ii) occur when $f$ is of only the first degree in $w$.

(iv). A multiform function has a number of different values for the same value of $z$, and these values vary with $z$: the aggregate of the variations of any one of the values is called a *branch* of the function. Although the function is multiform for unrestricted variation of the variable, it often happens that a branch is uniform when the variable is restricted to particular regions in the plane.

---

\* Also *monodromic*, or *monotropic*; with German writers the title is *eindeutig*, occasionally, *einändrig*.

† Also *polytropic*; with German writers the title is *mehrdeutig*.

(v). A point in the plane, at which two or more branches of a multiform function assume the same value, and near which those branches are interchanged (§ 94, Note) by appropriate modification in the path of $z$, is called a *branch-point** of the function. The relations of the branches in the immediate vicinity of a branch-point will be discussed hereafter.

(vi). A function, which is monogenic, uniform and continuous over any part of the $z$-plane, is called *holomorphic*† over that part of the plane. When a function is called holomorphic without any limitation, the usual implication is that the character is preserved over the whole of the plane which is not at infinity.

The simplest example of a holomorphic function is a polynomial in the variable.

(vii). A *root* (or a *zero*) of a function is a value of the variable for which the function vanishes.

The simplest case of occurrence of roots is in a rational integral function, various theorems relating to which (e.g., the number of roots included within a given contour) will be found in treatises on the theory of equations.

(viii). The *infinities* of a function are the points at which the value of the function is infinite. Among them, the simplest are the *poles*‡ of the function, a pole being an infinity such that in its immediate vicinity the reciprocal of the function is holomorphic.

Infinities other than poles (and also the poles) are called the *singular points*, or the *singularities*, of the function: their classification must be deferred until after the discussion of properties of functions.

(ix). A function, which is monogenic, uniform and, except at poles, continuous, is called a *meromorphic* function§. The simplest example is a rational fraction.

**13.** The following functions give illustrations of some of the preceding definitions.

(a) In the case of a meromorphic function

$$w = \frac{F(z)}{f(z)},$$

---

* Also *critical point*, which, however, is sometimes used to include all special points of a function; with German writers the title is *Verzweigungspunkt*, and sometimes *Windungspunkt*. French writers use *point de ramification*, and Italians *punto di giramento* and *punto di diramazione.*

† Also *synectic.*

‡ Also *polar discontinuities*; also (§ 32) *accidental singularities.*

§ Sometimes *regular*, but this term will be reserved for the description of another property of functions.

where $F$ and $f$ are polynomials in $z$ without a common factor, the roots are the roots of $F(z)$ and the poles are the roots of $f(z)$. Moreover, according as the degree of $F$ is greater or is less than that of $f$, $z = \infty$ is a pole or a zero of $w$.

(b)  If $w$ be a polynomial of order $n$, then each simple root of $w$ is a branch-point and a zero of $w^{\frac{1}{m}}$, where $m$ is a positive integer; $z = \infty$ is a pole of $w$; and $z = \infty$ is a pole but not a branch-point or is an infinity (though not a pole) and a branch-point of $w^{\frac{1}{2}}$ according as $n$ is even or odd.

(c)  In the case of the function

$$w = \frac{1}{\operatorname{sn} \dfrac{1}{z}}$$

(the notation being that of Jacobian elliptic functions), the zeros are given by

$$\frac{1}{z} = iK' + 2mK + 2m'iK',$$

for all positive and negative integral values of $m$ and of $m'$. If we take

$$\frac{1}{z} = iK' + 2mK + 2m'iK' + \zeta,$$

where $\zeta$ may be restricted to values that are not large, then

$$w = (-1)^m k \operatorname{sn} \zeta,$$

so that, in the neighbourhood of a zero, $w$ behaves like a holomorphic function. There is evidently a doubly-infinite system of zeros; they are distinct from one another except at the origin, where an infinite number practically coincide.

The infinities of $w$ are given by

$$\frac{1}{z} = 2nK + 2n'iK',$$

for all positive and negative integral values of $n$ and of $n'$. If we take

$$\frac{1}{z} = 2nK + 2n'iK' + \zeta,$$

then

$$\frac{1}{w} = (-1)^n \operatorname{sn} \zeta,$$

so that, in the immediate vicinity of $\zeta = 0$, $\dfrac{1}{w}$ is a holomorphic function. Hence $\zeta = 0$ is a pole of $w$. There is thus evidently a doubly-infinite system of poles; they are distinct from one another except at the origin, where an infinite number practically coincide. But the origin is not a pole; the function, in fact, is there not determinate, for it has an infinite number of zeros and an infinite number of infinities, and the variations of value are not necessarily exhausted by zeros and infinities.

For the function $\dfrac{1}{\operatorname{sn}\dfrac{1}{z}}$, the origin is a point which will hereafter be called an *essential singularity*.

*Ex.* Obtain essential singularities of the functions

$$e^{z}, \quad \sinh\frac{1}{z}, \quad \tanh z.$$

# CHAPTER II.

## INTEGRATION OF UNIFORM FUNCTIONS.

**14.** THE definition of an integral, that is adopted when the variables are complex, is the natural generalisation of that definition for real variables in which it is regarded as the limit of the sum of an infinite number of infinitesimally small terms. It is as follows:—

Let $a$ and $z$ be any two points in the plane; and let them be connected by a curve of specified form, which is to be the path of variation of the independent variable. Let $f(z)$ denote any function of $z$; if any infinity of $f(z)$ lie in the vicinity of the curve, the line of the curve will be chosen so as not to pass through that infinity. On the curve, let any number of points $z_1, z_2, \ldots, z_n$ in succession be taken between $a$ and $z$; then, if the sum

$$(z_1 - a)f(a) + (z_2 - z_1)f(z_1) + \ldots + (z - z_n)f(z_n)$$

have a limit, when $n$ is indefinitely increased so that the infinitely numerous points are in indefinitely close succession along the whole of the curve from $a$ to $z$, that limit is called the integral of $f(z)$ between $a$ and $z$. It is denoted, as in the case of real variables, by

$$\int_a^z f(z)\, dz.$$

It is known* that the value of the integral of a function of a real variable between limits $a$ and $b$ is independent of the manner in which, under the customary definition, the interval between $a$ and $b$ is divided up. Assuming this result, we infer at once that the same property holds for the complex integral

$$\int_a^z f(z)\, dz\, ;$$

for, if $f(z) = u + iv$, where $u$ and $v$ are real,

$$f(z)\, dz = u\, dx - v\, dy + iu\, dy + iv\, dx,$$

and each of the integrals

$$\int u\, dx, \quad \int v\, dy, \quad \int u\, dy, \quad \int v\, dx,$$

* Harnack's *Introduction to the Calculus*, (Cathcart's translation), §§ 103, 142.

taken between limits corresponding to the extremities of the curve, is independent of the way in which the range is divided up.

The limit, as the value of the integral, is associated with a particular curve: in order that the integral may have a definite value, the curve (called the *path of integration*) must, in the first instance, be specified[*]. The integral of any function whatever may not be assumed to depend in general only upon the limits.

We have to deal with converging series; it is therefore convenient to state the definitions of the terms used. For proofs of the statements, developments, and applications in the theory of convergence, as well as the various tests of convergence, see Bromwich's *Theory of infinite series*, Carslaw's *Fourier's series and integrals*, Hobson's *Functions of a real variable*, and Pringsheim's article in the *Encyclopädie der mathematischen Wissenschaften*, t. i, pp. 49—146, where full references are given.

A series, represented by
$$a_1, \quad a_2, \quad a_3, \ldots \text{ad inf.},$$
is said to *converge*, when the limit of $S_n$, where
$$S_n = a_1 + a_2 + \ldots + a_n,$$
as $n$ increases indefinitely, is a unique finite quantity, say $S$. When, in the same circumstances, the limit of $S_n$ either is infinite or, if finite, is not unique (that is, may be one of several quantities), the series is said[†] to *diverge*.

The necessary and sufficient condition that the series
$$a_1, \quad a_2, \quad a_3, \ldots$$
should converge is that, corresponding to every finite positive quantity $\epsilon$ taken as small as we please, an integer $m$ can be found such that
$$| a_{n+1} + a_{n+2} + \ldots + a_{n+r} | < \epsilon,$$
for all integers $n$ such that $n \geqslant m$, and for every positive integer $r$.

When the series
$$| a_1 |, \quad | a_2 |, \quad | a_3 |, \ldots$$
converges, the series
$$a_1, \quad a_2, \quad a_3, \ldots$$
converges; and it is said to converge *absolutely*. When the series of moduli $| a_1 |, | a_2 |, | a_3 |, \ldots$, does not converge, though the series $a_1, a_2, a_3, \ldots$ converges, the convergence of the latter is said to be *conditional*. In a conditionally converging series, the order of the terms must be kept: derangement of the order can lead to different limits; and any assigned sum, as a limit, can be obtained by appropriate derangement. In an absolutely converging series, the order of the terms can be deranged without affecting the limit to which the series converges; the convergence is sometimes called *unconditional*.

These definitions apply to all infinite series, whatever be the source of their terms. When the terms depend upon a variable quantity $z$, and the convergence of the series is considered as $z$ varies, we have further classifications. Denote the series by
$$f_1(z), \quad f_2(z), \quad f_3(z), \ldots \text{ad inf.},$$

---

[*] This specification is tacitly supplied when the variables are real: the variable point moves along the axis of $x$.

[†] Sometimes the series, such that the limit of $S_n$ when $n$ is infinitely large is one of a number of finite quantities (depending upon the way in which $S_n$ is formed), are called *oscillating*.

and suppose that it converges for all values of $z$ within a definite region. When any small quantity $\delta$ has been chosen, and a positive integer $m$ can be determined, such that

$$\left| \sum_{\nu=n}^{\infty} f_\nu(z) \right| < \delta$$

for every value of $n \geqslant m$ and for all values of $z$ in the region, the convergence is said to be *uniform* (sometimes *continuous*).

Convergence may be uniform without being absolute; it can be absolute without being uniform.

When a series converges for all values of $z$ such that $|z| < r$, but not for $|z| > r$, then the circle, centre the origin of the variable $z$ and radius equal to $r$, is called the *circle of convergence*: and the radius is sometimes called the *radius of convergence*. A series such as

$$a_0, \quad a_1 z, \quad a_2 z^2, \ldots \text{ad inf.},$$

converges absolutely within its circle of convergence, though not necessarily on its circumference. It does not necessarily converge uniformly within its circle of convergence; but if $r'$ is a positive quantity, less than the radius of convergence by a finite quantity which can be taken small, the series converges uniformly within the circle of radius $r'$ concentric with its circle of convergence.

Again, when a uniformly converging series is integrated term by term over a finite range, the resulting series also converges uniformly. But a uniformly converging series can be differentiated term by term only if the series of derivatives converges.

**15.** Some inferences can be made from the definition of an integral.

(I.) *The integral along any path from $a$ to $z$ passing through a point $\zeta$ is the sum of the integrals from $a$ to $\zeta$ and from $\zeta$ to $z$ along the same path.* Analytically, this is expressed by the equation

$$\int_a^z f(z)\,dz = \int_a^\zeta f(z)\,dz + \int_\zeta^z f(z)\,dz,$$

the paths on the right-hand side combining to form the path on the left.

(II.) *When the path is described in the reverse direction, the sign of the integral is changed*: that is,

$$\int_a^z f(z)\,dz = -\int_z^a f(z)\,dz,$$

the curve of variation between $a$ and $z$ being the same. .

(III.) *The integral of the sum of a finite number of terms is equal to the sum of the integrals of the separate terms, the path of integration being the same for all.*

(IV.) *If a function $f(z)$ be finite and continuous along any finite line between two points $a$ and $z$, the integral* $\int_a^z f(z)\,dz$ *is finite.*

Let $I$ denote the integral, so that we have $I$ as the limit of

$$\sum_{r=0}^{n} (z_{r+1} - z_r) f(z_r):$$

hence

$$|I| = \text{limit of} \left| \sum_{r=0}^{n} (z_{r+1} - z_r) f(z_r) \right|$$

$$< \dots\dots\dots\dots \Sigma |z_{r+1} - z_r| |f(z_r)|.$$

Because $f(z)$ is finite and continuous, its modulus is finite and therefore must have a superior limit, say $M$, for points on the line. Thus

$$|f(z_r)| < M,$$

so that

$$|I| < \text{limit of } M\Sigma |z_{r+1} - z_r|$$

$$< MS,$$

where $S$ is the finite length of the path of integration. Hence the modulus of the integral is finite; the integral itself is therefore finite.

No limitation has been assigned to the path, except finiteness in length; the proposition is still true when the curve is a closed curve of finite length.

Hermite and Darboux have given an expression for the integral which leads to the same result. We have as above

$$I = \int_a^z f(z)\, dz,$$

and

$$|I| < \int_a^z |f(z)|\, |dz|$$

$$= \theta \int_a^z |f(z)|\, |dz|,$$

where $\theta$ is a real positive quantity less than unity. The last integral involves only real variables; hence* for some point $\xi$ lying between $a$ and $z$, we have

$$\int_a^z |f(z)|\, |dz| = |f(\xi)| \int_a^z |dz|$$

$$= S|f(\xi)|,$$

so that

$$|I| = \theta S |f(\xi)|.$$

It therefore follows that there is some argument $\alpha$ such that, if $\lambda = \theta e^{i\alpha}$,

$$I = \lambda S f(\xi).$$

This form proves the finiteness of the integral; and the result is the generalisation† to complex variables of the theorem of mean value just quoted for real variables.

---

* By what is usually called the "First theorem of mean value," in the integral calculus; for a proof, see Carslaw's *Fourier's series and integrals*, § 39.

† Hermite, *Cours à la faculté des sciences de Paris* (4ème éd., 1891), p. 59, where the reference to Darboux is given.

(V.)   *When a function is expressed as a uniformly converging series, the integral of the function along any path of finite length is the sum of the integrals of the terms of the series along the same path, provided that path lies within the circle of convergence of the series:*—a result, which is an extension of (III.) above.

Let $u_0 + u_1 + u_2 + \ldots$ be the converging series ; take

$$f(z) = u_0 + u_1 + \ldots + u_n + R,$$

where $|R|$ can be made infinitesimally small with indefinite increase of $n$, because the series converges uniformly.   Then by (III.), or immediately from the definition of the integral, we have

$$\int_a^z f(z)\, dz = \int_a^z u_0 dz + \int_a^z u_1 dz + \ldots + \int_a^z u_n dz + \int_a^z R\, dz,$$

the path of integration being the same for all the integrals.   Hence, if

$$\Theta = \int_a^z f(z)\, dz - \sum_{m=0}^{n} \int_a^z u_m dz,$$

we have                                 $$\Theta = \int_a^z R\, dz.$$

Let $R'$ be the greatest value of $|R|$ for points in the path of integration from $a$ to $z$, and let $S$ be the length of this path, so that $S$ is finite ; then, by (IV.),

$$|\Theta| < SR'.$$

Now $S$ is finite ; and, as $n$ is increased indefinitely, the quantity $R'$ tends towards zero as a limit for all points within the circle of convergence and therefore for all points on the path of integration provided that the path lie within the circle of convergence.   When this proviso is satisfied, $|\Theta|$ becomes infinitesimally small and therefore also $\Theta$ becomes infinitesimally small, with indefinite increase of $n$.   Hence, under the conditions stated in the enunciation, we have

$$\int_a^z f(z)\, dz - \sum_{m=0}^{\infty} \int_a^z u_m dz = 0,$$

which proves the proposition.

**16.**   The following lemma* is of fundamental importance.

Let any region of the plane, on which the $z$-variable is represented, be bounded by one or more simple† curves which do not meet one another : each curve that lies entirely in the finite part of the plane will be considered to be a closed curve.

---

* It is proved by Riemann, *Ges. Werke*, p. 12, and is made by him (as also by Cauchy) the basis of certain theorems relating to functions of complex variables.

† For the immediate purpose, a curve is called simple, if it have no multiple points.   The aim, in constituting the boundary from such curves, is to prevent the superfluous complexity that arises from duplication of area on the plane.   If, in any particular case, multiple points existed, a method of meeting the difficulty would be to take each simple loop as a boundary.

*If p and q be any two functions of x and y, which, for all points within the region or along its boundary, are uniform, finite and continuous, then the integral*

$$\iint \left(\frac{\partial q}{\partial x} - \frac{\partial p}{\partial y}\right) dx dy,$$

*extended over the whole area of the region, is equal to the integral*

$$\int (p\,dx + q\,dy),$$

*taken in a positive direction round the whole boundary of the region.*

(As the proof of the proposition does not depend on any special form of region, we shall take the area to be (fig. 5) that which is included by the curve $Q_1 P_1 Q_3' P_3'$ and excluded by $P_2' Q_2' P_3 Q_3$ and excluded by $P_1' P_2$. The positive directions of description of the curves are indicated by the arrows; and for integration in the area the positive directions are those of increasing $x$ and increasing $y$.)

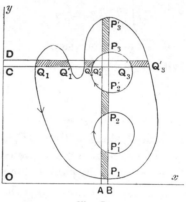

Fig. 5.

First, suppose that both $p$ and $q$ are real. Then, integrating with regard to $x$, we have*

$$\iint \frac{\partial q}{\partial x} dx dy = \int [q\,dy],$$

where the brackets imply that the limits are to be introduced. When the limits are introduced along a line $CQ_1 Q_1' \ldots$ parallel to the axis of $x$, then, since $CQ_1 Q_1' \ldots$ gives the direction of integration, we have

$$[q\,dy] = - q_1 dy_1 + q_1' dy_1' - q_2 dy_2 + q_2' dy_2' - q_3 dy_3 + q_3' dy_3',$$

where the various differential elements are the projections on the axis of $y$ of the various elements of the boundary at points along $CQ_1 Q_1' \ldots$.

---

* It is in this integration, and in the corresponding integration for $p$, that the properties of the function $q$ are assumed. Any deviation from uniformity, finiteness or continuity within the region of integration would render necessary some equation different from the one given in the text.

Now when integration is taken in the positive direction round the whole boundary, the part of $\int q\,dy$ arising from the elements of the boundary at the points on $CQ_1Q_1'...$ is the foregoing sum. For at $Q_3'$ it is $q_3'dy_3'$ because the positive element $dy_3'$, which is equal to $CD$, is in the positive direction of boundary integration; at $Q_3$ it is $-q_3dy_3$ because the positive element $dy_3$, also equal to $CD$, is in the negative direction of boundary integration; at $Q_2'$ it is $q_2'dy_2'$, for similar reasons; at $Q_2$ it is $-q_2dy_2$, for similar reasons; and so on. Hence

$$[q\,dy],$$

corresponding to parallels through $C$ and $D$ to the axis of $x$, is equal to the part of $\int q\,dy$ taken along the boundary in the positive direction for all the elements of the boundary that lie between those parallels. Then when we integrate for all the elements $CD$ by forming $\int[q\,dy]$, an equivalent is given by the aggregate of all the parts of $\int q\,dy$ taken in the positive direction round the whole boundary; and therefore

$$\iint \frac{\partial q}{\partial x}\,dx\,dy = \int q\,dy,$$

on the suppositions stated in the enunciation.

Again, integrating with regard to $y$, we have

$$\iint \frac{\partial p}{\partial y}\,dx\,dy = \int[p\,dx]$$
$$= -p_1dx_1 + p_1'dx_1' - p_2dx_2 + p_2'dx_2' - p_3dx_3 + p_3'dx_3',$$

when the limits are introduced along a line $BP_1P_1'...$ parallel to the axis of $y$: the various differential elements are the projections on the axis of $x$ of the various elements of the boundary at points along $BP_1P_1'...$.

It is proved, in the same way as before, that the part of $-\int p\,dx$ arising from the positively-described elements of the boundary at the points on $BP_1P_1'...$ is the foregoing sum. At $P_3'$ the part of $\int p\,dx$ is $-p_3'dx_3'$, because the positive element $dx_3'$, which is equal to $AB$, is in the negative direction of boundary integration; at $P_3$ it is $p_3dx_3$, because the positive element $dx_3$, also equal to $AB$, is in the positive direction of boundary integration; and so on for the other terms. Consequently

$$-[p\,dx],$$

corresponding to parallels through $A$ and $B$ to the axis of $y$, is equal to the part of $\int p\,dx$ taken along the boundary in the positive direction for all the elements of the boundary that lie between those parallels. Hence integrating for all the elements $AB$, we have as before

$$\iint \frac{\partial p}{\partial y}\,dx\,dy = -\int p\,dx;$$

and therefore $$\iint\left(\frac{\partial q}{\partial x} - \frac{\partial p}{\partial y}\right)dx\,dy = \int(p\,dx + q\,dy).$$

Secondly, suppose that $p$ and $q$ are complex. When they are resolved into real and imaginary parts, in the forms $p' + ip''$ and $q' + iq''$ respectively, then the conditions as to uniformity, finiteness and continuity, which apply to $p$ and $q$, apply also to $p'$, $q'$, $p''$, $q''$. Hence

$$\iint \left( \frac{\partial q'}{\partial x} - \frac{\partial p'}{\partial y} \right) dx dy = \int (p'dx + q'dy),$$

and

$$\iint \left( \frac{\partial q''}{\partial x} - \frac{\partial p''}{\partial y} \right) dx dy = \int (p''dx + q''dy),$$

and therefore

$$\iint \left( \frac{\partial q}{\partial x} - \frac{\partial p}{\partial y} \right) dx dy = \int (pdx + qdy):$$

which proves the proposition.

No restriction on the properties of the functions $p$ and $q$ at points that lie without the region is imposed by the proposition. They may have infinities outside, they may cease to be continuous at outside points, or they may have branch-points outside; but so long as they are finite and continuous everywhere inside, and in passing from any one point to any other point always acquire at that other the same value whatever be the path of passage in the region, that is, so long as they are uniform in the region, the lemma is valid.

**17.** The following theorem due to Cauchy\* can now be proved:—

*If a function $f(z)$ be holomorphic throughout any region of the z-plane, then the integral $\int f(z)dz$, taken round the whole boundary of that region, is zero.*

We apply the preceding result by assuming

$$p = f(z), \qquad q = ip = if(z);$$

owing to the character of $f(z)$, these suppositions are consistent with the conditions under which the lemma is valid. Since $p$ is a function of $z$, we have, at every point of the region,

$$\frac{\partial p}{\partial x} = \frac{1}{i} \frac{\partial p}{\partial y},$$

and therefore, in the present case,

$$\frac{\partial q}{\partial x} = i \frac{\partial p}{\partial x} = \frac{\partial p}{\partial y}.$$

There is no discontinuity or infinity of $p$ or $q$ within the region; hence

$$\iint \left( \frac{\partial q}{\partial x} - \frac{\partial p}{\partial y} \right) dx dy = 0,$$

---

\* For an account of the gradual development of the theory and, in particular, for a statement of Cauchy's contributions to the theory (with references), see Casorati, *Teorica delle funzioni di variabili complesse*, pp. 64—90, 102—106. The general theory of functions, as developed by Briot and Bouquet in their treatise *Théorie des fonctions elliptiques*, is based upon Cauchy's method.

the integral being extended over the region.　Hence also
$$\int(pdx + qdy) = 0,$$
when the integral is taken round the whole boundary of the region.　But
$$pdx + qdy = pdx + ipdy$$
$$= pdz$$
$$= f(z)\,dz,$$
and therefore　　　　　　　　　　$$\int f(z)\,dz = 0,$$
the integral being taken round the whole boundary of the region within which $f(z)$ is holomorphic.

It should be noted that the theorem requires no limitation on the character of $f(z)$ for points $z$ that are not included in the region.

The result can also be established by a slightly different use of the original theorem.　Writing
$$f(z) = u + iv,$$
where, after the hypotheses concerning $f(z)$, the real functions $u$ and $v$ are uniform, finite, and continuous for all points within the region or along the boundary, we have
$$\int f(z)\,dz = \int (u + iv)(dx + idy)$$
$$= \int(udx - vdy) + i\int(vdx + udy).$$
Owing to the character of $u$ and $v$, we have
$$\int(udx - vdy) = \iint\left(-\frac{\partial v}{\partial x} - \frac{\partial u}{\partial y}\right)dxdy,$$
taken over the whole region; but
$$\frac{\partial u}{\partial y} = -\frac{\partial v}{\partial x},$$
and therefore　　　　　　　　　　$$\int(udx - vdy) = 0.$$

Similarly
$$\int(vdx + udy) = \iint\left(\frac{\partial u}{\partial x} - \frac{\partial v}{\partial y}\right)dxdy,$$
taken over the whole region; but
$$\frac{\partial u}{\partial x} = \frac{\partial v}{\partial y},$$
and therefore　　　　　　　　　　$$\int(vdx + udy) = 0.$$
Hence, with the assumptions made as to $f(z)$, we have
$$\int f(z)\,dz = 0.$$

Some important propositions can be derived by means of the theorem, as follows.

**18.**  *When a function $f(z)$ is holomorphic over any continuous region of the plane, the integral $\int_a^z f(z)\,dz$ is a holomorphic function of $z$, provided the points $z$ and $a$ as well as the whole path of integration lie within that region.*

The general definition (§ 14) of an integral is associated with a specified path of integration.  In order to prove that the integral is a holomorphic function of $z$, it will be necessary to prove (i) that the integral acquires the same value in whatever way the point $z$ is attained, that is, that the value is independent of the path of integration, (ii) that it is finite, (iii) that it is continuous, and (iv) that it is monogenic.

Let two paths $a\gamma z$ and $a\beta z$ between $a$ and $z$ be drawn (fig. 6) in the continuous region of the plane within which $f(z)$ is holomorphic.  The line $a\gamma z\beta a$ is a contour over the area of which $f(z)$ is holomorphic ; and therefore $\int f(z)\,dz$ vanishes when the integral is taken along $a\gamma z\beta a$. Dividing the integral into two parts and implying by $z_\gamma$, $z_\beta$ that the point $z$ has been reached by the paths $a\gamma z$, $a\beta z$ respectively, we have

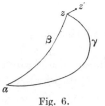

Fig. 6.

$$\int_a^{z_\gamma} f(z)\,dz + \int_{z_\beta}^{a} f(z)\,dz = 0,$$

and  therefore

$$\int_a^{z_\gamma} f(z)\,dz = -\int_{z_\beta}^{a} f(z)\,dz$$

$$= \int_a^{z_\beta} f(z)\,dz.$$

Thus the value of the integral is independent of the way in which $z$ has acquired its value ; and therefore $\int_a^z f(z)\,dz$ is uniform in the region.  Denote it by $F(z)$.

Secondly, $f(z)$ is finite for all points in the region.  After the result of § 17, we naturally consider only such paths between $a$ and $z$ as are finite in length, the distance between $a$ and $z$ being finite.  Hence (§ 15, IV.) the integral $F(z)$ is finite for all points $z$ in the region.

Thirdly, let $z'\,(= z + \delta z)$ be a point infinitesimally near to $z$ ; and consider $\int_a^{z'} f(z)\,dz$.  By what has just been proved, the path from $a$ to $z'$ can be taken $a\beta z z'$ ; therefore

$$\int_a^{z'} f(z)\,dz = \int_a^{z} f(z)\,dz + \int_z^{z'} f(z)\,dz$$

or

$$\int_a^{z+\delta z} f(z)\,dz - \int_a^{z} f(z)\,dz = \int_z^{z+\delta z} f(z)\,dz,$$

so that

$$F(z + \delta z) - F(z) = \int_z^{z+\delta z} f(z)\,dz.$$

Now at points in the infinitesimal line from $z$ to $z'$, the value of the continuous function $f(z)$ differs only by an infinitesimal quantity from its value at $z$; hence the right-hand side is

$$\{f(z) + \epsilon\}\, \delta z,$$

where $|\epsilon|$ is an infinitesimal quantity vanishing with $\delta z$. It therefore follows that

$$F(z + \delta z) - F(z)$$

is an infinitesimal quantity with a modulus of the same order of small quantities as $|\delta z|$. Hence $F(z)$ is continuous for points $z$ in the region.

Lastly, we have

$$\frac{F(z + \delta z) - F(z)}{\delta z} = f(z) + \epsilon\,;$$

and therefore

$$\frac{F(z + \delta z) - F(z)}{\delta z}$$

has a limit when $\delta z$ vanishes; and this limit, $f(z)$, is independent of the way in which $\delta z$ vanishes. Hence $F(z)$ has a differential coefficient; the integral is monogenic for points $z$ in the region.

Thus $F(z)$, which is equal to

$$\int_a^z f(z)\, dz,$$

is uniform, finite, continuous, and monogenic; it is therefore a holomorphic function of $z$.

As in § 16 for the functions $p$ and $q$, so here for $f(z)$, no restriction is placed on properties of $f(z)$ at points that do not lie within the region; so that elsewhere it may have infinities, or discontinuities, or branch-points. The properties, essential to secure the validity of the proposition, are (i) that no infinities or discontinuities lie within the region, and (ii) that the same value of $f(z)$ is acquired by whatever path in the continuous region the variable reaches its position $z$.

COROLLARY. *No change is caused in the value of the integral of a holomorphic function between two points when the path of integration between the points is deformed in any manner, provided only that, during the deformation, no part of the path passes outside the boundary of the region within which the function is holomorphic.*

This result is of importance, because it permits the adoption of special forms of the path of integration without affecting the value of the integral.

**19.** *When a function $f(z)$ is holomorphic over a part of the plane bounded by two simple curves (one lying within the other), equal values of $\int f(z)\, dz$ are obtained by integrating round each of the curves in a direction, which—relative to the whole area enclosed by each of them—is positive.*

The ring-formed portion of the plane (fig. 1, p. 3) which lies between the two curves is a region over which $f(z)$ is holomorphic; hence the integral $\int f(z)\,dz$ taken in the positive sense round the whole of the boundary of the included portion is zero. The integral consists of two parts: first, that round the outer boundary the positive sense of which is $DEF$; and second, that round the inner boundary the positive sense of which for the portion of area between $ABC$ and $DEF$ is $ACB$. Denoting the value of $\int f(z)\,dz$ round $DEF$ by $(DEF)$, and similarly for the other, we have

$$(ACB) + (DEF) = 0.$$

The direction of an integral can be reversed if its sign be changed, so that $(ACB) = -(ABC)$; and therefore

$$(ABC) = (DEF).$$

But $(ABC)$ is the integral $\int f(z)\,dz$ taken round $ABC$, that is, round the curve in a direction which, relative to the area enclosed by it, is positive.

The proposition is therefore proved.

The remarks made in the preceding case as to the freedom from limitations on the character of the function at places not within the bounded area are valid also in this case.

COROLLARY I. *When the integral of a function is taken round the whole of any simple curve in the plane, no change is caused in its value by continuously deforming the curve into any other simple curve provided the function is holomorphic over the part of the plane in which the deformation is effected.*

COROLLARY II. *When a function $f(z)$ is holomorphic over a continuous portion of a plane bounded by any number of simple non-intersecting curves, all but one of which are external to one another and the remaining one of which encloses them all, the value of the integral $\int f(z)\,dz$ taken positively round the single external curve is equal to the sum of the values taken round each of the other curves in a direction which is positive relative to the area enclosed by it.*

These corollaries are of importance in many instances, as will be seen later. The simplest instances arise in finding the value of the integrals of meromorphic functions round a curve which encloses one or more of the poles; the fundamental theorem, also due to Cauchy, for these integrals is the following.

**20.** *Let $f(z)$ denote a function which is holomorphic over any region in the z-plane, and let $a$ denote any point within that region; then*

$$\frac{1}{2\pi i}\int \frac{f(z)}{z-a}\,dz = f(a),$$

*the integral being taken positively round the whole boundary of the region.*

With $a$ as centre and a very small radius $\rho$, describe a circle $C$, which will be assumed to lie wholly within the region; this assumption is justifiable because the point $a$ lies within the region. Because $f(z)$ is holomorphic over the assigned region, the function $f(z)/(z-a)$ is holomorphic over the whole of the region excluded by the small circle $C$. Hence, by Corollary II. of § 19, we have

$$\int_B \frac{f(z)}{z-a} dz = \int_C \frac{f(z)}{z-a} dz,$$

the notation implying that the integrations are taken positively round the whole boundary $B$ and round the circumference of $C$ respectively.

For points on the circle $C$, let $z-a = \rho e^{\theta i}$, so that $\theta$ is the variable for the circumference and its range is from 0 to $2\pi$; then we have

$$\frac{dz}{z-a} = id\theta.$$

Along the circle $f(z) = f(a + \rho e^{\theta i})$; the quantity $\rho$ is very small and $f(z)$ is finite and continuous over the whole of the region, so that $f(a + \rho e^{\theta i})$ differs from $f(a)$ only by a quantity which vanishes with $\rho$. Let this difference be $\epsilon$, which is a continuous small quantity; thus $|\epsilon|$ is a small quantity which, for every point on the circumference of $C$, vanishes with $\rho$. Then

$$\int_C \frac{f(z)}{z-a} dz = i \int_0^{2\pi} \{f(a) + \epsilon\} d\theta$$

$$= 2\pi i f(a) + i \int_0^{2\pi} \epsilon d\theta.$$

If $E$ denote the value of the integral on the right-hand side, and $\eta$ the greatest value of the modulus of $\epsilon$ along the circle, we have, as in § 15,

$$|E| < \int_0^{2\pi} |\epsilon| d\theta$$

$$< \int_0^{2\pi} \eta d\theta$$

$$< 2\pi\eta.$$

Now let the radius of the circle diminish to zero. Then $\eta$ also diminishes to zero and therefore $|E|$, necessarily positive, becomes less than any finite quantity however small, that is, $E$ is itself zero; and thus we have

$$\int_C \frac{f(z)}{z-a} dz = 2\pi i f(a),$$

which proves the theorem.

When $a$ is not a zero of $f(z)$, this result is the simplest case of the integral of a meromorphic function. The subject of integration is $\dfrac{f(z)}{z-a}$, a function which is monogenic and uniform throughout the region and which, everywhere except at $z = a$, is finite and continuous; moreover, $z = a$ is a pole, because in the immediate vicinity of $a$ the reciprocal of the subject of integration, viz. $(z-a)/f(z)$, is holomorphic.

The theorem may therefore be expressed as follows :—

If $g(z)$ be a meromorphic function, which in the vicinity of $a$ can be expressed in the form $f(z)/(z-a)$ where $f(a)$ is not zero, and which at all other points in a region enclosing $a$ is holomorphic, then

$$\frac{1}{2\pi i}\int g(z)\,dz = \text{limit of } (z-a)\,g(z) \text{ when } z=a,$$

the integral being taken round a curve in the region enclosing the point $a$.

The pole $a$ of the function $g(z)$ is said to be simple, or of the first order, or of multiplicity unity.

*Corollary.* The more general case of a meromorphic function with a finite number of poles can easily be deduced. Let these be $a_1, \ldots, a_n$, each assumed to be simple; and let

$$G(z) = (z-a_1)(z-a_2)\ldots(z-a_n).$$

Let $f(z)$ be a holomorphic function within a region of the $z$-plane bounded by a simple contour enclosing the $n$ points $a_1, a_2, \ldots, a_n$, no one of which is a zero of $f(z)$. Then since

$$\frac{1}{G(z)} = \sum_{r=1}^{n} \frac{1}{G'(a_r)} \frac{1}{z-a_r},$$

we have

$$\frac{f(z)}{G(z)} = \sum_{r=1}^{n} \frac{1}{G'(a_r)} \frac{f(z)}{z-a_r}.$$

We therefore have

$$\int \frac{f(z)}{G(z)}\,dz = \sum_{r=1}^{n} \frac{1}{G'(a_r)} \int \frac{f(z)}{z-a_r}\,dz,$$

each integral being taken round the boundary. But the preceding proposition gives

$$\int \frac{f(z)}{z-a_r}\,dz = 2\pi i f(a_r),$$

because $f(z)$ is holomorphic over the whole region included in the contour; and therefore

$$\int \frac{f(z)}{G(z)}\,dz = 2\pi i \sum_{r=1}^{n} \frac{f(a_r)}{G'(a_r)},$$

the integral on the left-hand side being taken in the positive direction *.

The result just obtained expresses the integral of the meromorphic function round a contour which includes a finite number of its simple poles. It can be obtained otherwise from Corollary II. of § 19, by adopting

---

* We shall for the future assume that, if no direction for a complete integral be specified, the positive direction is taken.

a process similar to that adopted above, viz., by making each of the curves in that Corollary circles round the points $a_1, \ldots, a_n$ with radii sufficiently small to secure that each circle is outside all the others.

*Ex.* 1.  A function $f(z)$ is holomorphic over an area bounded by a simple closed curve; and $a$, $b$, $c$ are three points within the area.  Find the value of the integral

$$\frac{1}{2\pi i} \int \frac{f(z)}{(z-a)(z-b)(z-c)}\, dz$$

taken round the curve; and shew what it becomes

(i)  when $a$ and $b$ coincide,

(ii)  when $a$, $b$, $c$ coincide.

*Ex.* 2.  Let $S\left(\dfrac{\zeta}{z}\right)$ denote the sum of any set of selected terms of the series

$$1 + \frac{\zeta}{z} + \frac{\zeta^2}{z^2} + \ldots, \qquad\qquad |\zeta| < |z|,$$

and let $\qquad\qquad f(\zeta) = a_0 + a_1\zeta + a_2\zeta^2 + \ldots,$

where $f(\zeta)$ is a holomorphic function of $\zeta$ within the range; shew that the sum of the same set of terms selected from $f(\zeta)$ can be expressed in the form

$$\frac{1}{2\pi i} \int \frac{f(z)}{z} S\left(\frac{\zeta}{z}\right) dz.$$

**21.**  The preceding theorems have sufficed to evaluate the integral of a function with a number of simple poles.  We now proceed to obtain further theorems, which can be used among other purposes to evaluate the integral of a function with poles of order higher than the first.

We still consider a function $f(z)$ which is holomorphic within a given region.  Let $a$ be a point within the region which is not a zero of $f(z)$; we have

$$f(a) = \frac{1}{2\pi i} \int \frac{f(z)}{z-a}\, dz.$$

Let $a + \delta a$ be any other point within the region, so that, if $a$ be near the boundary, $|\delta a|$ is to be chosen less than the shortest distance from $a$ to the boundary; then

$$f(a + \delta a) = \frac{1}{2\pi i} \int \frac{f(z)}{z - a - \delta a}\, dz,$$

and  therefore

$$f(a + \delta a) - f(a) = \frac{1}{2\pi i} \int \left(-\frac{1}{z-a} + \frac{1}{z-a-\delta a}\right) f(z)\, dz$$

$$= \frac{1}{2\pi i} \int \left\{\frac{\delta a}{(z-a)^2} + \frac{(\delta a)^2}{(z-a)^2(z-a-\delta a)}\right\} f(z)\, dz,$$

the integral being in every case taken round the boundary.

Since $f(z)$ is monogenic, the definition of $f'(a)$, the first derivative of $f(a)$, gives $f'(a)$ as the limit of

$$\frac{f(a + \delta a) - f(a)}{\delta a},$$

when $\delta a$ ultimately vanishes; hence we may take

$$\frac{f(a + \delta a) - f(a)}{\delta a} = f'(a) + \sigma,$$

where $\sigma$ is a quantity which vanishes with $\delta a$ and is therefore such that $|\sigma|$ also vanishes with $\delta a$. Hence

$$\{f'(a) + \sigma\}\,\delta a = \frac{\delta a}{2\pi i} \int \left\{ \frac{1}{(z-a)^2} + \frac{\delta a}{(z-a)^2(z-a-\delta a)} \right\} f(z)\,dz;$$

dividing out by $\delta a$ and transposing, we have

$$f'(a) - \frac{1}{2\pi i} \int \frac{f(z)}{(z-a)^2}\,dz = -\sigma + \frac{\delta a}{2\pi i} \int \frac{f(z)}{(z-a)^2(z-a-\delta a)}\,dz.$$

As yet, there is no limitation on the value of $\delta a$; we now proceed to a limit by making $a + \delta a$ approach to coincidence with $a$, viz., by making $\delta a$ ultimately vanish. Taking moduli of each of the members of the last equation, we have

$$\left| f'(a) - \frac{1}{2\pi i} \int \frac{f(z)}{(z-a)^2}\,dz \right| = \left| -\sigma + \frac{\delta a}{2\pi i} \int \frac{f(z)}{(z-a)^2(z-a-\delta a)}\,dz \right|$$

$$< |\sigma| + \frac{|\delta a|}{2\pi} \left| \int \frac{f(z)}{(z-a)^2(z-a-\delta a)}\,dz \right|.$$

Let the greatest modulus of $\dfrac{f(z)}{(z-a)^2(z-a-\delta a)}$ for points $z$ along the boundary be $M$, which is a finite quantity on account of the conditions applying to $f(z)$ and of the fact that the points $a$ and $a + \delta a$ lie within the region and are not on the boundary. Then, by § 15,

$$\left| \int \frac{f(z)}{(z-a)^2(z-a-\delta a)}\,dz \right| < MS,$$

where $S$ is the whole length of the boundary, a finite quantity. Hence

$$\left| f'(a) - \frac{1}{2\pi i} \int \frac{f(z)}{(z-a)^2}\,dz \right| < |\sigma| + \frac{|\delta a|}{2\pi} MS.$$

When we proceed to the limit in which $\delta a$ vanishes, we have $|\delta a| = 0$ and $|\sigma| = 0$, ultimately; hence the modulus on the left-hand side ultimately vanishes, and therefore the quantity to which that modulus belongs is itself zero, that is,

$$f'(a) - \frac{1}{2\pi i} \int \frac{f(z)}{(z-a)^2}\,dz = 0,$$

so that

$$f'(a) = \frac{1}{2\pi i} \int \frac{f(z)}{(z-a)^2}\,dz.$$

This theorem evidently corresponds in complex variables to the well-known theorem of differentiation with respect to a constant under the integral sign when all the quantities concerned are real.

Proceeding in the same way, we can prove that

$$\frac{f'\,(a+\delta a)-f'\,(a)}{\delta a}=\frac{2\,!}{2\pi i}\int\frac{f\,(z)}{(z-a)^3}\,dz+\theta,$$

where $\theta$ is a small quantity which vanishes with $\delta a$. Moreover the integral on the right-hand side is finite, for the subject of integration is everywhere finite along the path of integration which itself is of finite length. Hence, first, a small change in the independent variable leads to a change of the same order of small quantities in the value of the function $f'\,(a)$, which shews that $f'\,(a)$ is a continuous function. Secondly, denoting

$$f'\,(a+\delta a)-f'\,(a)$$

by $\delta f'\,(a)$, we have the limiting value of $\dfrac{\delta f'\,(a)}{\delta a}$ equal to the integral on the right-hand side when $\delta a$ vanishes, that is, the derivative of $f'\,(a)$ has a value independent of the form of $\delta a$ and therefore $f'\,(a)$ is monogenic. Denoting this derivative by $f''\,(a)$, we have

$$f''\,(a)=\frac{2\,!}{2\pi i}\int\frac{f\,(z)}{(z-a)^3}\,dz.$$

Thirdly, the function $f'\,(a)$ is uniform: for it is the limit of the value of $\dfrac{f\,(a+\delta a)-f\,(a)}{\delta a}$; and both $f\,(a)$ and $f\,(a+\delta a)$ are uniform. Lastly, it is finite; for (§ 15) it is the value of the integral $\dfrac{1}{2\pi i}\int\dfrac{f\,(z)}{(z-a)^2}\,dz$, in which the length of the path is finite and the subject of integration is finite at every point of the path.

Hence $f'\,(a)$ is continuous, monogenic, uniform, and finite, throughout the whole of the region in which $f\,(z)$ has these properties: it is a holomorphic function. Hence :—

*When a function is holomorphic in any region of the plane bounded by a simple curve, its derivative is also holomorphic within that region.*

And, by repeated application of this theorem :—

*When a function is holomorphic in any region of the plane bounded by a simple curve, it has an unlimited number of successive derivatives each of which is holomorphic within the region.*

All these properties have been shewn to depend solely upon the holomorphic character of the fundamental function; but the inferences relating to the derivatives have been proved only for points within the region and not for points on the boundary. If the foregoing methods be used to prove them for points on the boundary, they require that a consecutive point shall be taken in any direction; in the absence of knowledge concerning the fundamental function for points outside (even though just outside), no inferences can be drawn justifiably.

An illustration of this statement is furnished by the hypergeometric series which, together with all its derivatives, is holomorphic within a circle of radius unity and centre the origin. The series converges everywhere on the circumference, provided $\gamma > \alpha + \beta$. But the corresponding condition for convergence on the circumference ceases to be satisfied for some one of the derivatives and for all which succeed it: as such functions do not then converge, the circumference of the circle must be excluded from the region within which the derivatives are holomorphic.

*Ex.* Let $F(z)$ and $G(z)$ denote two functions of $z$, holomorphic in a region enclosing the point $a$, which is a zero of $G(z)$ and a non-zero of $F(z)$; prove that

$$\frac{1}{2\pi i}\int\frac{F(z)}{\{G(z)\}^2}\,dz = \frac{F''(a)\,G'(a) - F(a)\,G''(a)}{\{G'(a)\}^3},$$

when $a$ is a simple root of $G(z)=0$, and that

$$\frac{1}{2\pi i}\int\frac{F(z)}{G(z)}\,dz = \frac{6F'(a)\,G''(a) - 2F(a)\,G'''(a)}{3\{G''(a)\}^2},$$

when $a$ is a double root of $G(z)=0$, both integrals being taken round a small contour which encloses $a$ but no other zero of $G(z)$.

**22.** Expressions for the first and the second derivatives have been obtained.

By a process similar to that which gives the value of $f'(a)$, the derivative of order $n$ is obtainable in the form

$$f^{(n)}(a) = \frac{n!}{2\pi i}\int\frac{f(z)}{(z-a)^{n+1}}\,dz,$$

the integral being taken round the whole boundary of the region or round any curves which arise from deformation of the boundary, provided that no point of the curves in the final form of the boundary or in any intermediate form of the boundary is indefinitely near to $a$.

In the case when the curve of integration is a circle, no point of which circle may lie outside the boundary of the region, we have a modified form for $f^{(n)}(a)$.

For points along the circumference of the circle with centre $a$ and radius $r$, let $z - a = re^{\theta i}$, so that, as before,

$$\frac{dz}{z - a} = id\theta:$$

then $0$ and $2\pi$ being taken as the limits of $\theta$, we have

$$f^{(n)}(a) = \frac{n!}{2\pi r^n}\int_0^{2\pi} e^{-n\theta i}f(a + re^{\theta i})\,d\theta.$$

Let $M$ be the greatest value of the modulus of $f(z)$ for points on the circumference (or, as it may be convenient to consider, for points on or within the circumference): then

$$|f^{(n)}(a)| < \frac{n!}{2\pi r^n} \int_0^{2\pi} |e^{-n\theta i}|\,|f(a + re^{\theta i})|\,d\theta$$

$$< \frac{n!}{2\pi r^n} \int_0^{2\pi} M d\theta$$

$$< n!\frac{M}{r^n}.$$

Now, let a function $\phi(z)$ be defined by the equation

$$\phi(z) = \frac{M}{1 - \dfrac{z-a}{r}};$$

evidently it can be expanded in a series of ascending powers of $z-a$ which converges within the circle. The series is

$$\phi(z) = M\left\{1 + \frac{z-a}{r} + \frac{(z-a)^2}{r^2} + \dots\right\},$$

so that

$$\frac{d^n\phi(z)}{dz^n} = n!\frac{M}{r^n}\left\{1 + (n+1)\frac{z-a}{r} + \dots\right\}.$$

Hence

$$\left[\frac{d^n\phi(z)}{dz^n}\right]_{z=a} = n!\frac{M}{r^n},$$

so that, if the value of the $n$th derivative of $\phi(z)$, when $z=a$, be denoted by $\phi^{(n)}(a)$, we have $|f^{(n)}(a)| < \phi^{(n)}(a)$.

These results can be extended to functions of more than one variable: the proof is similar to the foregoing proof. When there are two variables, say $z$ and $z'$, the results may be stated as follows:—

For all points $z$ within a given simple curve $C$ in the $z$-plane and all points $z'$ within a given simple curve $C'$ in the $z'$-plane, let $f(z, z')$ be a holomorphic function; then, if $a$ be any point within $C$ and $a'$ any point within $C'$,

$$\frac{n!\,n'!}{(2\pi i)^2}\iint \frac{f(z, z')}{(z-a)^{n+1}(z'-a')^{n'+1}}\,dz\,dz' = \frac{\partial^{n+n'}f(a, a')}{\partial a^n\partial a'^{n'}},$$

where $n$ and $n'$ are any integers and the integral is taken positively round the two curves $C$ and $C'$.

If $M$ be the greatest value of $|f(z, z')|$ for points $z$ and $z'$ within their respective regions when the curves $C$ and $C'$ are circles of radii $r$, $r'$ and centres $a$, $a'$, then

$$\left|\frac{\partial^{n+n'}f(a, a')}{\partial a^n\partial a'^{n'}}\right| < n!\,n'!\,\frac{M}{r^n r'^{n'}};$$

and if

$$\phi(z, z') = \frac{M}{\left(1 - \dfrac{z-a}{r}\right)\left(1 - \dfrac{z'-a'}{r'}\right)},$$

then
$$\left|\frac{\partial^{n+n'} f(a, a')}{\partial a^n \partial a'^{n'}}\right| < \frac{\partial^{n+n'} \phi(z, z')}{\partial z^n \partial z'^{n'}},$$

when $z = a$ and $z' = a'$ in the derivative of $\phi(z, z')$.

A function $\phi$, related in this manner to a function $f$ in association with which it is constructed, is sometimes called* a *dominant* function.

**23.**   All the integrals of meromorphic functions that have been considered have been taken along complete curves: it is necessary to refer to integrals along curves which are lines only from one point to another.   A single illustration will suffice at present.

Consider the integral $\int_{z_0}^{z} \frac{f(z)}{z - a} \, dz$; the function $f(z)$ is supposed holomorphic in the given region: $z$ and $z_0$ are any two points in that region.   Let some curves joining $z$ to $z_0$ be drawn as in the figure (fig. 7).

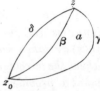

Fig. 7.

Then $\dfrac{f(z)}{z - a}$ is holomorphic over the whole area en-

closed by $z_0\beta z\delta z_0$: and therefore we have $\int \dfrac{f(z)}{z - a} \, dz = 0$, the integral being

taken round the boundary of that area.   Hence, as in the earlier case, we have

$$\int_{z_0}^{z\delta} \frac{f(z)}{z - a} \, dz = \int_{z_0}^{z\beta} \frac{f(z)}{z - a} \, dz.$$

The point $a$ lies within the area enclosed by $z_0 \gamma z \beta z_0$, and the function $\dfrac{f(z)}{z - a}$ is holomorphic, except in the immediate vicinity of $z = a$; hence

$$\int \frac{f(z)}{z - a} \, dz = 2\pi i f(a),$$

the integral on the left-hand side being taken round $z_0 \gamma z \beta z_0$.   Accordingly

$$\int_{z_0}^{z\gamma} \frac{f(z)}{z - a} \, dz = \int_{z_0}^{z\beta} \frac{f(z)}{z - a} \, dz + 2\pi i f(a).$$

We denote $\dfrac{f(z)}{z - a}$ by $g(z)$, so that $g(z)$ is a function which has one pole $a$ in the region considered.

The preceding results are connected only with the simplest form of meromorphic functions; other simple results can be derived by means of the other theorems proved in §§ 17—21.   Those which have been obtained are sufficient however to shew that: *The integral of a meromorphic function $\int g(z) \, dz$, from one point to another of the region of the function, is not in general a uniform function.*   The value of the integral is not altered by any deformation of the path which does not meet or cross a pole of the

* Poincaré uses the term *majorante*.

function; but the value is altered when the path of integration is so deformed as to pass over one or more poles. Therefore *it is necessary to specify the path of integration when the subject of integration is a meromorphic function;* only partial deformations of the path of integration are possible without modifying the value of the integral.

**24.** The following additional propositions* are deduced from limiting cases of integration round complete curves. In the first, the curve becomes indefinitely small; in the second, it becomes infinitely large. And in neither, are the properties of the functions to be integrated limited as in the preceding propositions, so that the results are of wider application.

I. *If $f(z)$ be a function which, whatever be its character at $a$, has no infinities and no branch-points in the immediate vicinity of $a$, the value of $\int f(z)\,dz$ taken round a small circle with its centre at $a$ tends towards zero when the circle diminishes in magnitude so as ultimately to be merely the point $a$, provided that, as $|z-a|$ diminishes indefinitely, the limit of $(z-a)f(z)$ tend uniformly to zero.*

Along the small circle, initially taken to be of radius $r$, let

$$z - a = re^{\theta i},$$

so that

$$\frac{dz}{z-a} = id\theta,$$

and therefore

$$\int f(z)\,dz = i\int_0^{2\pi} (z-a)f(z)\,d\theta.$$

Hence

$$\left|\int f(z)\,dz\right| = \left|\int_0^{2\pi}(z-a)f(z)\,d\theta\right|$$

$$< \int_0^{2\pi} |(z-a)f(z)|\,d\theta$$

$$< \int_0^{2\pi} M\,d\theta$$

$$< 2\pi M',$$

where $M'$ is the greatest value of $M$, the modulus of $(z-a)f(z)$, for points on the circumference. Since $(z-a)f(z)$ tends uniformly to the limit zero as $|z-a|$ diminishes indefinitely, $|\int f(z)\,dz|$ is ultimately zero. Hence the integral itself $\int f(z)\,dz$ is zero, under the assigned conditions.

*Note.* If the integral be extended over only part of the circumference of the circle, it is easy to see that, under the conditions of the proposition, the value of $\int f(z)\,dz$ still tends towards zero.

---

* The form of the first two propositions, which is adopted here, is due to Jordan, *Cours d'Analyse*, t. ii, § 256.

COROLLARY. *If $(z-a)f(z)$ tend uniformly to a limit $k$ as $|z-a|$ diminishes indefinitely, the value of $\int f(z)\,dz$ taken round a small circle, centre $a$, tends towards $2\pi i k$ in the limit.*

Thus the value of $\int \dfrac{dz}{(a^2-z^2)^{\frac{1}{2}}}$, taken round a very small circle centre $a$, where $a$ is not the origin, is zero: the value of $\int \dfrac{dz}{(a-z)(a+z)^{\frac{1}{2}}}$ round the same circle is $\dfrac{\pi}{i}\left(\dfrac{2}{a}\right)^{\frac{1}{2}}$.

Neither the theorem nor the corollary will apply to a function, such as $\operatorname{sn}\dfrac{1}{z-a}$, which has the point $a$ for an essential singularity: the value of $(z-a)\operatorname{sn}\dfrac{1}{z-a}$, as $|z-a|$ diminishes indefinitely, does not tend (§ 13) to a uniform limit. As a matter of fact, the function $\operatorname{sn}\dfrac{1}{z-a}$ has an infinite number of poles in the immediate vicinity of $a$ as the limit $z=a$ is being reached.

II. *Whatever be the character of a function $f(z)$ for infinitely large values of $z$, the value of $\int f(z)\,dz$, taken round a circle with the origin for centre, tends towards zero as the circle becomes infinitely large, provided that, as $|z|$ increases indefinitely, the limit of $zf(z)$ tend uniformly to zero.*

Along a circle, centre the origin and radius $R$, we have $z=Re^{\theta i}$, so that
$$\frac{dz}{z}=id\theta,$$

and therefore
$$\int f(z)\,dz = i\int_0^{2\pi} zf(z)\,d\theta.$$

Hence
$$\left|\int f(z)\,dz\right| = \left|\int_0^{2\pi} zf(z)\,d\theta\right|$$
$$< \int_0^{2\pi} |zf(z)|\,d\theta$$
$$< \int_0^{2\pi} M\,d\theta$$
$$< 2\pi M',$$

where $M'$ is the greatest value of $M$, the modulus of $zf(z)$, for points on the circumference. When $R$ increases indefinitely, the value of $M'$ is zero on the hypothesis in the proposition; hence $|\int f(z)\,dz|$ is ultimately zero. Therefore the value of $\int f(z)\,dz$ tends towards zero, under the assigned conditions.

*Note.* If the integral be extended along only a portion of the circumference, the value of $\int f(z)\,dz$ still tends towards zero.

COROLLARY. *If $zf(z)$ tend uniformly to a limit $k$ as $|z|$ increases indefinitely, the value of $\int f(z)\,dz$, taken round a very large circle, centre the origin, tends towards $2\pi i k$.*

Thus the value of $\int (1-z^n)^{-\frac{1}{2}}dz$ round an infinitely large circle, centre the origin, is zero if $n>2$, and is $2\pi$ if $n=2$.

III.   *If all the infinities and the branch-points of a function lie in a finite region of the z-plane, then the value of $\int f(z)\,dz$ round any simple curve, which includes all those points, is zero, provided the value of $zf(z)$, as $|z|$ increases indefinitely, tends uniformly to zero.*

The simple curve can be deformed continuously into the infinite circle of the preceding proposition, without passing over any infinity or any branch-point; hence, if we assume that the function exists all over the plane, the value of $\int f(z)\,dz$ is, by Cor. I. of § 19, equal to the value of the integral round the infinite circle, that is, by the preceding proposition, to zero.

Another method of stating the proof of the theorem is to consider the corresponding simple curve on Neumann's sphere (§ 4). The surface of the sphere is divided into two portions by the curve*: in one portion lie all the singularities and the branch-points, and in the other portion there is no critical point whatever. Hence in this second portion the function is holomorphic; since the area is bounded by the curve we see that, on passing back to the plane, the excluded area is one over which the function is holomorphic. Hence, by § 19, the integral round the curve is equal to the integral round an infinite circle having its centre at the origin and is therefore zero, as before.

Corollary.   *If, under the same circumstances, the value of $zf(z)$, as $|z|$ increases indefinitely, tend uniformly to $k$, then the value of $\int f(z)\,dz$ round the simple curve is $2\pi i k$.*

Thus the value of $\int \dfrac{dz}{(a^2-z^2)^{\frac12}}$ along any simple curve, which encloses the two points $a$ and $-a$, is $2\pi$; the value of

$$\int \frac{dz}{\{(1-z^2)(1-k^2z^2)\}^{\frac12}}$$

round any simple curve enclosing the four points $1, -1, \dfrac{1}{k}, -\dfrac{1}{k}$, is zero, $k$ being a non-vanishing constant; and the value of $\int(1-z^{2n})^{-\frac12}dz$, taken round a circle, centre the origin and radius greater than unity, is zero when $n$ is an integer greater than 1.

But the value of   $\int \dfrac{dz}{\{(z-e_1)(z-e_2)(z-e_3)\}^{\frac12}}$

round any circle, which has the origin for centre and includes the three distinct points $e_1, e_2, e_3$, is not zero. The subject of integration has $z=\infty$ for a branch-point, so that the condition in the proposition is not satisfied; and the reason that the result is no longer valid is that the deformation into an infinite circle, as described in Cor. I. of § 19, is not possible because the infinite circle would meet the branch-point at infinity.

---

* The fact that a single path of integration is the boundary of two portions of the surface of the sphere, within which the function may have different characteristic properties, will be used hereafter (§ 104) to obtain a relation between the two integrals that arise according as the path is deformed within one portion or within the other.

**25.**  The further consideration of integrals of functions, that do not possess the character of uniformity over the whole area included by the curve of integration, will be deferred until Chap. IX.  Some examples of the theorems proved in the present chapter will now be given.

*Ex.* 1.  It is sufficient merely to mention the indefinite integrals (that is, integrals from an arbitrary point to a point $z$) of rational integral functions of the variable.  After the preceding explanations it is evident that they follow the same laws as integrals of similar functions of real variables.

*Ex.* 2.  Consider the integral $\int \dfrac{dz}{(z-a)^{n+1}}$, taken round a simple curve.

When $n$ is 0, the value of the integral is zero if the curve do not include the point $a$, and it is $2\pi i$ if the curve include the point $a$.

When $n$ is a positive integer, the value of the integral is zero if the curve do not include the point $a$ (by § 17); and the value of the integral is still zero if the curve do include the point $a$ (by § 22, for the function $f(z)$ of the text is 1 and all its derivatives are zero).  Hence the value of the integral round any curve, which does not pass through $a$, is zero.

We can now at once deduce, by § 20, the result that, *if a holomorphic function be constant along any simple closed curve within its region, it is constant over the whole area within the curve.*  For let $t$ be any point within the curve, $z$ any point on it, and $C$ the constant value of the function for all the points $z$; then

$$\phi(t) = \frac{1}{2\pi i} \int \frac{\phi(z)}{z-t}\, dz,$$

the integral being taken round the curve, so that

$$\phi(t) = \frac{C}{2\pi i} \int \frac{dz}{z-t}$$
$$= C,$$

since the point $t$ lies within the curve.

*Ex.* 3.  The integral $\dfrac{1}{2\pi i} \int f'(z) \log \dfrac{z+1}{z-1}\, dz$ is taken round a circle, centre the origin and radius greater than unity; and the function $f(z)$ is holomorphic everywhere within the circle.  Prove that the value of the integral is

$$f(1) - f(-1).$$

*Ex.* 4.  Consider the integral $\int e^{-z^2}\, dz$.

In any finite part of the plane, the function $e^{-z^2}$ is holomorphic; therefore (§ 17) the integral round the boundary of a rectangle (fig. 8), bounded by the lines $x = \pm a$, $y = 0$, $y = b$, is zero: and this boundary can be extended, provided the deformation remain in the region where the function is holomorphic.  Now as $a$ tends towards infinity, the modulus of $e^{-z^2}$, being $e^{-x^2+y^2}$, tends towards zero when $y$ remains finite; and therefore the preceding rectangle can be

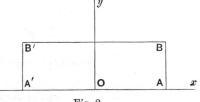

Fig. 8.

extended towards infinity in the direction of the axis of $x$, the side $b$ of the rectangle remaining unaltered.

Along $A'A$, we have $z=x$: so that the value of the integral along the part $A'A$ of the boundary is $\int_{-a}^{a} e^{-x^2}\,dx$.

Along $AB$, we have $z=a+iy$, so that the value of the integral along the part $AB$ is $i\int_{0}^{b} e^{-(a+iy)^2}\,dy$.

Along $BB'$, we have $z=x+ib$, so that the value of the integral along the part $BB'$ is $\int_{a}^{-a} e^{-(x+ib)^2}\,dx$.

Along $B'A'$, we have $z=-a+iy$, so that the value of the integral along the part $B'A'$ is $i\int_{b}^{0} e^{-(-a+iy)^2}\,dy$.

The second of these portions of the integral is $e^{-a^2}.\,i.\int_{0}^{b} e^{y^2-2ayi}\,dy$, which is easily seen to be zero when the (real) quantity $a$ is infinite.

Similarly the fourth of these portions is zero.

Hence as the complete integral is zero, we have, on passing to the limit,

$$\int_{-\infty}^{\infty} e^{-x^2}\,dx + \int_{\infty}^{-\infty} e^{-x^2-2ibx+b^2}\,dx = 0,$$

whence

$$e^{b^2}\int_{-\infty}^{\infty} e^{-x^2-2ibx}\,dx = \int_{-\infty}^{\infty} e^{-x^2}\,dx = \pi^{\frac{1}{2}},$$

or

$$\int_{-\infty}^{\infty} e^{-x^2}(\cos 2bx - i\sin 2bx)\,dx = \pi^{\frac{1}{2}}e^{-b^2};$$

and therefore, on equating real parts, we obtain the well-known result

$$\int_{-\infty}^{\infty} e^{-x^2}\cos 2bx\,dx = \pi^{\frac{1}{2}}e^{-b^2}.$$

This is only one of numerous examples* in which the theorems in the text can be applied to obtain the values of definite integrals with real limits and real variables.

*Ex.* 5.   By taking the integral $\int e^{-z^2}\,dz$ along the perimeter of a sector of a circle between the radii of a circle given $\theta=0$, $\theta=\frac{1}{4}\pi$, and the intercepted part of the circumference of radius $r$ which is ultimately increased without limit, establish the value $(\frac{1}{8}\pi)^{\frac{1}{2}}$ for each of Fresnel's integrals

$$\int_{0}^{\infty} \cos u^2\,du,\qquad \int_{0}^{\infty} \sin u^2\,du.$$

*Ex.* 6.   Prove that, when $a^2+b^2 < 1$, the value of the integral

$$\int_{0}^{2\pi} \frac{a\cos x + \beta\sin x + \gamma}{a\cos x + b\sin x + 1}\,dx,$$

for real values of $x$ within the range, is

$$\frac{2\pi}{(1-a^2-b^2)^{\frac{1}{2}}}\left\{\gamma - \frac{a\alpha+b\beta}{(1-a^2-b^2)^{\frac{1}{2}}+1}\right\}.$$

---

* See Briot and Bouquet, *Théorie des fonctions elliptiques*, (2nd ed.), pp. 141 et sqq., from which examples 4 and 8 are taken.

*Ex.* 7.   Evaluate the following integrals by the process of contour integration :—

(i)   $\displaystyle\int_{-\infty}^{\infty} \frac{\cos ax}{(x^2+1)(x^2+4)}\, dx$, where $a$ is real ;

(ii)   $\displaystyle\int_{0}^{\infty} \frac{\cos ax - \cos bx}{x^2}\, dx$ :       (iii)   $\displaystyle\int_{-\infty}^{\infty} \frac{e^{ax} - e^{bx}}{1 - e^x}\, dx,$

where $a$ and $b$ are real and lie between 0 and 1 ;

(iv)   $\displaystyle\int_{-\infty}^{\infty} \frac{e^{ax}}{1 + e^x}\, dx$, where $0 < a < 1$.

*Ex.* 8.   Consider the integral $\displaystyle\int \frac{z^{n-1}}{1+z}\, dz$, where $n$ is a real positive quantity less than unity.

The only infinities of the subject of integration are the origin and the point $-1$; the branch-points are the origin and $z = \infty$. Everywhere else in the plane the function behaves like a holomorphic function; and, therefore, when we take any simple closed curve enclosing neither the origin nor the point $-1$, the integral of the function round that curve is zero.

Choose the curve, so that it lies on the positive side of the axis of $x$ and that it is made up of :—

(i)   a semicircle $C_3$ (fig. 9), centre the origin and radius $R$ which is made to increase indefinitely :

(ii)   two semicircles, $c_1$ and $c_2$, with their centres at 0 and $-1$ respectively, and with radii $r$ and $r'$, which ultimately are made infinitesimally small :

(iii)   the diameter of $C_3$ along the axis of $x$ excepting those ultimately infinitesimal portions which are the diameters of $c_1$ and of $c_2$.

The subject of integration is uniform within the area thus enclosed although it is not uniform over the whole plane. We shall take that value of $z^{n-1}$ which has its argument equal to $(n-1)\,\theta$, where $\theta$ is the argument of $z$.

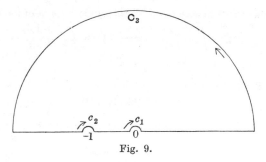

Fig. 9.

The integral round the boundary is made up of four parts.

(*a*)   The integral round $C_3$. The value of $z \cdot \dfrac{z^{n-1}}{1+z}$, as $|z|$ increases indefinitely, tends uniformly to the limit zero ; hence, as the radius of the semicircle is increased indefinitely, the integral round $C_3$ vanishes (§ 24, II., *Note*).

(*b*)   The integral round $c_1$. The value of $z \cdot \dfrac{z^{n-1}}{1+z}$, as $|z|$ diminishes indefinitely, tends uniformly to the limit zero ; hence as the radius of the semicircle is diminished indefinitely, the integral round $c_1$ vanishes (§ 24, I., *Note*).

(c)  The integral round $c_2$.  The value of $(1+z)\dfrac{z^{n-1}}{1+z}$, as $|1+z|$ diminishes indefinitely for points in the area, tends uniformly to the limit $(-1)^{n-1}$, i.e., to the limit $e^{(n-1)\pi i}$. Hence this part of the integral is

$$e^{(n-1)\pi i}\int\frac{dz}{1+z},$$

being taken in the direction indicated by the arrow round $c_2$, the infinitesimal semicircle. Evidently $\dfrac{dz}{1+z}=id\theta$ and the limits are $\pi$ to 0, so that this part of the whole integral is

$$e^{(n-1)\pi i}\int_{\pi}^{0}id\theta$$
$$=-i\pi e^{(n-1)\pi i}$$
$$=i\pi e^{n\pi i}.$$

(d)  The integral along the axis of $x$.  The parts at $-1$ and at 0 which form the diameters of the small semicircles are to be omitted ; so that the value is

$$\left\{\int_{-\infty}^{-1-r'}+\int_{-1+r'}^{-r}+\int_{r}^{\infty}\right\}\frac{x^{n-1}}{1+x}\,dx.$$

This is what Cauchy calls the principal value of the integral

$$\int_{-\infty}^{\infty}\frac{x^{n-1}}{1+x}\,dx.$$

Since the whole integral is zero, we have

$$i\pi e^{n\pi i}+\int_{-\infty}^{\infty}\frac{x^{n-1}}{1+x}\,dx=0.$$

Let
$$P=\int_{0}^{\infty}\frac{x^{n-1}}{1+x}\,dx,\quad P'=\int_{-\infty}^{0}\frac{x^{n-1}}{1+x}\,dx,$$

and
$$Q=\int_{0}^{\infty}\frac{x^{n-1}}{1-x}\,dx,$$

principal values being taken in each case.  Then, taking account of the arguments, we have

$$P'=\int_{0}^{\infty}\frac{(-x)^{n-1}}{1-x}\,dx=(-1)^{n-1}\int_{0}^{\infty}\frac{x^{n-1}\,dx}{1-x}$$
$$=e^{(n-1)\pi i}\,Q.$$

Since $i\pi e^{n\pi i}+P+P'=0$, we have

$$P-e^{n\pi i}Q=-i\pi e^{n\pi i},$$

so that
$$P-Q\cos n\pi=\pi\sin n\pi,\quad Q\sin n\pi=\pi\cos n\pi.$$

Hence
$$\int_{0}^{\infty}\frac{x^{n-1}}{1+x}\,dx=P=\pi\operatorname{cosec}n\pi,$$

$$\int_{0}^{\infty}\frac{x^{n-1}}{1-x}\,dx=Q=\pi\cot n\pi.$$

*Ex.* 9.  In the same way it may be proved that

$$\int_{-\infty}^{\infty}\frac{\cos ax}{1+x^{2n}}\,dx=-i\frac{\pi}{n}\sum_{r=1}^{n}\omega^{2r-1}e^{ai\omega^{2r-1}},$$

where $n$ is an integer, $a$ is positive and $\omega$ is $e^{i\frac{\pi}{2n}}$.

*Ex.* 10.   By considering the integral $\int e^{-z} z^{n-1} dz$ round the contour of the sector of a circle of radius $r$, bounded by the radii $\theta=0$, $\theta=a$, where $a$ is less than $\frac{1}{2}\pi$ and $n$ is positive, it may be proved that

$$\int_0^\infty \{r^{n-1} e^{-r\cos a} \cos(\beta + r\sin a)\}\, dr = \Gamma(n) \cos(\beta + na),$$

on proceeding to the limit when $r$ is made infinite.                    (Briot and Bouquet.)

*Ex.* 11.   By considering the integral $\int (z^2 - 1)^m z^{-ai-m-1} dz$, taken round a semicircle, prove that

$$\int_0^\pi \sin^m \theta\, e^{a\theta}\, d\theta = \frac{\pi e^{\frac{1}{2}\pi a}\, \Pi(m)}{2^m\, \Pi(\frac{1}{2}m + \frac{1}{2}ai)\, \Pi(\frac{1}{2}n - \frac{1}{2}ai)},$$

provided the real part of $m$ is greater than $-1$.

Similarly deduce the value of

$$\int_0^\pi \sin^m \theta \cos^n \theta\, e^{a\theta}\, d\theta,$$

where the real parts of $m$ and $n$ are each greater than $-1$, from a consideration of the integral

$$\int (z^2 - 1)^m (z^2 + 1)^n z^{-ai-m-n-1} dz,$$

taken round a semicircle.

(Many of the results stated in de Haan, *Nouvelles tables d'intégrales définies,* can be obtained in a similar manner.)

*Ex.* 12.   Consider the integral $\int \dfrac{dz}{z^n - 1}$, where $n$ is an integer.   The subject of integration is meromorphic; it has for its poles (each of which is simple) the $n$ points $\omega^r$ for $r=0$, 1, ..., $n-1$, where $\omega$ is a primitive $n$th root of unity; and it has no other infinities and no branch-points.   Moreover the value of $\dfrac{z}{z^n - 1}$, as $|z|$ increases indefinitely, tends uniformly to the limit zero; hence (§ 24, III.) the value of the integral, taken round a circle centre the origin and radius $> 1$, is zero.

This result can be derived by means of Corollary II. in § 19.   Surround each of the poles with an infinitesimal circle having the pole for centre; then the integral round the circle of radius $> 1$ is equal to the sum of the values of the integral round the infinitesimal circles.   The value round the circle having $\omega^r$ for its centre is, by § 20,

$$2\pi i \left( \text{limit of } \frac{z - \omega^r}{z^n - 1}, \text{ when } z = \omega^r \right)$$

$$= \frac{2\pi i}{n} \omega^{n-r}.$$

Hence the integral round the large circle

$$= \frac{2\pi i}{n} \sum_{r=0}^{n-1} \omega^{n-r}$$

$$= 0.$$

*Ex.* 13.   By considering the integral $\int \dfrac{e^{azi}}{z^3 + 1}\, dz$, taken round a semicircle, prove that

$$\int_{-\infty}^\infty \frac{\cos ax}{1 + x^3}\, dx = \frac{\pi}{3} \sin a, \qquad \int_{-\infty}^\infty \frac{\sin ax}{1 + x^3}\, dx = \frac{\pi}{3} \cos a,$$

provided $a$ is positive.

*Ex.* 14. Taking as the definition of Bernoulli's numbers that they are the coefficients in the expansion

$$\frac{1}{e^x - 1} - \frac{1}{x} + \frac{1}{2} = \sum_{m=1}^{\infty} (-1)^{m-1} \frac{B_m}{(2m)!} x^{2m-1},$$

prove (by contour integration) that

$$B_m = \frac{2(2m)!}{(2\pi)^{2m}} \sum_{n=1}^{\infty} \frac{1}{n^{2m}}.$$

In the same way, obtain expressions for the coefficients, in the expansion in powers of $x$, of the quantity

$$\frac{e^{xy}}{e^x - 1}.$$

(Hermite.)

*Ex.* 15. In all the preceding examples, the poles that have occurred have been simple: but the results proved in § 21 enable us to obtain the integrals of functions which have multiple poles within an area. As an instance, consider the integral $\int \frac{dz}{(1+z^2)^{n+1}}$ round any curve which includes the point $i$ but not the point $-i$, these points being the two poles of the subject of integration, each of multiplicity $n+1$.

We have seen that

$$f^{(n)}(a) = \frac{n!}{2\pi i} \int \frac{f(z)}{(z-a)^{n+1}} dz,$$

where $f(z)$ is holomorphic throughout the region bounded by the curve round which the integral is taken.

In the present case $a$ is $i$, and $f(z) = \frac{1}{(z+i)^{n+1}}$; so that

$$f^{(n)}(z) = \frac{2n!}{n!} \frac{(-1)^n}{(z+i)^{2n+1}},$$

and therefore

$$f^{(n)}(i) = \frac{2n!}{n!} \frac{(-1)^n}{(2i)^{2n+1}} = -\frac{2n!}{n!} 2^{-2n-1} i.$$

Hence we have

$$\int \frac{dz}{(1+z^2)^{n+1}} = \frac{2\pi i}{n!} f^{(n)}(i) = \frac{2n!}{n!\,n!} \frac{\pi}{2^{2n}}.$$

In the case of the integral of a function round a simple curve which contains several of its poles, we first (§ 20) resolve the integral into the sum of the integrals round simple curves each containing only one of the points, and then determine each of the latter integrals as above.

Another method, that is sometimes possible, makes use of the expression of the uniform function in partial fractions. After Ex. 2, we need retain only those fractions which are of the form $A/(z-a)$: the integral of such a fraction is $2\pi i A$, and the value of the whole integral is therefore $2\pi i \Sigma A$. It is thus sufficient to obtain the coefficients of the inverse first powers which arise when the function is expressed in partial fractions corresponding to each pole. Such a coefficient $A$, being the coefficient of $\frac{1}{z-a}$ in the expansion of the function, is called by Cauchy the *residue* of the function relative to the point.

For example,

$$\frac{1}{(z^3+1)^2} = \frac{2}{9}\left\{\frac{1}{z+1} + \frac{\omega}{z+\omega} + \frac{\omega^2}{z+\omega^2}\right\} + \frac{1}{9}\left\{\frac{1}{(z+1)^2} + \frac{\omega^2}{(z+\omega)^2} + \frac{\omega}{(z+\omega^2)^2}\right\},$$

so that the residues relative to the points $-1$, $-\omega$, $-\omega^2$ are $\frac{2}{9}$, $\frac{2}{9}\omega$, $\frac{2}{9}\omega^2$ respectively. Hence if we take a semicircle, of radius $>1$ and centre the origin with its diameter along the axis of $y$, so as to lie on the positive side of the axis of $y$, the area between the semi-circumference and the diameter includes the two points $-\omega$ and $-\omega^2$; and therefore the value of

$$\int \frac{dz}{(z^3+1)^2},$$

taken along the semi-circumference and the diameter, is

$$2\pi i\left(\tfrac{2}{9}\omega+\tfrac{2}{9}\omega^2\right);$$

that is, the value is $-\frac{4}{9}\pi i$.

*Ex.* 16.  Let $u$ denote $\int_{(C')}\int_{(C)} \dfrac{f(z,\,z')}{zz'-1}\,dz\,dz'$, $f$ being a rational integral function $\Sigma A_{mn} z^m z'^n$ of the complex variables $z$, $z'$, the integrations being taken in the positive sense round the closed contours $C$, $C'$, of which $C$ is a circle of unit radius with its centre at the origin.   Shew that $u=0$ if $C'$ lies wholly inside $C$, or if $C$ and $C'$ lie wholly outside one another, and that $u=-4\pi^2\Sigma A_{mm}$ ($m=0$, 1, 2, ...) if $C'$ completely surrounds $C$. Discuss also the value of $u$ if $C'$ is a circle passing through the points $\pm i$ but not coinciding with $C$, and $f(z,\,z')=f(-z,\,-z')$.

(Math. Trip., Part II., 1898.)

NOTE.   For further applications of Cauchy's theory of residues, together with many references to Cauchy's own results, Lindelöf's monograph *Le calcul des résidus* (Gauthier-Villars, 1905) may be consulted.

# CHAPTER III.

## Expansion of Functions in Series of Powers.

**26.** We are now in a position to obtain the two fundamental theorems relating to the expansion of functions in series of powers of the variable: they are due to Cauchy and Laurent respectively.

Cauchy's theorem is as follows[*] :—

*When a function is holomorphic over the area of a circle of centre a, it can be expanded as a series of positive integral powers of $z - a$, converging for all points within the circle.*

Let $z$ be any point within the circle; describe a concentric circle of radius $r$ such that

$$|z - a| = \rho < r < R,$$

where $R$ is the radius of the given circle. If $t$ denote a current point on the circumference of the new circle, we have

$$f(z) = \frac{1}{2\pi i} \int \frac{f(t)}{t - z} dt$$

$$= \frac{1}{2\pi i} \int \frac{f(t)}{t - a} \frac{dt}{1 - \dfrac{z - a}{t - a}},$$

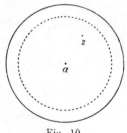

Fig. 10.

the integral extending along the whole circumference of radius $r$. Now

$$\frac{1}{1 - \dfrac{z - a}{t - a}} = 1 + \frac{z - a}{t - a} + \left(\frac{z - a}{t - a}\right)^2 + \ldots\ldots + \left(\frac{z - a}{t - a}\right)^n + \frac{\left(\dfrac{z - a}{t - a}\right)^{n+1}}{1 - \dfrac{z - a}{t - a}},$$

so that, by § 15 (III.), we have

$$f(z) = \frac{1}{2\pi i} \int \frac{f(t)}{t - a} dt + \frac{z - a}{2\pi i} \int \frac{f(t)}{(t - a)^2} dt + \ldots\ldots + \frac{(z - a)^n}{2\pi i} \int \frac{f(t)}{(t - a)^{n+1}} dt$$

$$+ \frac{1}{2\pi i} \int \frac{f(t)}{t - z} \left(\frac{z - a}{t - a}\right)^{n+1} dt.$$

---

[*] *Exercices d'Analyse et de Physique Mathématique*, t. ii, pp. 50 et seq.; the memoir was first made public at Turin in 1832.

Now $f(t)$ is holomorphic over the whole area of the circle; hence, if $t$ be not actually on the boundary of the region (§§ 21, 22), a condition secured by the hypothesis $r < R$, we have

$$f^{(s)}(a) = \frac{s!}{2\pi i} \int \frac{f(t)}{(t-a)^{s+1}}\, dt,$$

and therefore

$$f(z) = f(a) + (z-a)f'(a) + \ldots\ldots + \frac{(z-a)^n}{n!} f^{(n)}(a) + \frac{(z-a)^{n+1}}{2\pi i} \int \frac{f(t)}{t-z} \frac{dt}{(t-a)^{n+1}}.$$

Let the last term be denoted by $L$. Since $|z-a| = \rho$ and $|t-a| = r$; it is at once evident that $|t-z| \geqslant r - \rho$. Let $M$ be the greatest value of $|f(t)|$ for points along the circle of radius $r$; then $M$ must be finite, owing to the initial hypothesis relating to $f(z)$. Taking

$$t - a = re^{\theta i},$$

so that

$$dt = i(t-a)\, d\theta,$$

we have

$$|L| = \frac{\rho^{n+1}}{2\pi} \left| \int_0^{2\pi} \frac{f(t)}{t-z} \frac{d\theta}{(t-a)^n} \right|$$

$$< \frac{\rho^{n+1}}{2\pi} \frac{1}{r^n (r-\rho)} \int_0^{2\pi} |f(t)|\, d\theta$$

$$< \frac{\rho^{n+1}}{r^n (r-\rho)} M$$

$$< \left(\frac{\rho}{r}\right)^{n+1} M \left(1 - \frac{\rho}{r}\right)^{-1}.$$

Now $r$ was chosen to be greater than $\rho$; as $n$ becomes infinitely large, $\left(\frac{\rho}{r}\right)^{n+1}$ becomes infinitesimally small. Also $M\left(1 - \frac{\rho}{r}\right)^{-1}$ is finite. Hence as $n$ increases indefinitely, the limit of $|L|$, necessarily not negative, is infinitesimally small and therefore, in the same case, $L$ tends towards zero.

It thus appears, exactly as in § 15 (V.), that, when $n$ is made to increase without limit, the difference between the quantity $f(z)$ and the first $n+1$ terms of the series is ultimately zero; hence the series is a converging series having $f(z)$ as the limit of the sum, so that

$$f(z) = f(a) + (z-a)f'(a) + \frac{(z-a)^2}{2!} f''(a) + \ldots\ldots + \frac{(z-a)^n}{n!} f^{(n)}(a) + \ldots\ldots,$$

which proves the proposition under the assigned conditions. It is the form of Taylor's expansion for complex variables.

*Note.* A series, such as that on the right-hand side and not necessarily arising through the expansion of a given function $f(z)$, is frequently denoted by $P(z-a)$, where $P$ is a general symbol for a converging series of positive integral powers of $z-a$: it is also sometimes* denoted by $P(z \mid a)$. Conformably with this notation, a series of negative integral powers of $z - a$

---

* Weierstrass, *Ges. Werke*, t. ii, p. 77.

would be denoted by $P\left(\dfrac{1}{z-a}\right)$: a series of negative integral powers of $z$ either by $P\left(\dfrac{1}{z}\right)$ or by $P\left(z\mid\infty\right)$, the latter implying a series proceeding in positive integral powers of a quantity which vanishes when $z$ is infinite, that is, in positive integral powers of $z^{-1}$.

If, however, the circle can be made of infinitely great radius so that the function $f(z)$ is holomorphic over the finite part of the plane, the equivalent series is denoted by $G\left(z-a\right)$, and it converges over the whole plane*. Conformably with this notation, a series of negative integral powers of $z-a$ which converges over the whole plane is denoted by $G\left(\dfrac{1}{z-a}\right)$.

*Ex.* If the expansion, taken in the form $a_0 + a_1 z + a_2 z^2 + \dots$, be valid over the whole of the finite part of the plane, then the limit of

$$\left| a_m^{\frac{1}{m}} \right|,$$

as $m$ increases indefinitely, is zero. More generally, if the circle of convergence of the series be of radius $r$, then the limit of the preceding quantity is $1/r$.     (Cauchy.)

**27.** The following remarks on the proof and on inferences from it should be noted.

(i)   In order that $(t-z)^{-1}$ may be expanded in the required form, the point $z$ must be taken actually within the area of the circle of radius $R$; and therefore the convergence of the series $P\left(z-a\right)$ is not established for points on the circumference.

(ii)   The coefficients of the powers of $z-a$ in the series are the values of the function and its derivatives at the centre of the circle; and the character of the derivatives is sufficiently ensured (§ 21) by the holomorphic character of the function for all points within the region. It therefore follows that, if a function be holomorphic within a region bounded by a circle of centre $a$, its expansion in a series of ascending powers of $z-a$, which converges for all points within the circle, depends only upon the values of the function and its derivatives at the centre.

Conversely, a converging power-series in $z-a$, having assigned coefficients $f(a)$, $f'(a)$, ..., defines a uniform function within the radius of convergence of the series.

But instead of having the values of the function and of all its derivatives at the centre of the circle, it will suffice to have the values of the holomorphic function itself over any region at $a$ or along any line through $a$, the region or the line being not merely a point. The values of the derivatives at $a$ can be found in either case; for $f'(b)$ is the limit of $\{f(b+\delta b)-f(b)\}/\delta b$, so that the value of the first derivative can be found for any point in the region or on the line, as the case may be; and so for all the derivatives in succession.

---

* It then is often called an *integral* function.

(iii)   The form of Maclaurin's series for complex variables is at once derivable by supposing the centre of the circle at the origin. We then infer that, *if a function be holomorphic over a circle, centre the origin, it can be represented in the form of a series of ascending, positive, integral powers of the variable given by*

$$f(z) = f(0) + zf'(0) + \frac{z^2}{2!} f''(0) + \dots,$$

*where the coefficients of the various powers of z are the values of the derivatives of f(z) at the origin; and the series converges for all points within the circle.*

Thus, the function $e^z$ is holomorphic over the finite part of the plane; therefore its expansion is of the form $G(z)$. The function $\log(1+z)$ has a singularity at $-1$; hence within a circle, centre the origin and radius unity, it can be expanded in the form of an ascending series of positive integral powers of $z$, it being convenient to choose that one of the values of the function which is zero at the origin. Again, $\tan^{-1} z^2$ has singularities at the four points $z^4 = -1$, which lie on the same circumference; choosing the value at the origin which is zero there, we have a similar expansion in a series, converging for points within the circle.

Similarly for the function $(1+z)^n$, which has $-1$ for a singularity unless $n$ is a positive integer.

(iv)   Darboux's method* of derivation of the expansion of $f(z)$ in positive powers of $z - a$ depends upon the expression, obtained in § 15 (IV.), for the value of an integral.   When applied to the general term

$$\frac{1}{2\pi i} \int \left(\frac{z-a}{t-a}\right)^{n+1} f(t)\, dt,$$

$= L$ say, it gives                    $$L = \lambda r \left(\frac{z-a}{\zeta-a}\right)^{n+1} f(\zeta),$$

where $\zeta$ is some point on the circumference of the circle of radius $r$, and $\lambda$ is a complex quantity of modulus not greater than unity. The modulus of $\dfrac{z-a}{\zeta-a}$ is less than a quantity which is less than unity; the terms of the series of moduli are therefore less than the terms of a converging geometric progression, so that they form a converging series; the limit of $|L|$, and therefore of $L$, can, with indefinite increase of $n$, be made zero and Taylor's expansion can be derived as before.

*Ex.* 1.   Prove that the arithmetic mean of all values of $z^{-n} \sum\limits_{\nu=0}^{\infty} a_\nu z^\nu$, for points lying along a circle $|z| = r$ entirely contained in the region of continuity, is $a_n$. (Rouché, Gutzmer.)

Prove also that the arithmetic mean of the squares of the moduli of all values of $\sum\limits_{\nu=0}^{\infty} a_\nu z^\nu$, for points lying along a circle $|z| = r$ entirely contained in the region of continuity, is equal to the sum of the squares of the moduli of the terms of the series for a point on the circle.                                                                 (Gutzmer.)

* *Liouville*, 3ᵐᵉ Sér., t. ii, (1876), pp. 291—312.

*Ex.* 2.    Prove that the function    $\sum\limits_{n=0}^{\infty} a^n z^{n^2}$,

is finite and continuous, as well as all its derivatives, within and on the boundary of the circle $|z| = 1$, provided $|a| < 1$.          (Fredholm.)

*Ex.* 3.    The radii of convergence of the series
$$f(z) = a_0 + a_1 z + a_2 z^2 + \dots, \qquad g(z') = b_0 + b_1 z' + b_2 z'^2 + \dots,$$
are $\rho$ and $\rho'$; prove that $\rho\rho'$ is the radius of convergence of the series
$$h(z'') = a_0 b_0 + a_1 b_1 z'' + a_2 b_2 z''^2 + \dots.$$

Denoting the singularities of $f(z)$ by $s_1, s_2, \dots$, and those of $g(z')$ by $s_1', s_2', \dots$, prove that the singularities of $h(z'')$ are given by $s_m s_n'$, for all values of $m$ and $n$.    (Hadamard.)

*Ex.* 4.    (See also *Ex.* 2, § 20.)   It is possible to express the sum of selected terms in the form of a definite integral.   Thus, writing
$$c_m = \frac{1}{m!} f^{(m)}(a),$$
for $m = 1, 2, \dots$, consider the finite series
$$S = c_0 + c_1 (z-a) + \dots + c_n (z-a)^n$$
$$= \frac{1}{2\pi i} \int \frac{f(t)}{t-a} \left\{ 1 + \frac{z-a}{t-a} + \dots + \left(\frac{z-a}{t-a}\right)^n \right\} dt$$
$$= \frac{1}{2\pi i} \int \frac{f(t)}{t-a} \frac{1 - \left(\frac{z-a}{t-a}\right)^{n+1}}{1 - \frac{z-a}{t-a}} dt$$
$$= \frac{1}{2\pi i} \int \frac{f(t)}{t-z} \left\{ 1 - \left(\frac{z-a}{t-a}\right)^{n+1} \right\} dt$$
or
$$f(z) - S = \frac{1}{2\pi i} \int \frac{f(t)}{t-z} \left(\frac{z-a}{t-a}\right)^{n+1} dt.$$

*Ex.* 5    Establish the following results in a similar manner :—

(i)    $c_p (z-a)^p + c_{p+1} (z-a)^{p+1} + \dots + c_q (z-a)^q$
$$= \frac{1}{2\pi i} \int \frac{f(t)}{t-z} \left\{ \left(\frac{z-a}{t-a}\right)^p - \left(\frac{z-a}{t-a}\right)^{q+1} \right\} dt,$$

(ii)    $c_0 + c_2 (z-a)^2 + c_4 (z-a)^4 + \dots$
$$= \frac{1}{2\pi i} \int \frac{f(t)(t-a)}{(t-z)(t+z-2a)} dt,$$

(iii)    $c_1 + c_3 (z-a)^2 + c_5 (z-a)^4 + \dots$
$$= \frac{1}{2\pi i} \int \frac{f(t)}{(t-z)(t+z-2a)} dt.$$

**28.**    Laurent's theorem is as follows\* :—

*A function, which is holomorphic in a part of the plane bounded by two concentric circles with centre $a$ and finite radii, can be expanded in the form of a double series of integral powers, positive and negative, of $z - a$; and the series converges in the part of the plane between the circles.*

\* *Comptes Rendus*, t. xvii, (1843), p. 939.

Let $z$ be any point within the region bounded by the two circles of radii $R$ and $R'$; describe two concentric circles of radii $r$ and $r'$, such that

$$R > r > |z - a| > r' > R'.$$

Denoting by $t$ and by $s$ current points on the circumference of the outer and of the inner circles respectively, and considering the space which lies between them and includes the point $z$, we have, by § 20,

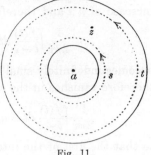

Fig. 11.

$$f(z) = \frac{1}{2\pi i}\int \frac{f(t)}{t - z}\, dt - \frac{1}{2\pi i}\int \frac{f(s)}{s - z}\, ds \ \ldots(\text{i}),$$

a negative sign being prefixed to the second integral because the direction indicated in the figure is the negative direction for the description of the inner circle regarded as a portion of the boundary.

Now we have

$$\frac{t - a}{t - z} = 1 + \frac{z - a}{t - a} + \left(\frac{z - a}{t - a}\right)^2 + \ldots\ldots + \left(\frac{z - a}{t - a}\right)^n + \frac{\left(\dfrac{z - a}{t - a}\right)^{n+1}}{1 - \dfrac{z - a}{t - a}},$$

this expansion being adopted with a view to an infinite converging series, because $\left|\dfrac{z - a}{t - a}\right|$ is less than unity for all points $t$; and hence, by § 15,

$$\int \frac{f(t)}{t - z}\, dt = \int \frac{f(t)}{t - a}\, dt + (z - a)\int \frac{f(t)}{(t - a)^2}\, dt + \ldots\ldots + (z - a)^n \int \frac{f(t)}{(t - a)^{n+1}}\, dt$$
$$+ \int \frac{f(t)}{t - z}\left(\frac{z - a}{t - a}\right)^{n+1} dt.$$

Now each of the integrals, which are the respective coefficients of powers of $z - a$, is finite, because the subject of integration is everywhere finite along the circle of finite radius, by § 15 (IV.). Let the value of

$$\int \frac{f(t)}{(t - a)^{r+1}}\, dt$$

be $2\pi i u_r$: the quantity $u_r$ is not necessarily equal to $f^{(r)}(a) \div r\,!$, because no knowledge of the function or of its derivatives is given for a point within the innermost circle of radius $R'$. Thus

$$\frac{1}{2\pi i}\int \frac{f(t)}{t - z}\, dt = u_0 + (z - a)\, u_1 + (z - a)^2\, u_2 + \ldots\ldots + (z - a)^n\, u_n$$
$$+ \frac{1}{2\pi i}\int \frac{f(t)}{t - z}\left(\frac{z - a}{t - a}\right)^{n+1} dt.$$

The modulus of the last term is less than

$$\frac{M}{1 - \dfrac{\rho}{r}}\left(\frac{\rho}{r}\right)^{n+1}$$

where $\rho$ is $|z-a|$ and $M$ is the greatest value of $|f(t)|$ for points along the circle. Because $\rho < r$, this quantity diminishes to zero with indefinite increase of $n$; and therefore the modulus of the expression

$$\frac{1}{2\pi i}\int\frac{f(t)}{t-z}\,dt - u_0 - (z-a)\,u_1 - \ldots\ldots - (z-a)^n\,u_n$$

becomes indefinitely small with unlimited increase of $n$. The quantity itself therefore vanishes in the same circumstances; and hence

$$\frac{1}{2\pi i}\int\frac{f(t)}{t-z}\,dt = u_0 + (z-a)\,u_1 + \ldots\ldots + (z-a)^m\,u_m + \ldots\ldots,$$

so that the first of the integrals is equal to a series of positive powers. This series converges within the outer circle, for the modulus of the $(m+1)^{\text{th}}$ term is less than

$$M\left(\frac{\rho}{r}\right)^m,$$

which is the $(m+1)^{\text{th}}$ term of a converging series.

As in § 27, the equivalence of the integral and the series can be affirmed only for points which lie within the outermost circle of radius $R$.

Again, we have

$$-\frac{z-a}{s-z} = 1 + \frac{s-a}{z-a} + \ldots\ldots + \left(\frac{s-a}{z-a}\right)^n + \frac{\left(\dfrac{s-a}{z-a}\right)^{n+1}}{1 - \dfrac{s-a}{z-a}},$$

this expansion being adopted with a view to an infinite converging series, because $\left|\dfrac{s-a}{z-a}\right|$ is less than unity for all points $s$. Hence

$$-\frac{1}{2\pi i}\int\frac{f(s)}{s-z}\,ds = \frac{1}{z-a}\frac{1}{2\pi i}\int f(s)\,ds + \ldots\ldots + \frac{1}{(z-a)^{n+1}}\frac{1}{2\pi i}\int(s-a)^n f(s)\,ds$$

$$+ \frac{1}{2\pi i}\int\left(\frac{s-a}{z-a}\right)^{n+1}\frac{f(s)}{z-s}\,ds.$$

The modulus of the last term is less than

$$\frac{M'}{1-\dfrac{r'}{\rho}}\left(\frac{r'}{\rho}\right)^{n+2},$$

where $M'$ is the greatest value of $|f(s)|$ for points along the circle of radius $r'$. With unlimited increase of $n$, the modulus of this last term is ultimately zero; and thus, by an argument similar to the one which was applied to the former integral, we have

$$-\frac{1}{2\pi i}\int\frac{f(s)}{s-z}\,ds = \frac{v_1}{z-a} + \frac{v_2}{(z-a)^2} + \ldots\ldots + \frac{v_m}{(z-a)^m} + \ldots\ldots,$$

where $v_m$ denotes the integral $\int(s-a)^{m-1}f(s)\,ds$ taken round the circle.

As in the former case, the series is one which converges, its convergence being without the inner circle; the equivalence of the integral and the series is valid only for points $z$ that lie without the innermost circle of radius $R'$.

The coefficients of the various negative powers of $z-a$ are of the form

$$\frac{1}{2\pi i}\int \frac{\frac{f(s)}{1}}{(s-a)^m}\,d\left(\frac{1}{s-a}\right),$$

a form that suggests values of the derivatives of $f(s)$ at the point given by $\frac{1}{s-a}=0$, that is, at infinity. But the outermost circle is of finite radius; and no knowledge of the function at infinity, lying without the circle, is given, so that the coefficients of the negative powers may not be assumed to be the values of the derivatives at infinity, just as, in the former case, the coefficients $u_r$ could not be assumed to be the values of the derivatives at the common centre of the circles.

Combining the expressions obtained for the two integrals, we have

$$f(z)=u_0+(z-a)\,u_1+(z-a)^2\,u_2+\dots$$
$$+(z-a)^{-1}\,v_1+(z-a)^{-2}\,v_2+\dots.$$

Both parts of the double series converge for all points in the region between the two circles, though not necessarily for points on the boundary of the region. The whole series therefore converges for all those points: and we infer the theorem as enunciated.

Conformably with the notation (§ 26, Note) adopted to represent Taylor's expansion, a function $f(z)$ of the character required by Laurent's Theorem can be represented in the form

$$P_1(z-a)+P_2\left(\frac{1}{z-a}\right),$$

the series $P_1$ converging within the outer circle and the series $P_2$ converging without the inner circle; their sum converges for the ring-space between the circles.

**29.** The coefficient $u_0$ in the foregoing expansion is

$$\frac{1}{2\pi i}\int\frac{f(t)}{t-a}\,dt,$$

the integral being taken round the circle of radius $r$. We have

$$\frac{dt}{t-a}=id\theta$$

for points on the circle ; and therefore

$$u_0 = \int \frac{d\theta}{2\pi} f(t),$$

so that
$$|u_0| < \int \frac{d\theta}{2\pi} M_t < M',$$

$M'$ being the greatest value of $M_t$, the modulus of $f(t)$, for points along the circle. If $M$ be the greatest value of $|f(z)|$ for any point in the whole region in which $f(z)$ is defined, so that $M' \leqslant M$, then we have

$$|u_0| < M,$$

that is, the modulus of the term independent of $z - a$ in the expansion of $f(z)$ by Laurent's Theorem is less than the greatest value of $|f(z)|$ at points in the region in which it is defined.

Again, $(z - a)^{-m} f(z)$ is a double series in positive and negative powers of $z - a$, the term independent of $z - a$ being $u_m$; hence, by what has just been proved, $|u_m|$ is less than $\rho^{-m} M$, where $\rho$ is $|z - a|$. But the coefficient $u_m$ does not involve $z$, and for any point $z$ we can therefore choose a limit. The lowest limit will evidently be given by taking $z$ on the outer circle of radius $R$, so that $|u_m| < MR^{-m}$. Similarly for each coefficient $v_m$; and therefore we have the result :—

*If $f(z)$ be expanded as by Laurent's Theorem in the form*

$$u_0 + \sum_{m=1}^{\infty} (z - a)^m u_m + \sum_{m=1}^{\infty} (z - a)^{-m} v_m,$$

*then*
$$|u_m| < MR^{-m}, \quad |v_m| < MR'^m,$$

*where $M$ is the greatest value of $|f(z)|$ at points within the region in which $f(z)$ is defined, and $R$ and $R'$ are the radii of the outer and the inner circles respectively.*

COROLLARY. *If $M(r)$ denote the greatest value of $|f(z)|$ for values of $z$ on the circumference of the circle $|z - a| = r$, then*

$$|u_m| < r^{-m} M(r), \quad |v_m| < r^m M(r):$$

which may be lower limits than the preceding. As above, we have

$$u_0 = \int \frac{d\theta}{2\pi} f(t)$$

taken round the circle $|z - a| = r$; so that

$$|u_0| \leqslant \int \frac{d\theta}{2\pi} |f(t)| \leqslant \int \frac{d\theta}{2\pi} M(r) \leqslant M(r).$$

Similarly, as $u_m$ is the term independent of $z - a$ in the Laurent expansion of $(z - a)^{-m} f(z)$, we have

$$|u_m| \leqslant \text{greatest value of } |(z - a)^{-m} f(z)| \text{ along } |z - a| = r$$
$$\leqslant r^{-m} M(r);$$

and so for $v_m$.

**30**.  The following proposition is practically a corollary from Laurent's Theorem :—

*When a function is holomorphic over all the plane which lies outside a circle of centre a, it can be expanded in the form of a series of negative integral powers of z − a, the series converging everywhere in that part of the plane.*

It can be deduced as the limiting case of Laurent's Theorem when the radius of the outer circle is made infinite.   We then take $r$ infinitely large, and substitute for $t$ by the relation

$$t - a = re^{\theta i},$$

so that the first integral in the expression (i), p. 55, for $f(z)$ is

$$\frac{1}{2\pi} \int_0^{2\pi} \frac{d\theta}{\dfrac{t - z}{t - a}} f(t).$$

Since the function is holomorphic over the whole of the plane which lies outside the assigned circle, $f(t)$ cannot be infinite at the circle of radius $r$ when that radius increases indefinitely.   If $f(t)$ tend towards a (finite) limit $k$, which must be uniform owing to the hypothesis as to the functional character of $f(z)$, then, since the limit of $(t - z)/(t - a)$ is unity, the preceding integral is equal to $k$.

The second integral in the same expression (i), p. 55, for $f(z)$ is unaltered by the conditions of the present proposition; hence we have

$$f(z) = k + (z - a)^{-1} v_1 + (z - a)^{-2} v_2 + \dots,$$

the series converging without the circle, though it does not necessarily converge on the circumference.

The series can be represented in the form

$$P\left(\frac{1}{z - a}\right),$$

conformably with the notation of § 26.

Of the three theorems in expansion which have been obtained, Cauchy's is the most definite, because the coefficients of the powers are explicitly obtained as values of the function and of its derivatives at an assigned point.   In Laurent's theorem, the coefficients are not evaluated into simple expressions.   In the corollary from Laurent's theorem the coefficients are, as is easily proved, the values of the function and of its derivatives for infinite values of the variable.   The essentially important feature of all the theorems is the expansibility of the function in converging series under assigned conditions.

**31**.   It was proved (§ 21) that, when a function is holomorphic in any region of the plane bounded by a simple curve, it has an unlimited number of successive derivatives each of which is holomorphic in the region.   Hence, by the preceding propositions, each such derivative can be expanded in converging series of integral powers, the series themselves being deducible by differentiation from the series which represents the function in the region.

In particular, when the region is a finite circle of centre $a$, within which $f(z)$ and consequently all the derivatives of $f(z)$ are expansible in converging series of positive integral powers of $z - a$, the coefficients of the various powers of $z - a$ are—save as to numerical factors—the values of the derivatives at the centre of the circle. Hence it appears that, *when a function is holomorphic over the area of a given circle, the values of the function and all its derivatives at any point $z$ within the circle depend only upon the variable of the point and upon the values of the function and its derivatives at the centre.*

**32.** Some of the classes of points in a plane that usually arise in connection with uniform functions may now be considered.

(i) A point $a$ in the plane may be such that a function of the variable has a determinate finite value there, always independent of the path by which the variable reaches $a$; the point $a$ is called an *ordinary* point\* of the function. The function, supposed continuous in the vicinity of $a$, is continuous at $a$: and it is said to behave *regularly* in the vicinity of an ordinary point.

Let such an ordinary point $a$ be at a distance $d$, not infinitesimal, from the nearest of the singular points (if any) of the function; and let a circle of centre $a$ and radius just less than $d$ be drawn. The part of the $z$-plane lying within this circle is called† the *domain* of $a$; and the function, holomorphic within this circle, is said to behave regularly (or to be regular) in the domain of $a$. From the preceding section, we infer that a function and its derivatives can be expanded in a converging series of positive integral powers of $z - a$ for all points $z$ in the domain of $a$, an ordinary point of the function: and the coefficients in the series are the values of the function and of its derivatives at $a$.

The property possessed by the series—that it contains only positive integral powers of $z - a$—at once gives a test which is both necessary and sufficient to determine whether a point is an ordinary point. *If the point $a$ be ordinary, the limit of $(z - a)f(z)$ necessarily is zero when $z$ becomes equal to $a$.* This necessary condition is also sufficient to ensure that the point is an ordinary point of the function $f(z)$, supposed to be uniform; for, since $f(z)$ is holomorphic, the function $(z - a)f(z)$ is also holomorphic and can be expanded in a series

$$u_0 + u_1(z - a) + u_2(z - a)^2 + \ldots,$$

---

\* Sometimes a *regular* point.

† The German title is *Umgebung*, the French is *domaine*.

converging in the domain of $a$. The quantity $u_0$ is zero, being the value of $(z - a)f(z)$ at $a$ and this vanishes by hypothesis; hence

$$(z - a)f(z) = (z - a)\{u_1 + u_2(z - a) + \ldots\},$$

shewing that $f(z)$ is expressible as a series of positive integral powers of $z - a$ converging within the domain of $a$, or, in other words, that $f(z)$ certainly has $a$ for an ordinary point in consequence of the condition being satisfied.

(ii)   A point $a$ in the plane may be such that a function $f(z)$ of the variable has a determinate infinite value there, always independent of the path by which the variable reaches $a$, the function behaving regularly for points in the vicinity of $a$; then $\dfrac{1}{f(z)}$ has a determinate zero value there, so that $a$ is an ordinary point of $\dfrac{1}{f(z)}$. The point $a$ is called a *pole* (§ 12) or an *accidental singularity*\* of the function.

A test, necessary and sufficient to settle whether a point is a pole of a function, will subsequently (§ 42) be given.

(iii)   A point $a$ in the plane may be such that $f(z)$ has not a determinate value there, either finite or infinite, though the function is definite in value at all points in the immediate vicinity of $a$ other than $a$ itself.

Such a point is called† an *essential singularity* of the function. No hypothesis is postulated as to the character of the function for points at infinitesimal distances from the essential singularity, while the relation of the singularity to the function naturally depends upon this character at points near it.   There may thus be various kinds of essential singularities all included under the foregoing definition, even for uniform functions; one classification is effected through the consideration of the character of the function at points in their immediate vicinity.   (See § 88.)

One sufficient test of discrimination between an accidental singularity and an essential singularity is furnished by the determinateness of the value at the point.   If the reciprocal of the function have the point for an ordinary point, the point is an accidental singularity—it is, indeed, a zero for the reciprocal.   But when the point is an essential singularity, the value of the reciprocal of the function is not determinate there; and then the reciprocal, as well as the function, has the point for an essential singularity.

In these statements and explanations, it is assumed that the essential singularity is an isolated point.   It will hereafter be seen that uniform functions can be constructed for which this is not the case; thus there are uniform functions which have lines of essential singularity.   For the present, we shall deal only with essential singularities that are isolated points.

---

\* Weierstrass, *Ges. Werke*, t. ii, p. 78, to whom the name is due, calls it *ausserwesentliche singuläre Stelle;* the term *non-essential* is suggested by Mr Cathcart, Harnack, p. 148.

† Weierstrass calls it *wesentliche singuläre Stelle.*

*Ex.* 1. Consider the function $\cos\dfrac{1}{z}$ in the vicinity of the origin.

The value at $z=0$ clearly is indeterminate; but it tends to limits that depend upon the mode by which $z$ approaches the origin.

Thus suppose that $z$ approaches the origin along the axis of imaginary quantities; and let $z=ai$, where $a$ is real and can be made as small as we please. Then

$$\cos\frac{1}{z}=\tfrac{1}{2}e^{\frac{1}{a}}+\tfrac{1}{2}e^{-\frac{1}{a}};$$

if $a$ be positive then the first term, and if $a$ be negative then the second term, can be made larger than any assigned finite quantity by sufficiently diminishing $a$: that is, by these methods of approach of $z$ to its origin, the function $\cos\dfrac{1}{z}$ ultimately acquires an infinite value.

Next suppose that $z$ approaches the origin along the axis of real quantities, and assume it to have positive values, (the same reasoning applies if it has negative values); in particular, consider real values of $z$, such that $0 \leqslant z \leqslant \beta$, where $\beta$ is a quantity that may be assigned as small as we please. When $\beta$ is assigned, take any positive integer $m$, such that

$$2m+1 > \frac{2}{\beta\pi}$$

so that $m$ will be any integer lying between some one integer (that will be large, in dependence upon the value of $\beta$) and infinity. Let

$$\frac{1}{z}=(2m+1)\frac{\pi}{2}+\zeta,$$

where $\zeta$ is a positive quantity such that $0 \leqslant \zeta \leqslant \pi$; then

$$\frac{1}{z} > \frac{1}{\beta},$$

and so $0 < z < \beta$. For such values we have

$$\cos\frac{1}{z}=(-1)^{m-1}\sin\zeta,$$

and therefore with the range of $\zeta$ from 0 to $\pi$, the function ranges continuously in numerical value between 0 and 1. In particular, when $\zeta=0$, the function has a zero value; (also when $\zeta=\pi$, but this in effect gives the next greater value of $m$); and this holds for each of the integers $m$ so assumed. Hence it follows that within the range $0 \leqslant z \leqslant \beta$ for real values of $z$, no matter how small the real quantity $\beta$ may be assigned, the function $\cos\dfrac{1}{z}$ has an unlimited number of zeros; also that, within the same range, the function $\cos\dfrac{1}{z}-\kappa$ (where $\kappa$ is a real quantity not greater than unity) has an unlimited number of zeros.

*Ex.* 2. Consider the function $\cos\dfrac{1}{z}$ in the vicinity of the origin, when the variable $z$ is made to approach the origin along the spiral $\theta=\mu r$, where $z=re^{\theta i}$, and $\mu$ is a parametric quantity; and shew that, in the immediate vicinity of the origin along this path,

$$\sinh\mu \leqslant \left|\cos\frac{1}{z}\right| \leqslant \cosh 2\mu.$$

Discuss the possibility of so choosing the approach of $z$ to the origin as, for values of $z$ such that $|z| < \gamma$ where $\gamma$ is a quantity that may be made as small as we please, to make $\cos\dfrac{1}{z}$ acquire a value $A+iB$.

*Ex.* 3.   Shew that the function $\operatorname{cosec}\dfrac{1}{z}$ has an unlimited number of poles in the immediate vicinity of its essential singularity $z=0$.

*Ex.* 4.   Consider the variations in value of the function $e^{\frac{1}{z}}$ for values of $z$, such that $|z|$ is not greater than some assigned small quantity $\kappa$.

In particular, consider the possibility of $e^{\frac{1}{z}}$ either acquiring, or tending to, any assigned value $A$.   The values of $z$ for which $e^{\frac{1}{z}}=A$ are given by

$$\frac{1}{z}=2k\pi i+\log A,$$

where $k$ is any integer, positive or negative.   Let $A=ae^{ai}$, where $a$ and $a$ are real; so that

$$\frac{1}{z}=(2k\pi+a)\,i+\log a.$$

If $z=x+iy$ as usual, then

$$\frac{x-iy}{x^2+y^2}=(2k\pi+a)\,i+\log a;$$

and therefore all the points, for which $e^{\frac{1}{z}}$ acquires the value $A$, lie upon the circle

$$x^2+y^2=\frac{x}{\log a}.$$

Accordingly, we consider an arc of this circle which lies within the circle

$$x^2+y^2=\kappa^2.$$

Not every point on the arc leads to the value $A$ of $e^{\frac{1}{z}}$; for taking any point $(\xi,\eta)$ on it, let

$$\frac{\eta}{\xi}\log a=2m\pi+\theta,$$

where $m$ is an integer, and $0\leqslant\theta<2\pi$; thus

$$\frac{\xi-i\eta}{\xi^2+\eta^2}=-i\,(2m\pi+\theta)+\log a,$$

so that the value of $e^{\frac{1}{z}}$ is $e^{\log a-i(2m\pi+\theta)}$, $=ae^{-\theta i}$, which is only the same as $ae^{ai}$ for particular points.   It is however clear that $\left|e^{\frac{1}{z}}\right|$ is the same for all points on the circular arc.

The values of $z$ for which $e^{\frac{1}{z}}=A$ are given by

$$z=\frac{1}{(2k\pi+a)\,i+\log a},$$

where $k$ is an integer.   It is manifest that a value of $k$ (say $k_1$) can be chosen for which

$$|z|<\kappa,$$

this inequality holding for all values of $k$ greater than $k_1$: so that the function $e^{\frac{1}{z}}$ acquires the value $A$ at an unlimited number of points in the region $|z|<\kappa$.   Further, by sufficiently increasing $k$, we can make $|z|$ smaller than any assigned quantity however small; and therefore $A$ is one of the (unlimited number of) values of $e^{\frac{1}{z}}$ as $z$ ultimately becomes zero.

It may be remarked at once that there must be at least one infinite value among the values which a uniform function can assume at an essential singularity. For if $f(z)$ cannot be infinite at $a$, then the limit of $(z-a)f(z)$ would be zero when $z=a$, no matter what the non-infinite values of $f(z)$ may be, and no matter by what path $z$ acquires the value $a$; that is, the limit would be a determinate zero. The function $(z-a)f(z)$ is regular in the vicinity of $a$: hence by the foregoing test for an ordinary point, the point $a$ would be ordinary and the value of the uniform function $f(z)$ would be determinate, contrary to hypothesis. Hence the function must have at least one infinite value at an essential singularity.

Further, a uniform function must be capable of assuming any value $C$ at an essential singularity. For an essential singularity of $f(z)$ is also an essential singularity of $f(z)-C$ and therefore also of $\dfrac{1}{f(z)-C}$. The last function must have at least one infinite value among the values that it can assume at the point; and, for this infinite value, we have $f(z)=C$ at the point, so that $f(z)$ assumes the assigned value $C$ at the essential singularity.

*Note.* This result, that a uniform function can acquire any assigned value at an isolated essential singularity, is so contrary to the general idea of the one-valuedness of the function, that the function is often regarded as not existing at the point; and the point then is regarded as not belonging to the region of significance of the function. The difference between the two views is largely a matter of definition, and depends upon the difference between two modes of considering the variable $z$. If no account is allowed to be taken of the mode by which $z$ approaches its value at an essential singularity $a$, the function does not tend uniformly to any one value there. If such account is allowed, then it can happen (as in Ex. 4, above) that $z$ may approach the value $a$ along a particular path through a limiting series of values, in such a way that the function can acquire any assigned value in the limit when $z$ coincides with $a$ after the specified mode of approach.

**33.** There is one important property possessed by every uniform function in the immediate vicinity of any of its isolated essential singularities; it was first stated by Weierstrass\*, as follows:—*In the immediate vicinity of an isolated essential singularity of a uniform function, there are positions at which the function differs from an assigned value by a quantity not greater than a non-vanishing magnitude that can be made as small as we please.*

\* Weierstrass, *Ges. Werke*, t. ii, pp. 122—124; Durège, *Elemente der Theorie der Funktionen*, p. 119; Hölder, *Math. Ann.*, t. xx, (1882), pp. 138—143; Picard, "Mémoire sur les fonctions entières," *Annales de l'École Norm. Sup.*, 2ᵐᵉ Sér., t. ix, (1880), pp. 145—166, which, in this regard, should be consulted in connection with the developments in Chapter V. See also § 62. Picard's proof is followed in the text.

Let $a$ be the singularity, $C$ an assigned value, and $\epsilon$ a non-vanishing magnitude which can be chosen arbitrarily small at our own disposal; and in the vicinity of $a$, represented by

$$|z - a| < \rho,$$

consider the function $\dfrac{1}{f(z) - C}$. For values of $z$ in the range

$$0 < |z - a| < \rho,$$

this function may have poles, or it may not.

If it has poles, then at each of them $f(z) - C = 0$: that is, the function $f(z)$ actually attains the value $C$, so that the difference between $f(z)$ and $C$ for such positions is not merely less than $\epsilon$, it actually is zero.

If it has no poles, then the function

$$\frac{1}{f(z) - C}$$

is regular everywhere through the domain

$$0 < |z - a| < \rho,$$

because no point in that domain is either a pole or an essential singularity. Accordingly, by Laurent's theorem, it can be expanded in that domain in a converging series of positive and negative powers, in the form

$$\frac{1}{f(z) - C} = u_0 + (z - a)\, u_1 + \ldots\ldots + (z - a)^n\, u_n + \ldots\ldots$$
$$+ \frac{v_1}{z - a} + \frac{v_2}{(z - a)^2} + \ldots\ldots + \frac{v_m}{(z - a)^m} + \ldots\ldots$$

Choose a quantity $\rho'$ such that $0 < \rho' < \rho$. The series of positive powers converges everywhere within and on a circle, centre $a$ and radius $\rho'$: let $S(z)$ denote its value at $z$. The series of negative powers converges everywhere in the plane outside the point $a$; and therefore the series

$$v_1 + \frac{v_2}{z - a} + \frac{v_3}{(z - a)^2} + \ldots\ldots$$

converges everywhere outside the point $a$: let $T(z)$ denote its value, so that

$$\frac{1}{f(z) - C} = S(z) + \frac{T(z)}{z - a}.$$

Accordingly, as $|S(z)|$ is finite and $|T(z)|$ not zero—it may be a rapidly increasing quantity as $|z - a|$ decreases—choose $|z - a|$ so that, while not being zero, it gives the modulus of the right-hand side as greater than $\dfrac{1}{\epsilon}$. As $z - a$ occurs in a denominator, this can be done. Then, for such a value of $z$,

$$\left| \frac{1}{f(z) - C} \right| > \frac{1}{\epsilon},$$

and therefore

$$|f(z) - C| < \epsilon,$$

which proves the theorem.

It may happen that the function attains the value $C$ only at the essential singularity, where $C$ is one of its unlimited number of values. Thus to find the zeros of the function $\operatorname{cosec} \dfrac{1}{z}$ in the vicinity of the origin, we must have $\sin \dfrac{1}{z}$ infinite at them; this can only occur when $z$ becomes zero along the axis of imaginaries, and cannot occur for any value of $z$ such that $|z| > 0$. Such a value is called an *exceptional* value; the discussion of exceptional values is effected by Picard in his memoir quoted.

*Ex.* Discuss the character of the functions $\cos (1/z)$, $\tan (1/z)$ for values of $|z|$ which are very small; and the character of the functions $\tan z$, $e^{e^z}$, $z^{-n} e^z$, $e^{\sin \frac{1}{z}}$, $z \log z$, for values of $|z|$ which are very large.

**34.** Let $f(z)$ denote the function represented by a series of powers $P_1(z - a)$, the circle of convergence of which is the domain of the ordinary point $a$, and the coefficients in which are the values of the derivatives of $f(z)$ at $a$. The region over which the function $f(z)$ is holomorphic may extend beyond the domain of $a$, although the circumference bounding that domain is the greatest of centre $a$ that can be drawn within the region. The region evidently cannot extend beyond the domain of $a$ in all directions.

Take an ordinary point $b$ in the domain of $a$. The value at $b$ of the function $f(z)$ is given by the series $P_1(b - a)$, and the values at $b$ of all its derivatives are given by the derived series. All these series converge within the domain of $a$ and they are therefore finite at $b$; and their expressions involve the values at $a$ of the function and its derivatives.

Let the domain of $b$ be formed. The domain of $b$ may be included in that of $a$, and then its bounding circle will touch the bounding circle of the domain of $a$ internally. If the domain of $b$ be not entirely included in that of $a$, part of it will lie outside the domain of $a$; but it cannot include the whole of the domain of $a$ unless its bounding circumference touch that of the domain of $a$ externally, for otherwise it would extend beyond $a$ in all directions, a result inconsistent with the construction of the domain of $a$. Hence there must be points excluded from the domain of $a$ which are also excluded from the domain of $b$.

For all points $z$ in the domain of $b$, the function can be represented by a series, say $P_2(z - b)$, the coefficients of which are the values at $b$ of the function and its derivatives. Since these values are partially dependent upon the corresponding values at $a$, the series representing the function may be denoted by $P_2(z - b, a)$.

At a point $z$ in the domain of $b$ lying also in the domain of $a$, the two series $P_1(z - a)$ and $P_2(z - b, a)$ must furnish the same value for the function $f(z)$; and therefore no new value is derived from the new series $P_2$ which cannot be derived from the old series $P_1$. For all such points the new series is of no advantage; and hence, if the domain of $b$ be included in that of $a$, the construction of the series $P_2(z - b, a)$ is superfluous. Thus, in choosing the ordinary point $b$ in the domain of $a$ we choose a point, if possible, that will not have its domain included in that of $a$.

At a point $z$ in the domain of $b$, which does not lie in the domain of $a$, the series $P_2(z-b, a)$ gives a value for $f(z)$ which cannot be given by $P_1(z-a)$. The new series $P_2$ then gives an additional representation of the function; it is called* a *continuation* of the series which represents the function in the domain of $a$. The derivatives of $P_2$ give the values of the derivatives of $f(z)$ for points in the domain of $b$.

It thus appears that, if the whole of the domain of $b$ be not included in that of $a$, the function can, by the series which is valid over the whole of the new domain, be continued into that part of the new domain excluded from the domain of $a$.

Now take a point $c$ within the region occupied by the combined domains of $a$ and $b$; and construct the domain of $c$. In the new domain, the function can be represented by a new series, say $P_3(z-c)$, or, since the coefficients (being the values at $c$ of the function and of its derivatives) involve the values at $a$ and possibly also the values at $b$ of the function and of its derivatives, the series representing the function may be denoted by $P_3(z-c, a, b)$. Unless the domain of $c$ include points, which are not included in the combined domains of $a$ and $b$, the series $P_3$ does not give a value of the function which cannot be given by $P_1$ or $P_2$: we therefore choose $c$, if possible, so that its domain will include points not included in the earlier domains. At such points $z$ in the domain of $c$ as are excluded from the combined domains of $a$ and $b$, the series $P_3(z-c, a, b)$ gives a value for $f(z)$ which cannot be derived from $P_1$ or $P_2$; and thus the new series is a continuation of the earlier series.

Proceeding in this manner by taking successive points and constructing their domains, we can reach all parts of the plane connected with one another where the function preserves its holomorphic character; their combined aggregate is called† the *region of continuity* of the function. With each domain, constructed so as to include some portion of the region of continuity not included in the earlier domains, a series is associated, which is a continuation of the earlier series and, as such, gives a value of the function not deducible from those earlier series; and all the associated series are ultimately deduced from the first.

Each of the continuations is called an *Element* of the function. The aggregate of all the distinct elements is called a *monogenic analytic function*: it is evidently the complete analytical expression of the function in its region of continuity.

Let $z$ be any point in the region of continuity, not necessarily in the circle of convergence of the initial element of the function; a value of the

---

* Biermann, *Theorie der analytischen Functionen*, p. 170, which may be consulted in connection with the whole of § 34; the German word is *Fortsetzung*.

† Weierstrass, *Ges. Werke*, t. ii, p. 77.

function at $z$ can be obtained through the continuations of that initial element. In the formation of each new domain (and therefore of each new element) a certain amount of arbitrary choice is possible; and there may, moreover, be different sets of domains which, taken together in a set, each lead to $z$ from the initial point. When the analytic function is uniform, as before defined (§ 12), the same value at $z$ for the function is obtained, whatever be the set of domains. If there be two sets of elements, differently obtained, which give at $z$ different values for the function, then the analytic function is multiform, as before defined (§ 12); but not every change in a set of elements leads to a change in the value at $z$ of a multiform function, and the analytic function is uniform within such a region of the plane as admits only equivalent changes of elements.

The whole process is reversible when the function is uniform. We can pass back from any point to any earlier point by the use, if necessary, of intermediate points. Thus, if the point $a$ in the foregoing explanation be not included in the domain of $b$ (there supposed to contribute a continuation of the first series), an intermediate point on a line, drawn in the region of continuity so as to join $a$ and $b$, would be taken; and so on, until a domain is formed which does include $a$. The continuation, associated with this domain, must give at $a$ the proper value for the function and its derivatives, and therefore for the domain of $a$ the original series $P_1(z-a)$ will be obtained, that is, $P_1(z-a)$ can be deduced from $P_2(z-b, a)$ the series in the domain of $b$. This result is general, so that *any one of the continuations of a uniform function, represented by a power-series, can be deduced from any other;* and therefore the expression of such a function in its region of continuity is potentially given by one element, for all the distinct elements can be deduced from any one element.

**35.** It has been assumed that the property, characteristic of some of the uniform functions adduced as examples, of possessing either accidental or essential singularities, is characteristic of all such functions; it will be proved (§ 40) to hold for every uniform function which is not a mere constant.

The singularities limit the region of continuity; for each of the separate domains is, from its construction, limited by the nearest singularity, and the combined aggregate of the domains constitutes the region of continuity when they form a continuous space*. Hence the complete boundary of the region of continuity is the aggregate of the singularities of the function†.

---

* Cases occur in which the region of continuity of a function is composed of isolated spaces, each continuous in itself, but not continuous into one another. The consideration of such cases will be dealt with briefly hereafter, an l they are assumed excluded for the present: meanwhile, it is sufficient to note that each continuous space could be deduced from an element belonging to some domain of that space and that a new element would be needed for a new space.

† See Weierstrass, *Ges. Werke*, t. ii, pp. 77—79; Mittag-Leffler, "Sur la représentation analytique des fonctions monogènes uniformes d'une variable indépendante," *Acta Math.*, t. iv, (1884), pp. 1 et seq., especially pp. 1—8.

It may happen that a function has no singularity except at infinity; the region of continuity then extends over the whole finite part of the plane but it does not include the point at infinity.

It follows from the foregoing explanations that, in order to know a uniform analytic function, it is necessary to know some element of the function, which has been shewn to be potentially sufficient for the derivation of the full expression of the function and for the construction of its region of continuity. But the process of continuation is mainly descriptive of the analytic function, and in actual practice it can prove too elaborate to be effected[*].

To avoid the continuation process, Mittag-Leffler has devised[†] another method of representing a uniform function. Let $a$ be an ordinary point of the function, and let a line, terminated at $a$, rotate round it. In the vicinity of $a$, let the element of the function be denoted by $P(z-a)$; and imagine the continuation of this element to be effected along the vector as far as possible. It may happen that the continuation can be effected to infinity along the vector; if not, there is some point $a'$ on the vector beyond which the continuation is impossible. In the latter case, the part of the vector[‡] from $a'$ to infinity is excluded from the range of variation of the variable. Let this be done for every position of the vector; then the part of the plane, which remains after these various ranges have been excluded, gives a star-shaped figure, which is a region of continuity of the uniform function of which $P(z-a)$ is the initial element. The function manifestly can be continued over the whole of this star, by means of appropriate elements; but there is no indication as to the necessary number of elements. Instead of using the elements to express the function, Mittag-Leffler constructs a single expression, which is the valid representation of the function over the whole star; the expression is an infinite series of polynomials, and not merely a power-series.

Thus let there be a power-series

$$b_0 + b_1(z-a) + \frac{1}{2!} b_2(z-a)^2 + \frac{1}{3!} b_3(z-a)^3 + \dots,$$

which converges uniformly in a region round the point $a$; the radius of convergence of the series is $r$, where $1/r$ is the upper limit of the quantities $(b_n/n!)^{\frac{1}{n}}$. Let the star-shaped figure be constructed; the following is the simplest form of expression as obtained by Mittag-Leffler to represent, over the whole star, the function of which the foregoing series is an element. Let the quantity

$$\sum_{\lambda_1=0}^{p^2} \sum_{\lambda_2=0}^{p^4} \dots \sum_{\lambda_p=0}^{p^{2p}} \frac{b_{\lambda_1+\lambda_2+\dots+\lambda_p}}{\lambda_1! \, \lambda_2! \dots \lambda_p!} \left(\frac{z-a}{p}\right)^{\lambda_1+\lambda_2+\dots+\lambda_p},$$

---

* Some examples have been constructed by Prof. M. J. M. Hill, *Proc. Lond. Math. Soc.*, vol. xxxv, (1903), pp. 388—416.

† Exact references are given at the beginning of Chapter VII.

‡ In effect, this is a *section*, in the sense used in § 103.

which is a polynomial, be denoted by $g_p(z)$; and take

$$G_0(z) = g_0(z) = b_0,$$
$$G_n(z) = g_n(z) - g_{n-1}(z), \quad \text{for } z = 1, 2, \ldots.$$

Mittag-Leffler's expression is

$$\sum_{\mu=0}^{\infty} G_\mu(z);$$

and it converges everywhere within the star.

Again, an element representing a function is effective only within its own circle of convergence, while it may be known that the function is holomorphic over some closed domain which touches the circle of convergence externally. The process of continuation would make it possible to obtain the analytical representation over the whole domain by means of appropriate elements: but again there is no indication as to the necessary number of elements. Painlevé* has shewn how to construct a single expression, which is the valid representation of the function over the whole domain; this expression also is an infinite series of polynomials, and not merely a power-series.

For the establishment of these results, we refer to the memoirs quoted.

**36.**  The method of continuation of a function, by means of successive elements, is quite general; there is one particular continuation, which is important in investigations on conformal representation. It is contained in the following proposition, due to Schwarz† :—

*If an analytic function w of z be defined only for a region S′ in the positive half of the z-plane, and if continuous real values of w correspond to continuous real values of z, then w can be continued across the axis of real quantities.*

Consider a region $S''$, symmetrical with $S'$ relative to the axis of real quantities (fig. 12). Then a function is defined for the region $S''$ by associating a value $w_0$, the conjugate of $w$, with $z_0$, the conjugate of $z$.

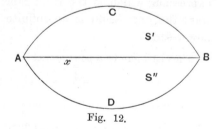

Fig. 12.

Let the two regions be combined along the portion of the axis of $x$ which is their common boundary; they then form a single region $S' + S''$.

Consider the integrals

$$\frac{1}{2\pi i} \int_{S'} \frac{w}{z - \zeta}\, dz \quad \text{and} \quad \frac{1}{2\pi i} \int_{S''} \frac{w_0}{z_0 - \zeta}\, dz_0,$$

taken round the boundaries of $S'$ and of $S''$ respectively. Since $w$ is continuous over the whole area of $S'$ as well as along its boundary, and

---

* *Comptes Rendus*, t. cxxvi, (1898), pp. 320, 321; see also the references to Painlevé at the beginning of Chapter VII.

† *Crelle*, t. lxx, (1869), pp. 106, 107, and *Ges. Math. Abh.*, t. ii, pp. 66—68.  See also Darboux, *Théorie générale des surfaces*, t. i, § 130.

likewise $w_0$ relative to $S''$, it follows that, if the point $\zeta$ be in $S'$, the value of the first integral is $w(\zeta)$ and that of the second is zero; while, if $\zeta$ be in $S''$, the value of the first integral is zero and that of the second is $w_0(\zeta)$. Hence the sum of the two integrals represents a unique function of a point in either $S'$ or $S''$. But the value of the first integral is

$$\frac{1}{2\pi i}\int_{B}^{A}\frac{wdz}{(C)\ z-\zeta}+\frac{1}{2\pi i}\int_{A}^{B}\frac{w(x)\,dx}{x-\zeta},$$

the first being taken along the curve $BCA$ and the second along the axis $AxB$; and the value of the second integral is

$$\frac{1}{2\pi i}\int_{B}^{A}\frac{w_0(x)\,dx}{x-\zeta}+\frac{1}{2\pi i}\int_{A}^{B}\frac{w_0\,dz_0}{(D)\ z_0-\zeta},$$

the first being taken along the axis $BxA$ and the second along the curve $ADB$. But

$$w_0(x)=w(x),$$

because conjugate values $w$ and $w_0$ correspond to conjugate values of the argument by definition of $w_0$, and because $w$ (and therefore also $w_0$) is real and continuous when the argument is real and continuous. Hence when the sum of the four integrals is taken, the two integrals corresponding to the two descriptions of the axis of $x$ cancel; we have as the sum

$$\frac{1}{2\pi i}\int_{B}^{A}\frac{wdz}{(C)\ z-\zeta}+\frac{1}{2\pi i}\int_{A}^{B}\frac{w_0\,dz_0}{(D)\ z_0-\zeta},$$

and this sum represents a unique function of a point in $S'+S''$. These two integrals, taken together, are

$$\frac{1}{2\pi i}\int\frac{w'dz}{z-\zeta},$$

taken round the whole contour of $S'+S''$, where $w'$ is equal to $w(\zeta)$ in the positive half of the plane and to $w_0(\zeta)$ in the negative half.

For all points $\zeta$ in the whole region $S'+S''$, this integral represents a single uniform, finite, continuous function of $\zeta$; its value is $w(\zeta)$ in the positive half of the plane and is $w_0(\zeta)$ in the negative half; and therefore $w_0(\zeta)$ is the continuation, into the negative half of the plane, of the function which is defined by $w(\zeta)$ for the positive half.

For a point $c$ on the axis of $x$, we have

$$w(z)-w(c)=A(z-c)+B(z-c)^2+C(z-c)^3+\dots;$$

and all the coefficients $A$, $B$, $C$, ... are real. If, in addition, $w$ be such a function of $z$ that the inverse functional relation makes $z$ a uniform analytic function of $w$, obviously $A$ must not vanish. Thus the functional relation may be expressed in the form

$$w(z)-w(c)=(z-c)P(z-c),$$

where $P(z-c)$ does not vanish when $z=c$.

# CHAPTER IV.

## General properties of Uniform Functions, particularly of those without Essential Singularities.

**37.** In the derivation of the general properties of functions, which will be deduced in the present and the next three chapters from the results already obtained, it is to be supposed, in the absence of any express statement to other effect, that the functions are uniform, monogenic and, except at either accidental or essential singularities, continuous*.

THEOREM I. *A function, which is constant throughout any region of the plane however small, or which is constant along any line however short, is constant throughout its region of continuity.*

For the first part of the theorem, we take any point $a$ in the region of the plane where the function is constant; and we draw a circle of centre $a$ and of any radius, taking care that the circle remains within the region of continuity of the function. At any point $z$ within this circle, we have

$$f(z) = f(a) + (z - a)f'(a) + \frac{(z - a)^2}{2!} f''(a) + \dots,$$

a converging series the coefficients of which are the values of the function and its derivatives at $a$. Let a point $a + \delta a$ be taken in the region; then

$$f'(a) = \text{Limit of } \frac{f(a + \delta a) - f(a)}{\delta a},$$

which is zero because $f(a + \delta a)$ is the same constant as $f(a)$: so that the first derivative is zero at $a$. Similarly, all the derivatives can be shewn to be zero at $a$; hence the above series after its first term is evanescent, and we have

$$f(z) = f(a),$$

that is, the function preserves its constant value throughout its region of continuity.

The second result follows in the same way, when once the derivatives are proved zero. Since the function is monogenic, the value of the first and

---

* It will be assumed, as in § 35 (note, p. 68), that the region of continuity consists of a single space. Functions, which exist in regions of continuity consisting of a number of separated spaces, will be discussed in Chap. VII.

of each of the successive derivatives will be obtained, if we make the differential element of the independent variable vanish along the line.

Now, if $a$ be a point on the line and $a + \delta a$ a consecutive point, we have $f(a + \delta a) = f(a)$; hence $f'(a)$ is zero. Similarly the first derivative at any other point on the line is zero. Therefore we have $f'(a + \delta a) = f'(a)$, for each has just been proved to be zero: hence $f''(a)$ is zero. Similarly the value of the second derivative at any other point on the line is zero. So on for all the derivatives: the value of each of them at $a$ is zero.

Using the same expansion as before and inserting again the zero values of all the derivatives at $a$, we find that

$$f(z) = f(a),$$

so that under the assigned condition the function preserves its constant value throughout its region of continuity.

It should be noted that, if in the first case the area and in the second the line reduce to a point, then consecutive points cannot be taken; the values at $a$ of the derivatives cannot be proved to be zero and the theorem cannot then be inferred.

COROLLARY I. *If two functions have the same value over any area of their common region of continuity however small or along any line in that region however short, then they have the same values at all points in their common region of continuity.*

This is at once evident: for their difference is zero over that area or along that line and therefore, by the preceding theorem, their difference has a constant zero value, that is, the functions have the same values, everywhere in their common region of continuity.

But two functions can have the same values at a succession of isolated points, without having the same values everywhere in their common region of continuity; in such a case the theorem does not apply, the reason being that the fundamental condition of equality over a continuous area or along a continuous line is not satisfied.

COROLLARY II. *A function cannot be zero over any area of its region of continuity however small, or along any line in that region however short, without being zero everywhere in its region of continuity.*

It is deduced in the same manner as the preceding corollary.

If, then, there be a function which is evidently not zero everywhere, we conclude that *its zeros are isolated points though such points may be multiple zeros.*

Further, *in any finite area of the region of continuity of a function that is subject to variation, there can be at most only a finite number of its zeros, when no point of the boundary of the area is an essential singularity.* For if there were an infinite number of such points in any such region, there must be a cluster in at least one area or a succession along at least one line, infinite in number. Either they must then constitute a continuous area or a continuous line where the function is everywhere zero: which would require that the function should be zero everywhere in its region of continuity, a condition excluded by the hypothesis. Or they must be so close to some point, say $c$, that the function has an unlimited number of zeros within a region

$$|z - c| < \epsilon,$$

where $\epsilon$ can be made as small as we please: and so for non-zero values of the function. After the general properties which have been established, and the proposition of § 33, it is clear that $c$ is an essential singularity of the function, contrary to the hypothesis as to the region of continuity of the function.

It immediately follows that the points within a region of continuity, at which a function assumes any the same value, are isolated points; and that only a finite number of such points occur in any finite area.

This result may be established in another way.

Let $f(z)$ be a uniform monogenic function; we proceed to shew that, when $f(a)$ is not zero, we can choose a region round $a$ in which $f(z)$ nowhere vanishes. We have

$$f(z) = a_0 + a_1(z - a) + a_2(z - a)^2 + \dots,$$

where $a_0$ is not zero, the series for $f(z)$ converging absolutely and uniformly for values of $z$ such that

$$|z - a| \leqslant r < R.$$

Within or on the circle $r$, let $M$ be the greatest value of

$$|a_1 + a_2(z - a) + \dots|,$$

so that $M$ is, of course, finite. Let

$$|a_0| = Ms,$$

so that $s$ is finite; and take values of $z$ such that

$$|z - a| \leqslant \sigma < s.$$

Then

$$|f(z)| \geqslant |a_0| - |z - a||a_1 + a_2(z - a) + \dots|$$
$$\geqslant a_0 - \sigma M$$
$$\geqslant (s - \sigma) M,$$

so that, at no place within this region can $f(z)$ vanish.

Now let $c$ be a zero of $f(z)$ of order $n$, so that

$$f(z) = (z - c)^n g(z),$$

where $g(c)$ is not zero and $g(z)$ is uniform and monogenic. By what has just been proved, we can choose a region round $c$ such that $g(z)$ has no zero within it. Then obviously $f(z)$ has no zero within that region except at the place $c$; in other words, the zero of $f(z)$ is an isolated point.

**38.** THEOREM II. *The multiplicity $m$ of any zero $a$ of a function is finite provided the zero be an ordinary point of the function, supposed not to be zero throughout its region of continuity; and the function can be expressed in the form*

$$(z-a)^m \phi(z),$$

*where $\phi(z)$ is holomorphic in the vicinity of $a$, and $a$ is not a zero of $\phi(z)$.*

Let $f(z)$ denote the function; since $a$ is a zero, we have $f(a) = 0$. Suppose that $f'(a), f''(a), \ldots\ldots$ vanish: in the succession of the derivatives of $f$, one of finite order must be reached which does not have a zero value. Otherwise, if all vanish, then the function and all its derivatives would vanish at $a$; the expansion of $f(z)$ in powers of $z-a$ would lead to zero as the value of $f(z)$, that is, the function would everywhere be zero in the region of continuity, if all the derivatives vanish at $a$.

Let, then, the $m$th derivative be the first in the natural succession which does not vanish at $a$, so that $m$ is finite. Using Cauchy's expansion, we have

$$f(z) = \frac{(z-a)^m}{m!} f^{(m)}(a) + \frac{(z-a)^{m+1}}{(m+1)!} f^{(m+1)}(a) + \ldots$$
$$= (z-a)^m \phi(z),$$

where $\phi(z)$ is a function that does not vanish with $a$ and, being the quotient of a converging series by a monomial factor, is holomorphic in the immediate vicinity of $a$.

COROLLARY I. *If infinity be a zero of a function of multiplicity $m$ and at the same time be an ordinary point of the function, then the function can be expressed in the form*

$$z^{-m} \phi\left(\frac{1}{z}\right),$$

*where $\phi\left(\frac{1}{z}\right)$ is a function that is continuous and different from zero for infinitely large values of $z$.*

The result can be derived from the expansion in § 30 in the same way as the foregoing theorem from Cauchy's expansion.

COROLLARY II. *The number of zeros of a function, account being taken of their multiplicity, which occur within a finite area of the region of continuity of the function, is finite, when no point of the boundary of the area is an essential singularity.*

By Corollary II. of § 37, the number of distinct zeros in the limited area is finite, and, by the foregoing theorem, the multiplicity of each is finite;

hence, when account is taken of their respective multiplicities, the total number of zeros is still finite.

The result is, of course, a known result for a polynomial in the variables; but the functions in the enunciation are not restricted to be of the type of polynomials.

*Note.* It is important to notice, both for Theorem II. and for its Corollary I., that the zero is an ordinary point of the function under consideration; the implication therefore is that the zero is a definite zero and that in the immediate vicinity of the point the function can be represented in the form $P(z-a)$ or $P\left(\frac{1}{z}\right)$, the function $P(a-a)$ or $P\left(\frac{1}{\infty}\right)$ being always a definite zero.

Instances do occur for which this condition is not satisfied. The point may not be an ordinary point, and the zero value may be an indeterminate zero; or zero may be only one of a set of distinct values though everywhere in the vicinity the function is regular. Thus the analysis of § 13 shews that $z=a$ is a point where the function $\operatorname{sn}\dfrac{1}{z-a}$ has any number of zero values and any number of infinite values, and there is no indication that there are not also other values at the point. In such a case the preceding proposition does not apply; there may be no limit to the order of multiplicity of the zero, and we certainly cannot infer that any finite integer $m$ can be obtained such that

$$(z-a)^{-m}\,\phi(z)$$

is finite at the point. Such a point is (§§ 32, 33) an essential singularity of the function.

**39.** THEOREM III. *A multiple zero of a function is a zero of its derivative; and the multiplicity for the derivative is less or is greater by unity according as the zero is not or is at infinity.*

If $a$ be a point in the finite part of the plane which is a zero of $f(z)$ of multiplicity $n$, we have

$$f(z) = (z-a)^n\,\phi(z),$$

and therefore $\qquad f'(z) = (z-a)^{n-1}\{n\phi(z)+(z-a)\,\phi'(z)\}.$

The coefficient of $(z-a)^{n-1}$ is holomorphic in the immediate vicinity of $a$ and does not vanish for $a$; hence $a$ is a zero for $f'(z)$ of decreased multiplicity $n-1$.

If $z=\infty$ be a zero of $f(z)$ of multiplicity $r$, then

$$f(z) = z^{-r}\,\phi\left(\frac{1}{z}\right),$$

where $\phi\left(\dfrac{1}{z}\right)$ is holomorphic for very large values of $z$ and does not vanish at infinity.   Therefore

$$f'(z) = -rz^{-r-1}\phi\left(\frac{1}{z}\right) - z^{-r-2}\phi'\left(\frac{1}{z}\right)$$

$$= z^{-r-1}\left\{-r\phi\left(\frac{1}{z}\right) - \frac{1}{z}\phi'\left(\frac{1}{z}\right)\right\}.$$

The coefficient of $z^{-r-1}$ is holomorphic for very large values of $z$, and does not vanish at infinity; hence $z = \infty$ is a zero of $f'(z)$ of increased multiplicity $r+1$.

*Corollary I.*   If a function be finite at infinity, then $z = \infty$ is a zero of the first derivative of multiplicity at least two.

*Corollary II.*   If $a$ be a finite zero of $f(z)$ of multiplicity $n$, we have

$$\frac{f'(z)}{f(z)} = \frac{n}{z-a} + \frac{\phi'(z)}{\phi(z)}.$$

Now $a$ is not a zero of $\phi(z)$; and therefore $\dfrac{\phi'(z)}{\phi(z)}$ is finite, continuous, uniform and monogenic in the immediate vicinity of $a$.   Hence, taking the integral of both members of the equation round a circle of centre $a$ and of radius so small as to include no infinity and no zero, other than $a$, of $f(z)$—and therefore no zero of $\phi(z)$—we have, by former propositions,

$$\frac{1}{2\pi i}\int\frac{f'(z)}{f(z)}\,dz = n.$$

**40.**   THEOREM IV.   *A function must have an infinite value for some finite or infinite value of the variable.*

If $M$ be a finite maximum value of the modulus for points in the plane, then (§ 22) we have

$$|f^{(n)}(a)| < \frac{n!\,M}{r^n},$$

where $r$ is the radius of an arbitrary circle of centre $a$, provided the whole of the circle is in the region of continuity of the function.   But as the function is uniform, monogenic, finite and continuous everywhere, this radius can be increased indefinitely; when this increase takes place, the limit of

$$|f^{(n)}(a)|$$

is zero, and therefore $f^{(n)}(a)$ vanishes.   This is true for all the indices $1, 2, \ldots$ of the derivatives.

Now the function can be represented at any point $z$ in the vicinity of $a$ by the series

$$f(a) + (z-a)f'(a) + \frac{(z-a)^2}{2!}f''(a) + \ldots,$$

which degenerates, under the present hypothesis, to $f(a)$, so that the function is everywhere constant. Hence, if a function has not an infinity somewhere in the plane, it must be a constant.

The given function is not a constant; and therefore there is no finite limit to the maximum value of its modulus, that is, the function acquires an infinite value somewhere in the plane.

COROLLARY I. *A function must have a zero value for some finite or infinite value of the variable.*

For the reciprocal of a uniform monogenic analytic function is itself a uniform monogenic analytic function; and the foregoing proposition shews that this reciprocal must have an infinite value for some value of the variable, which therefore is a zero of the original function.

COROLLARY II. *A function must assume any assigned value at least once.*

COROLLARY III. *Every function which is not a mere constant must have at least one singularity, either accidental or essential.* For it must have an infinite value: if this be a determinate infinity, the point is an accidental singularity (§ 32); if it be an infinity among a set of values at the point, the point is an essential singularity (§§ 32, 33).

**41.** Among the infinities of a function, the simplest class is that constituted by its poles or accidental singularities, already defined (§ 32) by the property that, in the immediate vicinity of such a point, the reciprocal of the function is regular, the point being an ordinary (zero) point for that reciprocal.

It follows from this property that, because (§ 37) an ordinary zero of a uniform function is an isolated point, every pole of a uniform function is also an isolated point: that is to say, in some non-infinitesimal region round a pole $a$, no other pole of the function can occur.

THEOREM V. *A function, which has a point c for an accidental singularity, can be expressed in the form*

$$(z - c)^{-n} \, \phi(z),$$

*where n is a finite positive integer and $\phi(z)$ is a continuous function in the vicinity of c.*

Since $c$ is an accidental singularity of the function $f(z)$, the function $\dfrac{1}{f(z)}$ is regular in the vicinity of $c$ and is zero there (§ 32). Hence, by § 38, there is a finite limit to the multiplicity of the zero, say $n$ (which is a positive integer), and we have

$$\frac{1}{f(z)} = (z - c)^n \, \chi(z),$$

where $\chi(z)$ is uniform, monogenic and continuous in the vicinity of $c$ and is not zero there. The reciprocal of $\chi(z)$, say $\phi(z)$, is also uniform, monogenic and continuous in the vicinity of $c$, which is an ordinary point for $\phi(z)$; hence we have

$$f(z) = (z - \dot{c})^{-n} \, \phi(z),$$

which proves the theorem.

The finite positive integer $n$ measures the *multiplicity* of the accidental singularity at $c$, which is sometimes said to be of multiplicity $n$ or of order $n$.

Another analytical expression for $f(z)$ can be derived from that which has just been obtained. Since $c$ is an ordinary point for $\phi(z)$ and not a zero, this function can be expanded in a series of ascending, positive, integral powers of $z - c$, converging in the vicinity of $c$, in the form

$$\phi(z) = P(z - c)$$
$$= u_0 + u_1(z - c) + \ldots + u_{n-1}(z - c)^{n-1} + u_n(z - c)^n + \ldots$$
$$= u_0 + u_1(z - c) + \ldots + u_{n-1}(z - c)^{n-1} + (z - c)^n \, Q(z - c),$$

where $Q(z - c)$, a series of positive, integral, powers of $z - c$ converging in the vicinity of $c$, is a monogenic analytic function of $z$. Hence we have

$$f(z) = \frac{u_0}{(z - c)^n} + \frac{u_1}{(z - c)^{n-1}} + \ldots + \frac{u_{n-1}}{z - c} + Q(z - c),$$

the indicated expression for $f(z)$, valid in the immediate vicinity of $c$, where $Q(z - c)$ is uniform, finite, continuous and monogenic.

COROLLARY. *A function, which has $z = \infty$ for an accidental singularity of multiplicity $n$, can be expressed in the form*

$$z^n \phi\left(\frac{1}{z}\right),$$

*where $\phi\left(\frac{1}{z}\right)$ is a continuous function for very large values of $|z|$, and is not zero when $z = \infty$. It can also be expressed in the form*

$$a_0 z^n + a_1 z^{n-1} + \ldots + a_{n-1} z + Q\left(\frac{1}{z}\right),$$

*where $Q\left(\frac{1}{z}\right)$ is uniform, finite, continuous and monogenic for very large values of $|z|$.*

The derivation of the form of the function in the vicinity of an accidental singularity has been made to depend upon the form of the reciprocal of the function.

As the accidental singularities of a function are isolated points, there is only a finite number of them in any limited portion of the plane.

**42.** We can deduce a criterion which determines whether a given singularity of a uniform function $f(z)$ is accidental or essential.

When the point is in the finite part of the plane, say at $c$, and a finite positive integer $n$ can be found such that

$$(z-c)^n f(z)$$

is not infinite at $c$, then $c$ is an accidental singularity.

When the point is at infinity and a finite positive integer $n$ can be found such that

$$z^{-n} f(z)$$

is not infinite when $z = \infty$, then $z = \infty$ is an accidental singularity.

If the condition be not satisfied in the respective cases, the singularity at the point is essential. But it must not be assumed that the failure of the limitation to finiteness in the multiplicity of the accidental singularity is the only source or the complete cause of essential singularity.

Since the association of a single factor with the function is effective in preventing an infinite value at the point when the condition is satisfied, it is justifiable to regard the discontinuity of the function at the point as not essential, and to call the singularity either non-essential or accidental (§ 32).

**43.** THEOREM VI. *The poles of a function, that lie in the finite part of the plane, are all the poles (of increased multiplicity) of the derivatives of the function that lie in the finite part of the plane.*

Let $c$ be a pole of the function $f(z)$ of multiplicity $p$: then, for any point $z$ in the vicinity of $c$,

$$f(z) = (z-c)^{-p} \phi(z),$$

where $\phi(z)$ is holomorphic in the vicinity of $c$, and does not vanish for $z = c$. We have

$$f'(z) = (z-c)^{-p} \phi'(z) - p(z-c)^{-p-1} \phi(z)$$
$$= (z-c)^{-p-1}\{(z-c)\phi'(z) - p\phi(z)\}$$
$$= (z-c)^{-p-1} \chi(z),$$

where $\chi(z)$ is holomorphic in the vicinity of $c$, and does not vanish for $z = c$.

Hence $c$ is a pole of $f'(z)$ of multiplicity $p+1$. Similarly it can be shewn to be a pole of $f^{(r)}(z)$ of multiplicity $p+r$.

This proves that all the poles of $f(z)$ in the finite part of the plane are poles of its derivatives. It remains to prove that a derivative cannot have a pole which the original function does not also possess.

Let $\alpha$ be a pole of $f'(z)$ of multiplicity $m$: then, in the vicinity of $\alpha$, $f'(z)$ can be expressed in the form

$$(z-\alpha)^{-m} \psi(z),$$

where $\psi(z)$ is holomorphic in the vicinity of $\alpha$ and does not vanish for $z = \alpha$. Thus

$$\psi(z) = \psi(\alpha) + (z - \alpha)\,\psi'(\alpha) + \dots,$$

and therefore

$$f'(z) = \frac{\psi(\alpha)}{(z - \alpha)^m} + \frac{\psi'(\alpha)}{(z - \alpha)^{m-1}} + \dots,$$

so that, integrating, we have

$$f(z) = -\frac{\psi(\alpha)}{(m-1)(z-\alpha)^{m-1}} - \frac{\psi'(\alpha)}{(m-2)(z-\alpha)^{m-2}} - \dots.$$

When there is no term in $\log(z - \alpha)$ in this expression, $f(z)$ is uniform: that is, $\alpha$ is a pole of $f(z)$. When there is a term in $\log(z - \alpha)$, then $f(z)$ is not uniform.

An exception occurs in the case when $m$ is unity: for then

$$f'(z) = \frac{\psi(\alpha)}{z-\alpha} + \psi'(\alpha) + \frac{z-\alpha}{2!}\psi''(\alpha) + \dots,$$

the integral of which leads to

$$f(z) = \psi(\alpha)\log(z - \alpha) + \dots,$$

so that $f(z)$ is no longer uniform, contrary to hypothesis. Hence *a derivative cannot have a simple pole in the finite part of the plane;* and so this exception is excluded.

The theorem is thus proved.

COROLLARY I. *The $r^{\text{th}}$ derivative of a function cannot have a pole in the finite part of the plane of multiplicity less than $r + 1$.*

COROLLARY II. *If $c$ be a pole of $f(z)$ of any order of multiplicity $\mu$, and if $f^{(r)}(z)$ be expressed in the form*

$$\frac{a_0}{(z-c)^{\mu+r}} + \frac{a_1}{(z-c)^{\mu+r-1}} + \dots,$$

*there are no terms in this expression with the indices $-1, -2, \dots, -r$.*

COROLLARY III. *If $c$ be a pole of $f(z)$ of multiplicity $p$, we have*

$$\frac{f'(z)}{f(z)} = \frac{-p}{z-c} + \frac{\phi'(z)}{\phi(z)},$$

where $\phi(z)$ is a holomorphic function that does not vanish for $z = c$, so that $\dfrac{\phi'(z)}{\phi(z)}$ is a holomorphic function in the vicinity of $c$. Taking the integral of $\dfrac{f'(z)}{f(z)}$ round a circle, with $c$ for centre, with radius so small as to exclude all other poles or zeros of the function $f(z)$, we have

$$\frac{1}{2\pi i}\int \frac{f'(z)}{f(z)}\,dz = -p.$$

COROLLARY IV. *If a simple closed curve include a number $N$ of zeros of a uniform function $f(z)$ and a number $P$ of its poles, in both of which* numbers account is taken of possible multiplicity, and if the curve contain no essential singularity of the function, then

$$\frac{1}{2\pi i} \int \frac{f'(z)}{f(z)}\, dz = N - P,$$

the integral being taken round the curve.

The only infinities of the function $\dfrac{f'(z)}{f(z)}$ within the curve are the zeros and the poles of $f(z)$. Round each of these draw a circle of radius so small as to include it but no other infinity; then, by Cor. II. § 19, the integral round the closed curve is the sum of the values when taken round these circles. By the Corollary II. § 39 and by the preceding Corollary III., the sum of these values is

$$= \Sigma n - \Sigma p$$
$$= N - P.$$

It is easy to infer the known theorem that the number of roots of a polynomial of order $n$ is $n$, as well as the further result that $2\pi (N - P)$ is the variation of the argument of $f(z)$, when $z$ describes the closed curve in a positive sense.

*Ex.* 1.  A function $f(z)$ is uniform over an area bounded by a contour; it has no essential singularity within that area; and it has no zero and no pole on the contour. Prove that the change in the argument of $f(z)$, as $z$ makes a complete description of the contour, is $2\pi (n \sim p)$, where $n$ is the number of zeros and $p$ is the number of poles within the area.                                                                    (Cauchy.)

*Ex.* 2.  Prove that, if $F(z)$ be holomorphic over an area of simple contour, which contains roots $a_1,\ a_2, \ldots$ of multiplicity $m_1,\ m_2, \ldots$ and poles $c_1,\ c_2, \ldots$ of multiplicity $p_1,\ p_2, \ldots$ respectively of a function $f(z)$ which has no other singularities within the contour, then

$$\frac{1}{2\pi i} \int F(z)\cdot\frac{f'(z)}{f(z)}\, dz = \underset{r=1}{\Sigma}\, m_r F(a_r) - \underset{r=1}{\Sigma}\, p_r F(c_r),$$

the integral being taken round the contour.

In particular, if the contour contains a single simple root $a$ and no singularity, then that root is given by

$$a = \frac{1}{2\pi i} \int z\, \frac{f'(z)}{f(z)}\, dz,$$

the integral being taken as before.                                                              (Laurent.)

*Ex.* 3.  Discuss the integral in the preceding example when $F(z) = \log z$, and the origin is excluded by a small circle of radius $\rho$, less than the smallest of the quantities $|\, a_r\, |$ and $|\, c_r\, |$.                                                                                          (Goursat.)

**44.**   THEOREM VII.   *If infinity be a pole of $f(z)$, it is also a pole of $f'(z)$ only when it is a multiple pole of $f(z)$.*

Let the multiplicity of the pole for $f(z)$ be $n$; then for very large values of $z$ we have

$$f(z) = z^n\, \phi\left(\frac{1}{z}\right),$$

where $\phi$ is holomorphic for very large values of $z$ and does not vanish at infinity; hence

$$f'(z) = z^{n-1}\left\{n\phi\left(\frac{1}{z}\right) - \frac{1}{z}\,\phi'\left(\frac{1}{z}\right)\right\}.$$

The coefficient of $z^{n-1}$ is holomorphic for very large values of $z$ and does not vanish at infinity; hence infinity is a pole of $f'(z)$ of multiplicity $n-1$.

If $n$ be unity, so that infinity is a simple pole of $f(z)$, then it is not a pole of $f'(z)$; the derivative is then finite at infinity.

**45.  THEOREM VIII.**  *A function, which has no singularity in a finite part of the plane, and has $z = \infty$ for a pole, is a polynomial in $z$.*

Let $n$, necessarily a finite integer, be the order of multiplicity of the pole at infinity: then the function $f(z)$ can be expressed in the form

$$a_0 z^n + a_1 z^{n-1} + \ldots\ldots + a_{n-1}z + Q\left(\frac{1}{z}\right),$$

where $Q\left(\dfrac{1}{z}\right)$ is a holomorphic function for very large values of $z$, and is finite (or zero) when $z$ is infinite.

Now the first $n$ terms of the series constitute a function which has no singularities in the finite part of the plane: and $f(z)$ has no singularities in that part of the plane.  Hence $Q\left(\dfrac{1}{z}\right)$ has no singularities in the finite part of the plane: it is finite for infinite values of $z$.  It thus can never have an infinite value: and it is therefore merely a constant, say $a_n$.  Then

$$f(z) = a_0 z^n + a_1 z^{n-1} + \ldots\ldots + a_{n-1}z + a_n,$$

a polynomial of degree equal to the multiplicity of the pole at infinity, supposed to be the only pole of the function.

The above result may be obtained also in the following manner.

Since $z = \infty$ is a pole of multiplicity $n$, the limit of $z^{-n}f(z)$ is not infinite when $z = \infty$.

Now in any finite part of the plane the function is everywhere finite, so that we can use the expansion

$$f(z) = f(0) + zf'(0) + \ldots\ldots + \frac{z^n}{n!}f^{(n)}(0) + R,$$

where $$R = \frac{z^{n+1}}{2\pi i}\int \frac{f(t)}{t^{n+1}}\frac{dt}{t - z},$$

the integral being taken round a circle of any radius $r$ enclosing the point $z$ and having its centre at the origin.  As the subject of integration is finite everywhere along the circumference, we have, by Darboux's expression in (IV.) § 15,

$$R = \lambda r \frac{z^{n+1}}{\tau^{n+1}}\frac{f(\tau)}{\tau - z},$$

where $\tau$ is some point on the circumference and $\lambda$ is a quantity of modulus not greater than unity.

Let $\tau = re^{ia}$; then .

$$R = \frac{\lambda}{r} z^{n+1} e^{-2ai} \frac{f(\tau)}{\tau^n} \frac{1}{1 - \frac{z}{r} e^{-ai}}.$$

By definition, the limit of $\frac{f(\tau)}{\tau^n}$ as $\tau$ (and therefore $r$) becomes infinitely large is not infinite; in the same case, the limit of $\left(1 - \frac{z}{r} e^{-ai}\right)^{-1}$ is unity. Since $|\lambda|$ is not greater than unity, the limit of $\lambda/r$ in the same case is zero; hence with indefinite increase of $r$, the limit of $R$ is zero, and so

$$f(z) = f(0) + zf'(0) + \ldots\ldots + \frac{z^n}{n!} f^{(n)}(0),$$

shewing as before that $f(z)$ is a polynomial in $z$.

**46.** As the quantity $n$ is necessarily a positive integer\*, there are two distinct classes of functions discriminated by the magnitude of $n$.

The first (and the simpler) is that for which $n$ has a finite value. The function then contains only a finite number of terms, each with a positive integral index; it is a polynomial or a *rational integral* function of $z$, of degree $n$.

The second (and the more extensive, as significant functions) is that for which $n$ has an infinite value. The point $z = \infty$ is not a pole, for then the function does not satisfy the test of § 42: it is an essential singularity of the function, which is expansible in an infinite converging series of positive integral powers. To functions of this class the general term *transcendental* is applied.

The number of zeros of a function of the former class is known: it is equal to the degree of the function. It has been proved that the zeros of a transcendental function are isolated points, occurring necessarily in finite number in any finite part of the region of continuity of the function, no point on the boundary of the part being an essential singularity; but no test has been assigned for the determination of the total number of zeros of a function in an infinite part of the region of continuity†.

Again, when the zeros of a polynomial are given, a product-expression can at once be obtained that will represent its analytical value. Also we know

---

\* It is unnecessary to consider the zero value of $n$, for the function is then a polynomial of order zero, that is, it is a constant.

† In connection with the zeros of a transcendental function, as expressed in a Taylor's series, a paper by Hadamard, *Liouville*, 4$^{me}$ Sér., t. viii, (1892), pp. 101—186, may be consulted with advantage.

that, if $a$ be a zero of any uniform analytic function of multiplicity $n$, the function can be represented in the vicinity of $a$ by the expression

$$(x-a)^n \phi(z),$$

where $\phi(z)$ is holomorphic in the vicinity of $a$. The other zeros of the function are zeros of $\phi(z)$; this process of modification in the expression can be continued for successive zeros so long as the number of zeros taken account of is limited. But when the number of zeros is unlimited, then the inferred product-expression for the original function is not necessarily a converging product; and thus the question of the formal factorisation of a transcendental function arises.

**47.** THEOREM IX. *A function, all the singularities of which are accidental, is a rational meromorphic function.*

Since all the singularities are accidental, each must be of finite multiplicity; and therefore infinity, if an accidental singularity, is of finite multiplicity. All the other poles are in the finite part of the plane; they are isolated points and therefore only finite in number, so that the total number of distinct poles is finite and each is of finite order. Let them be $a_1, a_2, \ldots\ldots, a_\mu$ of orders $m_1, m_2, \ldots\ldots, m_\mu$ respectively: let $m$ be the order of the pole at infinity: and let the poles be arranged in the sequence of decreasing moduli such that $|a_\mu| > |a_{\mu-1}| > \ldots\ldots > |a_1|$.

Then, since infinity is a pole of order $m$, we have

$$f(z) = a_m z^m + a_{m-1} z^{m-1} + \ldots\ldots + a_1 z + f_0(z),$$

where $f_0(z)$ is not infinite for infinite values of $z$. Now the polynomial $\sum_{i=1}^{m} a_i z^i$ is not infinite for any finite value of $z$; hence $f_0(z)$ is infinite for all the finite infinities of $f(z)$ and in the same way, that is, the function $f_0(z)$ has $a_1, \ldots\ldots, a_\mu$ for its poles and it has no other singularities.

Again, since $a_\mu$ is a finite pole of multiplicity $m_\mu$, we have

$$f_0(z) = \frac{b_{m_\mu}}{(z-a_\mu)^{m_\mu}} + \ldots\ldots + \frac{b_1}{z-a_\mu} + f_1(z),$$

where $f_1(z)$ is not infinite for $z = a_\mu$ and, as $f_0(z)$ is not infinite for $z = \infty$, evidently $f_1(z)$ is not infinite for $z = \infty$. Hence the singularities of $f_1(z)$ are merely the poles $a_1, \ldots\ldots, a_{\mu-1}$; and these are all its singularities.

Proceeding in this manner for the singularities in succession, we ultimately reach a function $f_\mu(z)$ which has only one pole $a_1$ and no other singularity, so that

$$f_\mu(z) = \frac{k_{m_1}}{(z-a_1)^{m_1}} + \ldots\ldots + \frac{k_1}{z-a_1} + g(z),$$

where $g(z)$ is not infinite for $z = a_1$. But the function $f_\mu(z)$ is infinite only for $z = a_1$, and therefore $g(z)$ has no infinity. Hence $g(z)$ is only a constant, say $k_0$: thus

$$g(z) = k_0.$$

Combining all these results we have a *finite* number of finite series to add together: and the result is that

$$f(z) = g_1(z) + \frac{g_2(z)}{g_3(z)},$$

where $g_1(z)$ is the series $k_0 + a_1 z + \ldots\ldots + a_m z^m$, and $\dfrac{g_2(z)}{g_3(z)}$ is the sum of the finite number of fractions. Evidently $g_3(z)$ is the product

$$(z - a_1)^{m_1}(z - a_2)^{m_2}\ldots\ldots(z - a_\mu)^{m_\mu};$$

and $g_2(z)$ is at most of degree

$$m_1 + m_2 + \ldots\ldots + m_\mu - 1.$$

If $F(z)$ denote $g_1(z)g_3(z) + g_2(z)$, the form of $f(z)$ is

$$\frac{F(z)}{g_3(z)},$$

that is, $f(z)$ is a rational meromorphic function.

It is evident that, when the function is thus expressed as a rational fraction, the degree of $F(z)$ is the sum of the multiplicities of all the poles when infinity is a pole.

COROLLARY I. *A function, all the singularities of which are accidental, has as many zeros as it has accidental singularities in the plane.*

When $z = \infty$ is a pole, it follows that, because $f(z)$ can be expressed in the form

$$\frac{F(z)}{g_3(z)},$$

the function has as many zeros as $F(z)$, unless one such should be also a zero of $g_3(z)$. But the zeros of $g_3(z)$ are known, and no one of them is a zero of $F(z)$, on account of the form of $f(z)$ when it is expressed in partial fractions. Hence the number of zeros of $f(z)$ is equal to the degree of $F(z)$, that is, it is equal to the number of poles of $f(z)$.

When $z = \infty$ is not a pole, two cases are possible; (i) the function $f(z)$ may be finite for $z = \infty$, or (ii) it may be zero for $z = \infty$. In the former case, the number of zeros is, as before, equal to the degree of $F(z)$, that is, it is equal to the number of infinities.

In the latter case, if the degree of the numerator $F(z)$ be $\kappa$ less than that of the denominator $g_3(z)$, then $z = \infty$ is a zero of multiplicity $\kappa$; and it follows that the number of zeros is equal to the degree of the numerator together with $\kappa$, so that their number is the same as the number of accidental singularities.

COROLLARY II. At the beginning of the proof of the theorem of the present section, it is proved that a function, all the singularities of which are accidental, has only a finite number of such singularities.

Hence, by the preceding Corollary, *such a function can have only a finite number of zeros.*

If, therefore, the number of zeros of a function be infinite, the function must have at least one essential singularity.

COROLLARY III. When a uniform function has no essential singularity, if the (finite) number of its poles, say $c_1, \ldots, c_m$, be $m$, no one of them being at $z = \infty$, and if the number of its zeros, say $a_1, \ldots, a_m$, be also $m$, no one of them being at $z = \infty$, then the function is

$$\prod_{r=1}^{m} \left( \frac{z - a_r}{z - c_r} \right),$$

except possibly as to a constant factor.

When $z = \infty$ is a zero of order $n$, so that the function has $m - n$ zeros, say $a_1, a_2, \ldots$, in the finite part of the plane, the form of the function is

$$\frac{\prod_{r=1}^{m-n} (z - a_r)}{\prod_{r=1}^{m} (z - c_r)};$$

and, when $z = \infty$ is a pole of order $p$, so that the function has $m - p$ poles, say $c_1, c_2, \ldots$, in the finite part of the plane, the form of the function is

$$\frac{\prod_{r=1}^{m} (z - a_r)}{\prod_{r=1}^{m-p} (z - c_r)}.$$

COROLLARY IV. *All the singularities of rational meromorphic functions are accidental.*

**48.** Some properties of the simplest functions thus defined may conveniently be given here[*]. We shall begin with polynomials.

(i) Let $P(z)$ denote

$$a_m z^m + a_{m-1} z^{m-1} + \ldots\ldots + a_1 z + a_0,$$

where the coefficients $a$ are constants which may be complex; it is continuous, for every one of the finite number of terms is continuous; it is finite for all finite values of $z$; and $|P(z)|$ tends to become infinite as $|z|$ tends to become infinite.

---

[*] For these and other properties, reference may be made to Jordan's *Cours d'Analyse*, t. i, p. 198.

Further, a finite value of $|z|$ can be determined which will make $|P(z)|$ greater than any assigned finite value, say $A$. For we have

$$|P(z)| > |a_m||z|^m - |a_{m-1}||z|^{m-1} - |a_{m-2}||z|^{m-2} - \ldots\ldots - |a_1||z| - |a_0|$$

$$> |z|^m \left\{ |a_m| - \frac{|a_{m-1}|}{|z|} - \frac{|a_{m-2}|}{|z|^2} - \ldots\ldots - \frac{|a_1|}{|z|^{m-1}} - \frac{|a_0|}{|z|^m} \right\},$$

so that, when $|z| > 1$,

$$|P(z)| > |z| \left[ |a_m| - \frac{1}{|z|} \{ |a_{m-1}| + |a_{m-2}| + \ldots\ldots + |a_1| + |a_0| \} \right].$$

Now take

$$c = \frac{1}{|a_m|} \{ |a_{m-1}| + |a_{m-2}| + \ldots\ldots + |a_1| + |a_0| + A \};$$

then
$$|P(z)| > A + |a_m|(|z| - c).$$

Hence if $|z|$, already supposed greater than unity, is also greater than $c$ should $c$ be greater than unity, we have

$$|P(z)| > A,$$

for values of $z$ such that $|z| > 1$, $|z| > c$.

(ii) Next, *the equation $P(z) = 0$ always has a root.* The quantity $|P(z)|$ is continuous, is never negative, and tends to become infinite as $|z|$ tends to become infinite. Hence, if it cannot be zero, there must be at least one minimum value greater than zero below which it cannot fall. Denote this value by $\mu$; and suppose it acquired for the value $c$ of $z$, so that

$$|P(c)| = \mu.$$

Construct a circle of radius greater than $|c|$, and take a place $c + h$ lying within that circle. Then

$$P(c + h) = P(c) + hP'(c) + \ldots\ldots + \frac{h^m}{m!} P^{(m)}(c),$$

where the coefficient of $h^m$ is $a_m$, a quantity different from zero. As (hypothetically) $P(c)$ is not zero, the first term and the last term in $P(c + h)$ do not disappear; but intervening terms may disappear, and so we write

$$P(c + h) = P(c) + b_r h^r + b_{r+1} h^{r+1} + \ldots\ldots + a_m h^m,$$

where $r$ is the lowest index of the powers of $h$ that survive. Now choose $h$ in such a way that $|h|$ is small enough to secure the inequality

$$|B_r||h|^r < |P(c)| < \mu,$$

while at the same time

$$r\{\arg. h\} + \{\arg. B_r\} = \{\arg. P(c)\} + (2n + 1)\pi,$$

so that the arguments of $B_r h^r$ and $P(c)$ differ by an odd multiple of $\pi$. Hence, if

$$P(c) = |P(c)| e^{\theta i},$$

then

$$B_r h^r = -|B_r h^r| e^{\theta i},$$

so that

$$P(c) + B_r h^r = \{|P(c)| - |B_r h^r|\} e^{\theta i},$$

and therefore

$$|P(c) + B_r h^r| = |P(c)| - |B_r h^r|.$$

Now

$$P(c+h) = P(c) + h^r B_r + h^{r+1} B_{r+1} + \ldots;$$

consequently

$$|P(c+h)| \leqslant |P(c) + h^r B_r| + |h^{r+1} B_{r+1}| + \ldots$$

$$\leqslant |P(c)| - |h^r B_r| + |h^{r+1}||B_{r+1}| + \ldots$$

$$\leqslant |P(c)| - |h|^r \{|B_r| - |h||B_{r+1}| - \ldots\}.$$

As $|B_r|$ differs from zero, the coefficient of $-|h|^r$ on the right-hand side is positive when $|h|$ is quite small; consequently, for such values of $h$,

$$|P(c+h)| < |P(c)|,$$

that is, the modulus of $P(z)$ in the immediate vicinity of $c$ can be made less than $|P(c)|$, contrary to the hypothesis that $|P(c)|$ is a minimum different from zero. Thus there cannot be a minimum different from zero, and $|P(z)|$ can always be diminished so long as it is different from zero. Hence there must be a value of $z$ which makes $P(z)$ zero.

It now follows, by the customary argument, that there are $m$ such values.

(iii)   Any rational function of $z$, say $w$, is of the form

$$w = \frac{Q(z)}{P(z)},$$

where $Q(z)$ and $P(z)$ are polynomials in $z$ of degrees $m$ and $n$ respectively.

Every zero of $Q(z)$ is a zero of $w$. Every zero of $P(z)$ is a pole of $w$. The place $z = \infty$ is a pole of $w$ if $m > n$, and it is of order $m - n$; it is a zero of $w$ if $m < n$, and it is of order $m - n$; it is neither if $m = n$. The number of poles is equal to the number of zeros, being the greater of the two integers $m$ and $n$.

Two results, which are of use in one method of establishing some of the special cases of Abel's theorem concerning integrals of algebraic functions, may be noted.

Let the roots of $P(z)$ be simple, say $a_1, \ldots, a_n$. Let $A$ be the coefficient of $z^n$ in $P(z)$. Then

(a)   when $m$, the order of $Q(z)$, is less than $n-1$,

$$\sum_{r=1}^{n} \frac{Q(a_r)}{P'(a_r)} = 0;$$

($\beta$)   when $m = n - 1$, and $B_1$ is the coefficient of $z^{n-1}$ in $Q(z)$,

$$\sum_{r=1}^{n} \frac{Q(a_r)}{P'(a_r)} = \frac{B_1}{A}.$$

# CHAPTER V.

## TRANSCENDENTAL INTEGRAL FUNCTIONS.

**49.** WE now proceed to consider the properties of uniform functions which have essential singularities.

The simplest instance of the occurrence of such a function has already been referred to in § 42; the function has no singularity except at $z = \infty$, and that value is an essential singularity solely through the failure of the limitation to finiteness that would render the singularity accidental. The function is then an integral function of transcendental character; and it is analytically represented (§ 26) by $G(z)$, an infinite series in positive powers of $z$, which converges everywhere in the finite part of the plane and acquires an infinite value at infinity alone.

The preceding investigations shew that uniform functions, all the singularities of which are accidental, are rational functions of the variable—their character being completely determined by their uniformity and the accidental nature of their singularities, and that among such functions having the same accidental singularities the discrimination is made, save as to a constant factor, by means of their zeros.

Hence the zeros and the accidental singularities of a rational function determine, save as to a constant factor, an expression of the function which is valid for the whole plane. A question therefore arises how far the zeros and the singularities of a transcendental function determine the analytical expression of the function for the whole plane.

We have to deal with converging products; it is therefore convenient to state, as for converging series, the definitions of the terms used. For proofs of the statements, developments, and applications, as well as the various tests of convergence, the references which were given at the beginning (p. 21) of Chapter II. may be consulted.

When a series of quantities
$$u_1, \; u_2, \; u_3, \ldots \text{ad inf.}$$
is given, the infinite product
$$\prod_{s=0}^{\infty} (1 + u_s)$$

is said to *converge* when the limit of $\Pi_n$, where

$$\Pi_n = \prod_{s=0}^{n} (1+u_s),$$

as $n$ increases indefinitely, is a unique finite quantity $P$ different from zero. (The last condition, that $P$ should not be zero, is omitted by some writers: as our products arise through quantities involving $z$ and do not vanish for every value of $z$, no difficulty is caused. See also Pringsheim, *Math. Ann.*, t. xxxiii, p. 125.) When, in the same circumstances, the limit of $\Pi_n$ either is infinite, or is zero, or if finite is not unique (that is, may be one of several quantities), the infinite product is said to *diverge*.

The necessary and sufficient conditions that the product should converge are: that $\Pi_n$ is finite and different from zero, however large $n$ may be; and that, corresponding to every finite positive quantity $\epsilon$ taken as small as we please, an integer $m$ can be found such that

$$\left| \frac{\Pi_{n+r}}{\Pi_n} - 1 \right| < \epsilon,$$

for all integers $n$ such that $n \geqslant m$ and for every integer $r$.

When the product

$$\prod_{s=0}^{\infty} (1 + |u_s|)$$

converges, the product

$$\prod_{s=0}^{\infty} (1+u_s)$$

also converges; and it is said to converge *absolutely*. In an absolutely converging product, the factors may be arranged in any order without affecting the convergence or the value of the product. The convergence is sometimes called *unconditional*. The necessary and sufficient condition for the absolute convergence of the product is that the series

$$u_1, \; u_2, \; u_3, \ldots$$

should converge absolutely.

When the series $u_1, u_2, u_3, \ldots$ does not converge absolutely, while the product $\prod_{s=0}^{\infty} (1+u_s)$ converges, the convergence of the infinite product is called *conditional*. The tests differ according as the quantities $u$ are real or complex: we shall not be concerned with conditionally converging infinite products.

The instances, which we shall have to consider, are those where the quantities $u$ depend upon a variable (complex) quantity $z$. The convergence is required as $z$ varies, the quantities $u$ being regular functions throughout the region in which $z$ varies. When any small quantity $\delta$ has been chosen, and a positive integer $m$ can be determined, such that

$$\left| \frac{\Pi_{n+r}}{\Pi_n} - 1 \right| < \delta,$$

for every value of $n \geqslant m$, for all positive integers $r$, and for all values of $z$ within the region, the convergence of the infinite product is said to be *uniform* within the region.

Convergence of an infinite product may be uniform without being unconditional; it may be unconditional without being uniform.

When an infinite product converges uniformly and unconditionally within a given region, then every partial product, which is formed by taking any number of factors in the original product, also converges uniformly and unconditionally within that region.

When an infinite product converges uniformly and unconditionally within a region, the series constituted by the logarithms of the factors (that is, taking the principal logarithms, whose imaginary part is $ia$, where $\pi \geqslant a \geqslant -\pi$) also converges uniformly and unconditionally at all points within the region except the zeros of the factors: and the logarithmic series can be differentiated, if the series of the derivatives of the terms in this logarithmic series itself converges uniformly. In other words, we can (under the condition stated) take logarithmic derivatives of an infinite product, which converges uniformly and unconditionally within a region; and the infinite series is equal to the logarithmic derivative of the value of the product.

**50.** We shall consider first how far the discrimination of transcendental integral functions, which have no infinite value except for $z = \infty$, is effected by means of their zeros\*.

Let the zeros $a_1, a_2, a_3, \ldots$ be arranged in order of increasing moduli; a finite number of terms in the series may have the same value so as to allow for the existence of a multiple zero at any point. After the results stated in § 46, it will be assumed that the number of zeros is infinite; that, subject to limited repetition, they are isolated points; and, in the present chapter, that, as $n$ increases indefinitely, the limit of $|a_n|$ is infinity. And it will be assumed that $|a_1| > 0$, so that the origin is temporarily excluded from the set of zeros.

Let $z$ be any point in the finite part of the plane. Then only a limited number of the zeros can lie within and on a circle centre the origin and radius equal to $|z|$; let these be $a_1, a_2, \ldots, a_{k-1}$, and let $a_r$ denote any one of the other zeros. We proceed to form the infinite product of quantities $u_r$, where $u_r$ denotes

$$\left(1 - \frac{z}{a_r}\right) e^{g_r},$$

and $g_r$ is a rational integral function of $z$ which, being subject to choice, will be chosen so as to make the infinite product converge everywhere in the plane. We have

$$\log u_r = g_r - \sum_{n=1}^{\infty} \frac{1}{n} \left(\frac{z}{a_r}\right)^n,$$

a series which converges because $|z| < |a_r|$. Now let

$$g_r = \sum_{n=1}^{s-1} \frac{1}{n} \left(\frac{z}{a_r}\right)^n$$

then

$$\log u_r = - \sum_{n=s}^{\infty} \frac{1}{n} \left(\frac{z}{a_r}\right)^n,$$

and therefore

$$u_r = e^{\sum_{n=s}^{\infty} \frac{1}{n} \left(\frac{z}{a_r}\right)^n}$$

---

\* The following investigations are based upon the famous memoir by Weierstrass, "Zur Theorie der eindeutigen analytischen Functionen," published in 1876: see his *Ges. Werke*, t. ii, pp. 77—124.

In connection with the product-expression of a transcendental function, Cayley, "Mémoire sur les fonctions doublement périodiques," *Liouville*, t. x, (1845), pp. 385—420, or *Collected Mathematical Papers*, vol. i, pp. 156—182, should be consulted.

Hence
$$\prod_{r=k}^{\infty} u_r = e^{-\sum\limits_{r=k}^{\infty} \sum\limits_{n=s}^{\infty} \frac{1}{n}\left(\frac{z}{a_r}\right)^n},$$

if the expression on the right-hand side is finite, that is, if the series

$$\sum_{r=k}^{\infty} \sum_{n=s}^{\infty} \frac{1}{n}\left(\frac{z}{a_r}\right)^n$$

converges.   Denoting the modulus of this series by $M$, we have

$$M < \sum_{r=k}^{\infty} \sum_{n=s}^{\infty} \frac{1}{n}\left|\frac{z}{a_r}\right|^n,$$

so that
$$sM < \sum_{r=k}^{\infty} \sum_{n=s}^{\infty} \left|\frac{z}{a_r}\right|^n$$

$$< \sum_{r=k}^{\infty} \frac{\left|\dfrac{z}{a_r}\right|^s}{1 - \left|\dfrac{z}{a_r}\right|},$$

whence, since $1 - \left|\dfrac{z}{a_k}\right|$ is the smallest of the denominators in terms of the last sum, we have

$$sM \left\{ 1 - \left|\frac{z}{a_k}\right| \right\} < \sum_{r=k}^{\infty} \left|\frac{z}{a_r}\right|^s$$

$$< |z|^s \sum_{r=k}^{\infty} \frac{1}{|a_r|^s}.$$

If, as is not infrequently the case, there be any finite integer $s$ for which (and therefore for all greater indices) the series

$$\sum_{r=1}^{\infty} \frac{1}{|a_r|^s},$$

and therefore the series $\sum\limits_{r=k}^{\infty} |a_r|^{-s}$, converges, we choose $s$ to be that least integer.   The value of $M$ then is finite for all finite values of $z$; the series

$$\sum_{r=k}^{\infty} \sum_{n=s}^{\infty} \frac{1}{n}\left(\frac{z}{a_r}\right)^n$$

converges unconditionally, and therefore

$$\prod_{r=k}^{\infty} u_r$$

is a product, which converges unconditionally, when

$$u_r = \left(1 - \frac{z}{a_r}\right) e^{\sum\limits_{n=1}^{s-1} \frac{1}{n}\left(\frac{z}{a_r}\right)^n}.$$

Moreover, it converges uniformly. We have

$$\left| \frac{\prod\limits_{r=k}^{l+l'} u_r}{\prod\limits_{r=k}^{l} u_r} - 1 \right| = \left| e^{-\sum\limits_{r=l}^{l+l'} \sum\limits_{n=s}^{\infty} \frac{1}{n} \left( \frac{z}{a_r} \right)^n} - 1 \right|$$

$$< e^{\sum\limits_{r=l}^{l+l'} \sum\limits_{n=s}^{\infty} \frac{1}{n} \left| \frac{z}{a_r} \right|^n} - 1$$

$$< e^{\frac{|z|^s}{s\left\{ 1 - \left| \frac{z}{a_l} \right| \right\}} \sum\limits_{r=l}^{\infty} \frac{1}{|a_l|^s}} - 1.$$

Now the series $\sum\limits_{r=1}^{\infty} \dfrac{1}{|a_r|^s}$ converges; hence when any finite quantity $\epsilon$ is assigned, we can choose an integer $l$ such that, for all integers $l'' \geqslant l$,

$$\sum\limits_{r=l''}^{\infty} \frac{1}{|a_r|^s} < \epsilon.$$

Denoting by $\rho$ any positive quantity which is less than $|a_l|$, consider a region in the $z$-plane given by $|z| < \rho$. Let $\delta$ denote any assigned finite quantity, however small; and, after $\delta$ is assigned, choose a quantity $\epsilon$ so that

$$\frac{\rho^s}{s\left\{ 1 - \dfrac{\rho}{|a_l|} \right\}} \epsilon < \mathrm{Log}\,(1 + \delta),$$

taking the principal logarithm. Then

$$\left| \frac{\prod\limits_{r=k}^{l+l'} u_r}{\prod\limits_{r=k}^{l} u_r} - 1 \right| < e^{\frac{\rho^s}{s\left\{ 1 - \frac{\rho}{|a_l|} \right\}} \epsilon} - 1 < (1 + \delta) - 1 < \delta;$$

shewing that the product converges uniformly for all values of $z$ such that $|z| < \rho$. But $l$ can be taken as large as we please: so that the product converges uniformly for all finite values of $z$.

Let the finite product

$$\prod\limits_{m=1}^{k-1} \left\{ \left( 1 - \frac{z}{a_m} \right) e^{\sum\limits_{n=1}^{s-1} \frac{1}{n} \left( \frac{z}{a_m} \right)^n} \right\}$$

be associated as a factor with the foregoing infinite converging product. Then *the expression*

$$f(z) = \prod\limits_{r=1}^{\infty} \left\{ \left( 1 - \frac{z}{a_r} \right) e^{\sum\limits_{n=1}^{s-1} \frac{1}{n} \left( \frac{z}{a_r} \right)^n} \right\}$$

*is an infinite product, converging uniformly and unconditionally for all finite values of $z$, provided the finite integer $s$ be such as to make the series* $\sum\limits_{r=1}^{\infty} |a_r|^{-s}$ *converge.*

**51.**   But it may happen that no finite integer $s$ can be found which will make the series

$$\sum_{r=1}^{\infty} |a_r|^{-s}$$

converge*.   We then proceed as follows.

Instead of having the same index $s$ throughout the series, we associate with every zero $a_r$ an integer $m_r$, chosen so as to make the series

$$\sum_{n=1}^{\infty} \left| \frac{1}{a_n} \left( \frac{z}{a_n} \right)^{m_n} \right|$$

converge.   To obtain these integers, we take any series of decreasing real positive quantities $\epsilon, \epsilon_1, \epsilon_2, \ldots$, such that (i) $\epsilon$ is less than unity and (ii) they form a converging series; and we choose integers $m_r$ such that

$$\epsilon^{m_r+1} \leqslant \epsilon_r.$$

These integers make the foregoing series of moduli converge.   For, neglecting the limited number of terms for which $|z| \geqslant |a|\,\epsilon$, and taking the first term for $a_k$ such that

$$\left| \frac{z}{a_k} \right| \leqslant \epsilon,$$

we have for all succeeding terms $(r = k+1, k+2, \ldots)$

$$\left| \frac{z}{a_r} \right| \leqslant \epsilon,$$

and   therefore

$$\left| \frac{z}{a_r} \right|^{m_r+1} \leqslant \epsilon^{m_r+1} \leqslant \epsilon_r.$$

Hence, except for the first $k-1$ terms, the sum of which is finite, we have

$$\sum_{n=k}^{\infty} \left| \frac{1}{a_n} \left( \frac{z}{a_n} \right)^{m_n} \right| \leqslant \frac{1}{|z|} (\epsilon_k + \epsilon_{k+1} + \ldots)$$

$$\leqslant \frac{1}{|z|} (\epsilon + \epsilon_1 + \epsilon_2 + \ldots),$$

which is finite because the series $\epsilon + \epsilon_1 + \epsilon_2 + \ldots$ converges.   Hence the series

$$\sum_{n=1}^{\infty} \left| \frac{1}{a_n} \left( \frac{z}{a_n} \right)^{m_n} \right|$$

is a converging series.

Just as in the preceding case a special expression was formed to serve as a typical factor in the infinite product, we now form a similar expression for the same purpose.   Evidently

$$1 - x = e^{\log (1-x)} = e^{-\sum\limits_{r=0}^{\infty} \frac{x^{r+1}}{r+1}},$$

* For instance, there is no finite integer $s$ that can make the infinite series

$$(\log 2)^{-s} + (\log 3)^{-s} + (\log 4)^{-s} + \ldots$$

converge.   This series is given in illustration by Hermite, *Cours à la faculté des Sciences*, (4$^{\text{me}}$ éd., 1891), p. 86.

if $|x| < 1$. Forming a function $E(x, m)$ defined by the equation

$$E(x, m) = (1 - x)\, e^{\sum_{r=1}^{m} \frac{x^r}{r}},$$

we have

$$E(x, m) = e^{-\sum_{r=1}^{\infty} \frac{x^{m+r}}{m+r}}$$

In the preceding case it was possible to choose the integer $m$ so that it should be the same for all the factors of the infinite product, which was ultimately proved to converge. Now, we take $x = \dfrac{z}{a_n}$ and associate $m_n$ as the corresponding value of $m$. Hence, if

$$f(z) = \prod_{n=k}^{\infty} E\left(\frac{z}{a_n}, m_n\right),$$

where $|a_{k-1}| < |z| < |a_k|$, we have

$$f(z) = e^{-\sum_{n=k}^{\infty} \sum_{r=1}^{\infty} \frac{1}{r+m_n}\left(\frac{z}{a_n}\right)^{r+m_n}}$$

The infinite product represented by $f(z)$ will converge, if the double series in the exponential be a converging series.

Denoting the double series by $S$, we have

$$|S| < \sum_{n=k}^{\infty} \sum_{r=1}^{\infty} \frac{1}{r+m_n}\left|\frac{z}{a_n}\right|^{r+m_n}$$

$$< \sum_{n=k}^{\infty} \sum_{r=1}^{\infty} \left|\frac{z}{a_n}\right|^{r+m_n}$$

$$< \sum_{n=k}^{\infty} \left|\frac{z}{a_n}\right|^{1+m_n} \frac{1}{1 - \left|\dfrac{z}{a_n}\right|},$$

on effecting the summation for $r$. Let $A$ be the value of $1 - \left|\dfrac{z}{a_k}\right|$; then for all the remaining values of $n$, we have

$$1 - \left|\frac{z}{a_n}\right| > A,$$

and so

$$|S| < \frac{1}{A} \sum_{n=k}^{\infty} \left|\frac{z}{a_n}\right|^{1+m_n}$$

$$< \frac{|z|}{A} \sum_{n=k}^{\infty} \left|\frac{1}{a_n}\left(\frac{z}{a_n}\right)^{m_n}\right|.$$

This series converges; hence for finite values of $|z|$, the value of $|S|$ is finite, so that $S$ is an unconditionally converging series. Hence it follows that $f(z)$ is an unconditionally converging product. We now associate with $f(z)$ as factors the $k - 1$ functions

$$E\left(\frac{z}{a_i}, m_i\right),$$

for $i = 1, 2, \ldots, k-1$; their number being finite, their product is finite and therefore the modified infinite product still converges. We thus have

$$G(z) = \prod_{n=1}^{\infty} E\left(\frac{z}{a_n}, m_n\right);$$

it is an unconditionally converging product.

In the same way as for the simpler case, we prove that the infinite product converges uniformly for finite values of $z$.

Denoting the series in the exponential by $g_n(z)$, so that

$$g_n(z) = \sum_{r=1}^{m_n} \frac{1}{r}\left(\frac{z}{a_n}\right)^r,$$

we have

$$E\left(\frac{z}{a_n}, m_n\right) = \left(1 - \frac{z}{a_n}\right) e^{g_n(z)};$$

and therefore the function obtained is

$$G(z) = \prod_{n=1}^{\infty} \left\{ \left(1 - \frac{z}{a_n}\right) e^{g_n(z)} \right\}.$$

The series $g_n$ usually contains only a limited number of terms; when the number of terms increases without limit, it is only with indefinite increase of $|a_n|$, and the series is then a converging series.

Since the product $G(z)$ converges uniformly and unconditionally, no product constructed from its factors $E$, say from all but one of them, can be infinite. The factor

$$E\left(\frac{z}{a_n}, m_n\right) = \left(1 - \frac{z}{a_n}\right) e^{\sum_{r=1}^{m_n} \frac{1}{r}\left(\frac{z}{a_n}\right)^r}$$

vanishes for the value $z = a_n$ and only for this value; hence $G(z)$ vanishes for $z = a_n$. It therefore appears that $G(z)$ has the assigned points $a_1, a_2, a_3, \ldots$ for its zeros.

Further, take any finite quantity, say $\rho$; and let $a_m$ be such that

$$\rho < |a_m| < |a_{m+1}| < \cdots.$$

Then

$$G(z) = \prod_{n=1}^{m} E\left(\frac{z}{a_n}, m_n\right) \prod_{\mu=m+1}^{\infty} \left(1 + \frac{z}{a_\mu}\right) e^{\sum_{r=1}^{m_\mu} \frac{1}{r}\left(\frac{z}{a_\mu}\right)^r}$$

But

$$\prod_{\mu=m+1}^{\infty} \left\{ \left(1 - \frac{z}{a_\mu}\right) e^{\sum_{r=1}^{m_\mu} \frac{1}{r}\left(\frac{z}{a_\mu}\right)^r} \right\} = e^{-\sum_{\mu=m+1}^{\infty} \sum_{s=1}^{\infty} \frac{1}{m_\mu + s}\left(\frac{z}{a_\mu}\right)^{m_\mu + s}}$$

The double sum in the index is a series, which converges unconditionally for values of $z$ such that $|z| < \rho$; and therefore it is expressible in the form $P(z, m+1)$, which is a power-series converging absolutely for those values. Hence $e^{-P(z, m)}$ can be expressed in the form

$$1 + m_1 z + m_2 z^2 + \cdots,$$

converging absolutely for values of $z$ such that $|z| < \rho$. Also each of the finite number of factors $E\left(\dfrac{z}{a_n}, m_n\right)$, for $n = 1, \ldots, m$, is expressible in a series of the form

$$1 + n_1 z + n_2 z^2 + \ldots,$$

which converges absolutely for finite values of $z$ and therefore for values of $z$ such that $|z| < \rho$. The product of all these $n + 1$ series is also an absolutely converging series, of the form

$$1 + g_1 z + g_2 z^2 + \ldots,$$

which is an expression for $G(z)$ representing it as a holomorphic uniform function. Clearly we can take $\rho$ as large as we please without affecting the foregoing argument.

In the first place, since $G(z)$ is a uniform analytic function which has no singularity in any finite part of the plane and which clearly is transcendental, the value $z = \infty$ is an essential singularity of $G(z)$.

In the second place, $G(z)$ has no zero other than the assigned zeros. For let $a$ be a value of $z$; and choose $m$ sufficiently large to secure that $a$ lies within the region of convergence of $P(z, m+1)$; hence $e^{-P(z, m+1)}$ is finite for $z = a$. No one of the factors

$$E\left(\frac{z}{a_n}, m_n\right) \qquad\qquad (n = 1, \ldots, m)$$

can vanish, if $a$ is not included in the set $a_1, a_2, \ldots, a_m$. Therefore $G$ could not vanish for $a$, proving the statement.

It should be noted that the factors of the infinite product $G(z)$ are the expressions $E$. No one of these expressions, for the purposes of the product, is resoluble into factors that can be distributed and recombined with similarly obtained factors from other expressions $E$; for there is no guarantee that the product of the factors, when so modified, would converge uniformly and unconditionally. It is to secure such convergence that the expressions $E$ have been constructed.

It was assumed, merely for temporary convenience, that the origin was not a zero of the required function; there obviously could not be a factor of exactly the same form as the factors $E$, if $a$ were the origin.

If, however, the origin were a zero of order $\lambda$, we should have merely to associate a factor $z^\lambda$ with the function already constructed.

We thus obtain Weierstrass's theorem :—

*It is possible to construct a transcendental integral function such that it shall have infinity as its only essential singularity and have the origin (of multiplicity $\lambda$), $a_1, a_2, a_3, \ldots$ as zeros; and such a function is*

$$z^\lambda \prod_{n=1}^{\infty} \left\{ \left(1 - \frac{z}{a_n}\right) e^{g_n(z)} \right\},$$

*where $g_n(z)$ is a rational, integral function of $z$, the form of which is dependent upon the law of succession of the zeros.*

**52.** But, unlike uniform functions with only accidental singularities, the function is not unique: there *are an unlimited number of transcendental integral functions with the same series of zeros and infinity as the sole essential singularity*, a theorem also due to Weierstrass.

For, if $G_1(z)$ and $G(z)$ be two transcendental, integral functions with the same series of zeros in the same multiplicity, and $z = \infty$ as their only essential singularity, then

$$\frac{G_1(z)}{G(z)}$$

is a function with no zeros and no infinities in the finite part of the plane. Denoting it by $G_2$, then

$$\frac{1}{G_2}\frac{dG_2}{dz}$$

is a function which, in the finite part of the plane, has no infinities; and therefore it can be expanded in the form

$$C_1 + 2C_2 z + 3C_3 z^2 + \dots,$$

a series converging everywhere in the finite part of the plane. Choosing a constant $C_0$ so that $G_2(0) = e^{C_0}$, we have on integration

$$G_2(z) = e^{\bar{g}(z)},$$

where $$\bar{g}(z) = C_0 + C_1 z + C_2 z^2 + \dots,$$

and $\bar{g}(z)$ is finite everywhere in the finite part of the plane. Hence it follows that, *if $\bar{g}(z)$ denote any integral function of $z$ which is finite everywhere in the finite part of the plane, and if $G(z)$ be some transcendental integral function with a given series of zeros and $z = \infty$ as its sole essential singularity, all transcendental integral functions with that series of zeros and $z = \infty$ as the sole essential singularity are included in the form*

$$G(z)\, e^{\bar{g}(z)}.$$

COROLLARY I. *A function which has no zeros in the finite part of the plane, no accidental singularities, and $z = \infty$ for its sole essential singularity, is necessarily of the form*

$$e^{\bar{g}(z)},$$

*where $\bar{g}(z)$ is an integral function of $z$ finite everywhere in the finite part of the plane.*

COROLLARY II. *Every transcendental function, which has the same zeros in the same multiplicity as a polynomial $A(z)$—the number, therefore, being necessarily finite—, which has no accidental singularities, and has $z = \infty$ for its sole essential singularity, can be expressed in the form*

$$A(z)\, e^{g(z)}.$$

COROLLARY III. *Every function, which has an assigned set of zeros and an assigned set of poles, and has $z = \infty$ for its sole essential singularity, is of the form*

$$\frac{G_0(z)}{G_p(z)} e^{\bar{g}(z)},$$

*where the zeros of $G_0(z)$ are the assigned zeros and the zeros of $G_p(z)$ are the assigned poles.*

For if $G_p(z)$ be any transcendental integral function, constructed as in the proposition, which has as its zeros the poles of the required function in the assigned multiplicity, the most general form of that function is

$$G_p(z) e^{h(z)},$$

where $h(z)$ is integral.   Hence, if the most general form of function which has those zeros for its poles be denoted by $f(z)$,

$$f(z)\, G_p(z)\, e^{h(z)}$$

is a function with no poles, with infinity as its sole essential singularity, and with the assigned series of zeros.   But if $G_0(z)$ be any transcendental integral function with the assigned zeros as its zeros, the most general form of function with those zeros is

$$G_0(z)\, e^{g(z)} \; ;$$

and so $\qquad\qquad f(z)\, G_p(z)\, e^{h(z)} = G_0(z)\, e^{g(z)},$

whence $\qquad\qquad f(z) = \frac{G_0(z)}{G_p(z)}\, e^{g(z)},$

in which $\bar{g}(z)$ denotes $g(z) - h(z)$.

If the number of zeros be finite, we evidently may take $G_0(z)$ as the polynomial in $z$ with those zeros as its only zeros.

If the number of poles be finite, we evidently may take $G_p(z)$ as the polynomial in $z$ with those poles as its only zeros.

And, lastly, if a function has a finite number of zeros, a finite number of accidental singularities, and $z = \infty$ as its sole essential singularity, it can be expressed in the form

$$\frac{P(z)}{Q(z)} e^{\bar{g}(z)},$$

where $P$ and $Q$ are polynomials.   This is valid, even though the number of assigned zeros be not the same as the number of assigned poles; the sole effect of the inequality of these numbers is to complicate the character of the essential singularity at infinity.

**53.**   It follows from what has been proved that any uniform function, having $z = \infty$ for its sole essential singularity and any number of assigned zeros, can be expressed as a product of expressions of the form

$$\left(1 - \frac{z}{a_n}\right) e^{g_n(z)}.$$

Such a quantity is called* a *primary factor* of the function.

It has also been proved that :—

    (i)   If there be no zero $a_n$, the primary factor has the form

$$e^{g_n(z)}.$$

    (ii)   The exponential index $g_n(z)$ may be zero for individual primary factors, though the number of such factors must, at the utmost, be finite†.

    (iii)  The factor takes the form $z$ when the origin is a zero.

Hence we have the theorem, due to Weierstrass :—

*Every uniform integral function of z can be expressed as a product of primary factors, each of the form*

$$(kz + l) e^{g(z)},$$

*where g(z) is an appropriate polynomial in z vanishing with z, and where k, l are constants. In particular factors, g(z) may vanish; and either k or l, but not both k and l, may vanish with or without a non-vanishing exponential index g(z).*

**54.**  It thus appears that an essential distinction between transcendental integral functions is constituted by the aggregate of their zeros : and we may conveniently consider that *all such functions are substantially the same when they have the same zeros.*

There are a few very simple sets of functions, thus discriminated by their zeros : of each set only one member will be given, and the factor $e^{\bar{g}(z)}$, which makes the variation among the members of the same set, will be neglected for the present. Moreover, it will be assumed that the zeros are isolated points.

I.   There may be a finite number of zeros; the simplest function is then a polynomial.

II.   There may be a singly-infinite set of zeros. Various functions will be obtained, according to the law of distribution of the zeros.

Thus let them be distributed according to a law of simple arithmetic progression along a given line. If $a$ be a zero, $\omega$ a quantity such that $|\omega|$ is the distance between two zeros and arg. $\omega$ is the inclination of the line, we have

$$a + m\omega,$$

---

* Weierstrass's term is *Primfunction* ; see *Ges. Werke*, t. ii, p. 91.

† Unless the *class* (§ 59) be zero, when the index is zero for all the factors.

for integer values of $m$ from $-\infty$ to $+\infty$, as the expression of the set of the zeros. Without loss of generality, we may take $a$ at the origin—this is merely a change of origin of coordinates—and the origin is then a simple zero: the zeros are given by $m\omega$, for integer values of $m$ from $-\infty$ to $+\infty$.

Now $\Sigma \dfrac{1}{m\omega} = \dfrac{1}{\omega} \Sigma \dfrac{1}{m}$ is a diverging series; but an integer $s$—the lowest value is $s = 2$—can be found for which the series $\Sigma \left(\dfrac{1}{m\omega}\right)^s$ converges uncon-ditionally. Taking $s = 2$, we have

$$g_m(z) = \sum_{n=1}^{s-1} \frac{1}{n}\left(\frac{z}{a_m}\right)^n = \frac{z}{m\omega},$$

so that the primary factor of the present function is

$$\left(1 - \frac{z}{m\omega}\right) e^{\frac{z}{m\omega}};$$

and therefore, by § 52, the product

$$f(z) = z \prod_{-\infty}^{\infty} \left\{ \left(1 - \frac{z}{m\omega}\right) e^{\frac{z}{m\omega}} \right\}$$

converges uniformly and unconditionally for all finite values of $z$.

The term corresponding to $m = 0$ is to be omitted from the product; and it is unnecessary to assume that the numerical value of the positive infinity for $m$ is the same as that of the negative infinity for $m$. If, however, the latter assumption be adopted, the expression can be changed into the ordinary product-expression for a sine, by combining the primary factors due to values of $m$ that are equal and opposite. In any case, we have

$$f(z) = \frac{\omega}{\pi} \sin \frac{\pi z}{\omega}.$$

This example is sufficient to shew the importance of the exponential term in the primary factor. If the product be formed exactly as for a polynomial, then the function is

$$z \prod_{m=-q}^{m=p} \left(1 - \frac{z}{m\omega}\right)$$

in the limit when both $p$ and $q$ are infinite. But this is known[*] to be

$$\left(\frac{q}{p}\right)^{\frac{z}{\omega}} \frac{\omega}{\pi} \sin \frac{\pi z}{\omega}.$$

Another illustration is afforded by Gauss's $\Pi$-function, which is the limit when $k$ is infinite of

$$\frac{1.2.3......k}{(z+1)(z+2)......(z+k)} k^z.$$

* Hobson's *Trigonometry*, § 287.

This is transformed by Gauss* into the reciprocal of the expression

$$(1+z) \prod_{m=2}^{\infty} \left\{ \left(1+\frac{z}{m}\right)\left(\frac{m}{m-1}\right)^{-z} \right\},$$

that is, of

$$(1+z) \prod_{m=2}^{\infty} \left\{ \left(1+\frac{z}{m}\right) e^{-z \log\left(\frac{m}{m-1}\right)} \right\},$$

the primary factors of which have the same characteristic form as in the preceding investigation, though not the same literal form. This is associated with the Gamma Function†.

It is chiefly for convenience that the index of the exponential part of the primary factor is taken, in § 50, in the form $\sum\limits_{n=1}^{s-1} \frac{1}{n}\left(\frac{z}{a_r}\right)^n$. With equal effectiveness it may be taken in the form $\sum\limits_{n=1}^{s-1} \frac{1}{n} b_{r,n} z^n$, provided the series

$$\sum_{r=k}^{\infty} \sum_{n=1}^{\infty} \left\{ \frac{1}{n} (b_{r,n} - a_r^{-n}) z^n \right\}$$

converges uniformly and unconditionally.

*Ex.* 1. Prove that each of the products

$$\prod \left\{ \left(1 - \frac{2z}{m\pi}\right) e^{\frac{2z}{m\pi}} \right\}, \quad \left(1 + \frac{2z}{\pi}\right) \prod_{n=-\infty}^{n=\infty} \left[ \left\{ 1 - \frac{2z}{(2n-1)\pi} \right\} e^{\frac{z}{n\pi}} \right],$$

for $m = \pm 1, \pm 3, \pm 5, \ldots\ldots$ to infinity, the term for $n=0$ being excluded from the latter product, converges uniformly and unconditionally, and that each of them is equal to $\cos z$.                                                                                 (Hermite and Weyr.)

*Ex.* 2. Prove that, if the zeros of a transcendental integral function be given by the series

$$0, \pm \omega, \pm 4\omega, \pm 9\omega, \ldots\ldots \text{ to infinity},$$

the simplest of the set of functions thereby determined can be expressed in the form

$$\sin\left\{ \pi \left(\frac{z}{\omega}\right)^{\frac{1}{2}} \right\} \sin\left\{ i\pi \left(\frac{z}{\omega}\right)^{\frac{1}{2}} \right\}.$$

*Ex.* 3. Construct the set of transcendental integral functions which have in common the series of zeros determined by the law $m^2\omega_1 + 2m\omega_2 + \omega_3$ for all integral values of $m$ between $-\infty$ and $+\infty$; and express the simplest of the set in terms of circular functions.

*Ex.* 4. A one-valued analytical function satisfies the equation

$$f(x) = -xf(ax),$$

where $|a| \neq 1$; it has a simple zero at each of the points $x = a^m (m=0, \pm 1, \ldots)$ and no other zero, and it is finite for all values of $x$ which are neither zero nor infinite. Shew that it has essential singularities at $x=0$, $x=\infty$; and resolve it into primary factors.
                                                                                 (Math. Trip., Part II., 1898.)

---

* *Ges. Werke*, t. iii, p. 145; the example is quoted in this connection by Weierstrass, *Ges. Werke*, t. ii, p. 15.

† On the theory of the Gamma Function, a paper by Barnes, *Messenger of Mathematics*, t. xxix, (1900), pp. 64—128, may be consulted. References to later memoirs on the subject are to be found in Whittaker and Watson's *Modern Analysis* (2nd ed.).

*Ex.* 5. Three straight lines are drawn through a point equally inclined to one another; and by means of three infinite series of lines, respectively parallel to these three lines, the plane is divided into an infinite number of equilateral triangles. Construct an integral uniform function which vanishes at the centre of each of the triangles.

(Math. Trip., Part II., 1894.)

*Ex.* 6. Take a series of concentric circles

$$x^2 + y^2 = n \qquad\qquad (n = 1, 2, 3, \dots).$$

in the plane; and four common radii

$$\theta = 0, \quad \theta = \tfrac{1}{2}\pi, \quad \theta = \pi, \quad \theta = \tfrac{3}{2}\pi.$$

Construct a function which shall vanish at every one of these radial points on the circumferences: and express it by means of circular functions.

**55.** The law of distribution of the zeros, next in importance and substantially next in point of simplicity, is that in which the zeros form a doubly-infinite double arithmetic progression, the points being the $\infty^2$ intersections of one infinite system of equidistant parallel straight lines with another infinite system of equidistant parallel straight lines.

The origin may, without loss of generality, be taken as one of the zeros. If $\omega$ be the coordinate of the nearest zero along the line of one system passing through the origin, and $\omega'$ be the coordinate of the nearest zero along the line of the other system passing through the origin, then the complete series of zeros is given by

$$\Omega = m\omega + m'\omega',$$

for all integral values of $m$ and all integral values of $m'$ between $-\infty$ and $+\infty$. The system of points may be regarded as doubly-periodic, having $\omega$ and $\omega'$ for periods..

It must be assumed that the two systems of lines intersect. Otherwise, $\omega$ and $\omega'$ would have the same argument, and their ratio would be a real quantity, say $\alpha$; and then

$$\frac{\Omega}{\omega} = m + m'\alpha.$$

If $\alpha$ be commensurable, let $\dfrac{p}{q}$ denote its value, where $p$ and $q$ are positive integers having no common factor; also let $\dfrac{p}{q}$ be expressed as a continued fraction, and let $\dfrac{p'}{q'}$ denote the convergent next before the last $\Big($which, of course, is $\dfrac{p}{q}\Big)$. Then

$$\frac{\omega'}{\omega} = \frac{p}{q}, \quad pq' - p'q = \pm 1;$$

and therefore

$$\frac{\omega'}{p} = \frac{\omega}{q} = \pm (q'\omega' - q\omega) = \omega'',$$

that is, $\omega'$ and $\omega$ are integral multiples of a single period $\omega''$; and the apparently double system of points would be singly-periodic.

When $\alpha$ is incommensurable, the number of pairs of integers for which $m + m'\alpha$ may be made less than any assigned small quantity $\delta$ is infinite; and then the function would have an unlimited number of zeros in any assigned small region round the origin. This would make the origin an essential singularity instead of, as required, an ordinary point of the transcendental integral function. Hence *the ratio of the quantities $\omega$ and $\omega'$ is not real.*

**56.** For the construction of the primary factor, it is necessary to render the series

$$\Sigma \Omega^{-s_{m, m'}}$$

converging, by appropriate choice of integers $s_{m, m'}$. It is found to be possible to choose an integer $s$ to be the same for every term of the series, corresponding to the simpler case of the general investigation, given in § 50.

As a matter of fact, the series

$$\Sigma \Omega^{-s}$$

diverges for $s = 1$ (we have not made any assumption that the positive and the negative infinities for $m$ are numerically equal, nor similarly as to $m'$); the series tends to a finite value for $s = 2$, but the value depends upon the relative values of the infinities for $m$ and $m'$; and $s = 3$ is the lowest integral value for which, as for all greater values, the series converges unconditionally.

There are various ways of proving the unconditional convergence of the series $\Sigma \Omega^{-\mu}$ when $\mu > 2$: the following proof is based upon a general method due to Eisenstein*.

First, the series $\displaystyle\sum_{m=-\infty}^{m=\infty} \sum_{n=-\infty}^{n=\infty} (m^2 + n^2)^{-\mu}$ converges unconditionally, if $\mu > 1$. Let the whole series be arranged in partial series: for this purpose, we choose integers $k$ and $l$, and include in each such partial series all the terms which satisfy the inequalities

$$2^k < m \leqslant 2^{k+1},$$
$$2^l < n \leqslant 2^{l+1},$$

so that the number of values of $m$ is $2^k$ and the number of values of $n$ is $2^l$.

Then, if $k + l = 2\kappa$, we have

$$2^{2\kappa} < 2^{2\kappa+1} < 2^{2k} + 2^{2l} < m^2 + n^2,$$

so that each term in the partial series $\leqslant \dfrac{1}{2^{2\kappa\mu}}$. The number of terms in the

---

* *Crelle*, t. xxxv, (1847), p. 161. A geometrical exposition is given by Halphen, *Traité des fonctions elliptiques*, t. i, pp. 358—362; and another by Goursat, *Cours d'Analyse Mathématique*, t. ii, § 324.

partial series is $2^k . 2^l$, that is, $2^{2\kappa}$: so that the sum of the terms in the partial series is.

$$\leqslant \frac{1}{2^{2\kappa\,(\mu-1)}} .$$

Expressing the latter in the form

$$\frac{1}{2^{k\,(\mu-1)}} \cdot \frac{1}{2^{l\,(\mu-1)}} ,$$

and taking the upper limit of $k$ and $l$ to be $p$, ultimately to be made infinite, we have the sum of all the partial series

$$\leqslant \sum_{k=0}^{p} \sum_{l=0}^{p} \frac{1}{2^{k\,(\mu-1)}} \cdot \frac{1}{2^{l\,(\mu-1)}}$$

$$\leqslant \left\{ \frac{1-2^{-(p+1)\,(\mu-1)}}{1-2^{-(\mu-1)}} \right\}^2 ,$$

which, when $p = \infty$, is a finite quantity if $\mu > 1$.

Next, let $\omega = \alpha + \beta i$, $\omega' = \gamma + \delta i$, so that

$$\Omega = m\omega + n\omega' = m\alpha + n\gamma + i\,(m\beta + n\delta) ;$$

hence, if $\qquad\qquad \theta = m\alpha + n\gamma, \quad \phi = m\beta + n\delta,$

we have $\qquad\qquad\qquad |\Omega|^2 = \theta^2 + \phi^2.$

Now take integers $r$ and $s$ such that

$$r < \theta < r+1, \quad s < \phi < s+1.$$

The number of terms $\Omega$ satisfying these conditions is definitely finite and is independent of $m$ and $n$. For since

$$m\,(\alpha\delta - \beta\gamma) = \theta\delta - \phi\gamma,$$

$$n\,(\alpha\delta - \beta\gamma) = -\,\theta\beta + \phi\alpha,$$

and $\alpha\delta - \beta\gamma$ does not vanish because $\omega'/\omega$ is not purely real, the number of values of $m$ is the integral part of

$$\frac{(r+1)\,\delta - s\gamma}{\alpha\delta - \beta\gamma}$$

less the integral part of

$$\frac{r\delta - (s+1)\,\gamma}{\alpha\delta - \beta\gamma} ,$$

that is, it is the integral part of $(\gamma + \delta)/(\alpha\delta - \beta\gamma)$, or is greater than it by unity. Similarly, the number of values of $n$ is the integral part of

$$(\alpha + \beta)/(\alpha\delta - \beta\gamma),$$

or is greater than it by unity. Let the product of the two numbers be $q$ ; then the number of terms $\Omega$ satisfying the inequalities is $q$.

Then
$$\Sigma\Sigma \, |\, \Omega\, |^{-2\mu} = \Sigma\Sigma \, (\theta^2 + \phi^2)^{-\mu},$$
$$\leqslant q\Sigma\Sigma \, (r^2 + s^2)^{-\mu},$$

which, by the preceding result, is finite when $\mu > 1$.   Hence

$$\Sigma\Sigma \, (m\omega + m'\omega')^{-2\mu}$$

converges unconditionally when $\mu > 1$; and therefore the least integer $s$, for which

$$\Sigma\Sigma \, (m\omega + m'\omega')^{-s}$$

converges unconditionally, is 3.   But this series converges unconditionally for any real value of $s$ which is definitely greater than 2.

The series $\Sigma\Sigma \, (m\omega + m'\omega')^{-2}$ has a finite sum, the value of which depends* upon the infinite limits for the summation with regard to $m$ and $m'$. This dependence is inconvenient, and it is therefore excluded in view of the present purpose.

*Ex.*   Prove in the same manner that the series

$$\Sigma\Sigma\ldots\ldots\Sigma \, (m_1{}^2 + m_2{}^2 + \ldots\ldots + m_n{}^2)^{-\mu},$$

the multiple summation extending over all integers $m_1, m_2, \ldots\ldots, m_n$ between $-\infty$ and $+\infty$, converges unconditionally if $2\mu > n$.                          (Eisenstein.)

**57.**   Returning now to the construction of the transcendental integral function the zeros of which are the various points $\Omega$, we use the preceding result in connection with § 50 to form the general primary factor.   Since $s = 3$, we have

$$g(z) = \sum_{n=1}^{s-1} \frac{1}{n} \left(\frac{z}{\Omega}\right)^n$$
$$= \frac{z}{\Omega} + \tfrac{1}{2} \frac{z^2}{\Omega^2},$$

and therefore the primary factor is

$$\left(1 - \frac{z}{\Omega}\right) e^{\frac{z}{\Omega} + \frac{1}{2}\frac{z^2}{\Omega^2}}$$

Moreover, the origin is a simple zero.   Hence, denoting the required function by $\sigma(z)$, we have

$$\sigma(z) = z \prod_{-\infty}^{\infty} \prod_{-\infty}^{\infty} \left\{\left(1 - \frac{z}{\Omega}\right) e^{\frac{z}{\Omega} + \frac{1}{2}\frac{z^2}{\Omega^2}}\right\}$$

*as a transcendental integral function which, since the product converges uniformly and unconditionally for all finite values of $z$, exists and has a finite value everywhere in the finite part of the plane;* the quantity $\Omega$ denotes $m\omega + m'\omega'$, and the double product is taken for all values of $m$ and of $m'$ between $-\infty$ and $+\infty$, simultaneous zero values alone being excluded.

This function will be called Weierstrass's $\sigma$-function; it is of importance in the theory of doubly-periodic functions which will be discussed in Chapter XI.

---

* See a paper by the author, *Quart. Journ. of Math.*, vol. xxi, (1886), pp. 261—280.

*Ex.* If the doubly-infinite series of zeros be the points given by

$$\Omega = m^2\omega_1 + 2mn\omega_2 + n^2\omega_3,$$

$\omega_1$, $\omega_2$, $\omega_3$ being complex constants such that $\Omega$ does not vanish for real values of $m$ and $n$, then the series

$$\sum_{-\infty}^{\infty} \sum_{-\infty}^{\infty} \Omega^{-s}$$

converges for $s=2$ but not for $s=1$. The primary factor is thus

$$\left(1 - \frac{z}{\Omega}\right) e^{\frac{z}{\Omega}},$$

and the simplest transcendental integral function having the assigned zeros is

$$z \prod_{-\infty}^{\infty} \prod_{-\infty}^{\infty} \left\{ \left(1 - \frac{z}{\Omega}\right) e^{\frac{z}{\Omega}} \right\}.$$

The actual points that are the zeros are the intersections of two infinite systems of parabolas.

**58.** One other result—of a negative character—will be adduced in this connection. We have dealt with the case in which the system of zeros is a singly-infinite arithmetical progression of points along one straight line, and with the case in which the system of zeros is a doubly-infinite arithmetical progression of points along two different straight lines. We proceed to prove that *a uniform transcendental integral function cannot exist with a triply-infinite arithmetical progression of points for zeros.*

A triply-infinite arithmetical progression of points would be represented by all the possible values of

$$p_1\Omega_1 + p_2\Omega_2 + p_3\Omega_3$$

for all possible integer values for $p_1$, $p_2$, $p_3$ between $-\infty$ and $+\infty$, where no two of the arguments of the complex constants $\Omega_1$, $\Omega_2$, $\Omega_3$ are equal. Let

$$\Omega_r = \omega_r + i\omega_r', \qquad\qquad (r=1, 2, 3);$$

then, as will be proved (§ 107) in connection with a later proposition, it is possible*—and possible in an unlimited number of ways—to determine integers $p_1$, $p_2$, $p_3$ so that, save as to infinitesimal quantities,

$$\frac{p_1}{\omega_2\omega_3' - \omega_3\omega_2'} = \frac{p_2}{\omega_3\omega_1' - \omega_1\omega_3'} = \frac{p_3}{\omega_1\omega_2' - \omega_2\omega_1'},$$

all the denominators in which equations differ from zero on account of the fact that no two arguments of the three quantities $\Omega_1$, $\Omega_2$, $\Omega_3$ are equal. For each such set of determined integers, the quantity

$$p_1\Omega_1 + p_2\Omega_2 + p_3\Omega_3$$

is zero or infinitesimal. If it is zero, then (as in § 107 for periods) the triple infinite is really only a double infinite. If it is infinitesimal, then (as at the end of § 55) the origin is an essential singularity, contrary to the

---

* Jacobi, *Ges. Werke*, t. ii, p. 27.

hypothesis that the only essential singularity is for $z = \infty$. Hence a uniform transcendental function cannot exist having a triply-infinite arithmetical succession of zeros.

**59.** In effecting the formation of a transcendental integral function by means of its primary factors, it has been proved that the expression of the primary factor depends upon the values of the integers which make

$$\sum_{n=1}^{\infty} |a_n|^{-m_n-1} |z|^{m_n}$$

a converging series. Moreover, the primary factors are not unique in form, because any finite number of terms of the proper form can be added to the exponential index in

$$\left(1 - \frac{z}{a_n}\right) e^{\sum_{r=1}^{m_n-1} \frac{1}{r} \frac{z^r}{a_n^r}};$$

the added terms will only the more effectively secure the convergence of the infinite product. But there is a lower limit to the removal of terms with the highest exponents from the index of the exponential; for there are, in general, least values for the integers $m_1, m_2, \ldots$, below which these integers cannot be reduced, if the convergence of the product is to be secured.

The simplest case, in which the exponential must be retained in the primary factor in order to secure the convergence of the infinite product, is that discussed in § 50, viz., when the integers $m_1, m_2, \ldots$ are equal to one another. Let $m$ denote this common value for a given function, and let $m$ be the least integer effective for the purpose: the function is then said[*] to be of *class* $m$, and the condition that it should be of class $m$ is, that the integer $m$ be the least integer to make the series

$$\sum_{n=1}^{\infty} |a_n|^{-m-1}$$

converge, the constants $a_n$ being the zeros of the function.

Thus algebraical polynomials are of class 0; the circular functions $\sin z$ and $\cos z$ are of class 1; Weierstrass's $\sigma$-function and the Jacobian elliptic function sn $z$ are of class 2, and so on: but for no one of these classes do the functions mentioned constitute the whole of the functions of that class.

**60.** One or two of the simpler properties of an aggregate of transcendental integral functions of the same class can easily be obtained.

Let a function $f(z)$, of class $n$, have a zero of order $r$ at the origin and have $a_1, a_2, \ldots$ for its other zeros, arranged in order of increasing moduli. Then, by § 50, the function $f(z)$ can be expressed in the form

$$f(z) = e^{G(z)} z^r \prod_{i=1}^{\infty} \left\{ \left(1 - \frac{z}{a_i}\right) e^{g_i(z)} \right\},$$

---

[*] The French word is *genre*; the Italian is *genere*. Laguerre (see references on p. 113) appears to have been the first to discuss the *class* of transcendental integral functions.

where $g_i(z)$ denotes the series $\sum\limits_{s=1}^{n} \dfrac{1}{s}\left(\dfrac{z}{a_i}\right)^s$ and $G(z)$ must be properly determined to secure the equality.

Now consider the series

$$\sum_{i=1}^{\infty} \frac{1}{a_i^{\,n}(a_i - z)}$$

for all values of $z$ that lie outside circles round the points $a$, taken as small as we please. The sum of the series of the moduli of its terms is

$$\sum_{i=1}^{\infty} \frac{1}{|a_i|^{n+1}} \frac{1}{\left|1 - \dfrac{z}{a_i}\right|}.$$

Let $d$ be the least of the quantities $\left|1 - \dfrac{z}{a_i}\right|$, necessarily non-evanescent because $z$ lies outside the specified circles; then the sum of the series

$$< \frac{1}{d} \sum_{i=1}^{\infty} \frac{1}{|a_i|^{n+1}},$$

which is a converging series since the function is of class $n$. Hence the series of moduli converges, and therefore the original series converges. Moreover, the series $\sum\limits_{i=1}^{\infty} |a_i|^{-n-1}$ converges. Denoting by $\epsilon$ any real positive quantity, as small as we please, we can choose an integer $m$ such that

$$\sum_{p=\mu}^{\mu+r} |a_i|^{-n-1} < \epsilon,$$

for all integers $\mu \geqslant m$ and for all positive integers $r$. Accordingly, for the values of $z$ considered, we have

$$\left| \sum_{p=\mu}^{\mu+r} \frac{1}{a_i^{n+1}} \frac{1}{1 - \dfrac{z}{a_i}} \right| \leqslant \frac{\epsilon}{d},$$

for all integers $\mu \geqslant m$, for all positive integers $r$, and for all the values of $z$. Hence the series converges unconditionally and uniformly within the specified region of variation of $z$; let it be denoted by $S(z)$, so that

$$S(z) = \sum_{i=1}^{\infty} \frac{1}{a_i^{\,n}(a_i - z)}.$$

We have

$$\frac{f'(z)}{f(z)} = G'(z) + \frac{r}{z} + \sum_{i=1}^{\infty} \frac{1}{a_i}\left\{1 + \frac{z}{a_i} + \ldots + \frac{z^{n-1}}{a_i^{n-1}} - \frac{1}{1 - \dfrac{z}{a_i}}\right\}$$

$$= G'(z) + \frac{r}{z} - z^n \sum_{i=1}^{\infty} \frac{1}{a_i^{\,n}(a_i - z)}$$

$$= G'(z) + \frac{r}{z} - z^n S(z).$$

Each step of this process is reversible in all cases in which the original product converges. If, therefore, it can be shewn of a function $f(z)$ that $\dfrac{f'(z)}{f(z)}$ takes this form, the function is thereby proved to be of class $n$.

If there be no zero at the origin, the term $\dfrac{r}{z}$ is absent.

If the exponential factor $G(z)$ be a constant so that $G'(z)$ is zero, the function $f(z)$ is said to be a *simple* function of class $n$.

**61.** There are several criteria, used to determine the class of a function: the simplest of them is contained in the following proposition, due to Laguerre*.

*If, as z tends to the value* $\infty$*, a very great value of* $|z|$ *can be found for which the limit of* $z^{-n}\dfrac{f'(z)}{f(z)}$*, where* $f(z)$ *is a transcendental integral function, tends uniformly to the value zero, then* $f(z)$ *is of class n.*

Take a circle, centre the origin and of radius $R$ equal to this value of $|z|$; then, by § 24, II., the integral

$$\frac{1}{2\pi i}\int \frac{1}{t^n}\frac{f'(t)}{f(t)}\frac{dt}{t-z},$$

taken round the circle, is zero when $R$ becomes indefinitely great. But the value of the integral is, by the Corollary in § 20,

$$\frac{1}{2\pi i}\int^{(0)}\frac{1}{t^n}\frac{f'(t)}{f(t)}\frac{dt}{t-z}+\frac{1}{2\pi i}\int^{(z)}\frac{1}{t^n}\frac{f'(t)}{f(t)}\frac{dt}{t-z}+\frac{1}{2\pi i}\sum_{i=1}^{\infty}\int^{(a_i)}\frac{1}{t^n}\frac{f'(t)}{f(t)}\frac{dt}{t-z},$$

taken round small circles enclosing the origin, the point $z$, and the points $a_i$, which are the infinities of the subject of integration; the origin being supposed a zero of $f(t)$ of multiplicity $r$. Now

$$\frac{1}{2\pi i}\int^{(z)}\frac{1}{t^n}\frac{f'(t)}{f(t)}\frac{dt}{t-z}=\frac{1}{z^n}\frac{f'(z)}{f(z)},$$

$$\frac{1}{2\pi i}\int^{(a_i)}\frac{1}{t^n}\frac{f'(t)}{f(t)}\frac{dt}{t-z}=\frac{1}{a_i^n}\frac{1}{a_i-z},$$

and

$$\frac{1}{2\pi i}\int^{(0)}\frac{1}{t^n}\frac{f'(t)}{f(t)}\frac{dt}{t-z}=-\frac{\phi(z)}{z^n}-\frac{r}{z^{n+1}},$$

where $\phi(z)$ denotes the polynomial

$$\left\{\frac{f'(t)}{f(t)}-\frac{r}{t}\right\}+z\frac{d}{dt}\left\{\frac{f'(t)}{f(t)}-\frac{r}{t}\right\}+\ldots+\frac{z^{n-1}}{(n-1)!}\frac{d^{n-1}}{dt^{n-1}}\left\{\frac{f'(t)}{f(t)}-\frac{r}{t}\right\},$$

when $t$ is made zero. Hence

$$\frac{1}{z^n}\frac{f'(z)}{f(z)}+\sum_{i=1}^{\infty}\frac{1}{a_i^n(a_i-z)}-\frac{\phi(z)}{z^n}-\frac{r}{z^{n+1}}=0,$$

---

* *Comptes Rendus*, t. xciv, (1882), p. 636; *Œuvres Complètes*, t. i, p. 172.

and therefore

$$\frac{f'(z)}{f(z)} = \phi(z) + \frac{r}{z} - z^n S(z),$$

which, by § 60, shews that $f(z)$ is of class $n$.

COROLLARY. *The product of any finite number of functions of the same class $n$ is a function of class not higher than $n$; and the class of the product of any finite number of functions of different classes is not greater than the highest class of the component functions.*

NOTE 1. In connection with Weierstrass's theorem in § 52, one remark may be made as to its influence upon the class of a function; it will be sufficiently illustrated by taking $e^{z^2} \sin z$ as an example. Laguerre's test shews that the class is two, whereas by the test of § 60 the class apparently is unity. The explanation of the difference is that, in § 60, the zeros of the generalising factor $e^{\bar{g}(z)}$ of § 52 are not taken into account. It is true that all these zeros are at infinity; but their existence may affect the integer, which is the least that secures the convergence of the series $\Sigma |a_i|^{-n-1}$. Thus the zeros of the function $e^{z^2} \sin z$ are $m\pi$, where $m = 0, \pm 1, ..., \pm \infty$, arising from $\sin z$: and

$$ip^{\frac{1}{2}}, \quad -ip^{\frac{1}{2}},$$

each occurring $p$ times, where $p$ is an infinite positive integer: the latter arising from $e^{z^2}$, by regarding it as the limit of

$$\left(1 + \frac{z^2}{p}\right)^p,$$

when $p$ is an infinite positive integer. In order that the critical series may converge, it is necessary that, as these new zeros are at infinity, the integer $n$ should be chosen so as to make

$$p|(ip^{\frac{1}{2}})^{-n-1}| + p|(-ip^{\frac{1}{2}})^{-n-1}|$$

vanish. The lowest value of $n$ is two; and therefore the function really is of class two, agreeing with the result of Laguerre's test.

More generally, consider a function

$$F(z) = e^{G(z)} f(z),$$

where $f(z)$ is of class $n$, and $G(z)$ is itself an integral function. On the application of Laguerre's test, the limit of

$$z^{-n} \frac{F'(z)}{F(z)},$$

when $|z|$ increases indefinitely, is the limit of $z^{-n} G'(z)$. Thus $F(z)$ is not of class $n$, unless $G(z)$ is a polynomial in $z$ of degree $\leqslant n$. If $G(z)$ is a polynomial of degree $m > n$, then $F(z)$ is of class $m$. If $G(z)$ is a transcendental integral function, $F(z)$ is of infinite class.

Of course, this is not the only manner in which functions of infinite class can arise. Thus consider an integral function having $\log 2$, $\log 3$, $\log 4$, ... for its infinite succession of zeros. It has been noted (p. 95, foot-note) that no finite integer $s$ exists such that the series $\sum\limits_{n=2}^{\infty} (\log n)^{-s}$ converges; consequently the class of the series is infinite*.

NOTE 2. Borel† introduces the notion of the *order* of an integral function as distinct from the *class* of the function. In the preceding investigation (§ 59), the class of the equation is taken to be the lowest integer $s$ (if any) for which the series

$$\sum a_n^{-s-1}$$

(where $a_1$, $a_2$, ... are the zeros arranged in non-descending magnitude of moduli) converges absolutely. Borel takes the order of the function to be the lowest real quantity for which the same series converges absolutely; so that, if $\mu$ be the class and $\mu'$ the order of a function,

$$\mu' \leqslant \mu < \mu' + 1.$$

Thus the class of the product

$$\prod_{n=1}^{\infty} \left\{ \left( 1 - \frac{z}{n} \right) e^{\frac{z}{n}} \right\}$$

is unity, because 2 is the lowest integer which makes the series $\sum\limits_{n=1}^{\infty} n^{-s}$ converge; its order is $1 + k$, where $k$ is any quantity greater than zero but as small as we please, because the series $\sum\limits_{n=1}^{\infty} n^{-1-k}$ converges.

The following are the chief references to memoirs discussing the class of functions :—

Laguerre, *Comptes Rendus*, t. xciv, (1882), pp. 160—163, pp. 635—638, ib. t. xcv, (1882), pp. 828—831, ib. t. xcviii, (1884), pp. 79—81‡ ; Poincaré, *Bull. des Sciences Math.*, t. xi, (1883), pp. 136—144 ; Cesàro, *Comptes Rendus*, t. xcix, (1884), pp. 26—27 (followed (p. 27) by a note by Hermite), *Giornale di Battaglini*, t. xxii, (1884), pp. 191—200 ; Vivanti, *Giornale di Battaglini*, t. xxii, (1884), pp. 243—261, pp. 378—380, ib. t. xxiii, (1885), pp. 96—122, ib. t. xxvi, (1888), pp. 303—314 ; Hermite, *Cours à la faculté des Sciences* (4me éd., 1891), pp. 91—93 ; Hadamard, *Liouville*, 4me Sér., t. ix, (1893), pp. 171—214 ; Borel, *Acta Math.*, t. xx, (1897), pp. 357—396, *Leçons sur les fonctions entières*, (1900), ch. ii.

*Ex.* 1.  Prove that the class of the functions $\sin z$, $1 + z \sin z$ is unity.

*Ex.* 2.  The function

$$\sum_{i=1}^{n} e^{c_i z} f_i(z),$$

where the quantities $c$ are constants, $n$ is a finite integer, and the functions $f_i(z)$ are polynomials, is of class unity.

---

* For functions of infinite class, reference may be made to Blumenthal's monograph *Principes de la théorie des fonctions entières d'ordre infini* (1910).

† *Leçons sur les fonctions entières*, p. 26.

‡ All these are included in the first volume of the *Œuvres de Laguerre*, (1898, Gauthier-Villars).

*Ex.* 3. If a simple function be of class $n$, its derivative is also of class $n$.

*Ex.* 4. Discuss the conditions under which the sum of two functions, each of class $n$, is also of class $n$.

*Ex.* 5. Examine the following test for the class of a function, due to Poincaré.

Let $a$ be any number, no matter how small provided its argument be such that $e^{az^{n+1}}$ vanishes when $z$ tends towards infinity. Then $f(z)$ is of class $n$, if the limit of

$$e^{az^{n+1}} f(z)$$

vanish with indefinite increase of $z$.

A possible value of $a$ is $\sum_{i=1}^{\infty} c_i a_i^{-n-1}$, where $c_i$ is a constant of modulus unity.

*Ex.* 6. Verify the following test for the class of a function, due to de Sparre*.

Let $\lambda$ be any positive non-infinitesimal quantity; then the function $f(z)$ is of class $n$, if the limit, for $m = \infty$, of

$$|a_m|^{n-1}\{|a_{m+1}| - |a_m|\}$$

be not less than $\lambda$. Thus $\sin z$ is of class unity.

*Ex.* 7. Let the roots of $\theta^{n+1} = 1$ be $1, a, a^2, \ldots\ldots, a^n$; and let $f(z)$ be a function of class $n$. Then forming the product

$$\prod_{s=0}^{n} f(a^s z),$$

we evidently have an integral function of $z^{n+1}$; let it be denoted by $F(z^{n+1})$. The roots of $F(z^{n+1}) = 0$ are $a_i a^s$, for $i = 1, 2, \ldots\ldots$, and $s = 0, 1, \ldots\ldots, n$; and therefore, replacing $z^{n+1}$ by $z$, the roots of $F(z) = 0$ are $a_i^{n+1}$, for $i = 1, 2, \ldots\ldots$.

Since $f(z)$ is of class $n$, the series

$$\sum_{i=1}^{\infty} \frac{1}{a_i^{n+1}}$$

converges unconditionally. This series is the sum of the first powers of the reciprocals of the roots of $F(z) = 0$; hence, according to the definition (p. 109), $F(z)$ is of class zero.

It therefore follows that *from a function of any class, a function of class zero with a modified variable can be deduced. Conversely, by appropriately modifying the variable of a given function of class zero, it is possible to deduce functions of any required class.*

*Ex.* 8. If all the zeros of the function

$$\prod_{n=1}^{\infty} \left\{ \left(1 - \frac{z}{a_n}\right) e^{\sum_{r=1}^{k-1} \frac{1}{r} \frac{z^r}{a_n^r}} \right\}$$

be real, then all the zeros of its derivative are also real. (Witting.)

* *Comptes Rendus*, t. cii, (1886), p. 741.

# CHAPTER VI.

## FUNCTIONS WITH A LIMITED NUMBER OF ESSENTIAL SINGULARITIES.

**62.** SOME indications regarding the character of a function at an essential singularity have already been given. Thus, though the function is regular in the vicinity of such a point $a$, it may, like sn $(1/z)$ at the origin, have a zero of unlimited multiplicity or an infinity of unlimited multiplicity at the point; and in either case the point is such that there is no factor of the form $(z - a)^\lambda$, which can be associated with the function so as to make the point an ordinary point for the modified function. Moreover, even when the path of approach to the essential singularity is specified, the value acquired may not be definite: thus, as $z$ approaches the origin along the axis of $x$, so that its value may be taken to be $1 \div (4mK + x)$, the value of sn $(1/z)$ is not definite in the limit when $m$ is made infinite. One characteristic of the point is the indefiniteness of value of the function at the essential singularity, though in the vicinity the function is uniform.

A brief statement and a proof of this characteristic were given in § 32; the theorem there proved—that a uniform analytical function can assume any value at an essential singularity—may also be proved as follows. The essential singularity will be taken at infinity—a supposition that does not detract from generality.

Let $f(z)$ be a function having any number of zeros and any number of accidental singularities and $z = \infty$ for its sole essential singularity; then it can be expressed in the form

$$f(z) = \frac{G_1(z)}{G_2(z)} e^{g(z)},$$

where $G_1(z)$ is polynomial or transcendental according as the number of zeros is finite or infinite, and $G_2(z)$ is polynomial or transcendental according as the number of accidental singularities is finite or infinite.

If $G_2(z)$ be transcendental, we can omit the generalising factor $e^{g(z)}$. Then $f(z)$ has an infinite number of accidental singularities; each of them .

in the finite part of the plane is of only finite multiplicity and therefore some of them must be at infinity. At each such point, the function $G_2(z)$ vanishes and $G_1(z)$ does not vanish; and so $f(z)$ has infinite values for $z = \infty$.

If $G_2(z)$ be polynomial and $G_1(z)$ be also polynomial, then the factor $e^{g(z)}$ may not be omitted, for its omission would make $f(z)$ a rational function. Now $z = \infty$ is either an ordinary point or an accidental singularity of

$$G_1(z)/G_2(z);$$

hence as $g(z)$ is integral, there are infinite values of $z$ which make

$$\frac{G_1(z)}{G_2(z)} e^{g(z)}$$

infinite.

If $G_2(z)$ be polynomial and $G_1(z)$ be transcendental, the factor $e^{g(z)}$ may be omitted. Let $a_1, a_2, \ldots, a_n$ be the roots of $G_2(z)$: then taking

$$f(z) = \sum_{r=1}^{n} \frac{A_r}{z - a_r} + G_n(z),$$

we have

$$A_r = \frac{G_1(a_r)}{G_2'(a_r)},$$

a non-vanishing constant; and so

$$f(z) = \frac{G_3(z)}{G_2(z)} + G_n(z),$$

where $G_n(z)$ is a transcendental integral function. When $z = \infty$, the value of $G_3(z)/G_2(z)$ is zero, but $G_n(z)$ is infinite; hence $f(z)$ has infinite values for $z = \infty$.

Similarly it may be shewn, as follows, that $f(z)$ has zero values for $z = \infty$.

In the first of the preceding cases, if $G_1(z)$ be transcendental, so that $f(z)$ has an infinite number of zeros, then some of them must be at an infinite distance; $f(z)$ has a zero value for each such point. And if $G_1(z)$ be polynomial, then there are infinite values of $z$ which, not being zeros of $G_2(z)$, make $f(z)$ vanish.

In the second case, when $z$ is made infinite with such an argument as to make the highest term in $g(z)$ a real negative quantity, then $f(z)$ vanishes for that infinite value of $z$.

In the third case, $f(z)$ vanishes for a zero of $G_1(z)$ that is at infinity.

Hence the value of $f(z)$ for $z = \infty$ is not definite. If, moreover, there be any value neither zero nor infinity, say $C$, which $f(z)$ cannot acquire for $z = \infty$, then

$$f(z) - C$$

is a function which cannot be zero at infinity, and therefore all its zeros are in the finite part of the plane: no one of them is an essential singularity, for

$f(z)$ has only a single value at any point in the finite part of the plane; hence they are finite in number and are isolated points. Let $H_1(z)$ be the polynomial having them for its zeros. The accidental singularities of $f(z) - C$ are the accidental singularities of $f(z)$; hence

$$f(z) - C = \frac{H_1(z)}{G_2(z)} e^{h(z)},$$

where, if $G_2(z)$ be polynomial, the exponential $h(z)$ must occur, since $f(z)$, and therefore $f(z) - C$, is transcendental. The function

$$F(z) = \frac{1}{f(z) - C} = \frac{G_2(z)}{H_1(z)} e^{-h(z)}$$

evidently has $z = \infty$ for an essential singularity, so that, by the second or the third case above, it certainly has an infinite value for $z = \infty$, that is, $f(z)$ certainly acquires the value $C$ for $z = \infty$.

Hence the function can acquire any value at an essential singularity.

**63.** We now proceed to obtain the character of the expression of a function at a point $z$ which, lying in the region of continuity, is in the vicinity of an essential singularity $b$ in the finite part of the plane.

With $b$ as centre describe two circles, so that their circumferences and the whole area between them lie entirely within the region of continuity. The radius of the inner circle is to be as small as possible consistent with this condition; and therefore, as it will be assumed that $b$ is the only singularity in its own immediate vicinity, this radius may be made very small.

The ordinary point $z$ of the function may be taken as lying within the circular ring-formed part of the region of continuity. At all such points in this band, the function is holomorphic; and therefore, by Laurent's Theorem (§ 28), it can be expanded in a converging series of positive and negative integral powers of $z - b$, in the form

$$u_0 + u_1(z - b) + u_2 \overline{(z - b)^2} + \dots$$
$$+ v_1(z - b)^{-1} + v_2(z - b)^{-2} + \dots;$$

the coefficients $u_n$ are determined by the equation

$$u_n = \frac{1}{2\pi i} \int \frac{f(t)}{(t - b)^{n+1}} dt, \qquad (n = 0, 1, 2, \dots),$$

the integrals being taken positively round the outer circle, and the coefficients $v_n$ are determined by the equation

$$v_n = \frac{1}{2\pi i} \int (t' - b)^{n-1} f(t') dt',$$

the integrals being taken positively round the inner circle.

The series of positive powers converges everywhere within the outer circle of centre $b$, and so (§ 26) it may be denoted by $P(z-b)$; and the function $P$ may be either polynomial or transcendental.

The series of negative powers converges everywhere without the inner circle of centre $b$; and, since $b$ is not an accidental but an essential singularity of the function, the series of negative powers contains an infinite number of terms. It may be denoted by $G\left(\dfrac{1}{z-b}\right)$, a series converging for all points in the plane except $z = b$, and vanishing when $z - b = \infty$.

Thus
$$f(z) = G\left(\frac{1}{z-b}\right) + P(z-b)$$

is the analytical representation of the function in the vicinity of its essential singularity $b$; the function $G$ is transcendental and converges everywhere in the plane outside an infinitesimal circle round $b$, and the function $P$, if transcendental, converges for sufficiently small values of $|z-b|$.

Had the singularity at $b$ been accidental, the function $G$ would have been polynomial.

COROLLARY I. If the function have any essential singularity other than $b$, it is an essential singularity of $P(z-b)$ continued outside the outer circle; but it is not an essential singularity of $G\left(\dfrac{1}{z-b}\right)$, for the latter function converges everywhere in the plane outside the inner circle.

COROLLARY II. Suppose the function has no singularity in the plane except at the point $b$; then the outer circle can have its radius made infinite. In that case, all positive powers except the constant term $u_0$ disappear: and even this term survives only in case the function have a finite value at infinity. The expression for the function is
$$u_0 + \frac{v_1}{z-b} + \frac{v_2}{(z-b)^2} + \cdots,$$

and the transcendental series converges everywhere outside the infinitesimal circle round $b$, that is, at every point in the plane for which $\dfrac{1}{|z-b|}$ remains less than any assigned quantity, however large. Hence the function can be represented by
$$G\left(\frac{1}{z-b}\right).$$

This special result is deduced by Weierstrass from the earlier investigations*, as follows. If $f(z)$ be such a function with an essential

* Weierstrass, *Ges. Werke*, t. ii, p. 102.

singularity at $b$, and if we change the independent variable by the relation

$$z' = \frac{1}{z - b},$$

then $f(z)$ changes into a function of $z'$, the only essential singularity of which is at $z' = \infty$. It has no other singularity in the plane; and the form of the function is therefore $G(z')$, that is, *a function having an essential singularity at $b$, but no other singularity in the plane, is*

$$G\left(\frac{1}{z-b}\right).$$

COROLLARY III.   *The most general expression of a function having its sole essential singularity at $b$, a point in the finite part of the plane, and any number of accidental singularities, is*

$$\frac{G_1\left(\dfrac{1}{z-b}\right)}{G_2\left(\dfrac{1}{z-b}\right)} e^{g\left(\frac{1}{z-b}\right)},$$

*where the zeros of the function are the zeros of $G_1$, the accidental singularities of the function are the zeros of $G_2$, and the function $g$ in the exponential is a function which is finite for all finite values of* $\dfrac{1}{z-b}$.

This can be derived in the same way as before; or it can be deduced from the corresponding theorem relating to transcendental integral functions, as above. It would be necessary to construct an integral function $G_2(z')$, having as its zeros

$$\frac{1}{a_1 - b}, \quad \frac{1}{a_2 - b}, \quad \dots,$$

and then to replace $z'$ by $\dfrac{1}{z-b}$; and $G_2$ is polynomial or transcendental, according as the number of zeros is finite or infinite.

Similarly we obtain the following result :—

COROLLARY IV.   *A uniform function of $z$, which has its sole essential singularity at $b$, a point in the finite part of the plane, and no accidental singularities, can be represented in the form of an infinite product of primary factors of the form*

$$\left(\frac{k}{z-b} + l\right) e^{g\left(\frac{1}{z-b}\right)},$$

*which converges uniformly and unconditionally everywhere in the plane outside an infinitesimal circle drawn round the point $b$.*

The function $g\left(\dfrac{1}{z-b}\right)$ is an integral function of $\dfrac{1}{z-b}$ vanishing when $\dfrac{1}{z-b}$ vanishes; and $k$ and $l$ are constants. In particular factors, $g\left(\dfrac{1}{z-b}\right)$ may vanish; and either $k$ or $l$ (but not both $k$ and $l$) may vanish, with or without a vanishing exponent $g\left(\dfrac{1}{z-b}\right)$.

If $a_i$ be any zero, the corresponding primary factor may evidently be expressed in the form

$$\left(\frac{z-a_i}{z-b}\right)e^{g_i\left(\frac{1}{z-b}\right)}$$

Similarly, for a uniform function of $z$ with its sole essential singularity at $b$ and any number of accidental singularities, the product-form is at once derivable by applying the result of the present Corollary to the result given in Corollary III.

These results, combined with the results of Chapter V., give the general theory of uniform functions with only one essential singularity.

**64.** We now proceed to the consideration of functions, which have a limited number of assigned essential singularities.

The theorem of § 63 gives an expression for the function at any point in the band between the two circles there drawn.

Let $c$ be such a point, which is thus an ordinary point for the function; then in the domain of $c$, the function is expansible in a form $P_1(z-c)$. This domain may extend as far as an infinitesimal circle round an essential singularity $b$, or it may be limited by a pole $d$ which is nearer to $c$ than $b$ is, or it may be limited by an essential singularity $f$ which is nearer to $c$ than $b$ is. In the first case, we form a continuation of the function in a direction away from $b$; in the second case, we continue the function by associating with the function a factor $(z-d)^n$ which takes account of the accidental singularity; in the third case, we form a continuation of the function towards $f$. Taking the continuations for successive domains of points in the vicinity of $f$, we can obtain the value of the function for points on two circles that have $f$ for their common centre. Using these values, as in § 63, to obtain coefficients, we ultimately construct a series of positive and negative powers converging outside an infinitesimal circle round $f$. Different expressions in different parts of the plane will thus be obtained, each being valid only in a particular portion: the aggregate of all of them is the analytical expression of the function for the whole of the region of the plane where the function exists.

We thus have one mode of representation of the function; its chief advantage is that it indicates the form in the vicinity of any point, though it gives no suggestion of the possible modification of character elsewhere. This deficiency renders the representation insufficiently precise and complete; and it is therefore necessary to have another mode of representation.

**65.** Suppose that the function has $n$ essential singularities $a_1, a_2, \ldots, a_n$, and that it has no other singularity. Let a circle, or any simple closed curve, be drawn enclosing them all, every point of the boundary as well as the included area (with the exception of the $n$ singularities*) lying in the region of continuity of the function.

Let $z$ be any ordinary point in the interior of the circle or curve; and consider the integral

$$\int \frac{f(t)}{t-z} dt,$$

taken round the curve. If we surround $z$ and each of the $n$ singularities by small circles with the respective points for centres, then the integral round the outer curve is equal to the sum of the values of the integral taken round the $n+1$ circles. Thus

$$\frac{1}{2\pi i} \int_s \frac{f(t)}{t-z} dt = \frac{1}{2\pi i} \int_z \frac{f(t)}{t-z} dt + \frac{1}{2\pi i} \Sigma \int_{a_r} \frac{f(t)}{t-z} dt,$$

and therefore

$$\frac{1}{2\pi i} \int_z \frac{f(t)}{t-z} dt = \frac{1}{2\pi i} \int_s \frac{f(t)}{t-z} dt - \frac{1}{2\pi i} \Sigma \int_{a_r} \frac{f(t)}{t-z} dt.$$

The left-hand side of the equation is $f(z)$.

Evaluating the integrals, we have

$$\frac{1}{2\pi i} \int_{a_r} \frac{f(t)}{t-z} dt = - G_r\left(\frac{1}{z-a_r}\right),$$

where $G_r$ is, as before, a transcendental function of $\dfrac{1}{z-a_r}$ vanishing when $\dfrac{1}{z-a_r}$ is zero.

Now, of these functions, $G_r\left(\dfrac{1}{z-a_r}\right)$ converges everywhere in the plane outside the infinitesimal circle round $a_r$, (say except at $a_r$): and therefore, as $n$ is finite,

$$\sum_{r=1}^{n} G_r\left(\frac{1}{z-a_r}\right)$$

is a function which converges everywhere in the plane except at the $n$ points $a_1, \ldots, a_n$.

Because $z = \infty$ is not an essential singularity of $f(z)$, the radius of the circle in the integral $\dfrac{1}{2\pi i} \int_s \dfrac{f(t)}{t-z} dt$ may be indefinitely increased. The value

---

* This phrase will frequently be used as an abbreviation for "the infinitesimal regions enclosed by infinitesimal circles round the singularities."

of $f(t)$ tends, with unlimited increase of $t$, to some determinate value $C$ which is not infinite; hence, as in § 24, II., Corollary, the value of the integral is $C$. We therefore have the result that $f(z)$ can be expressed in the form

$$C + \sum_{r=1}^{n} G_r \left(\frac{1}{z - a_r}\right),$$

or, absorbing the constant $C$ into the functions $G$ and replacing the limitation that the function $G_r\left(\dfrac{1}{z - a_r}\right)$ shall vanish for $\dfrac{1}{z - a_r} = 0$, by the limitation that, for the same value $\dfrac{1}{z - a_r} = 0$, it shall be finite, we have the theorem*:—

*If a given function $f(z)$ have $n$ singularities $a_1, \ldots, a_n$, all of which are in the finite part of the plane and are essential singularities, it can be expressed in the form*

$$\sum_{r=1}^{n} G_r \left(\frac{1}{z - a_r}\right),$$

*where $G_r$ is a transcendental function, converging everywhere in the plane outside an infinitesimal circle round $a_r$, and having a determinate finite value $g_r$ for $\dfrac{1}{z - a_r} = 0$, such that $\sum\limits_{r=1}^{n} g_r$ is the finite value of the given function at infinity.*

COROLLARY. If the given function have a singularity at $\infty$, and $n$ singularities in the finite part of the plane, then the function can be expressed in the form

$$G(z) + \sum_{r=1}^{n} G_r \left(\frac{1}{z - a_r}\right),$$

where $G_r$ is a transcendental or a polynomial function, according as $a_r$ is an essential or an accidental singularity: and so also for $G(z)$, according to the character of the singularity at infinity.

**66.** Any uniform function, which has an essential singularity at $z = a$, can (§ 63) be expressed in the form

$$g\left(\frac{1}{z - a}\right) + p(z - a),$$

for points $z$ in the vicinity of $a$. Suppose that, for points in this vicinity, the function $f(z)$ has no zero, and that it has no accidental singularity. Therefore, among such points $z$, the function

$$\frac{1}{f(z)} \frac{df(z)}{dz}$$

---

\* The method of proof, by an integration, is used for brevity: the theorem can be established by purely algebraical reasoning.

has no pole, and therefore no singularity except that at $a$ which is essential. Hence it can be expanded in the form

$$G\left(\frac{1}{z-a}\right) + P(z-a),$$

where $G$ converges everywhere in the plane except at $a$, and vanishes for $\frac{1}{z-a} = 0$. Let

$$G\left(\frac{1}{z-a}\right) = \frac{c}{z-a} + \frac{d}{dz}\left\{G_1\left(\frac{1}{z-a}\right)\right\},$$

where $G_1\left(\frac{1}{z-a}\right)$ converges everywhere in the plane except at $a$, and vanishes for $\frac{1}{z-a} = 0$.

Then $c$, evidently not an infinite quantity, is an integer. To prove this, describe a small circle of radius $\rho$ round $a$: then taking $z - a = \rho e^{\theta i}$, so that $\frac{dz}{z-a} = id\theta$, we have

$$\frac{1}{f(z)}\frac{df(z)}{dz}dz = P(z-a)\,dz + cid\theta + \frac{d}{dz}\left\{G_1\left(\frac{1}{z-a}\right)\right\}dz,$$

and therefore

$$f(z) = Ce^{ci\theta + \int P(z-a)\,dz + G_1\left(\frac{1}{z-a}\right)}.$$

Now $\int P(z-a)\,dz$ is a uniform function: and so is $f(z)$. But a change of $\theta$ into $\theta + 2\pi$ does not alter $z$ or any of the functions: thus

$$e^{ci2\pi} = 1;$$

and therefore $c$ is an integer.

**67.** If the function $f(z)$ have essential singularities $a_1, \ldots, a_n$ and no others, then it can be expressed in the form

$$C + \sum_{r=1}^{n} g_r\left(\frac{1}{z-a_r}\right).$$

If there be no zeros for this function $f(z)$ anywhere (except of course such as may enter through the indeterminateness at the essential singularities), then

$$\frac{1}{f(z)}\frac{df(z)}{dz}$$

has $n$ essential singularities $a_1, \ldots, a_n$ and no other singularities of any kind. Hence it can be expressed in the form

$$C + \sum_{r=1}^{n} G_r\left(\frac{1}{z-a_r}\right),$$

where the function $G_r$ vanishes with $\dfrac{1}{z - a_r}$.  Let

$$G_r\left(\frac{1}{z - a_r}\right) = \frac{c_r}{z - a_r} + \frac{d}{dz}\left\{\bar{G}_r\left(\frac{1}{z - a_r}\right)\right\},$$

where $\bar{G}_r\left(\dfrac{1}{z - a_r}\right)$ is a function of the same kind as $G_r\left(\dfrac{1}{z - a_r}\right)$.

Then all the coefficients $c_r$, evidently not infinite quantities, are integers. For, let a small circle of radius $\rho$ be drawn round $a_r$: then, if $z - a_r = \rho e^{\theta i}$, we have

$$\frac{c_r dz}{z - a_r} = c_r i d\theta,$$

and

$$\frac{c_s dz}{z - a_s} = dP_s\,(z - a_r).$$

We proceed as before: the expression for the function in the former case is changed so that now the sum $\Sigma P_s\,(z - a_r)$ for $s = 1, ..., r - 1$, $r + 1, ..., n$ is a uniform function; there is no other change.  In exactly the same way as before, we shew that every one of the coefficients $c_r$ is an integer.

Hence it appears that if a given function $f(z)$ have, in the finite part of the plane, $n$ essential singularities $a_1, ..., a_n$ and no other singularities, and if it have no zeros anywhere in the plane, then

$$\frac{1}{f(z)}\frac{df(z)}{dz} = C + \sum_{i=1}^{n}\frac{c_i}{z - a_i} + \sum_{i=1}^{n}\frac{d}{dz}\left\{\bar{G}_i\left(\frac{1}{z - a_i}\right)\right\},$$

where all the coefficients $c_i$ are integers, the functions $\bar{G}$ converge everywhere in the plane except at the essential singularities, and $\bar{G}_i$ vanishes for

$$\frac{1}{z - a_i} = 0.$$

Now, since $f(z)$ has no singularity at $\infty$, we have for very large values of $z$

$$f(z) = u_0 + \frac{v_1}{z} + \frac{v_2}{z^2} + ...,$$

and

$$f'(z) = -\frac{v_1}{z^2} - \frac{2v_2}{z^3} - ...,$$

and therefore, for very large values of $z$,

$$\frac{1}{f(z)}\frac{df(z)}{dz} = -\frac{v_1}{u_0}\frac{1}{z^2} + \frac{w_1}{z^3} + .....$$

Thus there is no constant term in $\dfrac{1}{f(z)}\dfrac{df(z)}{dz}$, and there is no term in $\dfrac{1}{z}$.  But the above expression for it gives $C$ as the constant term, which must therefore vanish; and it gives $\Sigma c_i$ as the coefficient of $\dfrac{1}{z}$, for $\dfrac{d}{dz}\left\{\bar{G}_i\left(\dfrac{1}{z-a_i}\right)\right\}$ will begin with $\dfrac{1}{z^2}$ at least; thus $\Sigma c_i$ must therefore also vanish.

Hence for a function $f(z)$, which has no singularity at $z=\infty$ and no zeros anywhere in the plane, and of which the only singularities are the $n$ essential singularities at $a_1, a_2, \dots, a_n$, we have

$$\frac{1}{f(z)}\frac{df(z)}{dz} = \sum_{i=1}^{n}\frac{c_i}{z-a_i} + \sum_{i=1}^{n}\frac{d}{dz}\left\{\bar{G}_i\left(\frac{1}{z-a_i}\right)\right\},$$

where the coefficients $c_i$ are integers subject to the condition

$$\sum_{i=1}^{n} c_i = 0.$$

If $a_n = \infty$, so that $z = \infty$ is an essential singularity in addition to $a_1, a_2, \dots, a_{n-1}$, there is a term $G(z)$ instead of $G_n\left(\dfrac{1}{z-a_n}\right)$; there is no term, that corresponds to $\dfrac{c_n}{z-a_n}$, but there may be a constant $C$. Writing

$$C + G(z) = \frac{d}{dz}\{\bar{G}(z)\},$$

with the condition that $\bar{G}(z)$ vanishes when $z=0$, we then have

$$\frac{1}{f(z)}\frac{df(z)}{dz} = \sum_{i=1}^{n-1}\frac{c_i}{z-a_i} + \frac{d}{dz}\{\bar{G}(z)\} + \sum_{i=1}^{n-1}\frac{d}{dz}\left\{\bar{G}_i\left(\frac{1}{z-a_i}\right)\right\},$$

where the coefficients $c_i$ are integers, but are no longer subject to the condition that their sum vanishes.

Let $R^*(z)$ denote the function

$$\prod_{i=1}(z-a_i)^{c_i},$$

the product extending over the factors associated with the essential singularities of $f(z)$ that lie in the finite part of the plane; thus $R^*(z)$ is a rational meromorphic function. Since

$$\frac{1}{R^*(z)}\frac{dR^*(z)}{dz} = \sum_{i=1}\frac{c_i}{z-a_i},$$

we have

$$\frac{1}{f(z)}\frac{df(z)}{dz} - \frac{1}{R^*(z)}\frac{dR^*(z)}{dz} = \sum_{i=1}^{n}\frac{d}{dz}\left\{\bar{G}_i\left(\frac{1}{z-a_i}\right)\right\},$$

where $\bar{G}_n\left(\dfrac{1}{z-a_n}\right)$ is to be replaced by $\bar{G}(z)$ if $a_n = \infty$, that is, if $z = \infty$ be an essential singularity of $f(z)$. Hence, except as to an undetermined constant factor, we have

$$f(z) = R^*(z)\prod_{i=1}^{n} e^{\bar{G}_i\left(\frac{1}{z-a}\right)},$$

which is therefore *an analytical representation of a function with n essential* *singularities, no accidental singularities, and no zeros : and the rational function $R^*(z)$ becomes zero or $\infty$ only at the singularities of $f(z)$.*

If $z = \infty$ be not an essential singularity, then $R^*(z)$ for $z = \infty$ is equal to unity because $\sum_{i=1}^{n} c_i = 0$.

COROLLARY. It is easy to see, from § 43, that, if the point $a_i$ be only an accidental singularity, then $c_i$ is a negative integer and $\bar{G}_i \left( \dfrac{1}{z - a_i} \right)$ is zero : so that the polar property at $a_i$ is determined by the occurrence of a factor $(z - a_i)^{c_i}$ solely in the denominator of the rational meromorphic function $R^*(z)$.

And, in general, each of the integral coefficients $c_i$ is determined from the expansion of the function $f'(z) \div f(z)$ in the vicinity of the singularity with which it is associated.

**68.** Another form of expression for the function can be obtained from the preceding; and it is valid even when the function possesses zeros not absorbed into the essential singularities†.

Consider a function with one essential singularity, and let $a$ be the point. Suppose that, within a finite circle of centre $a$ (or within a finite simple curve which encloses $a$), there are $m$ simple zeros $\alpha$, $\beta$, ..., $\lambda$ of the function $f(z)$; assume $m$ to be finite, and also assume that there are no accidental singularities within or on the circle, or at a merely infinitesimal distance from its circumference. Then, if

$$f(z) = (z - \alpha)(z - \beta) \dots (z - \lambda) F(z),$$

the function $F(z)$ has $a$ for an essential singularity and has no zeros within the circle. Hence, for points $z$ within the circle,

$$\frac{F'(z)}{F(z)} = \frac{c}{z - a} + \frac{d}{dz} \left\{ G_1 \left( \frac{1}{z - a} \right) \right\} + P(z - a),$$

where $G_1 \left( \dfrac{1}{z - a} \right)$ converges uniformly everywhere in the plane outside a small circle round $a$ and vanishes with $\dfrac{1}{z - a}$, and $P(z - a)$ is an integral function converging uniformly within the circle; moreover, $c$ is an integer. Thus

$$F(z) = A(z - a)^c\, e^{G_1 \left( \frac{1}{z-a} \right)}\, e^{\int P(z-a)\, dz}.$$

Let $(z - \alpha)(z - \beta) \dots (z - \lambda) = (z - a)^m \left\{ 1 + \frac{p_1}{z - a} + \dots + \frac{p_m}{(z - a)^m} \right\}$

$$= (z - a)^m\, g_1 \left( \frac{1}{z - a} \right);$$

† See Guichard, *Théorie des points singuliers essentiels*, (Thèse, Gauthier-Villars, Paris, 1883), especially the first part.

then $\qquad f(z) = (z-a)^m \, g_1\left(\dfrac{1}{z-a}\right) F(z)$

$$= A \, (z-a)^{m+c} \, g_1\left(\dfrac{1}{z-a}\right) e^{G_1\left(\frac{1}{z-a}\right)} \, e^{\int P(z-a)\,dz}$$

Now of this product-expression for $f(z)$ it should be noted :—

(i)   That $m+c$ is an integer, finite because $m$ and $c$ are finite :

(ii)   The function $e^{G_1\left(\frac{1}{z-a}\right)}$ can be expressed in the form of a series converging uniformly everywhere outside a small circle round $a$, and proceeding in powers of $\dfrac{1}{z-a}$ in the form

$$1 + \dfrac{b_1}{z-a} + \dfrac{b_2}{(z-a)^2} + \dots.$$

It has no zero within the circle considered, for $F(z)$ has no zero.  Also $g_1\left(\dfrac{1}{z-a}\right)$ is a polynomial in $\dfrac{1}{z-a}$, beginning with unity and containing only a finite number of terms: hence, multiplying the two series together, we have as the product a series proceeding in powers of $\dfrac{1}{z-a}$ in the form

$$1 + \dfrac{h_1}{z-a} + \dfrac{h_2}{(z-a)^2} + \dots,$$

which converges uniformly everywhere outside any small circle round $a$.  Let this series be denoted by $H\left(\dfrac{1}{z-a}\right)$; it has an essential singularity at $a$ and its only zeros are the points $a, \beta, \dots, \lambda$, because the series multiplied by $g_1\left(\dfrac{1}{z-a}\right)$ has no zeros :

(iii)   The function $\int P\,(z-a)\,dz$ is a series of positive powers of $z-a$, converging uniformly in the vicinity of $a$; and therefore $e^{\int P(z-a)dz}$ can be expanded in a series of positive integral powers of $z-a$, which converges in the vicinity of $a$.  Let it be denoted by $Q(z-a)$ which, since it is a factor of $F(z)$, has no zeros within the circle.

Hence we have

$$f(z) = A \, (z-a)^\mu \, Q(z-a) \, H\left(\dfrac{1}{z-a}\right),$$

where $\mu$ is an integer; $H\left(\dfrac{1}{z-a}\right)$ is a series that converges everywhere outside an infinitesimal circle round $a$, is equal to unity when $\dfrac{1}{z-a}$ vanishes, and has as its zeros the (finite) number of zeros assigned to $f(z)$ within a finite circle of centre $a$; and $Q(z-a)$ is a series of positive powers of $z-a$ beginning with unity which converges (but has no zero) within the circle.

The foregoing function $f(z)$ is supposed to have no essential singularity except at $a$. If, however, a given function have singularities at points other than $a$, then the circle would be taken of radius less than the distance of $a$ from the nearest essential singularity.

Introducing a new function $f_1(z)$ defined by the equation

$$f(z) = A\,(z-a)^\mu\,H\left(\frac{1}{z-a}\right) f_1(z),$$

the value of $f_1(z)$ is $Q(z-a)$ within the circle, but it is not determined by the foregoing analysis for points without the circle. Moreover, as $(z-a)^\mu$ and also $H\left(\dfrac{1}{z-a}\right)$ are finite everywhere except in the immediate vicinity of the isolated singularity at $a$, it follows that essential singularities of $f(z)$ other than $a$ must be essential singularities of $f_1(z)$. Also since $f_1(z)$ is $Q(z-a)$ in the immediate vicinity of $a$, this point is not an essential singularity of $f_1(z)$.

Thus $f_1(z)$ is a function of the same kind as $f(z)$; it has all the essential singularities of $f(z)$ except $a$, but it has fewer zeros, on account of the $m$ zeros of $f(z)$ possessed by $H\left(\dfrac{1}{z-a}\right)$. The foregoing expression for $f(z)$ is the one referred to at the beginning of the section.

If we choose to absorb into $f_1(z)$ the factors $e^{G_1\left(\frac{1}{z-a}\right)}$ and $e^{\int P(z-a)\,dz}$, which occur in

$$A\,(z-a)^{m+c}\,g_1\left(\frac{1}{z-a}\right) e^{G_1\left(\frac{1}{z-a}\right)} e^{\int P(z-a)\,dz}.$$

an expression that is valid within the circle considered, then we obtain a result that is otherwise obvious, by taking

$$f(z) = (z-a)^\mu\,g_1\left(\frac{1}{z-a}\right) f_1(z),$$

where now $g_1\left(\dfrac{1}{z-a}\right)$ is polynomial in $\dfrac{1}{z-a}$, and has for its zeros all the zeros within the circle; $\mu$ is an integer; and $f_1(z)$ is a function of the same kind as $f(z)$, which now possesses all the essential singularities of $f(z)$, but its zeros are fewer by the $m$ zeros that are possessed by $g_1\left(\dfrac{1}{z-a}\right)$.

**69.** Next, consider a function $f(z)$ with $n$ essential singularities $a_1$, $a_2, \ldots, a_n$ but without accidental singularities; and let it have any number of zeros.

When the zeros are limited in number, they may be taken to be isolated points, distinct in position from the essential singularities.

When the zeros are unlimited in number, then at least one of the singularities must be such that the zeros in infinite number lie within a circle of finite radius, described round it as centre and containing no other singularity. For if there be not an infinite number in such a vicinity of some one point (which must be an essential singularity: the only alternative is that the zeros should form a continuous aggregate, and then the function would be zero everywhere), the points are isolated and there must be an infinite number outside a circle $|z| = R$, where $R$ is a finite quantity .that can be made as large as we please, say an infinite number at $z = \infty$. If $z = \infty$ be an essential singularity, the above alternative is satisfied: if not, the function, as in the preceding alternative, must be zero at all other parts of the plane. Hence it follows that, if a uniform function have a finite number of essential singularities and an infinite number of zeros, all but a finite number of the zeros lie within circles of finite radii described round the essential singularities as centres; at least one of the circles contains an infinite number of the zeros, and some of the circles may contain only a finite number of them.

We divide the whole plane into regions, each containing one but only one singularity and containing also the circle round the singularity; let the region containing $a_i$ be denoted by $C_i$, and let the region $C_n$ be the part of the plane other than $C_1$, $C_2$, ..., $C_{n-1}$.

If the region $C_1$ contain only a limited number of the zeros, then, by § 68, we can choose a new function $f_1(z)$ such that, if

$$f(z) = (z - a_1)^{\mu_1} G_1 \left( \frac{1}{z - a_1} \right) f_1(z),$$

the function $f_1(z)$ has $a_1$ for an ordinary point, has no zeros within the region $C_1$, and has $a_2$, $a_3$, ..., $a_n$ for its essential singularities.

If the region $C_1$ contain an unlimited number of the zeros, then, as in Corollaries II. and III. of § 63, we construct any transcendental function $\bar{G}_1 \left( \frac{1}{z - a_1} \right)$, having $a_1$ for its sole essential singularity and the zeros in $C_1$ for all its zeros. When we introduce a function $g_1(z)$, defined by the equation

$$f(z) = \bar{G}_1 \left( \frac{1}{z - a_1} \right) g_1(z),$$

the function $g_1(z)$ has no zeros in $C_1$ and certainly has $a_2$, $a_3$, ..., $a_n$ for essential singularities; in the absence of the generalising factor of $\bar{G}_1$, it can have $a_1$ for an essential singularity. By § 67, the function $\bar{g}_1(z)$, defined by

$$\bar{g}_1(z) = (z - a_1)^{c_1} e^{h_1 \left( \frac{1}{z - a_1} \right)},$$

has no zero and no accidental singularity, and it has $a_1$ as its sole essential singularity : hence, properly choosing $c_1$ and $h_1$, we may take

$$g_1(z) = \bar{g}_1(z) f_1(z),$$

so that $f_1(z)$ does not have $a_1$ as an essential singularity, but it has all the remaining singularities of $g_1(z)$, and it has no zeros within $C_1$.

In either case, we have a new function $f_1(z)$ given by

$$f(z) = (z - a_1)^{\mu_1} G_1\left(\frac{1}{z - a_1}\right) f_1(z),$$

where $\mu_1$ is an integer. The zeros of $f(z)$ that lie in $C_1$ are the zeros of $G_1$; the function $f_1(z)$ has $a_2, a_3, \ldots, a_n$ (but not $a_1$) for its essential singularities, and it has the zeros of $f(z)$ in the remaining regions for its zeros.

Similarly, considering $C_2$, we obtain a function $f_2(z)$, such that

$$f_1(z) = (z - a_2)^{\mu_2} G_2\left(\frac{1}{z - a_2}\right) f_2(z),$$

where $\mu_2$ is an integer, $G_2$ is a transcendental function finite everywhere except at $a_2$ and has for its zeros all the zeros of $f_1(z)$—and therefore all the zeros of $f(z)$—that lie in $C_2$. Then $f_2(z)$ possesses all the zeros of $f(z)$ in the regions other than $C_1$ and $C_2$, and has $a_3, a_4, \ldots, a_n$ for its essential singularities.

Proceeding in this manner, we ultimately obtain a function $f_n(z)$ which has none of the zeros of $f(z)$ in any of the $n$ regions $C_1, C_2, \ldots, C_n$, that is, has no zeros in the plane, and it has no essential singularities; it has no accidental singularities, and therefore $f_n(z)$ is a constant. Hence, when we substitute, and denote by $S^*(z)$ the product $\prod\limits_{i=1}^{n}(z - a_i)^{\mu_i}$, we have

$$f(z) = S^*(z) \prod_{i=1}^{n} G_i\left(\frac{1}{z - a_i}\right),$$

*which is the most general form of a function with n essential singularities, no accidental singularities, and any number of zeros. The function $S^*(z)$ is a rational function of z, usually meromorphic in form, and it has the essential singularities of $f(z)$ as its zeros and poles; and the zeros of $f(z)$ are distributed among the functions $G_i$.*

As however the distribution of the zeros by the regions $C$ and therefore the functions $G\left(\frac{1}{z - a}\right)$ are somewhat arbitrary, the above form though general is not unique.

If any one of the singularities, say $a_m$, had been accidental and not essential, then in the corresponding form the function $G_m\left(\frac{1}{z - a_m}\right)$ would be polynomial and not transcendental.

**70.** A function $f(z)$, which has *any finite number of accidental singularities in addition to n assigned essential singularities and any number of assigned zeros*, can be constructed as follows.

Let $A(z)$ be the polynomial which has, for its zeros, the accidental singularities of $f(z)$, each in its proper multiplicity. Then the product

$$f(z) A(z)$$

is a function which has no accidental singularities; its zeros and its essential singularities are the assigned zeros and the assigned essential singularities of $f(z)$, and therefore it is included in the form

$$S^*(z) \prod_{i=1}^{n} \left\{ G_i \left( \frac{1}{z - a_i} \right) \right\},$$

where $S^*(z)$ is a rational meromorphic function having the points $a_1, a_2, \ldots, a_n$ for zeros and poles. The form of the function $f(z)$ is therefore

$$\frac{S^*(z)}{A(z)} \prod_{i=1}^{n} \left\{ G_i \left( \frac{1}{z - a_i} \right) \right\}.$$

**71.** A function $f(z)$, which has *an unlimited number of accidental singularities in addition to n assigned essential singularities and any number of assigned zeros*, can be constructed as follows.

Let the accidental singularities be $\alpha', \beta', \ldots$. Construct a function $f_1(z)$, having the $n$ essential singularities assigned to $f(z)$, no accidental singularities, and the series $\alpha', \beta', \ldots$ of zeros. It will, by § 69, be of the form of a product of $n$ transcendental functions $G_{n+1}, \ldots, G_{2n}$, which are such that a function $G$ has for its zeros the zeros of $f_1(z)$ lying within a region of the plane, divided as in § 69; and the function $G_{n+i}$ is associated with the point $a_i$. Thus

$$f_1(z) = T^*(z) \prod_{i=1}^{n} G_{n+i} \left( \frac{1}{z - a_i} \right),$$

where $T^*(z)$ is a rational meromorphic function having its zeros and its poles, each of finite multiplicity, at the essential singularities of $f(z)$.

Because the accidental singularities of $f(z)$ are the same points and have the same multiplicity as the zeros of $f_1(z)$, the function $f(z) f_1(z)$ has no accidental singularities. This new function has all the zeros of $f(z)$, and $a_1, \ldots, a_n$ are its essential singularities; moreover, it has no accidental singularities. Hence the product $f(z) f_1(z)$ can be represented in the form

$$S^*(z) \prod_{i=1}^{n} G_i \left( \frac{1}{z - a_i} \right),$$

and therefore we have

$$f(z) = \frac{S^*(z)}{T^*(z)} \prod_{i=1}^{n} \frac{G_i \left( \dfrac{1}{z - a_i} \right)}{G_{n+i} \left( \dfrac{1}{z - a_i} \right)}$$

as an expression of the function.

But, as by their distribution through the $n$ selected regions of the plane in § 69, the zeros can to some extent be arbitrarily associated with the functions $G_1$, $G_2$, ..., $G_n$ and likewise the accidental singularities can to some extent be arbitrarily associated with the functions $G_{n+1}$, $G_{n+2}$, ..., $G_{2n}$, the product-expression just obtained, though definite in character and general, is not unique in the detailed form of the functions which occur.

The fraction
$$\frac{S^*(z)}{T^*(z)}$$
is rational, neither $S^*$ nor $T^*$ being transcendental; it vanishes or becomes infinite only at the essential singularities $a_1$, $a_2$, ..., $a_n$, being the product of factors of the form $(z - a_i)^{m_i}$, for $i = 1, 2, ..., n$. Let the power $(z - a_i)^{m_i}$ be absorbed into the function $G_i/G_{n+i}$ for each of the $n$ values of $i$; no substantial change in the transcendental character of $G_i$ and of $G_{n+i}$ is thereby caused, and we may therefore use the same symbol to denote the modified function after the absorption. Hence† *the most general product-expression of a uniform function of $z$, which has $n$ essential singularities $a_1$, $a_2$, ..., $a_n$, any unlimited number of assigned zeros, and any unlimited number of assigned accidental singularities, is*

$$\prod_{i=1}^{n} \frac{G_i\left(\dfrac{1}{z - a_i}\right)}{G_{n+i}\left(\dfrac{1}{z - a_i}\right)}.$$

The resolution of a transcendental function with one essential singularity into its primary factors, each of which gives only a single zero of the function, has been obtained in § 63, Corollary IV.

We therefore resolve each of the functions $G_1$, ..., $G_{2n}$ into its primary factors. Each factor of the first $n$ functions will contain one and only one zero of the original functions $f(z)$; and each factor of the second $n$ functions will contain one and only one of the poles of $f(z)$. The sole essential singularity of each primary factor is one of the essential singularities of $f(z)$. Hence we have a method of constructing a uniform function with any finite number of essential singularities as a product of any number of primary factors, each of which has one of the essential singularities as its sole essential singularity and either (i) has as its sole zero either one of the zeros or one of the accidental singularities of $f(z)$, so that it is of the form

$$\left(\frac{z - \epsilon}{z - c}\right) e^{g\left(\frac{1}{z - c}\right)};$$

or (ii) it has no zero and then it is of the form

$$e^{g\left(\frac{1}{z - c}\right)}.$$

† Weierstrass, *Ges. Werke*, t. ii, p. 121.

When all the primary factors of the latter form are combined, they constitute a generalising factor in exactly the same way as in § 52 and in § 63, Cor. III., except that now the number of essential singularities is not limited to unity. The product converges uniformly for all finite values of $z$ that lie outside small circles round the singularities; and similarly for infinite values, if the function is regular for $z = \infty$.

Two forms of expression of a function with a limited number of essential singularities have been obtained: one (§ 65) as a sum, the other (§ 69) as a product, of functions each of which has only one essential singularity. Intermediate expressions, partly product and partly sum, can be derived, e.g. expressions of the form

$$\frac{\sum\limits_{i=1}^{n} G_i \left( \dfrac{1}{z - c_i} \right)}{\sum\limits_{i=1}^{n} G_{n+i} \left( \dfrac{1}{z - c_i} \right)}.$$

But the pure product-expression is the most general, in that it brings into evidence not merely the $n$ essential singularities but also the zeros and the accidental singularities, whereas the expression as a sum tacitly requires that the function shall have no singularities other than the $n$ which are essential.

*Note.* The formation of the various elements, the aggregate of which is the complete representation of the function with a limited number of essential singularities, can be carried out in the same manner as in § 34; each element is associated with a particular domain, the range of the domain is limited by the nearest singularities, and the aggregate of the singularities determines the boundary of the region of continuity.

To avoid the practical difficulty of the gradual formation of the region of continuity by the construction of the successive domains when there is a limited number of singularities (and also, if desirable to be considered, of branch-points), Fuchs devised a method which simplifies the process. The basis of the method is an appropriate change of the independent variable. The result of that change is to divide the plane of the modified variable $\zeta$ into two portions, one of which, $G_2$, is finite in area and the other of which, $G_1$, occupies the rest of the plane; and the boundary, common to $G_1$ and $G_2$, is a circle of finite radius, called the *discriminating circle** of the function. In $G_2$ the modified function is holomorphic; in $G_1$ the function is holomorphic except at $\zeta = \infty$; and all the singularities (and the branch-points, if any) lie on the discriminating circle.

The theory is given in Fuchs's memoir "Ueber die Darstellung der Functionen complexer Variabeln, ......," *Crelle*, t. lxxv, (1872), pp. 176—223. It is corrected in details and is amplified in *Crelle*, t. cvi, (1890), pp. 1—4, and in *Crelle*, t. cviii, (1891), pp. 181—192; see also Nekrassoff, *Math. Ann.*, t. xxxviii, (1891), pp. 82—90, and Anissimoff, *Math. Ann.*, t. xl, (1892), pp. 145—148.

* Fuchs calls it *Grenzkreis*.

# CHAPTER VII.

## Functions with unlimited Essential Singularities, and Expansion in Series of Functions.

In addition to the memoirs mentioned below, as being the basis of the present chapter, there are several others (alluded to at the end of § 35) of the greatest importance, dealing with the general theory of uniform analytic functions and particularly with their analytical representation by an infinite series of polynomials in the variable. Among these, specially worthy of note, are:—

Runge, *Acta Math.*, t. vi, (1885), pp. 229—248;

Hilbert, *Gött. Nachr.*, (1897), pp. 63—70;

Painlevé, *Comptes Rendus*, t. cxxvi, (1898), pp. 200—202, 318—321, 385—388, 459—461, ib. t. cxxviii, (1899), pp. 1277—1280, ib. t. cxxix, (1899), pp. 27—31; see also his thesis, quoted in § 86;

Phragmén, *Comptes Rendus*, t. cxxviii, (1899), pp. 1434—1437;

Mittag-Leffler, *Acta Math.*, t. xxiii, (1900), pp. 43—62, where references are given to earlier records of the investigations; also *Camb. Phil. Trans.*, (Stokes Jubilee volume), t. xviii, (1900), pp. 1—11; and *Acta Math.*, t. xxiv, (1901), pp. 183—244.

See also Borel, *Leçons sur la théorie des fonctions*, (Gauthier-Villars, Paris, 1898), ch. vi.

A comprehensive reference may here be given to the *Collection de monographies sur la théorie des fonctions, publiée sous la direction de M. Émile Borel.* The earliest of them is the monograph by Borel just quoted; and some of them deal solely with functions of real variables.

**72.** It now remains to consider functions which have an infinite number of essential singularities[*]. It will, in the first place, be assumed that the essential singularities are isolated points, that is, that they do not form a continuous line, however short, and that they do not constitute a continuous

---

[*] The results in the present chapter are founded, except where other particular references are given, upon the researches of Mittag-Leffler and Weierstrass. The most important investigations of Mittag-Leffler are contained in a series of short notes, constituting the memoir "Sur la théorie des fonctions uniformes d'une variable," *Comptes Rendus*, t. xciv, (1882), pp. 414, 511, 713, 781, 938, 1040, 1105, 1163, t. xcv, (1882), p. 335; and in a memoir "Sur la représentation analytique des fonctions monogènes uniformes," *Acta Math.*, t. iv, (1884), pp. 1—79. The investigations of Weierstrass referred to are contained in his two memoirs "Ueber einen functionentheoretischen Satz des Herrn G. Mittag-Leffler," (1880), and "Zur Functionenlehre," (1880), both included in the volume *Abhandlungen aus der Functionenlehre*, pp. 53—66, 67—101, 102—104, *Ges. Werke*, t. ii, pp. 189—199, 201—233. A memoir by Hermite, "Sur quelques points de la théorie des fonctions," *Acta Soc. Fenn.*, t. xii, pp. 67—94, *Crelle*, t. xci, (1881), pp. 54—78, may be consulted with great advantage.

area, however small, in the plane. Since their number is unlimited and their distance from one another is finite, there must be at least one point in the plane (it may be at $z = \infty$) where there is an infinite aggregate of such points. But no special note need be taken of this fact, for the character of an essential singularity does not enter into the question at this stage ; the essential singularity at such a point would merely be of a nature different from the essential singularity at some other point.

We take, therefore, an infinite series of quantities $a_1, a_2, a_3, \ldots$ arranged in order of increasing moduli, and such that no two are the same : and so we have infinity as the limit of $|a_\nu|$ when $\nu = \infty$.

Let there be an associated series of uniform functions of $z$ such that for all values of $i$, the function $G_i \left( \dfrac{1}{z - a_i} \right)$, vanishing with $\dfrac{1}{z - a_i}$, has $a_i$ as its sole singularity; the singularity is essential or accidental according as $G_i$ is transcendental or polynomial. These functions can be constructed by theorems already proved. Then we have the theorem, due to Mittag-Leffler :—*It is always possible to construct a uniform analytic function $F(z)$, having no singularities other than $a_1, a_2, a_3, \ldots$ and such that for each determinate value of $\nu$, the difference $F(z) - G_\nu \left( \dfrac{1}{z - a_\nu} \right)$ is finite for $z = a_\nu$ and therefore, in the vicinity of $a_\nu$, is expressible in the form $P(z - a_\nu)$.*

**73.** To prove Mittag-Leffler's theorem, we first form subsidiary functions $F_\nu(z)$, derived from the functions $G$ as follows. The function $G_\nu \left( \dfrac{1}{z - a_\nu} \right)$ converges everywhere in the plane except within an infinitesimal circle round the point $a_\nu$; hence within a circle $|z| = \rho$, where $\rho$ is less than $|a_\nu|$, it is a monogenic analytic function of $z$, and can therefore be expanded in a series of positive powers of $z$ which converges uniformly within the circle $|z| = \rho$, say

$$G_\nu \left( \frac{1}{z - a_\nu} \right) = \sum_{\mu=0}^{\infty} \nu_\mu z^\mu,$$

for values of $z$ such that $|z| \leqslant \rho < |a_\nu|$. If $a_\nu$ be zero, there is evidently no expansion.

Let $\epsilon$ be a positive quantity less than 1, and let $\epsilon_1, \epsilon_2, \epsilon_3, \ldots$ be arbitrarily chosen positive decreasing quantities, subject to the single condition that $\Sigma \epsilon$ is a converging series, say of sum $\Delta$ : and let $\epsilon_0$ be a positive quantity intermediate between 1 and $\epsilon$. Let $g$ be the greatest value of $\left| G_\nu \left( \dfrac{1}{z - a_\nu} \right) \right|$ for points on or within the circumference $|z| = \epsilon_0 |a_\nu|$; then, because the series $\sum_{\mu=0}^{\infty} \nu_\mu z^\mu$ is a converging series, we have, by § 29,

$$|\nu_\mu z^\mu| \leqslant g,$$

or

$$| \nu_\mu | \leqslant \frac{g}{\epsilon_0{}^\mu \, | \, a_\nu \, |^\mu} .$$

Hence, with values of $z$ satisfying the condition $| z | \leqslant \epsilon \, | \, a_\nu \, |$, we have, for any value of $m$,

$$\left| \sum_{\mu=m}^{\infty} \nu_\mu z^\mu \right| \leqslant \sum_{\mu=m}^{\infty} | \nu_\mu | \, | z |^\mu$$

$$\leqslant \sum_{\mu=m}^{\infty} g \, \frac{\epsilon^\mu}{\epsilon_0{}^\mu} \leqslant \frac{g}{1 - \dfrac{\epsilon}{\epsilon_0}} \left( \frac{\epsilon}{\epsilon_0} \right)^m ,$$

since $\epsilon < \epsilon_0$. Take the smallest integral value of $m$ such that

$$\frac{g}{1 - \dfrac{\epsilon}{\epsilon_0}} \left( \frac{\epsilon}{\epsilon_0} \right)^m \leqslant \epsilon_\nu \, ;$$

it will be finite and may be denoted by $m_\nu$. Thus we have

$$\left| \sum_{\mu=m_\nu}^{\infty} \nu_\mu z^\mu \right| \leqslant \epsilon_\nu ,$$

for values of $z$ satisfying the condition $| z | \leqslant \epsilon \, | \, a_\nu \, |$.

We now construct a subsidiary function $F_\nu(z)$ such that, for all values of $z$,

$$F_\nu(z) = G_\nu \left( \frac{1}{z - a_\nu} \right) - \sum_{\mu=0}^{m_\nu - 1} \nu_\mu z^\mu \, ;$$

then, for values of $| z |$ which are $\leqslant \epsilon \, | \, a_\nu \, |$,

$$| F_\nu(z) | \leqslant \epsilon_\nu .$$

Moreover, the function $\sum_{\mu=0}^{m_\nu - 1} \nu_\mu z^\mu$ is finite for all finite values of $z$; so that, if we take

$$\phi_\nu(z) = z^{-m_\nu} G_\nu \left( \frac{1}{z - a_\nu} \right) - \sum_{\mu=0}^{m_\nu - 1} \frac{\nu_\mu}{z^{m_\nu - \mu}} ,$$

then $\phi_\nu(z)$ is zero at infinity, because, when $z = \infty$, $G_\nu \left( \dfrac{1}{z - a_\nu} \right)$ is finite by hypothesis. Evidently $\phi_\nu(z)$ is infinite only at $z = a_\nu$, and its singularity is of the same kind as that of $G_\nu \left( \dfrac{1}{z - a_\nu} \right)$.

**74.** Now let $c$ be any point in the plane, which is not one of the points $a_1, a_2, a_3, \dots$ ; it is possible to choose a positive quantity $\rho$ such that all the points $a$ lie without the circle $| z - c | = \rho$. Let $a_\nu$ be the singularity, which is the point nearest to the origin satisfying the condition $| a_\nu | > | c | + \rho$ ; then, for points within or on the circle, we have

$$\left| \frac{z}{a_s} \right| \leqslant \epsilon ,$$

when $s$ has the values $\nu, \nu + 1, \nu + 2, \ldots$. Introducing the subsidiary functions $F_\nu(z)$, we have, for such values of $z$,

$$|F_s(z)| < \epsilon_s,$$

and therefore

$$\left| \sum_{s=\nu}^{\infty} F_s(z) \right| < \sum_{s=\nu}^{\infty} |F_s(z)|$$

$$< \sum_{s=\nu}^{\infty} \epsilon_s$$

$$< \Delta,$$

a finite quantity. Also let $\delta$ denote any assigned finite positive quantity, however small; an integer $\mu'$ can be chosen so that $\sum_{s=\mu}^{\mu+r} \epsilon_s < \delta$, for all integers $\mu \geqslant \mu'$, and for all positive integers $r$. For these same integers, we have

$$\left| \sum_{s=\mu}^{\mu+r} F_s(z) \right| < \sum_{s=\mu}^{\mu+r} |F_s(z)| < \sum_{s=\mu}^{\mu+r} \epsilon_s < \delta.$$

It therefore follows that the series $\sum_{s=\nu}^{\infty} F_s(z)$ converges uniformly for all values of $z$ which satisfy the condition $|z - c| < \rho$. Moreover, all the functions $F_1(z), F_2(z), \ldots, F_{r-1}(z)$ are finite for such values of $z$, because their singularities lie without the circle $|z - c| = \rho$; and therefore the series

$$\sum_{r=1}^{\infty} F_r(z)$$

converges uniformly for all points $z$ within or on the circle $|z - c| = \rho$, where $\rho$ is chosen so that all the points $a$ lie without the circle.

The function, represented by the series, can therefore be expanded in the form $P(z - c)$, in the domain of the point $c$.

If $a_m$ denote any one of the points $a_1, a_2, \ldots$, and we take $\rho'$ so small that all the points, other than $a_m$, lie without the circle

$$|z - a_m| = \rho',$$

then, since $F_m(z)$ is the only one of the functions $F$ which has a singularity at $a_m$, the series

$$\sum_{r=1}^{\infty} {}^m \{F_r(z)\},$$

where $\Sigma^m$ implies that $F_m(z)$ is omitted, converges uniformly in the vicinity of $a$, and therefore it can be expressed in the form $P(z - a_m)$. Hence

$$\sum_{r=1}^{\infty} F_r(z) = F_m(z) + P(z - a_m)$$

$$= G_m\left(\frac{1}{z - a_m}\right) + P_1(z - a_m),$$

the difference of $F_m$ and $G_m$ being absorbed into the series $P$ to make $P_1$. It thus appears that the series $\overset{\infty}{\underset{r=1}{\Sigma}} F_r(z)$ is a function which has infinities only at the points $a_1, a_2, \ldots$, and is such that

$$\overset{\infty}{\underset{r=1}{\Sigma}} F_r(z) - G_m\left(\frac{1}{z-a_m}\right)$$

can be expressed in the vicinity of $a_m$ in the form $P(z-a_m)$. Hence $\overset{\infty}{\underset{r=1}{\Sigma}} F_r(z)$ *is a function of the required kind.*

**75.** It may be remarked that the function is not unique. As the positive quantities $\epsilon$ were subjected to merely the single condition that they form a converging series, there is the possibility of wide variation in their choice: and a difference of choice might easily lead to a difference in the ultimate expression of the function.

This latitude of ultimate expression is not, however, entirely unlimited. For, suppose there are two functions $F(z)$ and $\bar{F}(z)$, enjoying all the assigned properties. Then as any point $c$, other than $a_1, a_2, \ldots$, is an ordinary point for both $F(z)$ and $\bar{F}(z)$, it is an ordinary point for their difference: and so

$$F(z) - \bar{F}(z) = P(z-c)$$

for points in the immediate vicinity of $c$. The points $a$ are, however, singularities for each of the functions: in the vicinity of such a point $a_i$, we have

$$F(z) = G_i\left(\frac{1}{z-a_i}\right) + P(z-a_i),$$

$$\bar{F}(z) = G_i\left(\frac{1}{z-a_i}\right) + \bar{P}(z-a_i),$$

since the functions are of the required form: hence

$$F(z) - \bar{F}(z) = P(z-a_i) - \bar{P}(z-a_i),$$

or the point $a_i$ is an ordinary point for the difference of the functions. Hence every finite point in the plane, whether an ordinary point or a singularity for each of the functions, is an ordinary point for the difference of the functions: and therefore that difference is a uniform integral function of $z$. It thus appears that, *if $F(z)$ be a function with the required properties, then every other function with those properties is of the form*

$$F(z) + G(z),$$

*where $G(z)$ is a uniform integral function of $z$ either transcendental or polynomial.*

The converse of this theorem is also true.

Moreover, the function $G(z)$ can always be expressed in a form $\overset{\infty}{\underset{\nu=1}{\Sigma}} g_\nu(z)$, if it be desirable to do so: and therefore it follows that any function with the assigned characteristics can be expressed in the form

$$\overset{\infty}{\underset{\nu=1}{\Sigma}} \{F_\nu(z) + g_\nu(z)\}.$$

*Note.* In the preceding investigation, the integers $m_\nu$ have not been limited to be the same for each of the functions $G$. The simplest sets of functions evidently arise when a common value can be assigned to the integers; they then correspond to Weierstrass's converging infinite products (§§ 50, 59—61), arranged according to their class. But as with the converging infinite products (§ 51), it may happen that no common value can be assigned: and then the preceding investigation, in its most general form, establishes the existence of the functions.

It does not, however, indicate that the expression is unique. If, for instance, the series of functions $G$ be

$$G_n = \frac{1}{x - \log_e n},$$

for $n = 1, 2, \ldots$, the function formed by the preceding method is

$$\overset{\infty}{\underset{n=1}{\Sigma}} \left\{ \frac{x^{m_n}}{(\log_e n)^{m_n}} + \frac{1}{x - \log_e n} \right\}:$$

and there is no finite integer which, when assigned as the common value of the integers $m_n$, will make the series converge.

But we may use the function

$$\overset{\infty}{\underset{n=1}{\Sigma}} \frac{x e^x}{n \log_e n (x - \log_e n)},$$

which satisfies all the conditions and is a converging series*.

**76.** The following applications, due to Weierstrass, can be made so as to give a new expression for functions, already considered in Chapter VI., having $z = \infty$ as their sole essential singularity and an unlimited number of poles at points $a_1, a_2, \ldots$.

If the pole at $a_i$ be of multiplicity $m_i$, then $(z - a_i)^{m_i} f(z)$ is regular at the point $a_i$ and can therefore be expressed in the form

$$\overset{\infty}{\underset{\mu=0}{\Sigma}} c_\mu (z - a_i)^\mu.$$

Hence, if we take $\qquad f_i(z) = \overset{m_i - 1}{\underset{\mu=0}{\Sigma}} c_\mu (z - a_i)^{-m_i + \mu},$

we have $\qquad f(z) = f_i(z) + P(z - a_i).$

Now deduce from $f_i(z)$ a function $F_i(z)$ as in § 73, and let this deduction be effected for each of the functions $f_i(z)$. Then we know that

$$\overset{\infty}{\underset{i=1}{\Sigma}} F_i(z)$$

---

\* This remark was made to me by Prof. A. C. Dixon.

is a uniform function of $z$ having the points $a_1$, $a_2$, ... for poles in the proper multiplicity and no essential singularity except $z = \infty$. The most general form of the function therefore is

$$\sum_{r=1}^{\infty} \{F_r(z) + g_r(z)\}.$$

Hence *any uniform analytical function which has no essential singularity except at infinity can be expressed as a sum of functions each of which has only one singularity in the finite part of the plane.* The form of $F_r(z)$ is

$$f_r(z) - G_r(z),$$

where $f_r(z)$ is infinite at $z = a_r$, and $G_r(z)$ is a properly chosen integral function.

We pass to the case of a function, having a single essential singularity at $c$ and at no other point, and any number of accidental singularities, by taking $z' = \dfrac{1}{z-c}$ as in § 63, Cor. II.: and so we obtain the theorem :—

*Any uniform function which has only one essential singularity, say at $c$, can be expressed as a sum of uniform functions each of which has only one singularity different from $c$.*

Evidently the typical summative function $F_r(z)$ for the present case is of the form

$$f_r(z) + G_r\left(\frac{1}{z-c}\right).$$

**77.** The results, which have been obtained for functions possessed of an infinitude of singularities, are valid on the supposition, stated in § 72, that the limit of $a_\nu$ with indefinite increase of $\nu$ is infinite; the terms in the sequence $a_1$, $a_2$, ... tend to one definite limiting point which is $z = \infty$ and, by the substitution $z'(z-c) = 1$, can be made any point $c$ in the finite part of the plane.

Such a sequence, however, does not necessarily tend to one definite limiting point: it may, for instance, tend to condensation on a curve, though the condensation does not imply that all points of the continuous arc of the curve must be included in the sequence. We shall not enter into the discussion of the most general case, but shall consider that case in which the sequence of moduli $|a_1|$, $|a_2|$, ... tends to one definite limiting value so that, with indefinite increase of $\nu$, the limit of $|a_\nu|$ is finite and equal to $R$; the points $a_1$, $a_2$, ... tend to condense on the circle $|z| = R$.

Such a sequence is given by

$$a_{n,k} = \left\{1 + \frac{(-1)^{n+1}}{n+1}\right\} e^{\frac{2k\pi i}{n+1}},$$

for $k=0, 1, \dots, n$, and $n=1, 2, \dots$ *ad inf.*; and another* by

$$a_n = \{1 + (-1)^n c^n\}\, e^{2n\pi i \sqrt{2}},$$

where $c$ is a positive proper fraction.

With each point $a_m$ we associate the point on the circumference of the circle, say $b_m$, to which $a_m$ is nearest : let

$$|a_m - b_m| = \rho_m,$$

so that $\rho_m$ approaches the limit zero with indefinite increase of $m$. There cannot be an infinitude of points $a_p$, such that $\rho_p \geq \Theta$, any assigned positive quantity; for then either there would be an infinitude of points $a$ within or on the circle $|z| = R - \Theta$, or there would be an infinitude of points $a$ within or on the circle $|z| = R + \Theta$, both of which are contrary to the hypothesis that, with indefinite increase of $\nu$, the limit of $|a_\nu|$ is $R$. Hence it follows that a finite integer $n$ exists for every assigned positive quantity $\Theta$, such that

$$|a_m - b_m| < \Theta$$

when $m \geq n$.

Then the theorem, which corresponds to Mittag-Leffler's as stated in § 72 and which also is due to him, is as follows :—

*It is always possible to construct a uniform analytical function of $z$ which is definite over the whole plane, except within infinitesimal circles round the points $a$ and $b$, and which, in the immediate vicinity of each one of the singularities $a$, can be expressed in the form*

$$G_i\left(\frac{1}{z - a_i}\right) + P(z - a_i),$$

*where the functions $G_i$ are assigned functions, vanishing with $\dfrac{1}{z - a_i}$, and finite everywhere in the plane except at the single points $a_i$ with which they are respectively associated.*

In establishing this theorem, we shall need a positive quantity $\epsilon$ less than unity and a converging series $\epsilon_1, \epsilon_2, \epsilon_3, \dots$ of positive quantities, all less than unity.

Let the expression of the function $G_n$ be

$$G_n\left(\frac{1}{z - a_n}\right) = \frac{c_{n,1}}{z - a_n} + \frac{c_{n,2}}{(z - a_n)^2} + \frac{c_{n,3}}{(z - a_n)^3} + \dots.$$

Then, since

$$z - a_n = (z - b_n)\left\{1 - \frac{a_n - b_n}{z - b_n}\right\},$$

the function $G_n$ can be expressed† in the form

$$G_n\left(\frac{1}{z - a_n}\right) = \sum_{\mu=1}^{\infty} A_{n,\mu}\left(\frac{a_n - b_n}{z - b_n}\right)^{\mu}$$

---

* The first of these examples is given by Mittag-Leffler, *Acta Math.*, t. iv, p. 11; the second was stated to me by Prof. Burnside.

† The justification of this statement is to be found in the proposition in § 82.

for values of $z$ such that
$$\left| \frac{a_n - b_n}{z - b_n} \right| < \epsilon;$$
and the coefficients $A$ are given by the equations
$$A_{n,\mu} = \sum_{r=1}^{\mu} \frac{c_{n,r}}{(a_n - b_n)^r} \frac{(\mu-1)!}{(\mu-r)!\,(r-1)!}.$$
Now, because $G_n$ is finite everywhere in the plane except at $a_n$, the series
$$\frac{|c_{n,1}|}{\xi_n} + \frac{|c_{n,2}|}{\xi_n^2} + \frac{|c_{n,3}|}{\xi_n^3} + \cdots$$
has a finite value, say $g$, for any non-zero value of the positive quantity $\xi_n$; then
$$|c_{n,r}| < g\xi_n^r.$$
Hence
$$|A_{n,\mu}| \leqslant \sum_{r=1}^{\mu} \frac{|c_{n,r}|}{|a_n - b_n|^r} \frac{(\mu-1)!}{(\mu-r)!\,(r-1)!}$$
$$< \sum_{r=1}^{\mu} g \frac{\xi_n^r}{|a_n - b_n|^r} \frac{(\mu-1)!}{(\mu-r)!\,(r-1)!}$$
$$< \frac{g\xi_n}{|a_n - b_n|} \left\{ 1 + \frac{\xi_n}{|a_n - b_n|} \right\}^{\mu-1}.$$
Introducing a positive quantity $\alpha$ such that
$$(1+\alpha)\,\epsilon < 1,$$
we choose $\xi_n$ so that
$$\xi_n < \alpha\,|a_n - b_n|;$$
and then
$$|A_{n,\mu}| < g\alpha\,(1+\alpha)^{\mu-1}.$$
Because $(1+\alpha)\,\epsilon$ is less than unity, a quantity $\theta$ exists such that
$$(1+\alpha)\,\epsilon < \theta < 1.$$
Then for values of $z$ determined by the condition $\left| \dfrac{a_n - b_n}{z - b_n} \right| < \epsilon$, we have
$$\sum_{\mu=m_n+1}^{\infty} |A_{n,\mu}| \left| \frac{a_n - b_n}{z - b_n} \right|^{\mu} < \frac{g\alpha}{1+\alpha} \frac{\theta^{m_n+1}}{1-\theta}.$$
Let the integer $m_n$ be chosen so that
$$\frac{g\alpha}{1+\alpha} \frac{\theta^{m_n+1}}{1-\theta} \leqslant \epsilon_n;$$
it will be a finite integer, because $\theta < 1$. Then
$$\sum_{\mu=m_n+1}^{\infty} |A_{n,\mu}| \left| \frac{a_n - b_n}{z - b_n} \right|^{\mu} < \epsilon_n.$$
We now construct, as in § 73, a subsidiary function $F_n(z)$, defining it by the equation
$$F_n(z) = G_n\left( \frac{1}{z - a_n} \right) - \sum_{\mu=0}^{m_n} A_{n,\mu} \left( \frac{a_n - b_n}{z - b_n} \right)^{\mu},$$

so that for points $z$ determined by the condition $\left| \dfrac{a_n - b_n}{z - b_n} \right| < \epsilon$, we have

$$| F_n(z) | < \epsilon_n.$$

A function with the required properties is

$$F(z) = \overset{\infty}{\underset{m=1}{\Sigma}} F_m(z).$$

To prove it, let $c$ be any point in the plane distinct from any of the points $a$ and $b$ ; we can always find a value of $\rho$ such that the circle

$$| z - c | = \rho$$

contains none of the points $a$ and $b$. Let $l$ be the shortest distance between this circle and the circle of radius $R$, on which all the points $b$ lie; then for all points $z$ within or on the circle $| z - c | = \rho$, we have

$$| z - b_m | \geqslant l.$$

Now we have seen that, for any assigned positive quantity $\Theta$, there is a finite integer $n$ such that

$$| a_m - b_m | < \Theta,$$

when $m \geqslant n$. Taking $\Theta = \epsilon l$, we have

$$\left| \frac{a_m - b_m}{z - b_m} \right| < \epsilon,$$

when $m \geqslant n$, $n$ being the finite integer associated with the positive quantity $\epsilon l$.

It therefore follows that, for points $z$ within or on the circle $| z - c | = \rho$,

$$| F_m(z) | < \epsilon_m,$$

when $m$ is not less than the finite integer $n$; hence

$$\overset{\infty}{\underset{m=n}{\Sigma}} | F_m(z) | < \epsilon_n + \epsilon_{n+1} + \epsilon_{n+2} + \dots.$$

Now the series of positive quantities $\epsilon_1, \epsilon_2, \dots$ converges; and therefore

$$\overset{\infty}{\underset{m=n}{\Sigma}} F_m(z)$$

is a series, which converges uniformly and unconditionally. Each of the functions $F_1(z), F_2(z), \dots, F_{n-1}(z)$ is finite when $| z - c | \leqslant \rho$; and therefore

$$\overset{\infty}{\underset{m=1}{\Sigma}} F_m(z)$$

is a series which converges uniformly and unconditionally for all values of $z$ within the circle

$$| z - c | = \rho.$$

Hence the function represented by the series can be expressed in the form $P(z-c)$ for all such values of $z$. The function therefore exists over the whole plane except at the points $a$ and $b$.

It may be proved, exactly as in § 74, that, for points $z$ in the immediate vicinity of a singularity $a_m$,

$$F(z) = G_m\left(\frac{1}{z - a_m}\right) + P(z - a_m).$$

The theorem is thus completely established.

The function thus obtained is not unique, for a wide variation of choice of the converging series $\epsilon_1 + \epsilon_2 + \dots$ is possible. But, in the same way as in the corresponding case in § 75, it is proved that, *if $F(z)$ be a function with the required properties, every other function with those properties is of the form*

$$F(z) + G(z),$$

*where $G(z)$ behaves regularly in the immediate vicinity of every point in the plane except the points $b$.*

*Ex.* If the points $a$ in Mittag-Leffler's theorem are given by

$$\left(1 + \frac{1}{n}\right)\epsilon^{\frac{2k\pi i}{n}}, \qquad (k = 0, 1, \dots, n-1;\ n = 1, 2, \dots, \infty),$$

and if $G_m\left(\dfrac{1}{z - a_m}\right) = \dfrac{1}{z - a_m}$, shew that

$$\sum_{n=1}^{\infty} \frac{n z^{n-1}\left\{\left(1 + \frac{1}{n}\right)^n - 1\right\}}{(z^n - 1)\left\{z^n - \left(1 + \frac{1}{n}\right)^n\right\}}$$

is a function of the character specified in the theorem.

Discuss the nature of the function defined by

$$\sum_{n=1}^{\infty} \frac{n z^{n-1}}{z^n - \left(1 + \frac{1}{n}\right)^n}.$$

(Math. Trip., Part II., 1899.)

**78.** The theorem just given regards the function in the light of an infinite converging series of functions of the variable: it is natural to suppose that a corresponding theorem holds when the function is expressed as an infinite converging product. With the same series of singularities as in § 77, when the limit of $|a_\nu|$ with indefinite increase of $\nu$ is finite and equal to $R$, the theorem* is:—

*It is always possible to construct a uniform analytic function, which behaves regularly everywhere in the plane except within infinitesimal circles*

---

* Mittag-Leffler, *Acta Math.*, t. iv, p. 32; it may be compared with Weierstrass's theorem in § 67.

*round the points a and b, and which in the vicinity of any one of the points $a_\nu$ can be expressed in the form*

$$(z - a_\nu)^{n_\nu} e^{P(z - a_\nu)},$$

*where the numbers $n_1$, $n_2$, ... are any assigned integers.*

The proof is similar in details to proofs of other propositions and it will therefore be given only in outline. We have

$$\frac{n_\nu}{z - a_\nu} = \frac{n_\nu}{z - b_\nu} + \frac{n_\nu}{z - b_\nu} \sum_{\mu=1}^{\infty} \left(\frac{a_\nu - b_\nu}{z - b_\nu}\right)^\mu,$$

provided $\left|\dfrac{a_\nu - b_\nu}{z - b_\nu}\right| < \epsilon$, the notation being the same as in § 77. Hence, for such values of $z$,

$$\left(\frac{z - a_\nu}{z - b_\nu}\right)^{n_\nu} = e^{-n_\nu \sum_{\mu=1}^{\infty} \frac{1}{\mu} \left(\frac{a_\nu - b_\nu}{z - b_\nu}\right)^\mu}.$$

If we denote

$$\left(1 - \frac{a_\nu - b_\nu}{z - b_\nu}\right)^{n_\nu} e^{n_\nu \sum_{\mu=1}^{m_\nu} \frac{1}{\mu} \left(\frac{a_\nu - b_\nu}{z - b_\nu}\right)^\mu}$$

by $E_\nu(z)$, we have $\quad E_\nu(z) = e^{n_\nu \sum_{\mu=m_\nu+1}^{\infty} \frac{1}{\mu} \left(\frac{a_\nu - b_\nu}{z - b_\nu}\right)^\mu}.$

Hence, if $F(z)$ denote the infinite product

$$\prod_{\nu=1}^{\infty} E_\nu(z),$$

we have $\quad F(z) = e^{-\sum_{\nu=1}^{\infty} \left\{n_\nu \sum_{\mu=m_\nu+1}^{\infty} \frac{1}{\mu} \left(\frac{a_\nu - b_\nu}{z - b_\nu}\right)^\mu\right\}};$

and $F(z)$ is a determinate function provided the double series in the index of the exponential converges.

Because $n_\nu$ is a finite integer, and because

$$\sum_{\mu=1}^{\infty} \frac{1}{\mu} \left(\frac{a_\nu - b_\nu}{z - b_\nu}\right)^\mu$$

is a converging series, it is possible to choose an integer $m_\nu$ so that

$$\left| n_\nu \sum_{\mu=m_\nu+1}^{\infty} \frac{1}{\mu} \left(\frac{a_\nu - b_\nu}{z - b_\nu}\right)^\mu \right| < \eta_\nu,$$

where $\eta_\nu$ is any assigned positive quantity. We take a converging series of positive quantities $\eta_\nu$; and then the moduli of the terms in the double series form a uniformly converging series. The double series itself therefore converges uniformly; and then the infinite product $F(z)$ converges uniformly for points $z$ such that

$$\left|\frac{a_\nu - b_\nu}{z - b_\nu}\right| < \epsilon.$$

As in § 77, let $c$ be any point in the plane, distinct from any of the points $a$ and $b$. We take a finite value of $\rho$ such that all the points $a$ and $b$ lie outside the circle $|z - c| = \rho$; and then, for all points within or on this circle,

$$\left| \frac{a_m - b_m}{z - b_m} \right| < \epsilon,$$

when $m \geqslant n$, $n$ being the finite integer associated with the positive quantity $\epsilon l$. The product

$$\prod_{\nu=n}^{\infty} E_\nu(z)$$

is therefore finite, for its modulus is less than

$$e^{\sum\limits_{\nu=n}^{\infty} \eta_\nu};$$

the product

$$\prod_{\nu=1}^{n-1} E_\nu(z)$$

is finite, because the circle $|z - c| = \rho$ contains none of the points $a$ and $b$; and therefore the function $F(z)$ is finite for all points within or on the circle. Hence in the vicinity of $c$, the function can be expanded in the form $P(z - c)$; and therefore the function is definite everywhere in the plane except within infinitesimal circles round the points $a$ and $b$.

The infinite product converges uniformly and unconditionally. As in § 51, it can be zero only at points which make one of the factors zero and, from the form of the factors, this can take place only at the points $a_\nu$ with positive integers $n_\nu$. In the vicinity of $a_\nu$, all the factors of $F(z)$ except $E_\nu(z)$ are regular; hence $F(z)/E_\nu(z)$ can be expressed as a function of $z - a_\nu$ in the vicinity. But the function has no zeros there, and therefore the form of the function is

$$e^{P_1(z - a_\nu)}.$$

Hence, in the vicinity of $a_\nu$, we have

$$F(z) = E_\nu(z)\, e^{P_1(z - a_\nu)}$$
$$= (z - a_\nu)^{n_\nu} e^{P(z - a_\nu)},$$

on combining the exponential index in $E_\nu(z)$ with $P_1(z - a_\nu)$. This is the required property.

Other general theorems will be found in Mittag-Leffler's memoir just quoted.

**79.** The investigations in §§ 72—75 have led to the construction of a function with assigned properties. It is important to be able to change, into the chosen form, the expression of a given function, having an infinite series of singularities tending to a definite limiting point, say to $z = \infty$. It is necessary for this purpose to determine (i) the functions $F_r(z)$ so that the series $\overset{\infty}{\underset{r=1}{\Sigma}} F_r(z)$ may converge uniformly and unconditionally, and (ii) the function $G(z)$.

Let $\Phi(z)$ be the given function, and let $S$ be a simple contour embracing the origin and $\mu$ of the singularities, viz., $a_1, \ldots, a_\mu$: then, if $t$ be any point, we have

$$\int^S \frac{\Phi(t)}{t-z} \left(\frac{z}{t}\right)^m dt = \int^{(0)} \frac{\Phi(t)}{t-z} \left(\frac{z}{t}\right)^m dt + \int^{(z)} \frac{\Phi(t)}{t-z} \left(\frac{z}{t}\right)^m dt$$
$$+ \overset{\mu}{\underset{\nu=1}{\Sigma}} \int^{(a_\nu)} \frac{\Phi(t)}{t-z} \left(\frac{z}{t}\right)^m dt,$$

where $\int^{(a)}$ implies an integral taken round a very small circle centre $a$.

If the origin be one of the points $a_1, a_2, \ldots$, then the first term will be included in the summation.

Assuming that $z$ is neither the origin nor any one of the points $a_1, \ldots, a_\mu$, we have

$$\int^{(z)} \frac{\Phi(t)}{t-z} \left(\frac{z}{t}\right)^m dt = 2\pi i \Phi(z),$$

so that
$$\Phi(z) = \frac{1}{2\pi i} \int^S \frac{\Phi(t)}{t-z} \left(\frac{z}{t}\right)^m dt - \frac{1}{2\pi i} \int^{(0)} \frac{\Phi(t)}{t-z} \left(\frac{z}{t}\right)^m dt$$
$$- \frac{1}{2\pi i} \overset{\mu}{\underset{\nu=1}{\Sigma}} \int^{(a_\nu)} \frac{\Phi(t)}{t-z} \left(\frac{z}{t}\right)^m dt.$$

Now
$$\frac{1}{2\pi i} \int^{(0)} \frac{\Phi(t)}{t-z} \left(\frac{z}{t}\right)^m dt$$

$$= \frac{z^m}{(m-1)!} \left[\frac{d^{m-1}}{dt^{m-1}} \frac{\Phi(t)}{t-z}\right]_{t=0}$$

$$= -\frac{z^m}{(m-1)!} \left[\frac{d^{m-1}}{dt^{m-1}} \left\{\frac{\Phi(t)}{z} + \frac{t\Phi(t)}{z^2} + \ldots\right\}\right]_{t=0}$$

$$= -\frac{z^m}{(m-1)!} \left[\frac{1}{z} \Phi^{m-1}(0) + \frac{m-1}{z^2} \Phi^{m-2}(0) + \ldots\right]$$

$$= -\left[\Phi(0) + \frac{z}{1} \Phi'(0) + \ldots + \frac{z^{m-1} \Phi^{m-1}(0)}{(m-1)!}\right] = -G(z),$$

unless $z = 0$ be a singularity and then there will be no term $G(z)$. Similarly, it can be shewn that

$$-\frac{1}{2\pi i} \int^{(a_\nu)} \frac{\Phi(t)}{t-z} \left(\frac{z}{t}\right)^m dt$$

is equal to
$$G_\nu \left(\frac{1}{z-a_\nu}\right) - \overset{m-1}{\underset{\lambda=0}{\Sigma}} \nu_\lambda \left(\frac{z}{a_\nu}\right)^\lambda = F_\nu(z),$$

where
$$G_\nu \left(\frac{1}{z-a_\nu}\right) = -\frac{1}{2\pi i} \int^{(a_\nu)} \frac{\Phi(t)}{t-z} dt,$$

and the subtractive sum of $m$ terms is the sum of the first $m$ terms in the development of $G_\nu$ in ascending powers of $z$.   Hence

$$\Phi(z) = G(z) + \sum_{\nu=1}^{\mu} F_\nu(z) + \frac{1}{2\pi i} \int^S \frac{\Phi(t)}{t-z} \left(\frac{z}{t}\right)^m dt.$$

If, for an infinitely large contour, $m$ can be chosen so that the integral

$$\frac{1}{2\pi i} \int \frac{\Phi(t)}{t-z} \left(\frac{z}{t}\right)^m dt$$

diminishes indefinitely with increasing contours enclosing successive singularities, then

$$\Phi(z) = G(z) + \sum_{\nu=1}^{\infty} F_\nu(z).$$

The integer $m$ may be called the *critical integer*.

If the origin be a singularity, we take

$$F_0(z) = G_0\left(\frac{1}{z}\right),$$

and there is then no term $G(z)$: hence, including the origin in the summation, we have

$$\Phi(z) = \sum_{\nu=0}^{\infty} F_\nu(z) + \frac{1}{2\pi i} \int^S \frac{\Phi(t)}{t-z} \left(\frac{z}{t}\right)^m dt;$$

so that if, for this case also, there be some finite value of $m$ which makes the integral vanish, then

$$\Phi(z) = \sum_{\nu=0}^{\infty} F_\nu(z).$$

Other expressions can be obtained by choosing for $m$ a value greater than the critical integer; but it is usually most advantageous to take $m$ equal to its lowest effective value.

*Ex.* 1.   The singularities of the function $\pi \cot \pi z$ are given by $z=\lambda$, for all integer values of $\lambda$ from $-\infty$ to $+\infty$ including zero, so that the origin is a singularity.

The integral to be considered is

$$J = \frac{1}{2\pi i} \int^{(s)} \frac{\pi \cot \pi t}{t-z} \left(\frac{z}{t}\right)^m dt.$$

We take the contour to be a circle of very large radius $R$ chosen so that the circumference does not pass infinitesimally near any one of the singularities of $\pi \cot \pi t$ at infinity; this is, of course, possible because there is a finite distance between any two of them.   Then, round the circumference so taken, $\pi \cot \pi t$ is never infinite: hence its modulus is never greater than some finite quantity $M$.

Let $t = Re^{\theta i}$, so that $\dfrac{dt}{t} = i d\theta$; then

$$J = \frac{1}{2\pi} \int_0^{2\pi} \pi \cot \pi t \frac{z}{t-z} \left(\frac{z}{t}\right)^{m-1} d\theta,$$

and therefore
$$|J| \lessdot M \frac{|z|}{|t-z|} \left|\frac{z}{t}\right|^{m-1},$$

for some point $t$ on the circle. Now, as the circle is very large, we have $|t-z|$ infinite: hence $|J|$ can be made zero merely by taking $m$ unity.

Thus, for the function $\pi \cot \pi z$, the critical integer is unity.

Hence, by the general theorem, we have the equation
$$\pi \cot \pi z = -\frac{1}{2\pi i}. \Sigma \int \frac{\pi \cot \pi t}{t-z} \frac{z}{t} \, dt,$$

the summation extending to all the points $\lambda$ for integer values of $\lambda = -\infty$ to $+\infty$, and each integral being taken round a small circle centre $\lambda$.

Now if, in
$$\frac{1}{2\pi i} \int^{(\lambda)} \frac{\pi \cot \pi t}{t-z} \frac{z}{t} \, dt,$$

we take $t = \lambda + \zeta$, we have
$$\pi \cot \pi t = \frac{1}{\zeta} + P(\zeta),$$

where $P(\zeta) = 0$ when $\zeta = 0$; and therefore the value of the integral is
$$= \frac{1}{2\pi i} \int \frac{\frac{1}{\zeta} + P(\zeta)}{\lambda - z + \zeta} \frac{z}{\lambda + \zeta} \, d\zeta$$
$$= \frac{1}{2\pi i} \int \frac{\{1 + \zeta P(\zeta)\} z}{(\lambda - z + \zeta)(\lambda + \zeta)} \frac{d\zeta}{\zeta}.$$

In the limit when $|\zeta|$ is infinitesimal, this integral
$$= \frac{z}{(\lambda - z)\lambda}$$
$$= \frac{1}{\lambda - z} - \frac{1}{\lambda},$$

and therefore
$$F_\lambda(z) = \frac{1}{z - \lambda} + \frac{1}{\lambda},$$

if $\lambda$ be not zero.

And for the zero of $\lambda$, the value of the integral is
$$-\frac{1}{2\pi i} \int \{1 + \zeta P(\zeta)\} \frac{z}{z - \zeta} \frac{d\zeta}{\zeta^2}$$
$$= -\frac{d}{d\zeta} \left[ \{1 + \zeta P(\zeta)\} \frac{z}{z - \zeta} \right]_{\zeta=0}$$
$$= -\left[ \frac{z}{(z-\zeta)^2} \{1 + \zeta P(\zeta)\} + \frac{z}{z - \zeta} \{P(\zeta) + \zeta P'(\zeta)\} \right]_{\zeta=0}$$
$$= -\frac{1}{z},$$

so that $F_0(z)$ is $\frac{1}{z}$. In fact, in the notation of § 72, we have
$$G_0\left(\frac{1}{z}\right) = \frac{1}{z},$$
$$G_\lambda\left(\frac{1}{z-\lambda}\right) = \frac{1}{z-\lambda},$$

and the expansion of $G_\lambda$ needs to be carried only to one term.

We thus have $\qquad \pi \cot \pi z = \dfrac{1}{z} + \sum\limits_{\lambda = -\infty}^{\lambda = \infty}{}' \left( \dfrac{1}{z - \lambda} + \dfrac{1}{\lambda} \right),$

the summation not including the zero value of $\lambda$.

*Ex.* 2.   Obtain, *ab initio*, the relation

$$\frac{1}{\sin^2 z} = \sum_{\lambda = -\infty}^{\lambda = \infty} \frac{1}{(z - \lambda \pi)^2}.$$

*Ex.* 3.   Shew that, if

$$R(z) = \left\{ 1 - \left( \frac{2z}{1} \right)^2 \right\} \left\{ 1 - \left( \frac{2z}{3} \right)^2 \right\} \cdots \left\{ 1 - \left( \frac{2z}{2n+1} \right)^2 \right\},$$

then $\qquad \dfrac{\pi \cot \pi z}{R(z)} = \dfrac{1}{z} + 2z \sum\limits_{\lambda = 1}^{\infty} \dfrac{1}{R(\lambda)} \dfrac{1}{z^2 - \lambda^2}.$

$\hfill$ (Gyldén, Mittag-Leffler.)

*Ex.* 4.   Obtain an expression, in the form of a sum, for

$$\frac{\pi \cot \pi z}{Q(z)},$$

where $Q(z)$ denotes $\qquad (1 - z) \left( 1 - \dfrac{z}{2} \right)^2 \left( 1 - \dfrac{z}{3} \right)^3 \cdots \left( 1 - \dfrac{z}{n} \right)^n.$

*Ex.* 5.   Construct a uniform analytical function $F(x)$, which is finite at all finite points except at the points 0, 1, 2, 3, ..., at which it is infinite in such a way that

$$F(x) - e^x \cot \pi x$$

is finite at each of the points.

$\hfill$ (Math. Trip., Part II., 1897.)

**80.**   The results obtained in the present chapter relating to functions which have an unlimited number of singularities, whether distributed over the whole plane or distributed over only a finite portion of it, shew that analytical functions can be represented, not merely as infinite converging series of powers of the variable, but also as infinite converging series of functions of the variable.   The properties of functions when represented by series of powers of the variable depended in their proof on the condition that the series proceeded in powers; and it is therefore necessary at least to revise those properties in the case of functions when represented as series of functions of the variable.

Let there be a series of uniform functions $f_1(z)$, $f_2(z)$, ...; then the aggregate of values of $z$, for which the series

$$\sum_{i=1}^{\infty} f_i(z)$$

has a finite value, is the region of continuity of the series.   If a positive quantity $\rho$ can be determined such that, for all points $z$ within the circle

$$|z - a| = \rho,$$

the series $\sum\limits_{i=1}^{\infty} f_i(z)$ converges uniformly[*], the series is said to converge

---

[*] In connection with most of the investigations in the remainder of this chapter, Weierstrass's memoir " Zur Functionenlehre " already quoted (p. 134, note) should be consulted.

uniformly in the vicinity of $a$.   If $R$ be the greatest value of $\rho$ for which this holds, then the area within the circle

$$| z - a | = R$$

is called the domain of $a$; and the series converges uniformly in the vicinity of any point in the domain of $a$.

It will be proved in § 82 that the function, represented by the series of functions, can be represented by power-series, each such series being equivalent to the function within the domain of some one point.   In order to be able to obtain all the power-series, it is necessary to distribute the region of continuity of the function into domains of points where it has a uniform finite value.   We therefore form the domain of a point $b$ in the domain of $a$ from a knowledge of the singularities of the function, then the domain of a point $c$ in the domain of $b$, and so on ; the aggregate of these domains is a continuous part of the plane which has isolated points and which has one or several lines for its boundaries.   Let this part be denoted by $A_1$.

For most of the functions, which have already been considered, the region $A_1$, thus obtained, is the complete region of continuity.   But examples will be adduced almost immediately to shew that $A_1$ does not necessarily include all the region of continuity of the series under consideration.   Let $a'$ be a point not in $A_1$, within whose vicinity the function has a uniform finite value ; then a second portion $A_2$ can be separated from the whole plane, by proceeding from $a'$ as before from $a$.   The limits of $A_1$ and $A_2$ may be wholly or partially the same, or may be independent of one another : but no point within either can belong to the other.   If there be points in the region of continuity which belong to neither $A_1$ nor $A_2$, then there must be at least another part of the plane $A_3$ with properties similar to $A_1$ and $A_2$.   And so on.   The series $\sum\limits_{i=1}^{\infty} f_i(z)$ converges uniformly in the vicinity of every point within each of the separate portions of its region of continuity.

It was proved that a function represented by a series of powers has a definite finite derivative at every point lying actually within the circle of convergence of the series, but that this result cannot be affirmed for a point on the boundary of the circle of convergence even though the value of the series itself should be finite at the point, an illustration being provided by the hypergeometric series at a point on the circumference of its circle of convergence.   It will appear that a function represented by a series of functions has a definite finite derivative at every point lying actually within its region of continuity, but that the result cannot be affirmed for a point on the boundary ; and an example will be given (§ 83) in which the derivative is indefinite.

Again, it has been seen that a function, initially defined by a given power-series, is, in most cases, represented by different analytical expressions in different parts of the plane, each of the elements being a valid expression of the function within a certain region. The questions arise whether a given analytical expression, either a series of powers or a series of functions: (i) can represent different functions in the same continuous part of its region of continuity, (ii) can represent different functions in distinct, that is, non-continuous, parts of its region of continuity.

**81.**    Consider first a function defined by a given series of powers.

Let there be a region $A'$ in the plane and let the region of continuity of the function, say $g(z)$, have parts common with $A'$. Then if $a_0$ be any point in one of these common parts, we can express $g(z)$ in the form $P(z - a_0)$ in the domain of $a_0$.

As already explained, the function can be continued from the domain of $a_0$ by a series of elements, so that the whole region of continuity is gradually covered by domains of successive points ; to find the value in the domain of any point $a$, it is sufficient to know any one element, say, the element in the domain of $a_0$. The function is *the same* through its region of continuity.

Two distinct cases may occur in the continuations.

First, it may happen that the region of continuity of the function $g(z)$ extends beyond $A'$. Then we can obtain elements for points outside $A'$, their aggregate being a uniform analytical function. The aggregate of elements then represents within $A'$ a single analytical function : but as that function has elements for points without $A'$, the aggregate within $A'$ does not completely represent the function.   Hence :—

*If a function be defined within a continuous region of a plane by an aggregate of elements in the form of power-series, which are continuations of one another, the aggregate represents in that part of the plane one (and only one) analytical function : but if the power-series can be continued beyond the boundary of the region, the aggregate of elements within the region is not the complete representation of the analytical function.*

This is the more common case, so that examples need not be given.

Secondly, it may happen that the region of continuity of the function does not extend beyond $A'$ in any direction. There are then no elements of the function for points outside $A'$ and the function cannot be continued beyond the boundary of $A'$. The aggregate of elements is then the complete representation of the function and therefore :—

*If a function be defined within a continuous region of a plane by an aggregate of elements in the form of power-series, which are continuations of one another, and if the power-series cannot be continued across the boundary of that region, the aggregate of elements in the region is the complete representation of a single uniform monogenic function which exists only for values of the variable within the region.*

The boundary of the region of continuity of the function is, in the latter case, called the *natural limit* of the function\*, as it is a line beyond which the function cannot be continued.   Such a line arises for the series

$$1 + 2z + 2z^4 + 2z^9 + \ldots,$$

in the circle $|z| = 1$, a remark due to Kronecker; other illustrations occur in connection with the modular functions, the axis of real variables being the natural limit, and in connection with the automorphic functions (see Chapter XXII.) when the fundamental circle is the natural limit.   A few examples will be given at the end of the present chapter.

It appears that Weierstrass was the first to announce the existence of natural limits for analytic functions, *Berlin. Monatsber.* (1866), p. 617; see also Schwarz, *Ges. Werke*, t. ii, pp. 240—242, who adduces other illustrations and gives some references; Klein and Fricke, *Vorl. über die Theorie der elliptischen Modulfunctionen*, t. i, (1890), p. 110.   Some interesting examples and discussions of functions, which have the axis of real variables for a natural limit, are given by Hankel, "Untersuchungen über die unendlich oft oscillirenden und unstetigen Functionen," *Math. Ann.*, t. xx, (1870), pp. 63—112.

**82.**   Consider next a series of functions $f_1(z)$, $f_2(z)$, $f_3(z)$, ... of the variable $z$.

In the first place, let each of them occur in the form of power-series in $z$, with (it may be) positive and negative indices, say in the form

$$f_s(z) = \sum_\mu a_{s\mu} z^\mu.$$

Assume that the power-series for the separate functions, as well as the series

$$\sum_{s=1}^\infty f_s(z)$$

of functions, have a common region of continuity in the vicinity of the origin such that, for values of $z$ given by

$$R < |z| = r < R',$$

the function-series and each of the power-series converge uniformly.   Then *the sum*

$$\sum_{s=1}^\infty a_{s\mu}$$

*has a definite finite value, say $A_\mu$; for the values of $z$ considered, the series*

$$\sum_\mu A_\mu z^\mu$$

*converges; and we have*

$$\sum_{s=1}^\infty f_s(z) = \sum_\mu A_\mu z^\mu.$$

\* *Die natürliche Grenze*, according to German mathematicians.

Let $k$ denote any arbitrary positive quantity, taken as small as we please. In consequence of the uniform convergence of the function-series, it is possible to choose an integer $m$, such that

$$\left| \sum_{s=n}^{\infty} f_s(z) \right| < \tfrac{1}{2}k,$$

for all integers $n \geqslant m$, and for all values of $z$ such that $R < r_1 < r < r_2 < R'$, where $r_1 - R$ and $R' - r_2$ are non-vanishing quantities, no matter how small they may be assigned; and therefore for the same range of variables, it is possible to choose an integer $m$ so that, for all integers $n \geqslant m$ and for all finite positive integers $p$, we have

$$\left| \sum_{s=n}^{n+p} f_s(z) \right| = \left| \sum_{s=n}^{\infty} f_s(z) - \sum_{n+p+1}^{\infty} f_s(z) \right|$$

$$\leqslant \left| \sum_{s=n}^{\infty} f_s(z) \right| + \left| \sum_{n+p+1}^{\infty} f_s(z) \right|$$

$$\leqslant \tfrac{1}{2}k + \tfrac{1}{2}k \leqslant k.$$

Owing to the finiteness of the integer $p$, we have

$$\sum_{s=n}^{n+p} f_s(z) = \sum_{\mu} \left( \sum_{s=n}^{n+p} a_{s\mu} \right) z^{\mu},$$

so that

$$\left| \sum_{\mu} \left( \sum_{s=n}^{n+p} a_{s\mu} \right) z^{\mu} \right| < k,$$

for all integers $n \geqslant m$, and for all positive integers $p$.    Hence (Corollary, § 29)

$$\left| \sum_{s=n}^{n+p} a_{s\mu} \right| < kr^{-\mu},$$

where $|z| = r$; because $k$, being greater than the upper limit of the modulus of the above series for all the values of $z$ considered, is greater than the upper limit of its modulus for values of $z$ such that $|z| = r$. It therefore follows that, because $kr^{-\mu}$ is an arbitrary quantity assigned as small as we please, and because an integer $m$ can be chosen such that the above inequality holds for all integers $n \geqslant m$ and for all positive integers $p$, the series $\sum\limits_{s=1}^{\infty} a_{s\mu}$ converges to a unique finite limit.    Denote this by $A_{\mu}$.

Let

$$\sum_{s=1}^{n-1} a_{s\mu} = A_{\mu}', \quad \sum_{s=n}^{\infty} a_{s\mu} = A_{\mu}'';$$

then regarding $kr_1^{-\mu}$ and $kr_2^{-\mu}$ as two assigned quantities, as small as we please (because $k$ can be assigned as small as we please, and $r_1$, $r_2$ are finite non-vanishing magnitudes), the convergence of the series whose sum is $A_{\mu}$ enables us to choose an integer $n$ such that $A_{\mu}''$ is smaller than each of the quantities $kr_1^{-\mu}$ and $kr_2^{-\mu}$; thus

$$A_{\mu}'' < kr_1^{-\mu}, \quad A_{\mu}'' < kr_2^{-\mu}.$$

Now consider the series $\Sigma A_\mu z^\mu$ for a value of $z$ such that $r_1 < |z| = r < r_2$. We have

$$\sum_{\mu=0}^{\infty} |A_\mu'' z^\mu| < \sum_{\mu=0}^{\infty} k \left(\frac{r}{r_2}\right)^\mu < k \frac{r_2}{r_2 - r},$$

$$\sum_{\mu=-\infty}^{-1} |A_\mu'' z^\mu| < \sum_{\mu=-\infty}^{-1} k \left(\frac{r}{r_1}\right)^\mu < k \frac{r_1}{r - r_1},$$

and therefore

$$\sum_{\mu=-\infty}^{\infty} |A_\mu'' z^\mu| < k \frac{r_1}{r - r_1} + k \frac{r_2}{r_2 - r}.$$

Hence the series $\Sigma A_\mu'' z^\mu$ converges. Moreover, each of the power-series $f_1(z), \ldots, f_{n-1}(z)$ converges uniformly; therefore

$$\sum_{s=1}^{n-1} f_s(z) = \Sigma A_\mu' z^\mu,$$

and the latter series converges uniformly. The two series $\Sigma A_\mu' z^\mu$, $\Sigma A_\mu'' z^\mu$, can therefore be combined into the series

$$\Sigma A_\mu z^\mu,$$

which accordingly is a converging series.

Finally, we have

$$\sum_{s=1}^{\infty} f_s(z) - \sum_\mu A_\mu z^\mu = \sum_{s=1}^{\infty} f_s(z) - \Sigma A_\mu' z^\mu - \Sigma A_\mu'' z^\mu$$

$$= \sum_{s=n}^{\infty} f_s(z) - \Sigma A_\mu'' z^\mu,$$

and therefore

$$\left| \sum_{s=1}^{\infty} f_s(z) - \sum_\mu A_\mu z^\mu \right| = \left| \sum_{s=n}^{\infty} f_s(z) - \Sigma A_\mu'' z^\mu \right|$$

$$\leqslant \left| \sum_{s=n}^{\infty} f_s(z) \right| + \Sigma |A_\mu'' z^\mu|$$

$$\leqslant \tfrac{1}{2} k + k \frac{r_1}{r - r_1} + k \frac{r_2}{r_2 - r}.$$

As the assigned quantity $k$ is at our disposal, we can choose it so that the quantity on the right-hand side is smaller than any assignable magnitude: consequently, for the values of $z$ under consideration, we have

$$\sum_{s=1}^{\infty} f_s(z) = \Sigma A_\mu z^\mu.$$

**83.** In the second place, consider the series of functions $f_1(z)$, $f_2(z)$, $f_3(z)$, ... more generally. The region of continuity may be supposed to consist of one part or of more than one part: let such a part be denoted by

$A$, and let $F(z)$ denote the function represented by the series within $A$, so that

$$F(z) = \sum_{s=1}^{\infty} f_s(z),$$

and assume that within $A$ (though not necessarily at points on its boundary) the function-series converges uniformly. Let $a$ denote any arbitrarily assumed position within $A$; each of the functions $f_s(z)$ is regular in the vicinity of $a$ and is expressible in the form of a power-series $P_s(z-a)$ containing only positive powers of $z-a$. By the preceding investigation, the function-series can be represented as a power-series, and we have

$$F(z) = P(z-a).$$

In $P(z-a)$, the coefficient of $(z-a)^\mu$ is $A_\mu$, which is $\sum_{s=1}^{\infty} a_{s\mu}$, where $a_{s\mu}$ is the coefficient of $(z-a)^\mu$ in $f_s(z)$; accordingly

$$\left[ \frac{d^\mu P(z-a)}{dz^\mu} \right]_{z=a} = \left[ \sum_{s=1}^{\infty} \frac{d^\mu f_s(z)}{dz^\mu} \right]_{z=a}$$

for all values of $\mu$. Since $a$ is any arbitrarily chosen point in $A$, it follows that, for all points within $A$, we have

$$\frac{d^\mu F(z)}{dz^\mu} = \sum_{s=1}^{\infty} \frac{d^\mu f_s(z)}{dz^\mu}.$$

As the function-series $\sum_{s=1}^{\infty} f_s(z)$ converges uniformly, and as $f_s(z)$ is regular in the vicinity of $a$, it is easy to see that the series

$$\sum_{s=1}^{\infty} \frac{d^\mu f_s(z)}{dz^\mu}$$

also converges uniformly; and therefore the derivatives of the function-series within the region of continuity are the derivatives of the function the series represents.

The expression $P(z-a)$ is an *Element* of the function $F(z)$: and within the domain of $a$, contained in the region $A$, it represents the function. It can be used for the continuation of $F(z)$ so long as the domains of successive points lie within $A$; but this restriction is necessary, and the full continuation of $P(z-a)$ as an element of a power-series is not necessarily limited by the region $A$. It is solely in that part of its region of continuity which is included within $A$ that it represents the function $F(z)$; the boundary of the region $A$ must not be crossed in forming the continuations of $P(z-a)$.

It therefore appears that a converging series of functions of a variable can be expressed in the form of series of powers of the variable, which converge within the parts of the plane where the series of functions converges uniformly; but the equivalence of the two expressions is limited to such parts of the plane, and cannot be extended beyond the boundary of the region of continuity of the series of functions.

If the region of continuity of a series of functions consist of several parts of the plane, then the series of functions can in each part be expressed in the form of a set of converging series of powers : but the sets of series of powers are not necessarily the same for the different parts, and they are not necessarily continuations of one another, regarded as power-series.

Suppose, then, that the region of continuity of a series of functions

$$F(z) = \sum_{s=1}^{\infty} f_s(z)$$

consists of several parts $A_1$, $A_2$, .... Within the part $A_1$ let $F(z)$ be represented, as above, by a set of power-series. At every point within $A_1$, the values of $F(z)$ and of its derivatives are each definite and unique ; so that, at every point which lies in the regions of convergence of two of the power-series, the values which the two power-series, as the equivalents of $F(z)$ in their respective regions, furnish for $F(z)$ and for its derivatives must be the same. Hence the various power-series, which are the equivalents of $F(z)$ in the region $A_1$, are continuations of one another : and they are sufficient to determine a uniform monogenic analytic function, say $F_1(z)$. The functions $F(z)$ and $F_1(z)$ are equivalent in the region $A_1$ ; and therefore, by § 81, *the series of functions represents one and the same function for all points within one continuous part of its region of continuity.* It may (and frequently does) happen that the region of continuity of the analytical function $F_1(z)$ extends beyond $A_1$ ; and then $F_1(z)$ can be continued beyond the boundary of $A_1$ by a succession of elements. Or it may happen that the region of continuity of $F_1(z)$ is completely bounded by the boundary of $A_1$ ; and then that function cannot be continued across that boundary. In either case, the equivalence of $F_1(z)$ and $\sum_{s=1}^{\infty} f_s(z)$ does not extend beyond the boundary of $A_1$, one complete and distinct part of the region of continuity of $\sum_{s=1}^{\infty} f_s(z)$ ; and therefore, by using the theorem proved in § 81, it follows that :—

*A series of functions of a variable, which converges within a continuous part of the plane of the variable z, is either a partial or a complete representation of a single uniform analytic function of the variable in that part of the plane.*

Further, it has just been proved that the converging series of functions can, in any of the regions $A$, be changed into an equivalent uniform analytic function, the equivalence being valid for all points in that region, say

$$\sum_{s=1}^{\infty} f_s(z) = F_1(z).$$

We have seen that every derivative of $F_1(z)$ at any point within $A$ is the sum of the corresponding derivatives of $f_s(z)$, this sum converging uniformly within $A$. The equivalence of the analytic function and the series of functions has not been proved for points on the boundary; even if they are equivalent there, the function $F_1(z)$ cannot be proved to have a uniform finite derivative at every point on the boundary of $A$, and therefore *it cannot be affirmed that* $\sum\limits_{s=1}^{\infty} f_s(z)$ *has, of necessity, a uniform finite derivative at points on the boundary of $A$, even though the value of* $\sum\limits_{s=1}^{\infty} f_s(z)$ *be uniform and finite at every point on the boundary\**.

*Ex.* In illustration of the last inference, regarding the derivative of a function at a point on the boundary of its region of continuity, consider the series

$$g(z) = \sum_{n=0}^{\infty} b^n z^{a^n},$$

where $b$ is a positive quantity less than unity, and $a$ is a positive quantity which will be taken to be an odd integer.

For points within and on the circumference of the circle $|z| = 1$, the series converges uniformly and unconditionally; and for all points without the circle the series diverges. It thus defines a function for points within the circle and on the circumference, but not for points without the circle.

Moreover, for points actually within the circle, the function has a first derivative and consequently has any number of derivatives. But it cannot be declared to have a derivative for points on the circle : and it will in fact now be proved that, if a certain condition be satisfied, the derivative for variations at any point on the circle is not merely infinite but that the sign of the infinite value depends upon the direction of the variation, so that the function is not monogenic for the circumference†.

Let $z = e^{\theta i}$ : then, as the function converges unconditionally for all points along the circle, we take

$$f(\theta) = \sum_{n=0}^{\infty} b^n e^{a^n \theta i},$$

where $\theta$ is a real variable. Hence

$$\frac{f(\theta + \phi) - f(\theta)}{\phi} = \sum_{n=0}^{\infty} \frac{b^n}{\phi} \{ e^{a^n(\theta+\phi)i} - e^{a^n \theta i} \}$$

$$= \sum_{n=0}^{m-1} a^n b^n \left\{ \frac{e^{a^n(\theta+\phi)i} - e^{a^n \theta i}}{a^n \phi} \right\}$$

$$+ \sum_{n=0}^{\infty} b^{m+n} \left\{ \frac{e^{a^{m+n}(\theta+\phi)i} - e^{a^{m+n}\theta i}}{\phi} \right\},$$

\* It should be remarked here, as at the end of § 21, that the result in itself does not contravene Riemann's definition of a function, according to which (§ 8) $\dfrac{dw}{dz}$ must have the same value whatever be the direction of the vanishing quantity $dz$; at a point on the boundary of the region there are outward directions for which $dw$ is not defined.

† The following investigation is due to Weierstrass, who communicated it to Du Bois-Reymond : see *Crelle*, t. lxxix, (1875), pp. 29—31 ; Weierstrass, *Ges. Werke*, t. ii, pp. 71—74.

assuming $m$, in the first place, to be any positive integer. To transform the first sum on the right-hand side, we take

$$e^{a^n(\theta+\phi)i} - e^{a^n\theta i} = 2ie^{a^n(\theta+\frac{1}{2}\phi)i}\sin(\tfrac{1}{2}a^n\phi),$$

and therefore

$$\left| \sum_{n=0}^{m-1} (ab)^n \frac{e^{a^n(\theta+\phi)i} - e^{a^n\theta i}}{a^n\phi} \right|$$

$$< \sum_{n=0}^{m-1} (ab)^n \left| \frac{\sin(\frac{1}{2}a^n\phi)}{\frac{1}{2}a^n\phi} \right|$$

$$< \sum_{n=0}^{m-1} (ab)^n < \frac{(ab)^m}{ab-1},$$

if $ab > 1$. Hence, on this hypothesis, we have

$$\sum_{n=0}^{m-1} (ab)^n \left\{ \frac{e^{a^n(\theta+\phi)i} - e^{a^n\theta i}}{a^n\phi} \right\} = \gamma \frac{(ab)^m}{ab-1},$$

where $\gamma$ is a complex quantity with modulus $< 1$.

To transform the second sum on the right-hand side, let the integer nearest to $a^m\dfrac{\theta}{\pi}$ be $a_m$, so that

$$\tfrac{1}{2} \geqslant a^m \frac{\theta}{\pi} - a_m > -\tfrac{1}{2}$$

for any value of $m$: then taking

$$x = a^m\theta - \pi a_m,$$

we have

$$\tfrac{1}{2}\pi \geqslant x > -\tfrac{1}{2}\pi,$$

and $\cos x$ is not negative. We choose the quantity $\phi$ so that

$$\frac{\theta+\phi}{\pi} = \frac{a_m+1}{a^m},$$

and therefore

$$\phi = \frac{\pi-x}{a^m},$$

which, by taking $m$ sufficiently large ($a$ is $>1$), can be made as small as we please. We now have

$$e^{a^{m+n}(\theta+\phi)i} = e^{a^n\pi i(1+a_m)} = -(-1)^{a_m},$$

if $a$ be an odd integer, and

$$e^{a^{m+n}\theta i} = e^{a^n i(x+\pi a_m)} = (-1)^{a_m}e^{a^n xi}.$$

Hence

$$\frac{e^{a^{m+n}(\theta+\phi)i} - e^{a^{m+n}\theta i}}{\phi} = -(-1)^{a_m}\frac{1+e^{a^n xi}}{\pi-x}a^m,$$

and therefore

$$\sum_{n=0}^{\infty} b^{m+n} \left\{ \frac{e^{a^{m+n}(\theta+\phi)i} - e^{a^{m+n}\theta i}}{\phi} \right\} = -(-1)^{a_m}\frac{a^m b^m}{\pi-x}\sum_{n=0}^{\infty} b^n(1+e^{a^n xi}).$$

The real part of the series on the right-hand side is

$$\sum_{n=0}^{\infty} b^n\{1+\cos a^n x\};$$

every term of this is positive and therefore, as the first term is $1+\cos x$, the real part

$$> 1+\cos x$$

$$> 1,$$

for $\cos x$ is not negative.   Also it is finite, for it is

$$< 2 \sum_{n=0}^{\infty} b^n$$

$$< \frac{2}{1-b}.$$

Moreover  $\qquad\qquad \frac{1}{2}\pi < \pi - x < \frac{3}{2}\pi,$

so that $\dfrac{\pi}{\pi - x}$ is positive and $> \dfrac{2}{3}$.   Hence

$$\sum_{n=0}^{\infty} b^{m+n} \left\{ \frac{e^{a^{m+n}(\theta+\phi)i} - e^{a^{m+n}\theta i}}{\phi} \right\} = -(-1)^{a_m} \frac{a^m b^m}{\pi} \frac{2}{3}\eta,$$

where $\eta$ is a finite complex quantity, the real part of which is positive and greater than unity.   We thus have

$$\frac{f(\theta+\phi)-f(\theta)}{\phi} = -(-1)^{a_m}(ab)^m \left[ \frac{2}{3}\frac{\eta}{\pi} + \gamma' \frac{1}{ab-1} \right],$$

where $|\gamma'| < 1$, and the real part of $\eta$ is positive and $> 1$.

Proceeding in 'the same way and taking

$$\frac{\theta-\chi}{\pi} = \frac{a_m - 1}{a^m},$$

so that  $\qquad\qquad\qquad \chi = \frac{\pi+x}{a^m},$

we find  $\qquad \frac{f(\theta-\chi)-f(\theta)}{\chi} = -(-1)^{a_m}(ab)^m \left[ \frac{2}{3}\frac{\eta_1}{\pi} + \gamma_1' \frac{1}{ab-1} \right]$

where $|\gamma_1'| < 1$ and the real part of $\eta_1$, a finite complex quantity, is positive and greater than unity.

If now we take  $\qquad\qquad\qquad ab - 1 > \frac{3}{2}\pi,$

the real parts of  $\qquad\qquad \frac{2}{3}\frac{\eta}{\pi} + \gamma' \frac{1}{ab-1}$, say of $\zeta$,

and of  $\qquad\qquad\qquad \frac{2}{3}\frac{\eta_1}{\pi} + \gamma_1' \frac{1}{ab-1}$, say of $\zeta_1$,

are both positive and different from zero.   Then, since

$$\frac{f(\theta+\phi)-f(\theta)}{\phi} = -(-1)^{a_m}(ab)^m \zeta,$$

and  $\qquad\qquad \frac{f(\theta-\chi)-f(\theta)}{-\chi} = (-1)^{a_m}(ab)^m \zeta_1,$

$m$ being at present any positive integer, we have the right-hand sides essentially different quantities, because the real part of the first is of sign opposite to the real part of the second.

Now let $m$ be indefinitely increased; then $\phi$ and $\chi$ are infinitesimal quantities which ultimately vanish; and the limit of $\frac{1}{\phi}[f(\theta+\phi)-f(\theta)]$ for $\phi=0$ is a complex infinite quantity with its real part opposite in sign to the real part of the complex infinite quantity which is the limit of $\frac{1}{-\chi}[f(\theta-\chi)-f(\theta)]$ for $\chi=0$.   If $f(\theta)$ had a differential coefficient, these two limits would be equal: hence $f(\theta)$ *has not, for any value of* $\theta$, *a determinate differential coefficient.*

From this result, a remarkable inference relating to real functions may be at once derived. The real part of $f(\theta)$ is

$$\sum_{n=0}^{\infty} b^n \cos(a^n\theta),$$

which is a series converging uniformly and unconditionally. The real parts of

$$-(-1)^{a_m}(ab)^m\zeta$$

and of $+(-1)^{a_m}(ab)^m\zeta_1$

are the corresponding magnitudes for the series of real quantities : and they are of opposite signs. Hence for no value of $\theta$ has the series

$$\sum_{n=0}^{\infty} b^n \cos(a^n\theta)$$

a determinate differential coefficient, that is, we can choose an increase $\phi$ and a decrease $\chi$ of $\theta$, both being made as small as we please and ultimately zero, such that the limits of the expressions

$$\frac{f(\theta+\phi)-f(\theta)}{\phi}, \quad \frac{f(\theta-\chi)-f(\theta)}{-\chi}$$

are different from one another, provided $a$ be an odd integer and $ab > 1+\frac{3}{2}\pi$.

The chief interest of the above investigation lies in its application to functions of real variables, continuity in the value of which is thus shewn not necessarily to imply the existence of a determinate differential coefficient defined in the ordinary way. The application is due to Weierstrass, as has already been stated. Further discussions will be found in a paper by Wiener, *Crelle*, t. xc, (1881), pp. 221—252, in a remark by Weierstrass, *Ges. Werke*, t. ii, p. 229, and in a paper by Lerch, *Crelle*, t. ciii, (1888), pp. 126—138, who constructs other examples of continuous functions of real variables; and an example of a continuous function without a derivative is given by Schwarz, *Ges. Werke*, t. ii, pp. 269—274.

The simplest classes of ordinary functions are characterised by the properties :—

(i)    Within some region of the plane of the variable they are uniform, finite, and continuous :

(ii)   At all points within that region (but not necessarily on its boundary) they have a differential coefficient :

(iii)  When the variable is real, the number of maximum values and the number of minimum values within any given range is finite.

The function $\sum_{n=0}^{\infty} b^n \cos(a^n\theta)$, suggested by Weierstrass, possesses the first but not the second of these properties. Köpcke (*Math. Ann.*, t. xxix, pp. 123—140) gives an example of a function which possesses the first and the second but not the third of these properties.

**84.** In each of the distinct portions $A_1, A_2, \ldots$ of the complete region of continuity of a series of functions, the series can be represented by a monogenic analytic function, the elements of which are converging power-series. But the equivalence of the function-series and the monogenic analytic function for any portion $A_1$ is limited to that region. When the monogenic analytic function can be continued from $A_1$ into $A_2$, the continuation is not necessarily the same as the monogenic analytic function which is the equivalent of the series $\sum\limits_{s=1}^{\infty} f_s(z)$ in $A_2$. Hence, if the monogenic analytic functions for the two portions $A_1$ and $A_2$ be different, the function-series represents different functions in the distinct parts of its region of continuity.

A simple example will be an effective indication of the actual existence of such variety of representation in particular cases; that, which follows, is due to Tannery*.

Let $a$, $b$, $c$ be any three constants; then the fraction

$$\frac{a + bcz^m}{1 + bz^m},$$

when $m$ is infinite, is equal to $a$ if $|z| < 1$, and is equal to $c$ if $|z| > 1$.

Let $m_0$, $m_1$, $m_2$, ... be any set of positive integers arranged in ascending order and be such that the limit of $m_n$, when $n = \infty$, is infinite. Then, since

$$\frac{a + bcz^{m_n}}{1 + bz^{m_n}} = \frac{a + bcz^{m_0}}{1 + bz^{m_0}} + \sum_{i=1}^{n} \left\{ \frac{a + bcz^{m_i}}{1 + bz^{m_i}} - \frac{a + bcz^{m_{i-1}}}{1 + bz^{m_{i-1}}} \right\}$$

$$= \frac{a + bcz^{m_0}}{1 + bz^{m_0}} + b(c - a) \sum_{i=1}^{n} \left\{ \frac{(z^{m_i - m_{i-1}} - 1) z^{m_{i-1}}}{(1 + bz^{m_i})(1 + bz^{m_{i-1}})} \right\},$$

*the function $\phi(z)$, defined by the equation*

$$\phi(z) = \frac{a + bcz^{m_0}}{1 + bz^{m_0}} + b(c - a) \sum_{i=1}^{\infty} \left\{ \frac{(z^{m_i - m_{i-1}} - 1) z^{m_{i-1}}}{(1 + bz^{m_i})(1 + bz^{m_{i-1}})} \right\},$$

*converges uniformly to a value $a$ if $|z| \leqslant \rho < 1$, and converges uniformly to a value $c$ if $|z| \geqslant \rho' > 1$.* But if $|z| = 1$, the value to which the series tends depends upon the argument of $z$: the series cannot be said to converge for values of $z$ such that $|z| = 1$.

The simplest case occurs when $b = -1$ and $m_i = 2^i$; then, denoting the function by $\phi(z)$, we have

$$\phi(z) = \frac{a - cz}{1 - z} + (a - c) \sum_{i=0}^{\infty} \frac{z^{2^i}}{z^{2^{i+1}} - 1}$$

$$= \frac{a - cz}{1 - z} + (a - c) \left\{ \frac{z}{z^2 - 1} + \frac{z^2}{z^4 - 1} + \frac{z^4}{z^8 - 1} + \dots \right\},$$

that is, the function $\phi(z)$ is equal to $a$ if $|z| < 1$, and it is equal to $c$ if

$$|z| > 1.$$

---

* It is contained in a letter of Tannery's to Weierstrass, who communicated it to the Berlin Academy in 1881, *Ges. Werke*, t. ii, pp. 231—233. A similar series, which indeed is equivalent to the special form of $\phi(z)$, was given by Schröder, *Schlöm. Zeitschrift*, t. xxii, (1876), p. 184; and Pringsheim, *Math. Ann.*, t. xxii, (1883), p. 110, remarks that it can be deduced, without material modifications, from an expression given by Seidel, *Crelle*, t. lxxiii, (1871), pp. 297—299.

When $|z| = 1$, the function can have any value whatever. Hence a circle of radius unity is a line of singularities, that is, it is a line of discontinuity for the series. The circle evidently has the property of dividing the plane into two parts such that *the analytical expression represents different functions in the two parts.*

If we introduce a new variable $\zeta$ connected with $z$ by the relation*

$$\zeta = \frac{1 + z}{1 - z},$$

then, if $\zeta = \xi + i\eta$ and $z = x + iy$, we have

$$\xi = \frac{1 - x^2 - y^2}{(1 - x)^2 + y^2},$$

so that $\xi$ is positive when $|z| < 1$, and $\xi$ is negative when $|z| > 1$. If then

$$\phi(z) = \chi(\zeta),$$

the function $\chi(\zeta)$ is equal to $a$ or to $c$ according as the real part of $\zeta$ is positive or negative.

And, generally if we take $\zeta$ a rational function of $z$ and denote the modified form of $\phi(\zeta)$, which will be a sum of rational functions of $z$, by $\phi_1(z)$, then $\phi_1(z)$ will be equal to $a$ in some parts of the plane and to $c$ in other parts of the plane. The boundaries between these parts are lines of singular points: and they are constituted by the $z$-curves which correspond to $|\zeta| = 1$.

**85.** Now let $F(z)$ and $G(z)$ be two functions of $z$ with any number of singularities in the plane: it is possible to construct a function which shall be equal to $F(z)$ within a circle centre the origin and to $G(z)$ without the circle, the circumference being a line of singularities. For, when we make $a = 1$ and $c = 0$ in $\phi(z)$ of § 84, the function

$$\theta(z) = \frac{1}{1 - z} + \frac{z}{z^2 - 1} + \frac{z^2}{z^4 - 1} + \frac{z^4}{z^8 - 1} + \dots$$

is unity for all points within the circle and is zero for all points without it: and therefore

$$G(z) + \{F(z) - G(z)\}\, \theta(z)$$

is a function which has the required property.

Similarly $\qquad F_3(z) + \{F_1(z) - F_2(z)\}\, \theta(z) + \{F_2(z) - F_3(z)\}\, \theta\left(\dfrac{z}{r}\right)$

is a function which has the value $F_1(z)$ within a circle of radius unity, the value $F_2(z)$ between a circle of radius unity and a concentric circle of radius $r$ greater than unity, and the value $F_3(z)$ without the latter circle. All the singularities of the functions $F_1, F_2, F_3$ are singularities of the function thus represented: and it has, in addition to these, the two lines of singularities given by the circles.

---

\* The significance of a relation of this form will be discussed in Chapter XIX.

Again,
$$G\,(z)+\{F\,(z)-G\,(z)\}\,\theta\left(\frac{z-1}{z+1}\right)$$

is a function of $z$, which is equal to $F(z)$ on the positive side of the axis of $y$, and is equal to $G(z)$ on the negative side of that axis.

Also, if we take
$$\zeta e^{-ia_1}-p_1=\frac{1+z}{1-z},$$

where $a_1$ and $p_1$ are real constants, as an equation defining a new variable $\xi+i\eta$, we have
$$\xi\cos a_1+\eta\sin a_1-p_1=\frac{1-x^2-y^2}{(1-x)^2+y^2},$$

so that the two regions of the $z$-plane determined by $|z|<1$ and $|z|>1$ correspond to the two regions of the $\zeta$-plane into which the line $\xi\cos a_1+\eta\sin a_1-p_1=0$ divides it.   Let
$$\theta\,(z)=\theta\left(\frac{\zeta e^{-ia_1}-p_1-1}{\zeta e^{-ia_1}-p_1+1}\right)$$
$$=\theta_1\,(\zeta),$$

so that on the positive side of the line $\xi\cos a_1+\eta\sin a_1-p_1=0$ the function $\theta_1$ is unity and on the negative side of that line it is zero.   Take any three lines defined by $a_1,\ p_1;\ a_2,\ p_2;\ a_3,\ p_3$ respectively ; then

$$\tfrac{1}{2}\{-F+F\,(\theta_1+\theta_2+\theta_3)\}$$

is a function which has the value $F$ within the triangle, the value $-F$ in three of the spaces without it, and the value zero in the remaining three spaces without it, as indicated in the figure (fig. 13).

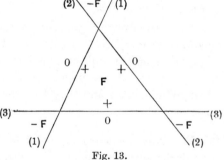

Fig. 13.

And for every division of the plane by lines, into which a circle can be transformed by rational equations, as will be explained when conformal representation is discussed hereafter, there is a possibility of representing discontinuous functions, by expressions similar to those just given.

These examples are sufficient to lead to the following result\*, which is complementary to the theorem of § 82 :—

*When the region of continuity of an infinite series of functions consists of several distinct parts, the series represents a single function in each part but it does not necessarily represent the same function in different parts.*

It thus appears that an analytical expression of given form, which converges uniformly and unconditionally in different parts of the plane separated from one another, can represent different functions of the variable in those different parts; and hence *the idea of monogenic functionality of a complex variable is not coextensive with the idea of functional dependence expressible through arithmetical operations,* a distinction first established by Weierstrass.

**86.**   We have seen that an analytic function has not a definite value at an essential singularity and that, therefore, every essential singularity is excluded from the region of definition of the function.

---

\* Weierstrass, *Ges. Werke*, t. ii, p. 221.

Again, it has appeared that not merely must single points be on occasion excluded from the region of definition but also that functions exist with continuous lines of essential singularities which must therefore be excluded. One method for the construction of such functions has just been indicated: but it is possible to obtain other analytical expressions for functions which possess what may be called a *singular line*. Thus let a function have a circle of radius $c$ as a line of essential singularity*; let it have no other singularities in the plane and let its zeros be $a_1, a_2, a_3, ...$, supposed arranged in such order that, if $\rho_n e^{i\theta_n} = a_n$, then

$$|\rho_n - c| \geqslant |\rho_{n+1} - c|,$$

so that the limit of $\rho_n$, when $n$ is infinite, is $c$.

Let $c_n = c e^{i\theta_n}$, a point on the singular circle, corresponding to $a_n$ which is assumed not to lie on it. Then, proceeding as in Weierstrass's theory in § 51, if

$$G(z) = \prod_{n=1}^{n=\infty} \left\{ \frac{z - a_n}{z - c_n} e^{g_n(z)} \right\},$$

where $\quad g_n(z) = \dfrac{a_n - c_n}{z - c_n} + \dfrac{1}{2}\left(\dfrac{a_n - c_n}{z - c_n}\right)^2 + ... + \dfrac{1}{m_n - 1}\left(\dfrac{a_n - c_n}{z - c_n}\right)^{m_n - 1},$

$G(z)$ is a uniform function, continuous everywhere in the plane except along the circumference of the circle which may be a line of essential singularities.

Special simpler forms can be derived according to the character of the series of quantities constituted by $|a_n - c_n|$. If there be a finite integer $m$, such that $\sum_{n=1}^{\infty} |a_n - c_n|^m$ is a converging series, then in $g_n(z)$ only the first $m-1$ terms need be retained.

*Ex.* Construct the function when

$$a_n = \left(1 - \frac{1}{n^r}\right) e^{\frac{2m\pi i}{n}},$$

$m$ being a given positive integer and $r$ a positive quantity.

Again, the point $c_n$ was associated with $a_n$ so that they have the same argument: but this distribution of points on the circle is not necessary, and it can be made in any manner which satisfies the condition that in the limited case just quoted the series $\sum_{n=1}^{\infty} |a_n - c_n|^m$ is a converging series.

Singular lines of other classes, for example, *sections*† in connection with functions defined by integrals, arise in connection with analytical functions. They are discussed by Painlevé, *Sur les lignes singulières des fonctions analytiques*, (Thèse, Gauthier-Villars, Paris, 1887).

*Ex.* 1. Shew that, if the zeros of a function be the points

$$A = \frac{b + c - (a - d)i}{a + d + (b - c)i},$$

---

* This investigation is due to Picard, *Comptes Rendus*, t. xci, (1881), pp. 690—692.
† Called *coupures* by Hermite; see § 103.

where $a$, $b$, $c$, $d$ are integers satisfying the condition $ad - bc = 1$, so that the function has a circle of radius unity for an essential singular line, then if

$$B = \frac{b + di}{d + bi},$$

the function

$$\Pi \left\{ \frac{z - A}{z - B} e^{\frac{A-B}{z-B}} \right\},$$

where the product extends to all positive integers subject to the foregoing condition $ad - bc = 1$, is a uniform function finite for all points in the plane not lying on the circle of radius unity. (Picard.)

*Ex.* 2. Examine the character of the distribution of points $z_n$ in the plane of $z$ which are given by

$$z_n = \left( 1 + \frac{1}{n} \right) e^{\sqrt{2}n\pi i}, \qquad (n = 1, 2, 3, \ldots).$$

Consider especially the neighbourhood of the circle whose centre is the origin and whose radius is 1.

Shew that

$$\sum_{n=1}^{\infty} \frac{1}{n^2 (z_r - z)}$$

represents a monogenic function of $z$ at all points within the circle; and investigate the possibility of an analytical continuation of this function beyond the circle.

(Math. Trip., Part II., 1896.)

**87.** In the earlier examples, instances were given of functions which have only isolated points for their essential singularities: and, in the latter examples, instances have been given of functions which have lines of essential singularities, that is, there are continuous lines for which the functions do not exist. We now proceed to shew how functions can be constructed which do not exist in assigned continuous spaces in the plane. Weierstrass was the first to draw attention to *lacunary* functions, as they may be called; the following investigation in illustration of Weierstrass's theorem is due to Poincaré*.

Take any convex curve in the plane, say $C$: and consider a function-series of the form

$$\phi(z) = \sum_{n=0}^{\infty} \frac{A_n}{z - b_n},$$

where the constants $A_n$ and $b_n$ are subject to the conditions

(i)　　The series $\sum_{n=0}^{\infty} A_n$ converges unconditionally:

(ii)　　Each of the points $b_n$ is either within or upon the curve $C$:

(iii)　　When any arc whatever of $C$ is taken, as small as we please, that arc contains an unlimited number of the points $b_n$.

* *Acta Soc. Fenn.*, t. xii, (1883), pp. 341—350; *Amer. Journ. Math.*, t. xiv, (1892),

It will be seen that, for values of $z$ outside $C$, $\phi(z)$ is represented by a power-series, which cannot be continued across the curve $C$ into the interior, and which therefore has the area of $C$ for a lacunary space.

Let $S$ denote the sum of the converging series $\sum\limits_{n=0}^{\infty} |A_n|$: then denoting by $\kappa$ any assigned quantity, as small as we please, an integer $p$ can always be determined so that

$$S_p = \sum_{n=p}^{\infty} |A_n| < \kappa.$$

Consider the function-series in the vicinity of any point $c$ outside $C$. Let $R$ denote the distance of $c$ from the nearest point of the boundary* of $C$, so that $R$ is a finite non-vanishing quantity; and draw a circle of radius $R$ and centre $c$, which thus touches $C$ externally. Thus for all the points $b$ except at the point of contact, we have

$$|b_n - c| > R.$$

Let $z$ be any point within the circle, so that

$$|z - c| < R$$
$$= \theta R,$$

say, where $\theta$ is a positive quantity less than 1. Then

$$|z - b_n| \geqslant |b_n - c| - |z - c|$$
$$\geqslant R(1 - \theta);$$

and therefore

$$\left| \frac{A_n}{z - b_n} \right| \leqslant \frac{|A_n|}{R(1 - \theta)}.$$

Consequently

$$\sum_{n=0}^{\infty} \left| \frac{A_n}{z - b_n} \right| \leqslant \sum_{n=0}^{\infty} \frac{|A_n|}{R(1 - \theta)} \leqslant \frac{S}{R(1 - \theta)},$$

so that the function-series converges unconditionally. Also

$$\left| \sum_{n=m}^{\infty} \frac{A_n}{z - b_n} \right| \leqslant \sum_{n=m}^{\infty} \frac{|A_n|}{|z - b_n|}$$

$$\leqslant \frac{\kappa}{R(1 - \theta)},$$

and therefore the function-series converges uniformly: that is,

$$\sum_{n=0}^{\infty} \frac{A_n}{z - b_n}$$

* This will be either the shortest normal from $c$ to the boundary, or the distance of $c$ from some point of abrupt change of direction, as for instance at the angular point of a polygon; for brevity of description we shall assume the former to be the case.

converges uniformly and unconditionally within any circle concentric with the circle of radius $R$ and lying within it. Accordingly, by Weierstrass's investigation (§§ 82, 83), this is expressible in the form of a converging series $P(z-c)$; manifestly

$$P(z-c) = -\sum_{m=0}^{\infty}\sum_{n=0}^{\infty} \frac{A_n}{(b_n-c)^{m+1}}(z-c)^m.$$

We have

$$\left| \frac{A_n}{(b_n-c)^{m+1}}(z-c)^m \right| = \frac{|A_n|\,\theta^m R^m}{|b_n-c|^{m+1}}$$

$$< \frac{|A_n|\,\theta^m}{R};$$

and therefore

$$\sum_{m=0}^{\infty}\sum_{n=0}^{\infty}\left| \frac{A_n}{(b_n-c)^{m+1}}(z-c)^m \right| < \frac{1}{R}\sum_{m=0}^{\infty}\sum_{n=0}^{\infty}|A_n|\,\theta^m$$

$$< \frac{S}{R(1-\theta)},$$

that is, the series $P(z-c)$ converges unconditionally. Let $C_m$ denote $\sum_{n=0}^{\infty} A_n (b_n-c)^{-m-1}$; then

$$P(z-c) = -\sum_{m=0}^{\infty} C_m (z-c)^m.$$

The point $c$ is any arbitrarily chosen point outside the curve $C$; and therefore the function represented by $\phi(z)$ for points $z$ outside the curve $C$ is a uniform analytic function.

Any power-series representing this function can be used as an element for continuation outside $C$ and away from $C$: we proceed to prove that *it cannot be continued across the boundary of $C$*. If this were possible, it would arise through the construction of the domain of some point $z_0$, where $z_0$ is a point outside $C$ (say within such a circle as the above, centre $c$), and where the circle bounding the domain of $z_0$ would cut off some arc from the boundary of $C$. The preceding analysis shews that, in the domain of $z_0$, the function is represented by a power-series

$$Q(z-z_0) = -\sum_{m=0}^{\infty} B_m (z-z_0)^m,$$

where

$$B_m = \sum_{n=0}^{\infty} A_n (b_n - z_0)^{-m-1}:$$

it must be shewn that the series diverges for points $z$ within $C$.

In the first place, consider the series $P(z-c)$; in order that it may converge, only such values of $z$ are admissible as make the limit of $C_m(z-c)^m$ zero, when $m$ is infinite. Let a point be taken on the circumference of the circle $C$ of radius $R$; then the above limit can only be zero if

$$\underset{m=\infty}{\mathrm{Lt}}\ C_m R^m = 0,$$

a condition that is not satisfied, as will now be proved. This circle touches $C$ externally; let the point of contact be a point $b_k$ (such a circle can always be constructed, by drawing the outward normal at a point $b$ and choosing some point $c$ upon it). Let any arbitrary quantity $\epsilon$ be assigned, as small as we please; and let an integer $p$ be chosen large enough to secure that

$$S_p < \tfrac{1}{2}\epsilon R,$$

this being possible because $S_p$, the remainder of the converging series $\Sigma\,|A_n|$, can (by choice of $p$) be made less than any assigned quantity. Either the chosen number $p$ is greater than $k$: or if it is less than $k$, then some other number $(> p)$ can be chosen so that it is greater than $k$: we may therefore assume $p > k$.

Draw a circle, centre $c$ and radius $R'$ greater than $R$, so as to include the point $b_k$, and exclude the points $b_0, \ldots, b_p$ with the exception of $b_k$. This can be done; for if

$$|b_k - b_{k-1}| > \lambda R, \qquad |b_k - b_{k+1}| > \lambda R,$$

where $\lambda$ is some positive quantity as small as we please (but not absolutely zero), we can take

$$R'^2 = R^2 + \lambda^2 R^2;$$

and then

$$|b_n - c| < R', \quad \text{for} \quad n = 0, 1, \ldots, k-1, k+1, \ldots, p.$$

Let $q$ denote a number sufficiently large to secure that

$$\frac{S}{R'}\left(\frac{R}{R'}\right)^q < \tfrac{1}{2}\epsilon.$$

Then as

$$C_q = \sum_{n=0}^{\infty} A_n (b_n - c)^{-q-1},$$

we have

$$C_q - A_k (b_k - c)^{-q-1} = \sum_{n=0}^{k-1} \frac{A_n}{(b_n - c)^{q+1}} + \sum_{n=k+1}^{p-1} \frac{A_n}{(b_n - c)^{q+1}} + \sum_{n=p}^{\infty} \frac{A_n}{(b_n - c)^{q+1}};$$

and therefore

$$|R^q\{C_q - A_k(b_k - c)^{-q-1}\}| < \sum_{n=0}^{k-1}\left|\frac{A_n R^q}{(b_n - c)^{q+1}}\right| + \sum_{n=k+1}^{p-1}\left|\frac{A_n R^q}{(b_n - c)^{q+1}}\right| + \sum_{n=p}^{\infty}\left|\frac{A_n R^q}{(b_n - c)^{q+1}}\right|$$

$$< \sum_{n=0}^{k-1}\frac{|A_n|}{R'}\left(\frac{R}{R'}\right)^q + \sum_{n=k+1}^{p-1}\frac{|A_n|}{R'}\left(\frac{R}{R'}\right)^q + \sum_{n=p}^{\infty}\frac{|A_n|}{R}$$

$$< \tfrac{1}{2}\frac{\epsilon}{S}\sum_{n=0}^{k-1}|A_n| + \tfrac{1}{2}\frac{\epsilon}{S}\sum_{n=k+1}^{p-1}|A_n| + \frac{S_p}{R}$$

$$< \tfrac{1}{2}\frac{\epsilon}{S}\{S - |A_k|\} + \tfrac{1}{2}\epsilon$$

$$< \epsilon,$$

a quantity arbitrarily assigned as small as we please.   Accordingly we have

$$\text{Limit}_{q=\infty} | R^q \{C_q - A_k (b_k - c)^{-q-1}\} | = 0,$$

that is,

$$\text{Limit}_{q=\infty} |C_q R^q| = \text{Limit}_{q=\infty} | A_k R^q (b_k - c)^{-q-1}| = \frac{|A_k|}{R},$$

so that $C_q R^q$ does not tend to zero when $q$ is infinitely large, as it should if $P(z - c)$ converges.   Thus $P(z - c)$ does not converge for points given by $|z - c| = R$.

Consider now the domain of $z_0$, assumed to include points within $C$ and therefore some arc of $C$; the function is represented throughout that domain by $Q(z - z_0)$.   On the included arc of $C$ take any one (say $b_k$) of the unlimited number of points $b$; at $b_k$ draw an outward normal to $C$ and choose a point $z_1$ on it such that the circle

$$|z - z_1| = |b_k - z_1|$$

lies wholly within the domain of $z_0$.   The function is represented by a power-series in $z - z_1$ throughout this circle; and as the circle lies wholly within the domain of $z_0$, the representation is included in $Q(z - z_0)$.   But, by the preceding investigation, the power-series does not converge on the circumference of the circle $|z - z_1| = |b_k - z_1|$: contradicting the supposition that $Q(z - z_0)$ converges in a domain of $z_0$ enclosing this circle.   Hence the power-series $P(z - c)$ cannot be continued across the boundary of $C$; in other words, the function represented by $P(z - c)$ and its continuations has the area of $C$ for a lacunary space.

The discussion of the significance (if any) of $\phi(z)$ for points $z$ within $C$ depends on the distribution of the points $b_n$ within $C$, as to which no hypothesis has been made.

As an example, take a convex polygon having $a_1, \ldots, a_p$ for its angular points; then any point

$$\frac{m_1 a_1 + \ldots + m_p a_p}{m_1 + \ldots + m_p},$$

where $m_1, \ldots, m_p$ are positive integers or zero (simultaneous zeros being excluded), is either within the polygon or on its boundary: and any rational point within the polygon or on its boundary can be represented by

$$\frac{\sum_{r=1}^{p} m_r a_r}{\sum_{r=1}^{p} m_r},$$

by proper choice of $m_1, \ldots, m_p$, a choice which can be made in an infinite number of ways.

Let $u_1, \ldots, u_p$ be given quantities, the modulus of each of which is less than unity: then the series

$$\sum_{0}^{\infty} u_1{}^{m_1} \ldots u_p{}^{m_p}$$

converges unconditionally.  Then all the assigned conditions are satisfied for the function

$$\Sigma \left\{ \frac{u_1{}^{m_1} \dots \dots u_p{}^{m_p}}{z - \dfrac{m_1 a_1 + \dots \dots + m_p a_p}{m_1 + \dots \dots + m_p}} \right\},$$

and therefore it is a function which converges uniformly and unconditionally everywhere outside the polygon and which has the polygonal space (including the boundary) for a lacunary space.

If, in particular, $p = 2$, we obtain a function which has the straight line joining $a_1$ and $a_2$ as a line of essential singularity.  When we take $a_1 = 0$, $a_2 = 1$, and slightly modify the summation, we obtain the function

$$\sum_{n=1}^{\infty} \sum_{m=0}^{n} \frac{u_1{}^m u_2{}^{n-m}}{z - \dfrac{m}{n}},$$

which, when $|u_1| < 1$ and $|u_2| < 1$, converges uniformly and unconditionally everywhere in the plane except at points between 0 and 1 on the axis of real quantities, this part of the axis being a line of essential singularity.

For the general case, the following remarks may be made :—

(i)   The quantities $u_1$, $u_2$, ... need not be the same for every term ; a numerator, quite different in form, might be chosen, such as $(m_1{}^2 + \dots + m_p{}^2)^{-\mu}$ where $2\mu > p$; all that is requisite is that the series, made up of the numerators, should converge unconditionally.

(ii)  The preceding is only a particular illustration, and is not necessarily the most general form of function having the assigned lacunary space.

It is evident that one mode of constructing a function, which shall have any assigned lacunary space, would begin by the formation of some expression which, by the variation of the constants it contains, can be made to represent indefinitely nearly any point within or on the contour of the space.   Thus for the space between two concentric circles, of radii $a$ and $c$ and centre the origin, we could take

$$\frac{m_1 a + (n - m_1)\, b\; e^{\frac{m_2}{n} 2\pi i}}{n},$$

which, by giving $m_1$ all values from 0 to $n$, $m_2$ all values from 0 to $n - 1$, and $n$ all values from 1 to infinity, will represent all rational points in the space : and a function, having the space between the circles as lacunary, would be given by

$$\sum_{n=1}^{\infty} \sum_{m_1=0}^{n} \sum_{m_2=0}^{n-1} \left[ \frac{u^n u_1{}^{m_1} u_2{}^{m_2}}{\left\{ z - \dfrac{m_1 a + (n - m_1)\, b\; e^{\frac{m_2}{n} 2\pi i}}{n} \right\}} \right],$$

provided $|u| < 1$, $|u_1| < 1$, $|u_2| < 1$.

In particular, if $a = b$, then the common circumference is a line of essential singularity for the corresponding function. It is easy to see that the function

$$\sum_{n=0}^{\infty} \sum_{m=0}^{2n-1} \frac{\overset{m}{u} \overset{n}{v}}{z - ae^{\frac{m}{n}\pi i}},$$

provided the series $\displaystyle\sum_{n=1}^{\infty} \sum_{m=0}^{2n-1} \overset{m}{u} \overset{n}{v}$

converges unconditionally, is a function having the circle $|z| = a$ as a line of essential singularity. It can be expressed as an analytic function within the circle, and as another analytic function without the circle.

Other examples will be found in memoirs by Goursat\*, Poincaré†, and Homén‡.

*Ex.* 1. Shew that the function

$$\sum_{m=-\infty}^{m=\infty} \sum_{n=-\infty}^{n=\infty} (m + nz)^{-2-r},$$

where $r$ is a real positive quantity and the summation is for all integers $m$ and $n$ between the positive and the negative infinities, is a uniform function in all parts of the plane except the axis of real quantities which is a line of essential singularity.

*Ex.* 2. Discuss the region in which the function

$$\sum_{n=1}^{\infty} \sum_{m=1}^{\infty} \sum_{p=1}^{\infty} \frac{n^{-2} m^{-2} p^{-2}}{z - \left(\frac{p}{n} + \frac{m}{n}i\right)}$$

is definite.                                                       (Homén.)

*Ex.* 3. Prove that the function

$$\sum_{n=0}^{\infty} 2^{-n} x^{3^{n}}$$

exists only within a circle of radius unity and centre the origin.           (Poincaré.)

*Ex.* 4. Prove that the series

$$\sum_{n=1}^{\infty} \frac{A_n}{z - a_n}$$

represents a uniform meromorphic function, if the quantities $|a_n|$ increase without limit as $n$ increases and if the series $|A_n / a_n|$ converges.

*Ex.* 5. An infinite number of points $a_1, a_2, a_3, \ldots\ldots$ are taken on the circumference of a given circle, centre the origin, so that they form the aggregate of rational points on the circumference. Shew that the series

$$\sum_{n=1}^{\infty} \frac{1}{n^3} \frac{z}{a_n - z}$$

can be expanded in a series of ascending powers of $z$ which converges for points within the circle, but that the function cannot be continued across the circumference of the circle.

                                                              (Stieltjes.)

---

\* *Comptes Rendus*, t. xciv, (1882), pp. 715—718 ; *Bulletin de Darboux*, 2$^{\text{me}}$ Sér., t. xi, (1887), pp. 109—114.

† In the memoirs, quoted p. 166, and *Comptes Rendus*, t. xcvi, (1883), pp. 1134—1136.

‡ *Acta Soc. Fenn.*, t. xii, (1883), pp. 445—464.

*Ex.* 6.   Prove that the infinite continued fraction

$$\frac{1}{a_1 z +}\ \frac{1}{a_2 +}\ \frac{1}{a_3 z +}\ \frac{1}{a_4 +}\ \ldots\ldots$$

converges for all values of $z$, provided the series

$$\sum_{n=1}^{\infty} a_n$$

diverges, the quantities $a$ being real. Discuss, in particular, the cases, (i) when $z$ has real positive values, (ii) when $z$ has real negative values.

(Stieltjes.)

*Ex.* 7.   Denoting by $\epsilon_n$ a positive quantity less than 1, prove that the infinite product

$$\prod_{n=1}^{\infty} \left\{ \left(1 - \frac{z}{n}\right) e^{\frac{z}{n}} \left(1 - \frac{z}{n + \epsilon_n}\right) e^{\frac{z}{n + \epsilon_n}} \right\}$$

converges ; and that the series

$$\sum_{n=1}^{\infty} \frac{1}{\epsilon_n} \left( \frac{1}{z - n - \epsilon_n} - \frac{1}{z - n} \right)$$

converges.

Shew that, if a new series be constructed by separating the two fractions in the single term so as to provide two terms, this new series does not converge when $\epsilon_n = n^{-3}$. Does the same consequence follow when $\epsilon_n = n^{-2}$?

(Borel.)

*Ex.* 8.   Prove that the series

$$\frac{2}{\pi} (z + z^{-1}) + \frac{2}{\pi} \sum_{-\infty}^{\infty} \sum_{-\infty}^{\infty} \left\{ \frac{z}{(1 - 2m - 2nzi)\,(2m + 2nzi)^2} \right\}$$

$$+ \frac{2}{\pi} \sum_{-\infty}^{\infty} \sum_{-\infty}^{\infty} \left\{ \frac{z^{-1}}{(1 - 2m - 2nz^{-1}i)\,(2m + 2nz^{-1}i)^2} \right\},$$

where the summation extends over all positive and negative integral values of $m$ and of $n$ except simultaneous zeros, converges uniformly and unconditionally for all points in the finite part of the plane which do not lie on the axis of $y$; and that it has the value $+1$ or $-1$, according as the real part of $z$ is positive or negative.

(Weierstrass.)

*Ex.* 9.   Prove that the region of continuity of the series

$$\sum_{n=0}^{\infty} \frac{1}{z^n + z^{-n}}$$

consists of two parts, separated by the circle $|z| = 1$ which is a line of infinities for the series: and that, in these two parts of the plane, it represents two different functions.

If two complex quantities $\omega$ and $\omega'$ be taken, such that $z = e^{-\frac{\omega' \pi}{\omega i}}$ and the real part of $\frac{\omega'}{\omega i}$ is positive, and if they be associated with the elliptic function $\wp(u)$ as its half-periods, then for values of $z$, which lie within the circle $|z| = 1$,

$$\sum_{n=0}^{\infty} \frac{1}{z^n + z^{-n}} = \frac{\omega}{2\pi} \frac{\sigma_3(\omega)}{\sigma(\omega)} + \tfrac{1}{4},$$

in the usual notation of Weierstrass's theory of elliptic functions.

Find the function which the series represents for values of $z$ without the circle $|z| = 1$.

(Weierstrass.)

*Ex.* 10. Discuss the descriptive properties of the functions represented by the expressions :

(i) $\int_0^\infty \dfrac{\cos zu}{1+u^2}\,du$, (ii) $\prod_1^\infty \left[1+\dfrac{1}{n^2(z-1)}\right]$, (iii) $\prod_1^\infty \left[1+\dfrac{1}{n^2(z^n-1)}\right]$, (iv) $\prod_1^\infty \dfrac{1+e^{2nz}}{1+e^{(2n-1)z}}$,

for all values of the complex argument $z$. (Math. Trip., Part II., 1893.)

*Ex.* 11. Four circles are drawn each of radius $\dfrac{1}{\sqrt 2}$ having their centres at the points $1, i, -1, -i$ respectively; the two parts of the plane, excluded by the four circumferences, are denoted the interior and the exterior parts. Shew that the function

$$\sum_{n=1}^{n=\infty} \frac{\sin\frac14 n\pi}{2^{\frac12 n} n}\left\{\frac{1}{(1-z)^n}+\frac{1}{(1+iz)^n}+\frac{1}{(1+z)^n}+\frac{1}{(1-iz)^n}\right\}$$

is equal to $\pi$ in the interior part and is zero in the exterior part. (Appell.)

*Ex.* 12. Obtain the values of the function

$$\sum_{n=1}^{n=\infty} \frac{1-(-1)^n}{n}\left\{(\tfrac12 z)^n-\frac{1}{(z+1)^n}-\frac{1}{(z-1)^n}\right\}$$

in the two parts of the area within a circle centre the origin and radius 2 which lie without two circles of radius unity, having their centres at the points 1 and $-1$ respectively. (Appell.)

*Ex.* 13. If $\qquad\qquad f(z)=U_1+U_2+\ldots\ldots+U_n,$

and $\qquad U_m=F_m(z)-\dfrac{1}{z-a_m}+(z-a_m-1)\left\{\dfrac{1}{(z-a_m)^2}+\dfrac{1}{(z-a_m)^3}+\ldots\ldots\right\},$

where the regions of continuity of the functions $F$ extend over the whole plane, then $f(z)$ is a function existing everywhere except within the circles of radius unity described round the points $a_1, a_2, \ldots\ldots, a_n$. (Teixeira.)

*Ex.* 14. Let there be $n$ circles having the origin for a common centre, and let $C_1, C_2, \ldots\ldots, C_n, C_{n+1}$ be $n+1$ arbitrary constants; also let $a_1, a_2, \ldots\ldots, a_n$ be any $n$ points lying respectively on the circumferences of the first, the second, $\ldots\ldots$, the $n$th circles. Shew that the expression

$$\frac{1}{2\pi}\int_0^{2\pi}\left(\frac{C_1}{ze^{i\theta}}+\frac{C_2-C_1}{ze^{i\theta}-a_1}+\ldots\ldots+\frac{C_{n+1}-C_n}{ze^{i\theta}-a_n}\right)ze^{i\theta}\,d\theta$$

has the value $C_m$ for points $z$ lying between the $(m-1)$th and the $m$th circles, and the value $C_{n+1}$ for points lying without the $n$th circle.

Construct a function which shall have any assigned values in the various bands into which the plane is divided by the circles. (Pincherle.)

*Ex.* 15. Examine the nature of the functions defined by the series

(i) $\displaystyle\sum_{n=1}^{\infty}\frac{(z^2-a^2)^n}{2(z-a)^{2n}-5(z^2-a^2)^n+2(z+a)^{2n}}$,

(ii) $\displaystyle\sum_{n=1}^{\infty}\frac{(z^2-a^2)^n}{(z-a)^{2n}+2(z+a)^{2n}}$,

where $a$ is a real positive constant. (Math. Trip., Part II., 1897.)

**88.** In § 32 it was remarked that the discrimination of the various species of essential singularities could be effected by means of the properties of the function in the immediate vicinity of the point.

Now it was proved, in § 63, that in the vicinity of an isolated essential singularity $b$ the function could be represented by an expression of the form

$$G\left(\frac{1}{z-b}\right) + P(z-b)$$

for all points in the space without a circle centre $b$ of small radius and within a concentric circle of radius not large enough to include singularities at a finite distance from $b$. Because the essential singularity at $b$ is isolated, the radius of the inner circle can be diminished to be all but infinitesimal: the series $P(z-b)$ is then unimportant compared with $G\left(\frac{1}{z-b}\right)$, which can be regarded as characteristic for the singularity of the function.

Another method of obtaining a function, which is characteristic of the singularity, is provided by § 68. It was there proved that, in the vicinity of an essential singularity $a$, the function could be represented by an expression of the form

$$(z-a)^n H\left(\frac{1}{z-a}\right) Q(z-a),$$

where, within a circle of centre $a$ and radius not sufficiently large to include the nearest singularity at a finite distance from $a$, the function $Q(z-a)$ is finite and has no zeros: all the zeros of the given function within this circle (except such as are absorbed into the essential singularity at $a$) are zeros of the factor $H\left(\frac{1}{z-a}\right)$, and the integer-index $n$ is affected by the number of these zeros. When the circle is made small, the function

$$(z-a)^n H\left(\frac{1}{z-a}\right)$$

can be regarded as characteristic of the immediate vicinity of $a$ or, more briefly, as characteristic of $a$.

It is easily seen that the two characteristic functions are distinct. For if $F$ and $F_1$ be two functions, which have essential singularities at $a$ of the same kind as determined by the first characteristic, then

$$F(z) - F_1(z) = P(z-a) - P_1(z-a)$$
$$= P_2(z-a),$$

while if their singularities at $a$ be of the same kind as determined by the second characteristic, then

$$\frac{F(z)}{F_1(z)} = \frac{Q(z-a)}{Q_1(z-a)} = Q_2(z-a)$$

in the immediate vicinity of $a$, since $Q_1$ has no zeros.   Two such equations cannot subsist simultaneously, except in one instance.

Without entering into detailed discussion, the results obtained in the preceding chapters are sufficient to lead to an indication of the classification of singularities*.

Singularities are said to be of the *first class* when they are accidental; and a function is said to be of the first class when all its singularities are of the first class.   It can, by § 48, have only a finite number of such singularities, each singularity being isolated.

It is for this case alone that the two characteristic functions are in accord.

When a function, otherwise of the first class, fails to satisfy the last condition, solely owing to failure of finiteness of multiplicity at some point, say at $z = \infty$, then that point ceases to be an accidental singularity.   It has been called (§ 32) an essential singularity; it belongs to the simplest kind of essential singularity; and it is called a singularity of the *second class*.

A function is said to be of the second class when it has some singularities of the second class; it may possess singularities of the first class.   By an argument similar to that adopted in § 48, a function of the second class can have only a limited number of singularities of the second class, each singularity being isolated.

When a function, otherwise of the second class, fails to satisfy the last condition solely owing to unlimited condensation at some point, say at $z = \infty$, of singularities of the second class, that point ceases to be a singularity of the second class: it is called a singularity (necessarily essential) of the *third class*.

A function is said to be of the third class when it has some singularities of the third class; it may possess singularities of the first and the second classes.   But it can have only a limited number of singularities of the third class, each singularity being isolated.

Proceeding in this gradual sequence, we obtain an unlimited number of classes of singularities: and functions of the various classes can be constructed by means of the theorems which have been proved.   A function of class $n$ has a limited number of singularities of class $n$, each singularity being isolated, and any number of singularities of lower classes which, except in so far as they are absorbed in the singularities of class $n$, are isolated points.

---

* For a detailed discussion, reference should be made to Guichard, *Théorie des points singuliers essentiels* (Thèse, Gauthier-Villars, Paris, 1883), who gives adequate references to the investigations of Mittag-Leffler in the introduction of the classification and to the researches of Cantor.  See also Mittag-Leffler, *Acta Math.*, t. iv, (1884), pp. 1—79 ; Cantor, *Crelle*, t. lxxxiv, (1878), pp. 242—258, *Acta Math.*, t. ii, (1883), pp. 311—328.

The effective limit of this sequence of classes is attained when the number of the class increases beyond any integer, however large. When once such a limit is attained, we have functions with essential singularities of unlimited class, each singularity being isolated ; when we pass to functions which have their essential singularities no longer isolated but, as in previous class-developments, of infinite condensation, it is necessary to add to the arrangement in classes an arrangement in a wider group, say, in species*.

Calling, then, all the preceding classes of functions functions of the first species, we may, after Guichard (l.c.), construct, by the theorems already proved, a function which has at the points $a_1$, $a_2$, ... singularities of classes 1, 2, .. , both series being continued to infinity. Such a function is called a function of the second species.

By a combination of classes in species, this arrangement can be continued indefinitely ; each species will contain an infinitely increasing number of classes; and when an unlimited number of species is ultimately obtained, another wider group must be introduced.

This gradual construction, relative to essential singularities, can be carried out without limit; the singularities are the characteristics of the functions.

* Guichard (l.c.) uses the term *genre*.

# CHAPTER VIII.

## Multiform Functions.

**89.** Having now discussed some of the more important general properties of uniform functions, we proceed to discuss some of the properties of multiform functions.

Deviations from uniformity in character may arise through various causes: the most common is the existence of those points in the $z$-plane, which have already (§ 12) been defined as branch-points.

As an example, consider the two power-series

$$u = 1 - \tfrac{1}{2}z' - \tfrac{1}{8}z'^2 - \dots, \qquad v = -(1 - \tfrac{1}{2}z' - \tfrac{1}{8}z'^2 - \dots),$$

which, for points in the plane such that $|z'|$ is less than unity, are the two values of $(1 - z')^{\frac{1}{2}}$; they may be regarded as representing the two branches of the function $w$, say $w_1$ and $w_2$, defined by the equation

$$w^2 = 1 - z' = z.$$

Let $z'$ describe a small curve (say a circle of radius $r$) round the point $z' = 1$, beginning on the axis of $x$; the point 1 is the origin for $z$. Then $z$ is $r$ initially, and at the end of the first description of the circle $z$ is $re^{2\pi i}$. The branch of the function, which initially is equal to $u$, changes continuously during the description of the circle. The series for $u$, and the continuations of that series, give rise to the complete variation of the branch of the function which originally is $u$. Its initial value is $r^{\frac{1}{2}}$, and its final value is $r^{\frac{1}{2}}e^{\pi i}$, that is, $-r^{-\frac{1}{2}}$; so that the final value of the branch is $v$. Similarly for the branch of the function, which initially is equal to $v$; it is continuously changed during the description of the circle; the series for $v$, and the continuations of that series, give rise to the complete variation of the branch of the function which originally is $v$; and the branch acquires $u$ as its final value. Thus the effect of the single circuit is to change $w_1$ into $w_2$ and $w_2$ into $w_1$, that is, the effect of a circuit round the point, at which $w_1$ and $w_2$ coincide in value, is to interchange the values of the two branches.

If, however, $z$ describe a circuit which does not include the branch-point, $w_1$ and $w_2$ return each to its initial value.

Instances have already occurred, e.g. integrals of uniform functions, in which a variation in the path of the variable has made a difference in the result; but this interchange of value is distinct from any of the effects produced by points belonging to the families of critical points which have been considered. The critical point is of a new nature; it is, in fact, a characteristic of multiform functions at certain associated points.

We now proceed to indicate more generally the character of the relation of such points to functions affected by them.

The method of constructing a monogenic analytic function, described in § 34, by forming all the continuations of a power-series, regarded as a given initial element of the function, leads to the aggregate of the elements of the function and determines its region of continuity. When the process of continuation has been completely carried out, two distinct cases may occur.

In the first case, the function is such that any and every path, leading from one point $a$ to another point $z$ by the construction of a series of successive domains of points along the path, gives a single value at $z$ as the continuation of one initial value at $a$. When, therefore, there is only a single value of the function at $a$, the process of continuation leads to only a single value of the function at any other point in the plane. The function is uniform throughout its region of continuity. The detailed properties of such functions have been considered in the preceding chapters.

In the second case, the function is such that different paths, leading from $a$ to $z$, do not give a single value at $z$ as the continuation of one and the same initial value at $a$. There are different sets of elements of the function, associated with different sets of consecutive domains of points on paths from $a$ to $z$, which lead to different values of the function at $z$; but any change in a path from $a$ to $z$ does not necessarily cause a change in the value of the function at $z$. The function is multiform in its region of continuity. The detailed properties of such functions will now be considered.

**90.** In order that the process of continuation may be completely carried out, continuations must be effected, beginning at the domain of any point $a$ and proceeding to the domain of any other point $b$ by all possible paths in the region of continuity, and they must be effected for all points $a$ and $b$. Continuations must be effected, beginning in the domain of every point $a$ and returning to that domain by all possible closed paths in the region of continuity. When they are effected from the domain of one point $a$ to that of another point $b$, all the values at any point $z$ in the domain of $a$ (and not merely a single value at such points) must be continued: and similarly when they are effected, beginning in the domain of $a$ and returning to that domain. The complete region of the plane will then be obtained in which the function can be represented by a series of positive integral powers: and the boundary of that region will be indicated.

In the first instance, let the boundary of the region be constituted by a
number, either finite or infinite, of
isolated points, say $L_1$, $L_2$, $L_3$, ....
Take any point $A$ in the region, so
that its distance from any of the
points $L$ is not infinitesimal; and
in the region draw a closed path
$ABC...EFA$ so as to enclose one
point, say $L_1$, but only one point, of
the boundary and to have no point

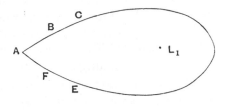

Fig. 14.

of the curve at a merely infinitesimal distance from $L_1$.  Let such curves be
drawn, beginning and ending at $A$, so that each of them encloses one and
only one of the points of the boundary: and let $K_r$ be the curve which
encloses the point $L_r$.

Let $w_1$ be one of the power-series defining the function in a domain with
its centre at $A$ : let this series be continued along each of the curves $K_s$ by
successive domains of points along the curve returning to $A$.  The result
of the description of all the curves will be that the series $w_1$ cannot be
reproduced at $A$ for all the curves, though it may be reproduced for some
of them; otherwise, $w_1$ would be a uniform function.  Suppose that $w_2$, $w_3$, ...,
each in the form of a power-series, are the aggregate of new distinct values
thus obtained at $A$ ; let the same process be effected on $w_2$, $w_3$, ... as has
been effected on $w_1$, and let it further be effected on any new distinct values
obtained at $A$ through $w_2$, $w_3$, ..., and so on.  When the process has
been carried out so far that all values obtained at $A$, by continuing any
series round any of the curves $K$ back to $A$, are included in values already
obtained, the aggregate of the values of the function at $A$ is complete : they
are the values at $A$ of the *branches* of the function.

We shall now assume that the number of values thus obtained is finite,
say $n$, so that the function has $n$ branches at $A$ : if their values be denoted
by $w_1$, $w_2$, ..., $w_n$, these $n$ quantities are all the values of the function at $A$.
Moreover, $n$ is the same for all points in the plane, as may be seen by continuing the series at $A$ to any other point and taking account of the corollaries
at the end of the present section.

The boundary-points $L$ may be of two kinds.  It may (and not infrequently does) happen that a point $L_s$ is such that, whatever branch is taken
at $A$ as the initial value for the description of the circuit $K_s$, that branch is
reproduced at the end of the circuit.  Let the aggregate of such points be
$I_1$, $I_2$, ....  Then each of the remaining points $L$ is such that a description
of the circuit round it effects a change on at least one of the branches, taken
as an initial value for the description; let the aggregate of these points be
$B_1$, $B_2$, ....  They are the branch-points; their association with the definition
in § 12 will be made later.

When account is taken of the continuations of the function from a point $A$ to another point $B$, we have $n$ values at $B$ as the continuations of $n$ values at $A$. The selection of the individual branch at $B$, which is the continuation of a particular branch·at $A$, depends upon the path of $z$ between $A$ and $B$; it is governed by the following fundamental proposition :—

*The final value of a branch of a function for two paths of variation of the independent variable from one point to another will be the same, if one path can be deformed into the other without passing over a branch-point.*

Let the initial and the final points be $a$ and $b$, and let one path of variation be $acb$. Let another path of variation be $aeb$, both paths lying in the region in which the function can be expressed by series of positive integral powers : the two paths are assumed to have no point within an infinitesimal distance of any of the boundary-points $L$ and to be taken so close together, that the circles of convergence of pairs of points (such as $c_1$ and $e_1$, $c_2$ and $e_2$, and so on) along the two paths have common areas. When we begin at $a$ with a branch of the function, values at $c_1$ and at $e_1$ are obtained,

Fig. 15.

depending upon the values of the branch and its derivatives at $a$ and upon the positions of $c_1$ and $e_1$; hence, at any point in the area common to the circles of convergence of these two points, only a single value arises as derived through the initial value at $a$. Proceeding in this way, only a single value is obtained at any point in an area common to the circles of convergence of points in the two paths. Hence ultimately one and the same value will be obtained at $b$ as the continuation of the value of the one branch at $a$ by the two different paths of variation which have been taken so that no boundary-point $L$ lies between them or infinitesimally near to them.

Now consider any two paths from $a$ to $b$, say $acb$ and $adb$, such that neither of them is near a boundary-point and that the contour they constitute does not enclose a boundary-point. Then by a series of successive infinitesimal deformations we can change the path $acb$ to $adb$; and as at $b$ the same value of $w$ is obtained for variations of $z$ from $a$ to $b$ along the successive deformations, it follows that the same value of $w$ is obtained at $b$ for variations of $z$ along $acb$ as for variations along $adb$.

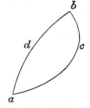

Fig. 16.

Next, let there be two paths $acb$, $adb$ constituting a closed contour, enclosing one (but not more than one) of the points $I$ and none of the points $B$. When the original curve $K$ which contains the point $I$ is described, the initial value is restored : and hence the branches of the function obtained at any point of $K$ by the two paths from any point, taken as initial point, are the same. By what precedes, the parts of this curve $K$ can be deformed into the parts of *acbda* without affecting the branches of the function : hence the value obtained at *b*, by continuation along *acb*, is the same as the value there obtained by continuation along *adb*. It therefore follows that a path between two points *a* and *b* can be deformed over, any point *I* without affecting the value of the function at *b* ; so that, when the preceding results are combined, the proposition enunciated is proved.

By the continued application of the theorem, we are led to the following results :—

COROLLARY I. *Whatever be the effect of the description of a circuit on the initial value of a function, a reversal of the circuit restores the original value of the function.*

For the circuit, when described positively and negatively, may be regarded as the contour of an area of infinitesimal breadth, which encloses no branch-point within itself and the description of the contour of which therefore restores the initial value of the function.

COROLLARY II. *A circuit can be deformed into any other circuit without affecting the final value of the function, provided that no branch-point be crossed in the process of deformation.*

It is thus justifiable, and it is often convenient, to deform a path containing a single branch-point into a loop round the point. A *loop*\* consists of a line nearly to the point, nearly the whole of a very small circle round the point, and a line back to the initial point ; see figure 17.

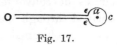

Fig. 17.

COROLLARY III. *The value of a function is unchanged when the variable describes a closed circuit containing no branch-point ; it is likewise unchanged when the variable describes a closed circuit containing all the branch-points.*

The first part is at once proved by remarking that, without altering the value of the function, the circuit can be deformed into a point.

For the second part, the simplest plan is to represent the variable on Neumann's sphere. The circuit is then a curve on the sphere enclosing all the branch-points: the effect on the value of the function is unaltered by any deformation of this curve which does not make it cross a branch-point. The curve can, without crossing a branch-point, be deformed into a point in that other part of the area of the sphere which contains none of the branch-points ; and the point, which is the limit of the curve, is not a branch-point. At such a point, the value of the function is unaltered ; and therefore the description of a circuit, which encloses all the branch-points, restores the initial value of the function.

COROLLARY IV. *If the values of w at b for variations along two paths*

---

\* French writers use the word *lacet*, German writers the word *Schleife*.

*acb, adb be not the same, then a description of acbda will not restore the initial value of w at a.*

In particular, let the path be the loop $O\epsilon c\epsilon O$ (fig. 17), and let it change $w$ at $O$ into $w'$. Since the values of $w$ at $O$ are different and because there is no branch-point in $O\epsilon$ (or in the evanescent circuit $O\epsilon O$), the values of $w$ at $\epsilon$ cannot be the same: that is, the value with which the infinitesimal circle round $a$ begins to be described is changed by the description of that circle. Hence *the part of the loop that is effective for the change in the value of w is the small circle round the point;* and it is because the description of a small circle changes the value of $w$ that the value of $w$ is changed at $O$ after the description of a loop.

If $f(z)$ be the value of $w$ which is changed into $f_1(z)$ by the description of the loop, so that $f(z)$ and $f_1(z)$ are the values at $O$, then the foregoing explanation shews that $f(\epsilon)$ and $f_1(\epsilon)$ are the values at $\epsilon$, the branch $f(\epsilon)$ being changed by the description of the circle into the branch $f_1(\epsilon)$.

From this result the inference can be derived that the points $B_1$, $B_2$, ... are branch-points as defined in § 12. Let $a$ be any one of the points, and let $f(z)$ be the value of $w$ which is changed into $f_1(z)$ by the description of a very small circle round $a$. Then as the branch of $w$ is monogenic, the difference between $f(z)$ and $f_1(z)$ is an infinitesimal quantity of the same order as the length of the circumference of the circle: so that, as the circle is infinitesimal and ultimately evanescent, $|f(z) - f_1(z)|$ can be made as small as we please with decrease of $|z - a|$ or, in the limit, the values of $f(a)$ and $f_1(a)$ at the branch-point are equal. Hence each of the points $B$ is such that *two or more branches of the function have the same value at the point, and there is interchange among these branches when the variable describes a small circuit round the point:* which affords a definition of a branch-point, more complete than that given in § 12.

Corollary V. *If a closed circuit contain several branch-points, the effect which it produces can be obtained by a combination of the effects produced in succession by a set of loops each going round only one of the branch-points.*

If the circuit contain several branch-points, say three as at $a$, $b$, $c$, then a path such as $AEFD$, in fig. 18, can without crossing any branch-point, be deformed into the loops $AaB$, $BbC$, $CcD$; and therefore the complete circuit $AEFDA$ can be deformed validly into $AaBbCcDA$, and the same effect will be produced by the two forms of circuit. When $D$ is made practically to coincide with $A$, the whole of the second circuit is composed of the three loops. Hence the corollary.

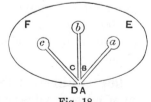

Fig. 18.

This corollary is of especial importance in the consideration of integrals of multiform functions.

COROLLARY VI. *In a continuous part of the plane where there are no branch-points, each branch of a multiform function is uniform.*

Each branch is monogenic and, except. at isolated points, continuous; hence, in such regions of the plane, all the propositions which have been proved for monogenic analytic functions can be applied to each of the branches of a multiform function.

**91.** If there be a branch-point within the circuit, then the value of the function at $b$ consequent on variations along $acb$ may, but will not necessarily, differ from its value at the same point consequent on variations along $adb$. Should the values be different, then the description of the whole curve $acbda$ will lead at $a$ not to the initial value of $w$, but to a different value. The test as to whether such a change is effected by the description is immediately derivable from the foregoing proposition; and as in Corollary IV., § 90, it is proved that the value is or is not changed by the loop, according as the value of $w$ for a point near the circle of the loop is or is not changed by the description of that circle. Hence it follows that, *if there be a branch-point which affects the branch of the function, a path of variation of the independent variable cannot be deformed across the branch-point without a change in the value of $w$ at the extremity of the path.*

And it is evident that *a point can be regarded as a branch-point for a function only if a circuit round the point interchange some (or all) of the branches of the function which are equal at the point.* It is not necessary that all the branches of the function should be thus affected by the point: it is sufficient that some should be interchanged*.

Further, *the change in the value of $w$ for a single description of a circuit enclosing a branch-point is unique.*

For, if a circuit could change $w$ into $w'$ or $w''$, then, beginning with $w''$ and describing it in the negative sense we should return to $w$ and afterwards describing it in the positive sense with $w$ as the initial value we should obtain $w'$. Hence the circuit, described and then reversed, does not restore the original value $w''$ but gives a different branch $w'$; and no point on the circuit is a branch-point. This result is in opposition to Corollary I., of § 90; and therefore the hypothesis of alternative values at the end of the circuit is not valid, that is, the change for a single description is unique.

But repetitions of the circuit may, of course, give different values at the end of successive descriptions.

---

* In what precedes, certain points were considered which were regular singularities (see p. 192, note) and certain which were branch-points. Frequently points will occur which are at once branch-points and infinities; proper account must of course be taken of them.

**92.** Let $O$ be any ordinary point of the function; join it to all the branch-points (generally assumed finite in number) in succession by lines which do not meet each other: then each branch is uniform for each path of variation of the variable which meets none of these lines. The effects produced by the various branch-points and their relations on the various branches can be indicated by describing curves, each of which begins at a point indefinitely near $O$ and returns to another point indefinitely near it after passing round one of the branch-points,

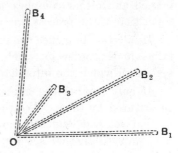

Fig. 19.

and by noting the value of each branch of the function after each of these curves has been described.

The law of interchange of branches of a function after description of a circuit round a branch-point is as follows:—

*All the branches of a function, which are affected by a branch-point as such, can either be arranged so that the order of interchange (for description of a path round the point) is cyclical, or be divided into sets in each of which the order of interchange is cyclical.*

Let $w_1$, $w_2$, $w_3$, ... be the branches of a function for values of $z$ near a branch-point $a$ which are affected by the description of a small closed curve $C$ round $a$: they are not necessarily all the branches of the function, but only those affected by the branch-point.

The branch $w_1$ is changed after a description of $C$; let $w_2$ be the branch into which it is changed. Then $w_2$ cannot be unchanged by $C$; for a reversed description of $C$, which ought to restore $w_1$, would otherwise leave $w_2$ unchanged. Hence $w_2$ is changed after a description of $C$; it may be changed either into $w_1$ or into a new branch, say $w_3$. If into $w_1$, then $w_1$ and $w_2$ form a cyclical set.

If the change be into $w_3$, then $w_3$ cannot remain unchanged after a description of $C$, for reasons similar to those that before applied to the change of $w_2$; and it cannot be changed into $w_2$, for then a reversed description of $C$ would change $w_2$ into $w_3$, and it ought to change $w_2$ into $w_1$. Hence, after a description of $C$, $w_3$ is changed either into $w_1$ or into a new branch, say $w_4$. If into $w_1$, then $w_1$, $w_2$, $w_3$ form a cyclical set.

If the change be into $w_4$, then $w_4$ cannot remain unchanged after a description of $C$; and it cannot be changed into $w_2$ or $w_3$, for by a reversal of the circuit that earlier branch would be changed into $w_4$ whereas it ought to be changed into the branch, which gave rise to it by the forward description—a branch which is not $w_4$. Hence, after a description of $C$, $w_4$ is changed either into $w_1$ or into a new branch. If into $w_1$, then $w_1$, $w_2$, $w_3$, $w_4$ form a cyclical set.

If $w_4$ be changed into a new branch, we proceed as before with that new branch and either complete a cyclical set or add one more to the set. By repetition of the process, we complete a cyclical set sooner or later.

If all the branches be included, then evidently their complete system taken in the order in which they come in the foregoing investigation is a system in which the interchange is cyclical.

If only some of the branches be included, the remark applies to the set constituted by them. We then begin with one of the branches not included in that set and evidently not inclusible in it, and proceed as at first, until we complete another set which may include all the remaining branches or only some of them. In the latter case, we begin again with a new branch and repeat the process; and so on, until ultimately all the branches are included. The whole system is then arranged in sets, in each of which the order of interchange is cyclical.

**93**. *The analytical test of a branch-point* is easily obtained by constructing the general expression for the branches of a function which are interchanged there.

Let $z = a$ be a branch-point where $n$ branches $w_1$, $w_2$, ..., $w_n$ are cyclically interchanged. Since by a first description of a small curve round $a$, the branch $w_1$ changes into $w_2$, the branch $w_2$ into $w_3$, and so on, it follows that by $r$ descriptions $w_1$ is changed into $w_{r+1}$ and by $n$ descriptions $w_1$ reverts to its initial value. Similarly for each of the branches. Hence *each branch returns to its initial value after $n$ descriptions of a circuit round a branch-point where $n$ branches of the function are interchangeable.*

Now let
$$z - a = Z^n ;$$
then, when $z$ describes circles round $a$, $Z$ moves in a circular arc round its origin. For each circumference described by $z$, the variable $Z$ describes $\frac{1}{n}$th part of its circumference; and the complete circle is described by $Z$ round its origin when $n$ complete circles are described by $z$ round $a$. Now the substitution changes $w_r$ as a function of $z$ into a function of $Z$, say into $W_r$; and, after $n$ complete descriptions of the $z$-circle round $a$, $w_r$ returns to its initial value. Hence, after the description of a $Z$-circle round its origin, $W_r$ returns to its initial value, that is, $Z = 0$ ceases to be a branch-point for $W_r$. Similarly for all the branches $W$.

But no other condition has been associated with $a$ as a point for the function $w$; and therefore $Z = 0$ may be any point for the function $W$, that is, it may be an ordinary point, or a singularity. In every case, we have $W$ a uniform function of $Z$ in the immediate vicinity of the origin; and therefore in that vicinity it can be expressed in the form

$$G\left(\frac{1}{Z}\right) + P(Z),$$

with the significations of $P$ and $G$ already adopted. When $Z = 0$ is an ordinary point, $G$ is a constant or zero; when it is an accidental singularity, $G$ is a polynomial function; and, when it is an essential singularity, $G$ is a transcendental function.

The simpler cases are, of course, those in which the form of $G$ is polynomial or constant or zero; and then $W$ can be put into the form

$$Z^m \bar{P}(Z),$$

where $\bar{P}$ is an infinite series of positive powers and $m$ is an integer. As this is the form of $W$ in the vicinity of $Z = 0$, it follows that the form of $w$ in the vicinity of $z = a$ is

$$(z-a)^{\frac{m}{n}} \bar{P}\left\{(z-a)^{\frac{1}{n}}\right\};$$

and the various $n$ branches of the function are easily seen to be given by substituting in the above for $(z-a)^{\frac{1}{n}}$ the values

$$e^{\frac{2\pi s i}{n}} (z-a)^{\frac{1}{n}},$$

where $s = 0, 1, \ldots, n-1$. We therefore infer that *the general expression for the $n$ branches of a function, which are interchanged by circuits round a branch-point $z = a$, assumed not to be an essential singularity, is*

$$(z-a)^{\frac{m}{n}} \bar{P}\left\{(z-a)^{\frac{1}{n}}\right\},$$

*where $m$ is an integer, and where to $(z-a)^{\frac{1}{n}}$ its $n$ values are in turn assigned to obtain the different branches of the function.*

There may be, however, more than one cyclical set of branches. If there be another set of $r$ branches, then it may similarly be proved that their general expression is

$$(z-a)^{\frac{m_1}{r}} \bar{Q}\left\{(z-a)^{\frac{1}{r}}\right\},$$

where $m_1$ is an integer, and $\bar{Q}$ is an integral function; the various branches are obtained by assigning to $(z-a)^{\frac{1}{r}}$ its $r$ values in turn.

And so on, for each of the sets, the members of which are cyclically interchangeable at the branch-point.

When the branch-point is at infinity, a different form is obtained. Thus in the case of a set of $n$ cyclically interchangeable branches we take

$$z = u^{-n},$$

so that $n$ negative descriptions of a closed $z$-curve, excluding infinity and no other branch-point, require a single positive description of a closed curve round the $u$-origin. These $n$ descriptions restore the value of $w$ as a function of $z$ to its initial value; and therefore the single description of the $u$-curve round the origin restores the value of $U$—the equivalent of $w$ after the change of the independent variable—as a function of $u$. Thus $u = 0$ ceases to be a branch-point for the function $U$; and therefore the form of $U$ is

$$G\left(\frac{1}{u}\right) + P(u),$$

where the symbols have the same general signification as before.

If, in particular, $z = \infty$ be a branch-point but not an essential singularity, then $G$ is either a constant or a polynomial function; and then $U$ can be expressed in the form

$$u^{-m}\,\bar{P}(u),$$

where $m$ is an integer. When the variable is changed from $u$ to $z$, then *the general expression for the n branches of a function which are interchangeable at $z = \infty$, assumed not to be an essential singularity, is*

$$z^{\frac{m}{n}} P(z^{-\frac{1}{n}}),$$

*where $m$ is an integer and where to $z^{\frac{1}{n}}$ its n values are assigned to obtain the different branches of the function.*

If, however, the branch-point $z = a$ in the former case or $z = \infty$ in the latter be an essential singularity, the forms of the expressions in the vicinity of the point are

$$G\{(z-a)^{-\frac{1}{n}}\} + P\{(z-a)^{\frac{1}{n}}\},$$

and

$$G(z^{\frac{1}{n}}) + P(z^{-\frac{1}{n}}),$$

respectively.

*Note.* When a multiform function is defined, either explicitly or implicitly, it is practically always necessary to consider the relations of the branches of the function for $z = \infty$ as well as their relations for points that are infinities of the function. The former can be determined by either of the processes suggested in § 4 for dealing with $z = \infty$; the latter can be determined as in the present section.

Moreover, the total number of branches of the function has been assumed to be finite. The cases, in which the number of branches is unlimited, need not be discussed in general: it will be sufficient to consider them when they arise, as they do arise, e.g., when the function is of the form of an algebraical irrational with an irrational index such as $z^{\sqrt{2}}$—hardly a function in the ordinary sense—, or when the function is the logarithm of a function of $z$, or is the inverse of a periodic function. In the nature of their multiplicity of branching and of their sequence of interchange, they are for the most part distinct from the multiform functions with only a finite number of branches.

*Ex.* The simplest illustrations of multiform functions are furnished by functions defined by algebraical equations, in particular, by algebraic irrationals.

The general type of the algebraical irrational is the product of a number of functions of the form $w = \{A\,(z-a_1)\,(z-a_2)\ldots\ldots(z-a_n)\}^{\frac{1}{m}}$, $m$ and $n$ being integers.

This particular function has $m$ branches; the points $a_1, a_2, \ldots\ldots, a_n$ are branch-points. To find the law of interchange, we take $z - a_r = \rho e^{\theta i}$; then when a small circle of radius $\rho$ is described round $a_r$, so that $z$ returns to its initial position, the value of $\theta$ increases by $2\pi$ and the new value of $w$ is $aw$, where $a$ is the $m$th root of unity defined by $e^{\frac{1}{m}2\pi i}$. Taking then the various branches as given by $w, aw, a^2 w, \ldots\ldots, a^{m-1}w$, we have the law of interchange for description of a small curve round any one branch-point as given by this succession in cyclical order. The law of succession for a circuit enclosing more than one of the branch-points is derivable by means of Corollary V., § 90.

To find the relation of $z = \infty$ to $w$, we take $zz' = 1$ and consider the new function $W$ in the vicinity of the $z'$-origin. We have

$$W = \{A\,(1-a_1 z')\,(1-a_2 z')\ldots\ldots(1-a_n z')\}^{\frac{1}{m}} z'^{-\frac{n}{m}}.$$

If the variable $z'$ describe a very small circle round the origin in the negative sense, then $z'$ is multiplied by $e^{-2\pi i}$ and so $W$ acquires a factor $e^{2\pi i \frac{n}{m}}$, that is, $W$ is changed unless this acquired factor is unity. It can be unity only when $n/m$ is an integer; and therefore, except when $n/m$ is an integer, $z = \infty$ is a branch-point of the function. The law of succession is the same as that for negative description of the $z'$-circle, viz., $w, a^n w, a^{2n} w, \ldots\ldots$; the $m$ values form a single cycle only if $n$ be prime to $m$, and a set of cycles if $n$ be not prime to $m$.

Thus $z = \infty$ is a branch-point for $w = (4z^3 - g_2 z - g_3)^{-\frac{1}{2}}$; it is not a branch-point for $w = \{(1-z^2)(1-k^2 z^2)\}^{-\frac{1}{2}}$; and $z = b$ is a branch-point for the function defined by

$$(z-b)\,w^2 = z - a,$$

but $z = b$ is not a branch-point for the function defined by $(z-b)^2 w^2 = z - a$.

Again, if $p$ denote a particular value of $z^{\frac{1}{2}}$, when $z$ has a given value, and $q$ similarly denote a particular value of $\left(\dfrac{z-1}{z+1}\right)^{\frac{1}{3}}$, then $w = p + q$ is a six-valued function, the values being

$$w_1 = \phantom{-}p + q, \qquad w_3 = \phantom{-}p + aq, \qquad w_5 = \phantom{-}p + a^2 q,$$
$$w_2 = -p + q, \qquad w_4 = -p + aq, \qquad w_6 = -p + a^2 q,$$

where $a$ is a primitive cube root of unity. The branch-points are $-1, 0, 1, \infty$; and the orders of change for small circuits round one (and only one) of these points are as follows:—

| For a small circuit round | $-1$ | $0$ | $1$ | $\infty$ |
|---|---|---|---|---|
| $w_1$ changes to | $w_5$ | $w_2$ | $w_3$ | $w_2$ |
| $w_2$ ,, | $w_6$ | $w_1$ | $w_4$ | $w_1$ |
| $w_3$ ,, | $w_1$ | $w_4$ | $w_5$ | $w_4$ |
| $w_4$ ,, | $w_2$ | $w_3$ | $w_6$ | $w_3$ |
| $w_5$ ,, | $w_3$ | $w_6$ | $w_1$ | $w_6$ |
| $w_6$ ,, | $w_4$ | $w_5$ | $w_2$ | $w_5$ |

Combinations can at once be effected; thus, for a positive circuit enclosing both 1 and $\infty$ but* not $-1$ or 0, the succession is

$$w_1, \ w_4, \ w_5, \ w_2, \ w_3, \ w_6$$

in cyclical order.

**94.** It has already been remarked that algebraic irrationals are a special class of functions defined by algebraical equations. Functions thus generally defined by equations, which are polynomial so far as concerns the dependent variable but need not be so in reference to the independent variable, are often called *algebraical*. The term, in one sense, cannot be strictly applied to the roots of an equation of every degree, seeing that the solution of equations of the fifth and higher degrees can be effected only by transcendental functions; but what is implied is that a finite number of determinations of the dependent variable is given by the equation†.

The equation is polynomial in relation to the dependent variable $w$, that is, it will be taken to be of finite degree $n$ in $w$. The coefficients of the different powers will be supposed to be uniform functions of $z$: were they multiform (with a limited number of values for each value of $z$) in any given equation, the equation could be transformed into another, the coefficients of which are uniform functions. And the equation is supposed to be irreducible, that is, if the equation be taken in the form

$$f(w, z) = 0,$$

the left-hand member $f(w, z)$ cannot be resolved into factors of a form and character as regards $w$ and $z$ similar to $f$ itself.

The existence of equal roots of the equation for general values of $z$ requires that

$$f(w, z) \quad \text{and} \quad \frac{\partial f(w, z)}{\partial w}$$

shall have a common factor, which will be uniform owing to the form of $f(w, z)$. This form of factor is excluded by the irreducibility of the equation; so that $f = 0$, as an equation in $w$, has not equal roots for *general* values of $z$. But though the two equations are not both satisfied in virtue of a simpler equation, they are two equations determining values of $w$ and $z$; and their form is such that they will give equal values of $w$ for *special* values of $z$.

Since the equation is of degree $n$, it may be taken to be

$$w^n + w^{n-1} F_1(z) + w^{n-2} F_2(z) + \ldots + w F_{n-1}(z) + F_n(z) = 0,$$

where the functions $F_1, F_2, \ldots$ are uniform. If all their singularities be accidental, they are rational meromorphic functions of $z$ (unless $z = \infty$ is the

---

* Such a circuit, if drawn on the Neumann's sphere, may be regarded as excluding $-1$ and 0, or taking account of the other portion of the surface of the sphere, it may be regarded as a negative circuit including $-1$ and 0, the cyclical interchange for which is easily proved to be $w_1, \ w_4, \ w_5, \ w_2, \ w_3, \ w_6$ as in the text.

† Such a function is called *bien défini* by Liouville.

only singularity, in which case they are holomorphic); and the equation can then be replaced by one which is equivalent and has all its coefficients holomorphic, the coefficient of $w^n$ being the least common multiple of all the denominators of the meromorphic functions in the first form. This form cannot however be deduced, if any of the singularities be essential.

The equation, as an equation in $w$, has $n$ roots, all functions of $z$; let these be denoted by $w_1, w_2, ..., w_n$, which are the $n$ branches of the function $w$. When the geometrical interpretation is associated with the analytical relation, there are $n$ points in the $w$-plane, say $a_1, ..., a_n$, which correspond with a point in the $z$-plane, say with $a_1$; and in general these $n$ points are distinct. Further, as will appear from the investigations in § 97 (p. 207), the $n$ roots $w$ are continuous functions of $z$; that is to say, any small change in the value of $z$ entails corresponding small changes in the value of each of the $n$ roots $w$. Hence, when $z$ varies so as to move in its own plane, each of the $w$-points moves in their common plane; and thus there are $n$ $w$-paths corresponding to a given $z$-path. These $n$ curves may or may not meet one another.

If they do not, there are $n$ distinct $w$-paths, leading from $a_1, ..., a_n$ to $\beta_1, ..., \beta_n$, respectively corresponding to the single $z$-path leading from $a$ to $b$.

If two or more of the $w$-paths do meet one another, and if the describing $w$-points coincide at their point of intersection, then at such a point of intersection in the $w$-plane, the associated branches $w$ are equal; and therefore the point in the $z$-plane is a point that gives equal values for $w$. It is one of the roots of the equation obtained by the elimination of $w$ between

$$ f(w, z) = 0, \quad \frac{\partial f(w, z)}{\partial w} = 0 \, ; $$

the analytical test as to whether the point is a branch-point will be considered later. The march of the concurrent $w$-branches from such a point of intersection of two $w$-paths depends upon their relations in its immediate vicinity.

When no such point lies on a $z$-path from $a$ to $b$, no two of the $w$-points coincide during the description of their paths. By § 90, the $z$-path can be deformed (provided that, in the deformation, it does not cross a branch-point) without causing any two of the $w$-points to coincide. Further, if $z$ describe a closed curve which includes none of the branch-points, then each of the $w$-branches describes a closed curve and no two of the tracing points ever coincide.

*Note.* The limitation for a branch-point, that the tracing $w$-points coincide at the point of intersection of the $w$-curves, is of essential importance.

What is required to establish a point in the $z$-plane as a branch-point, is not a mere geometrical intersection of a couple of completed $w$-paths but the coincidence of the $w$-points as those paths are traced, together with interchange of the branches for a small circuit round the point. Thus let there be such a geometrical intersection of two $w$-curves, without coincidence of the tracing points. There are two points in the $z$-plane corresponding to the geometrical intersection; one belongs to the intersection as a point of the $w$-path which first passed through it, and the other to the intersection as a point of the $w$-path which was the second to pass through it. The two branches of $w$ for the respective values of $z$ are undoubtedly equal; but the equality would not be for the same value of $z$. And unless the equality of branches subsists for the same value of $z$, the point is not a branch-point.

A simple example will serve to illustrate these remarks. Let $w$ be defined by the equation

$$f = c^2 (w^2 - 2zw) - z^4 = 0,$$

so that the branches $w_1$ and $w_2$ are given by

$$cw_1 = cz + z (z^2 + c^2)^{\frac{1}{2}}, \qquad cw_2 = cz - z (z^2 + c^2)^{\frac{1}{2}};$$

it is easy to prove that the equation resulting from the elimination of $w$ between $f = 0$ and $\dfrac{\partial f}{\partial w} = 0$ is

$$z^2 (z^2 + c^2) = 0,$$

and that only the two points $z = \pm ic$ are branch-points.

The values of $z$ which make $w_1$ equal to the value of $w_2$ for $z = a$ (supposed not equal to either $0$, $ci$ or $-ci$) are given by

$$cz + z (z^2 + c^2)^{\frac{1}{2}} = ca - a (a^2 + c^2)^{\frac{1}{2}},$$

which evidently has not $z = a$ for a root. Rationalising the equation so far as concerns $z$ and removing the factor $z - a$, as it has just been seen not to furnish a root, we find that $z$ is determined by

$$z^3 + z^2 a + za^2 + a^3 + 2ac^2 - 2ac (a^2 + c^2)^{\frac{1}{2}} = 0,$$

the three roots of which are distinct from $a$, the assumed point, and from $\pm ci$, the branch-point. Each of these three values of $z$ will make $w_1$ equal to the value of $w_2$ for $z = a$: we have geometrical intersection without coincidence of the tracing points.

**95.** When the characteristics of a function are required, the most important class are its infinities: these must therefore now be investigated. It is preferable to obtain the infinities of the function rather than the singularities alone, in the vicinity of which each branch of the function is uniform* : for the former will include these singularities as well as those branch-points which, giving infinite values, lead to regular singularities when the variables are transformed as in § 93. The theorem which determines them is :—

*The infinities of a function determined by an algebraical equation are the singularities of the coefficients of the equation.*

Let the equation be

$$w^n + w^{n-1} F_1 (z) + w^{n-2} F_2 (z) + \ldots + w F_{n-1} (z) + F_n (z) = 0,$$

---

\* These singularities will, for the sake of brevity, be called *regular*.

and let $w'$ be any branch of the function; then, if the equation which determines the remaining branches be

$$w^{n-1} + w^{n-2}G_1(z) + w^{n-3}G_2(z) + \ldots + wG_{n-2}(z) + G_{n-1}(z) = 0,$$

we have
$$F_n(z) = -w'G_{n-1}(z),$$

$$F_{n-1}(z) = -w'G_{n-2}(z) + G_{n-1}(z),$$

$$F_{n-2}(z) = -w'G_{n-3}(z) + G_{n-2}(z),$$

$$\vdots$$

$$F_1(z) = -w' + G_1(z).$$

Now suppose that $a$ is an infinity of $w'$; then, unless it be a zero of order at least equal to that of $G_{n-1}(z)$, $a$ is an infinity of $F_n(z)$. If, however, it be a zero of $G_{n-1}(z)$ of sufficient order, then from the second equation it is an infinity of $F_{n-1}(z)$ unless it is a zero of order at least equal to that of $G_{n-2}(z)$; and so on. The infinity must be an infinity of some coefficient not earlier than $F_i(z)$ in the equation, or it must be a zero of all the functions $G$ which are later than $G_{i-1}(z)$. If it be a zero of all the functions $G_r$, so that we may not, without knowing the order, assert that it is of rank at least equal to its order as an infinity of $w'$, still from the last equation it follows that $a$ must be an infinity of $F_1(z)$. Hence *any infinity of $w$ is an infinity of at least one of the coefficients of the equation.*

Conversely, from the same equations it follows that a singularity of one of the coefficients is an infinity either of $w'$ or of at least one of the co-efficients $G$. Similarly the latter alternative leads to an inference that the infinity is either an infinity of another branch $w''$ or of the coefficients of the (theoretical) equation which survives when the two branches have been removed. Proceeding in this way, we ultimately find that the infinity either is an infinity of one of the branches or is an infinity of the coefficient in the last equation, that is, of the last of the branches. Hence *any singularity of a coefficient is an infinity of at least one of the branches of the function.*

It thus appears that all the infinities of the function are included among, and include, all the singularities of the coefficients; but the order of the infinity for a branch does not necessarily make that point a regular singularity nor, if it be a regular singularity, is the order necessarily the same as for the coefficient.

The following method is effective for the determination of the order of the infinity of the branch.

Let $a$ be an accidental singularity of one or more of the $F$ functions, say of order $m_i$ for the function $F_i$; and assume that, in the vicinity of $a$, we have

$$F_i(z) = (z-a)^{-m_i}[c_i + d_i(z-a) + e_i(z-a)^2 + \ldots].$$

Then the equation which determines the first term of the expansion of $w$ in a series in the vicinity of $a$ is

$$w^n + c_1 (z - a)^{-m_1} w^{n-1} + c_2 (z - a)^{-m_2} w^{n-2} + \cdots$$
$$+ c_{n-1} (z - a)^{-m_{n-1}} w + c_n (z - a)^{-m_n} = 0.$$

Mark in a plane, referred to two rectangular axes, points $n$, $0$; $n - 1$, $-m_1$; $n - 2$, $-m_2$; ..., $0$, $-m_n$; let these be $A_0, A_1, \ldots, A_n$ respectively. Any line through $A_i$ has its equation of the form

$$y + m_i = \lambda \{x - (n - i)\};$$

that is,

$$y - \lambda x = - \lambda (n - i) - m_i.$$

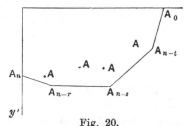

Fig. 20.

If then $w = (z - a)^{-\lambda} f(z)$, where $f(z)$ is finite when $z = a$, the intercept of the foregoing line on the negative side of the axis of $y$ is equal to the order of the infinity in the term

$$w^{n-i} F_i (z).$$

This being so, we take a line through $A_n$ coinciding in direction with the negative part of the axis of $y$, and we turn it about $A_n$ in a trigonometrically positive direction until it first meets one of the other points, say $A_{n-r}$; then we turn it about $A_{n-r}$ until it meets one of the other points, say $A_{n-s}$; and so on until it passes through $A_0$. There will thus be a line from $A_n$ to $A_0$, generally consisting of a number of parts; and none of the points $A$ will be outside the figure bounded by this line and the axes.

The perpendicular from the origin on the line through $A_{n-r}$ and $A_{n-s}$ is evidently greater than the perpendicular on any parallel line through a point $A$, that is, on any line through a point $A$ with the same value of $\lambda$; and, as this perpendicular is

$$\{\lambda (n - i) + m_i\} (1 + \lambda^2)^{-\frac{1}{2}},$$

it follows that the order of the infinite terms in the equation, when the particular substitution is made for $w$, is greater for terms corresponding to points lying on the line than it is for any other terms.

If $f(z) = \theta$ when $z = a$, then the terms of lowest order after the substitution of $(z - a)^{-\lambda} f(z)$ for $w$ are

$$(z - a)^{-m_{n-r} - \lambda r} [c_{n-r} \theta^r + \cdots + c_{n-s} \theta^s],$$

as many terms occurring in the bracket as there are points $A$ on the line joining $A_{n-r}$ to $A_{n-s}$. Since the equation determining $w$ must be satisfied, terms of all orders must disappear, and therefore

$$c_{n-s} \theta^{s-r} + \cdots + c_{n-r} = 0,$$

an equation determining $s - r$ values of $\theta$, that is, the first terms in the expansions of $s - r$ branches $w$.

Similarly for each part of the line: for the first part, there are $r$ branches with an associated value of $\lambda$; for the second, $s - r$ branches with another associated value; for the third, $t - s$ branches with a third associated value; and so on.

The order of the infinity for the branches is measured by the tangent of the angle which the corresponding part of the broken line makes with the axis of $x$; thus for the line joining $A_{n-r}$ to $A_{n-s}$ the order of the infinity for the $s - r$ branches is

$$\frac{m_{n-r} - m_{n-s}}{s - r},$$

where $m_{n-r}$ and $m_{n-s}$ are the orders of the accidental singularities of $F_{n-r}(z)$ and $F_{n-s}(z)$.

If any part of the broken line should have its inclination to the axis of $x$ greater than $\frac{1}{2}\pi$ so that the tangent is negative and equal to $-\mu$, then the form of the corresponding set of branches $w$ is $(z - a)^{\mu} g(z)$ for all of them, that is, the point is not an infinity for those branches. But when the inclination of a part of the line to the axis is $< \frac{1}{2}\pi$, so that the tangent is positive and equal to $\lambda$, then the form of the corresponding set of branches $w$ is $(z - a)^{-\lambda} f(z)$ for all of them, that is, the point is an infinity of order $\lambda$ for those branches.

In passing from $A_n$ to $A_0$, there may be parts of the broken line which have the tangential coordinate negative, implying therefore that $a$ is not an infinity of the corresponding set or sets of branches $w$. But as the revolving line has to change its direction from $A_n y'$ to some direction through $A_0$, there must evidently be some part or parts of the broken line which have their tangential coordinate positive, implying therefore that $a$ is an infinity of the corresponding set or sets of branches.

Moreover, the point $a$ is, by hypothesis, an accidental singularity of at least one of the coefficients, and it has been supposed to be an essential singularity of none of them; hence the points $A_0, A_1, ..., A_n$ are all in the finite part of the plane. And as no two of their abscissæ are equal, no line joining two of them can be parallel to the axis of $y$, that is, the inclination of the broken line is never $\frac{1}{2}\pi$ and therefore the tangential coordinate is finite, that is, the order of the infinity for the branches is finite for any accidental singularity of the coefficients.

If the singularity at $a$ be essential for some of the coefficients, the corresponding result can be inferred by passing to the limit which is obtained by making the corresponding value or values of $m$ infinite. In that case the corresponding points $A$ move to infinity and then parts of the broken line pass through $A_0$ (which is always on the axis of $x$) parallel to the axis of $y$, that is, the tangential coordinate is infinite and the order of the infinity at $a$ for the corresponding branches is also infinite. The point is then an essential singularity (and it may be also a branch-point).

It has been assumed implicitly that the singularity is at a finite point in the $z$-plane; if, however, it be at $\infty$, we can, by using the transformation $zz' = 1$ and discussing as above the function in the vicinity of the origin, obtain the relation of the singularity to the various branches. We thus have the further proposition:—

*The order of the infinity of a branch of an algebraical function at a singularity of a coefficient of the equation, which determines the function, is finite or infinite according as the singularity is accidental or essential.*

If the coefficients $F_i$ of the equation be holomorphic functions, then $z = \infty$ is their only singularity and it is consequently the only infinity for branches of the function. If some of or all the coefficients $F_i$ be meromorphic functions, the singularities of the coefficients are the zeros of the denominators and, possibly, $z = \infty$; and, if the functions be rational, all such singularities are accidental. In that case, the equation can be modified to

$$h_0(z) w^n + h_1(z) w^{n-1} + h_2(z) w^{n-2} + \ldots = 0,$$

where $h_0(z)$ is the least common multiple of all the denominators of the functions $F_i$. The preceding results therefore lead to the more limited theorem:—

*When a function $w$ is determined by an algebraical equation the coefficients of which are holomorphic functions of $z$, then each of the zeros of the coefficient of the highest power of $w$ is an infinity of some of (and it may be of all) the branches of the function $w$, each such infinity being of finite order. The point $z = \infty$ may also be an infinity of the function $w$; the order of that infinity is finite or infinite according as $z = \infty$ is an accidental or an essential singularity of any of the coefficients.*

It will be noticed that no precise determination of the forms of the branches $w$ at an infinity has been made. The determination has, however, only been deferred: the infinities of the branches for a singularity of the coefficients are usually associated with a branch-point of the function, and therefore the relations of the branches at such a point will be of a general character independent of the fact that the point is an infinity.

If, however, in any case a singularity of a coefficient should prove to be, not a branch-point of $w$ but only a regular singularity, then in the vicinity of that point the branch of $w$ is a uniform function. A necessary (but not sufficient) condition for uniformity is that $(m_{n-r} - m_{n-s}) \div (s - r)$ be an integer.

*Note.* The preceding method can be applied to determine the leading terms of the branches in the vicinity of a point $a$ which is an ordinary point for each of the coefficients $F$.

**96.** There remains therefore the consideration of the branch-points of a function determined by an algebraical equation.

The characteristic property of a branch-point is the equality of branches of the function for the associated value of the variable, coupled with the interchange of some of (or all) the equal branches after description by the variable of a small contour enclosing the point.

So far as concerns the first part, the general indication of the form of the value has already (§ 93) been given. The points, for which values of $w$ determined as a function of $z$ by the equation

$$f(w, z) = 0$$

are equal, are determined by the solution of this equation treated simultaneously with

$$\frac{\partial f(w, z)}{\partial w} = 0 ;$$

and when a point $z$ is thus determined, the corresponding values of $w$, which are equal there, are obtained by substituting that value of $z$ and taking $M$, the greatest common measure of $f$ and $\frac{\partial f}{\partial w}$. The factors of $M$ then lead to the value or the values of $w$ at the point; the index $m$ of a linear factor gives at the point the multiplicity of the value which it determines, and shews that $m + 1$ values of $w$ have a common value there, though they are distinct at infinitesimal distances from the point. Values of $w$, determined by $f = 0$ but not occurring in a factor of $M$, are isolated values; each of them determines a branch that is uniform at the point.

Let $z = a$, $w = \alpha$ be a value of $z$ and a value of $w$ thus obtained; and suppose that $m$ is the number of values of $w$ that are equal to one another. The point $z = a$ is not a branch-point unless some interchange among the $m$ values of $w$ is effected by a small circuit round $a$; and it is therefore necessary to investigate the values of the branches* in the vicinity of $z = a$.

Let $w = \alpha + w'$, $z = a + z'$; then we have

$$f(\alpha + w', a + z') = 0,$$

that is, on the supposition that $f(w, z)$ has been freed from fractions,

$$f(\alpha, a) + \sum_{r, s} \sum A_{rs} z'^r w'^s = 0,$$

so that, since $\alpha$ is a value of $w$ corresponding to the value $a$ of $z$, we have $w'$ and $z'$ connected by the relation

$$\sum_r \sum_s A_{rs} z'^r w'^s = 0.$$

---

* The following investigations are founded on the researches of Puiseux on algebraic functions; they are contained in two memoirs, *Liouville*, 1$^{\text{re}}$ Sér., t. xv, (1850), pp. 365—480, ib., t. xvi, (1851), pp. 228—240. See also the chapters on algebraic functions, pp. 19—76, in the second edition of Briot and Bouquet's *Théorie des fonctions elliptiques*.

When $z'$ is 0, the zero value of $w'$ must occur $m$ times, since $\alpha$ is a root $m$ times repeated; hence there are terms in the foregoing equation independent of $z'$, and the term of lowest index among them is $w'^m$. Also when $w' = 0$, $z' = 0$ is a possible root; hence there must be a term or terms independent of $w'$ in the equation.

First, suppose that the lowest power of $z'$ among the terms independent of $w'$ is the first. The equation has the form

$$A z' + \text{higher powers of } z'$$

$$+ B w'^m + \text{higher powers of } w'$$

$$+ \text{terms involving } z' \text{ and } w' = 0,$$

where $A$ is the value of $\dfrac{\partial f(w, z)}{\partial z}$ for $w = \alpha$, $z = a$. Let $z' = \zeta^m$, $w' = v\zeta$; the last form changes to

$$(A + Bv^m)\, \zeta^m + \text{terms with } \zeta^{m+1} \text{ as a factor} = 0 \,;$$

and therefore $\qquad A + Bv^m + \text{terms involving } \zeta = 0.$

Hence in the immediate vicinity of $z = a$, that is, of $\zeta = 0$, we have

$$A + Bv^m = 0.$$

Neither $A$ nor $B$ is zero, so that all the $m$ values of $v$ are finite. Let them be $v_1, \ldots, v_m$, so arranged that their arguments increase by $2\pi/m$ through the succession. The corresponding values of $w'$ are

$$w_r' = v_r \zeta$$

$$= v_r z'^{\frac{1}{m}},$$

for $r = 1, \ldots, m$. Now a $z$-circuit round $a$, that is, a $z'$-circuit round its origin, increases the argument of $z'$ by $2\pi$; hence after such a circuit, we have the new value of $w_r'$ as $v_r z'^{\frac{1}{m}} e^{\frac{2\pi i}{m}}$, that is, it is $v_{r+1} z'^{\frac{1}{m}}$ which is the value of $w'_{r+1}$. Hence the set of values $w'_1$, $w'_2$, $\ldots$, $w'_m$ form a complete set of interchangeable values in their cyclical succession; all the $m$ values, which are equal at $a$, form a single cycle and the point is a branch-point.

Next, suppose that the lowest power of $z'$ among the terms independent of $w'$ is $z'^l$, where $l > 1$. The equation now has the form

$$0 = A z'^l + \text{higher powers of } z'$$

$$+ B w'^m + \text{higher powers of } w'$$

$$+ \sum_{r=1}^{l-1} \sum_{s=1}^{m-1} A_{rs} z'^r w'^s + \Sigma\Sigma C_{rs} z'^r w'^s,$$

where in the last summation $r$ and $s$ are not zero and in every term either (i), $r$ is equal to or greater than $l$ or (ii), $s$ is equal to or greater than $m$ or (iii), both (i) and (ii) are satisfied. As only terms of the lowest orders need be retained for the present purpose, which is the derivation of the first term of $w'$ in its expansion in powers of $z'$, we may use the foregoing equation in the form

$$Az'^l + \sum_{r=1}^{l-1} \sum_{s=1}^{m-1} A_{rs} z'^r w'^s + Bw'^m = 0.$$

To obtain this first term we proceed in a manner similar to that in § 95 [*] Points $A_0, \ldots, A_m$ are taken in a plane referred to rectangular axes having as co-ordinates $0, l \,; \ldots \,; s, r \,; \ldots \,; m, 0$ respectively. A line is taken through $A_m$ and is made to turn round $A_m$ from the position $A_m O$ until it first meets one of the other points; then round the last point which lies in this direction, say round $A_j$, until it first meets another; and so on.

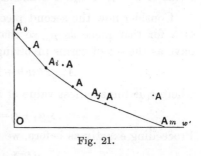

Fig. 21.

Any line through $A_i$ (the point $s_i, r_i$) is of the form

$$y - r_i = -\lambda (x - s_i).$$

The intercept on the axis of $z'$-indices is $\lambda s_i + r_i$, that is, the order of the term involving $A_{r_i s_i}$ for a substitution $w' = vz'^\lambda$. The perpendicular from the origin for a line through $A_i$ and $A_j$ is less than for any parallel line through other points with the same inclination; and, as this perpendicular is

$$(\lambda s_i + r_i)(1 + \lambda^2)^{-\frac{1}{2}},$$

it follows that, for the particular substitution $w' = vz'^\lambda$, the terms corresponding to the points lying on the line with coordinate $\lambda$ are the terms of lowest order, and consequently they are the terms which give the initial terms for the associated set of quantities $w'$.

Evidently, from the indices retained in the equation, the quantities $\lambda$ for the various pieces of the broken line from $A_m$ to $A_0$ are positive and finite.

Consider the first piece, from $A_m$ to $A_j$ say; then taking the value of $\lambda$ for that piece as $\mu_1$, so that we write $v_1 z'^{\mu_1}$ as the first term of $w'$, we have as the set of terms involving the lowest indices

$$Bw'^m + \Sigma\Sigma A_{rs} z'^r w'^s + A_{r_j s_j} z'^{r_j} w'^{s_j},$$

$s_j$ being the smallest value of $s$ retained; and then

$$m\mu_1 = s\mu_1 + r = s_j \mu_1 + r_j,$$

so that

$$\mu_1 = \frac{r}{m-s} = \frac{r_j}{m-s_j}.$$

---

[*] Reference in this connection may be made to Chrystal's *Algebra*, ch. xxx., with great advantage, as well as the authorities quoted on p. 197, note.

Let $p/q$ be the equivalent value of $\mu_1$ as the fraction in its lowest terms; and write $z' = \zeta^q$. Then $w' = v_1 z'^{\frac{p}{q}} = v_1 \zeta^p$; all the terms except the above group are of order $> mp$, and therefore the equation leads after division by $\zeta^{mp} v^{s_j}$ to

$$Bv_1^{m-s_j} + \Sigma A_{rs} v_1^{s-s_j} + A_{r_j s_j} = 0,$$

an equation which determines $m - s_j$ values for $v_1$, and therefore the initial terms of $m - s_j$ of the $w$-branches.

Consider now the second piece, from $A_j$ to $A_i$ say; then taking the value of $\lambda$ for that piece as $\mu_2$, so that we write $v_2 z'^{\mu_2}$ as the first term of $w'$, we have as the set of terms involving the lowest indices for this value of $\mu_2$

$$A_{r_j s_j} z'^{r_j} w'^{s_j} + \Sigma\Sigma A_{rs} z'^r w'^s + A_{r_i s_i} z'^{r_i} w'^{s_i},$$

where $s_i$ is the smallest value of $s$ retained.   Then

$$s_j \mu_2 + r_j = s\mu_2 + r = s_i \mu_2 + r_i.$$

Proceeding exactly as before, we find

$$A_{r_j s_j} v_2^{s_j - s_i} + \Sigma\Sigma A_{rs} v_2^{s-s_i} + A_{r_i s_i} = 0$$

as the equation determining $s_j - s_i$ values for $v_2$, and therefore the initial terms of $s_j - s_i$ of the $w$-branches.

And so on, until all the pieces of the line are used; the initial terms of all the $w$-branches are thus far determined in groups connected with the various pieces of the line $A_m A_j A_i \ldots A_0$.   By means of these initial terms, the $m$ branches can be arranged for their interchanges, by the description of a small circuit round the branch-point, according to the following theorem :—

*Each group can be resolved into systems, the members of each of which are cyclically interchangeable.*

It will be sufficient to prove this theorem for a single group, say the group determined by the first piece of broken line: the argument is general.

Since $\dfrac{p}{q}$ is the equivalent of $\dfrac{r}{m-s}$ and of $\dfrac{r_j}{m-s_j}$ and since $s_j < s$, we have

$$m - s = kq, \qquad m - s_j = k_j q, \qquad k_j > k;$$

and then the equation which determines $v_1$ is

$$Bv_1^{k_j q} + \Sigma A_{rs} v_1^{(k_j - k)q} + A_{r_j s_j} = 0,$$

that is, an equation of degree $k_j$ in $v_1^q$ as its variable.   Let $U$ be any root of it; then the corresponding values of $v_1$ are the values of $U^{\frac{1}{q}}$.   Suppose these $q$ values to be arranged so that the arguments increase by $2\pi \dfrac{p}{q}$, which is possible, because $p$ is prime to $q$.   Then the $q$ values of $w'$, being the values of $v_1 z'^{\mu_1}$, are

$$v_{11} z'^{\frac{p}{q}}, \qquad v_{12} z'^{\frac{p}{q}}, \qquad v_{13} z'^{\frac{p}{q}}, \ldots,$$

where $v_{1a}$ is that value of $U^{\frac{1}{q}}$ which has $\dfrac{2\pi p\alpha}{q}$ for its argument. A circuit round the $z'$-origin evidently increases the argument of any one of these $w'$-values by $2\pi p/q$, that is, it changes it into the value next in the succession; and so the set of $q$ values is a system the members of which are cyclically interchangeable.

This holds for each value of $U$ derived from the above equation; so that the whole set of $m - s_j$ branches are resolved into $k_j$ systems, each containing $q$ members with the assigned properties.

It is assumed that the above equation of order $k_j$ in $v_1{}^q$ has its roots unequal. If, however, it should have equal roots, it must be discussed *ab initio* by a method similar to that for the general equation; as the order $k_j$ (being a factor of $m - s_j$) is less than $m$, the discussion will be shorter and simpler, and will ultimately depend on equations with unequal roots as in the case above supposed.

It may happen that some of the quantities $\mu$ are integers, so that the corresponding integers $q$ are unity: a number of the branches would then be uniform at the point.

It thus appears that $z = a$ is a branch-point and that, under the present circumstances, the $m$ branches of the function can be arranged in systems, the members of each one of which are cyclically interchangeable.

Lastly it has been tacitly assumed in what precedes that the common value of $w$ for the branch-point is finite. If it be infinite, this infinite value can, by § 95, arise only out of singularities of the coefficients of the equation: and there is therefore a reversion to the discussion of §§ 95, 96. The distribution of the various branches into cyclical systems can be carried out exactly as above.

Another method of proceeding for these infinities would be to take $ww' = 1$, $z = c + z'$; but this method has no substantial advantage over the earlier one and, indeed, it is easy to see that there is no substantial difference between them.

*Note.* In the first case considered, a single transformation of the variables represented by $z' = \zeta^m$, $w' = v\zeta$, was sufficient to discriminate among the $m$ branches.

In the second case, the number of different directions in the broken line of fig. 21 is finite ($< m$); to each such direction there corresponds a transformation of the variables which leads to a discrimination among one of the groups out of the $m$ branches, and therefore the whole number of transformations needed to discriminate among the $m$ branches is finite.

If the $m$ branches are infinite at the point, the corresponding analysis shews that the whole number of transformations needed to discriminate among those $m$ branches is finite.

Moreover $m$ is finite, being $\leqslant n$; hence the various branches of the function $w$ are discriminated, at a branch-point, by a finite number of transformations.

*Ex.* 1. As an example, consider the function determined by the equation
$$8zw^3 + (1-z)(3w+1) = 0.$$
The equation determining the values of $z$ which give equal roots for $w$ is
$$8z(z-1)^2 = 4(z-1)^3,$$
so that the values are $z=1$ (repeated) and $z=-1$.

When $z=1$, then $w=0$, occurring thrice; and if $z=1+z'$, then
$$8w'^3 = z',$$
that is,
$$w' = \tfrac{1}{2}z'^{\frac{1}{3}}.$$
The three values are branches of one system in cyclical order for a circuit round $z=1$.

When $z=-1$, the equation for $w$ is
$$4w^3 - 3w - 1 = 0,$$
that is,
$$(w-1)(2w+1)^2 = 0,$$
so that $w=1$, or $w=-\tfrac{1}{2}$, occurring twice.

For the former of these we easily find that, for $z=-1+z'$, the value of $w$ is $1 + \tfrac{2}{9}z' + \ldots\ldots$, an isolated branch as is to be expected, for the value 1 is not repeated.

For the latter we take $w = -\tfrac{1}{2} + w'$, and find
$$w'^2 = \tfrac{1}{24}z' + \ldots\ldots,$$
so that the two branches are
$$w = -\tfrac{1}{2} + \frac{1}{2\sqrt{6}}z'^{\frac{1}{2}} + \ldots\ldots,$$
$$w = -\tfrac{1}{2} - \frac{1}{2\sqrt{6}}z'^{\frac{1}{2}} + \ldots\ldots,$$
and they are cyclically interchangeable for a small circuit round $z=-1$.

These are the finite values of $w$ at branch-points. For the infinities of $w$, which may arise in connection with the singularities of the coefficients, we take the zeros of the coefficient of the highest power of $w$ in the integral equation, viz., $z=0$, which is thus the only infinity of $w$. To find its order we take $w = z^{-n}f(z) = \gamma z^{-n} + \ldots\ldots$, where $\gamma$ is a constant and $f(z)$ is finite for $z=0$; and then we have
$$-\frac{8z^{1-3n}}{1-z}\gamma^3 + \ldots\ldots = 3\gamma z^{-n} + \ldots\ldots + 1.$$
Thus
$$1 - 3n = -n,$$
provided both of them be negative; the equality gives $n=\tfrac{1}{2}$ and satisfies the condition. And $8\gamma^3 = -3\gamma$. Of these values one is zero, and gives a branch of the function without an infinity; the other two are $\pm\tfrac{1}{2}\sqrt{-\tfrac{3}{2}}$ and they give the initial term of the two branches of $w$, which have an infinity of order $-\tfrac{1}{2}$ at the origin and are cyclically interchangeable for a small circuit round it. The three values of $w$ for infinitesimal values of $z$ are

$$w_1 = \sqrt{\tfrac{3}{8}}\,iz^{-\frac{1}{2}} + \tfrac{1}{6} - \tfrac{7}{18}\sqrt{\tfrac{3}{8}}\,iz^{\frac{1}{2}} - \tfrac{4}{81}z - \tfrac{275}{1944}\sqrt{\tfrac{3}{8}}\,iz^{\frac{3}{2}} - \tfrac{4}{729}z^2 + \ldots\ldots$$

$$w_2 = -\sqrt{\tfrac{3}{8}}\,iz^{-\frac{1}{2}} + \tfrac{1}{6} + \tfrac{7}{18}\sqrt{\tfrac{3}{8}}\,iz^{\frac{1}{2}} - \tfrac{4}{81}z + \tfrac{275}{1944}\sqrt{\tfrac{3}{8}}\,iz^{\frac{3}{2}} - \tfrac{4}{729}z^2 - \ldots\ldots$$

$$w_3 = -\tfrac{1}{3} + \tfrac{8}{81}z + \tfrac{8}{729}z^2 + \ldots\ldots$$

The first two of these form the system for the branch-point at the origin, which is neither an infinity nor a critical point for the third branch of the function.

*Ex.* 2.  Obtain the branch-points of the functions which are defined by the following equations, and determine the cyclical systems at the branch-points :—

    (i)   $w^3 - w + z = 0$ ;

    (ii)   $w^3 - 3w^2 + z^6 = 0$ ;

    (iii)  $w^3 - 3w + 2z^2 (2 - z^2) = 0$ ;

    (iv)  $w^3 - 3zw + z^3 = 0$ ;

    (v)   $w^5 - (1 - z^2) w^4 - \dfrac{4^4}{5^5} z^2 (1 - z^2)^4 = 0.$         (Briot and Bouquet.)

Also discuss the branches, in the vicinity of $z = 0$ and of $z = \infty$, of the functions defined by the following equations :—

    (vi)  $aw^7 + bw^5z + cw^4z^4 + dw^2z^5 + ewz^7 + fz^9 + gw^8 + hw^4z^5 + kz^{10} = 0$ ;

    (vii) $w^m z^n + w^n + z^m = 0.$

**97.**  Having shewn how to discriminate at any point among the various branches of the algebraic function defined by the equation

$$f(w, z) = h_0(z) w^n + h_1(z) w^{n-1} + h_2(z) w^{n-2} + \ldots = 0,$$

where the quantities $h_0(z)$, $h_1(z)$, $h_2(z)$, ... are holomorphic functions, we proceed to indicate the character of the various branches near the point. After the preceding discussions, it will be sufficient to consider only finite values of $z$ ; the consideration of infinite values can be obtained through the zero values of $z'$, where $\dfrac{1}{z'}$ is substituted for $z$. It is only for zeros of $h_0(z)$ that an infinite value (or several infinite values) of $w$ can arise : they can be discussed through the zero values of $w'$, where $\dfrac{1}{w'}$ is substituted for $w$.

Accordingly, let $a$ denote a finite value of $z$, and let $\alpha$ denote a finite value of $w$ for $z = a$, where $\alpha$ may be a simple root or multiple root of $f(\alpha, a) = 0$. Take $w = \alpha + y$, $z = a + x$, so as to consider some vicinity of the point $a$ and the character of $w$ in that vicinity ; and let

$$f(w, z) = f(\alpha + y, a + x) = F(y, x),$$

where $F$ is a polynomial in $y$ of degree not greater than $n$, and the coefficients are holomorphic functions of $x$ which are polynomials when all the coefficients $h_0, h_1, \ldots$ are polynomials. We have $F(0, 0) = 0$, so that there is no term free from $x$ and $y$ in $F(y, x)$. Also $F(y, 0)$ does not vanish for all values of $y$ ; for that would imply that some integral power of $x$ is a factor of $F(y, x)$ and therefore that some integral power of $z - a$ is a factor of $f(w, z)$, which is not the case. Hence there is at least one term in the polynomial $F(y, x)$, which has a constant for its coefficient, and there may be more than one such term ; let the term of lowest order in $y$ be $By^m$, and let the aggregate of such terms be denoted by $F_0(y)$. Denoting the rest by $F_1(y, x)$, where $F_1$ is a polynomial in $y$ that has holomorphic functions of $x$ for its coefficients, we have

$$F(y, x) = F_0(y) - F_1(y, x) ;$$

clearly $F_1(y, x)$ vanishes when $x = 0$ for all values of $y$, in any vicinity of $y = 0$. Hence* we can choose a region in the vicinity of $y = 0$, $x = 0$, such that

$$|F_0| > |F_1|;$$

but as $F_0$ vanishes when $y = 0$, there may be some limit of $|y|$ other than zero, at and below which the inequality does not hold. Accordingly, assume as the range for the inequality

$$|\rho_0| < |y| < \rho, \qquad |x| < r.$$

For such values we have, on taking logarithmic derivatives of the equation

$$F = F_0\left(1 - \frac{F_1}{F_0}\right),$$

the relation

$$\frac{1}{F}\frac{\partial F}{\partial y} = \frac{1}{F_0}\frac{\partial F_0}{\partial y} - \frac{\partial}{\partial x}\sum_{\lambda=1}^{\infty}\frac{1}{\lambda}\frac{F_1^\lambda}{F_0^\lambda}.$$

Since $F_0$ is a polynomial in $y$ that is divisible by $y^m$, we have

$$\frac{1}{F_0}\frac{\partial F_0}{\partial y} = \frac{m}{y} + G(y),$$

where $G$ is a converging series of integral powers. Similarly

$$\frac{F_1^\lambda}{F_0^\lambda} = \sum_{\mu=0}^{\infty} G_{\lambda,\mu}\, y^{-m\lambda+\mu},$$

where the quantities $G_{\lambda,\mu}$ are converging series of integral powers of $x$, each of them vanishing with $x$. As the series $\sum_{\lambda=1}^{\infty}\frac{1}{\lambda}\frac{F_1^\lambda}{F_0^\lambda}$ converges uniformly, we may gather together the various terms that involve the same power of $y$; and we then have

$$\sum_{\lambda=1}^{\infty}\frac{1}{\lambda}\frac{F_1^\lambda}{F_0^\lambda} = \sum_{p=-\infty}^{\infty} G_p y^p,$$

where each of the coefficients $G_p$ is a converging power-series in $x$ which vanishes with $x$. Thus

$$\frac{1}{F}\frac{\partial F}{\partial y} = \frac{m}{y} + G(y) - \frac{\partial}{\partial y}\sum_{p=-\infty}^{\infty} G_p y^p,$$

where the only term on the right-hand side in $y^{-1}$ is $\dfrac{m}{y}$.

Now let $\eta_1, \ldots, \eta_s$ denote the zeros of $F(y, \kappa)$, for values of $y$ such that $|y| < \rho$ and for a parametric value $\kappa$ of $x$ such that $|\kappa| < r$: it might be that there are no such zeros (though this will be seen not to be the case): repeated zeros are given by repetition in the quantities $\eta$. Then

$$\frac{1}{F}\frac{\partial F(y, \kappa)}{\partial y} - \sum_{l=1}^{s}\frac{1}{y - \eta_l}$$

* What follows is a special case of an important theorem, due to Weierstrass, *Ges. Werke*, t. ii, p. 135.

is finite for all values of $y$ within the range, and therefore it can be expanded in a converging series of positive powers, so that

$$\frac{1}{F}\frac{\partial F(y, \kappa)}{\partial y} = \sum_{l=1}^{s} \frac{1}{y-\eta_l} + P(y).$$

Now choose values of $y$, still such that $|y| < \rho$, and also such that they give moduli greater than the greatest of the quantities $|\eta_l|$; the fractions on the right-hand side can be expanded in descending powers of $y$, and we have

$$\frac{1}{F}\frac{\partial F(y, \kappa)}{\partial y} = P(y) + \frac{s}{y} + \sum_{\mu=1}^{\infty} S_\mu y^{-\mu-1},$$

where

$$S_\mu = \eta_1{}^\mu + \eta_2{}^\mu + \ldots + \eta_l{}^\mu.$$

The parametric value $\kappa$ in this expansion can be replaced by $x$; and thus comparing the two expansions for $\frac{1}{F}\frac{\partial F}{\partial y}$, we have

$$s = m, \qquad S_\mu = \mu G_{-\mu}.$$

The first of these results shews that there are $m$ roots of $F$ within the range. The second of them expresses the sums of the positive powers of $\eta_1, \ldots, \eta_l$ as converging series of positive powers of $x$ which vanish with $x$; hence the symmetric integral functions of $\eta_1, \ldots, \eta_l$ are regular functions of $x$ in the vicinity of $x = 0$ and vanish with $x$. Let

$$g(y, x) = (y-\eta_1)(y-\eta_2)\ldots(y-\eta_l)$$
$$= y^m + g_1 y^{m-1} + \ldots + g_l,$$

where $g_l$ are regular functions of $x$ and vanish with $x$.

A further comparison of the expansions shews that

$$P(y) = G(y) - \sum_{q=0}^{\infty}(q+1)G_{q+1}y^q$$

$$= \frac{\partial}{\partial y}\Gamma(y, x),$$

where $\Gamma(y, x)$ is a regular function of $y$ and $x$, given by

$$\Gamma(y, x) = \int_0^y G(y)\,dy - \sum_{q=0}^{\infty} G_{q+1}y^{q+1}.$$

Hence

$$\frac{1}{F}\frac{\partial F}{\partial y} = \sum_{l=1}^{s}\frac{1}{y-\eta_l} + \frac{\partial}{\partial y}\Gamma(y, x),$$

and therefore

$$F = Ug(y, x)\, e^{\Gamma(y, x)},$$

where $U$ is a quantity independent of $y$. Now when $x$ is zero, $U$ is $B$; hence generally

$$U = B\,(1 + \text{positive powers of } x)$$
$$= Be^\xi,$$

where $\xi$ is a regular function of $x$ vanishing with $x$. Writing $G(y, x)$ for $\Gamma(y, x) + \xi$, where $G(0, 0) = 0$, we have

$$F = Bg(y, x)\, e^{G(y, x)},$$

with the defined significance of $g(y, x)$ and $G(y, x)$.

Our immediate purpose is with such values of $y$, being functions of $x$, as make $F$ vanish in the region considered. Clearly the exponential term does not vanish; and therefore we have the values of $y$ given by

$$g(y, x) = y^m + g_1 y^{m-1} + g_2 y^{m-2} + \ldots + g_m = 0,$$

where $g_1, g_2, \ldots, g_m$ are regular functions of $x$ that vanish with $x$.

*Case* 1. The simplest case arises when $m = 1$; the root $\alpha$ is then a simple root of $f(\alpha, a) = 0$, and we have

$$y + g_1 = 0,$$

that is,

$$w - \alpha = y = -g_1 = Q(z - a),$$

or in the vicinity of the point $a$, the branch associated with the simple root of $f(\alpha, a) = 0$ is a regular function of $z - a$.

The same result holds for each simple root $\alpha$ of the equation $f(\alpha, a) = 0$.

*Case* 2. Let $m > 1$, so that the root $\alpha$ is a multiple root of $f(\alpha, a) = 0$, and $z = a$ may be (and generally is) a branch-point. The equation

$$g(y, x) = y^m + g_1 y^{m-1} + g_2 y^{m-2} + \ldots + g_m = 0$$

determines $m$ branches. By § 96 these branches can be arranged in groups, each group corresponding to a particular order $|y| \propto |x|^{\frac{p}{q}}$ for sufficiently small values of $|y|$ and $|x|$, and the order being determined by a portion of a broken line in a Puiseux diagram.

Thus for the first portion of the line, take $x = \zeta^q$, $y = v\zeta^p$; then the equation becomes of the form

$$v^m + \Sigma \kappa_r v^{m-r} + \kappa_s v^{m-s} + \zeta P(v, \zeta) = 0,$$

where $P(v, \zeta)$ is a regular function of its arguments. When $\zeta = 0$, we have

$$v^s + \Sigma \kappa_r v^{s-r} + \kappa_s = 0,$$

rejecting the zero values of $v$. If $v = v_1$ be a simple root of this equation, then in the earlier equation we write $v = v_1 + u$; and it then follows, by Case 1 above, that

$$u = R(\zeta),$$

where $R$ is a regular function of $\zeta$ that vanishes when $\zeta = 0$. Accordingly for every simple root of the equation in $v$ when $\zeta$ is zero, we have

$$z - a = \zeta^q, \qquad w - \alpha = \zeta^p \{v_1 + R(\zeta)\},$$

shewing that the corresponding branch of the algebraic function is a uniform function of $(z-a)^{\frac{1}{q}}$. When $q$ is 1, the branch is a regular function of $z-a$. When $q>1$, there is a system of roots of the same form.

It may happen that $v_1$ is a multiple root* of

$$v^s + \Sigma \kappa_r v^{s-r} + \kappa_s = 0.$$

This equation is of degree $s$, being less than $m$, the degree of the original equation. To it we apply, for the multiple root, the preceding process: and so gradually reach the stage in which each of the branches is discriminated and analytically expressed.

Similarly for the remaining portions of the broken line in the Puiseux diagram of § 96.

It therefore follows that all the branches (if the branches be more than one) of the function, defined by the equation $f(w, z) = 0$ and acquiring the value $\alpha$ when $z = a$, where $f(\alpha, a) = 0$, can be represented in the analytical form

$$z - a = \zeta^q, \qquad w - \alpha = \zeta^p S(\zeta),$$

where $S(\zeta)$ is a regular function of its argument which does not vanish when $\zeta = 0$, and where $p$, $q$ are positive integers not necessarily the same for all the branches. (As already remarked, we have assumed $\alpha$ and $a$ to be finite. It is easy to see that for an infinite value of $w$ when $z = a$, we have a branch of the form

$$z - a = \zeta^q, \qquad w = \zeta^{-p'} T(\zeta),$$

where $p'$ is a finite integer; and similarly for infinite values of $z$.) Consequently the function defined by the equation $f(w, z) = 0$, which is polynomial in $w$ and uniform in $z$, has $m$ branches at any point $a$, each of the branches being expressible as a uniform analytic function of $(z-a)^{\frac{1}{q}}$. If $f(w, z)$ is polynomial in $z$ as well as in $w$, the non-regular points of the branches are poles and branch-points: no point in the plane is an essential singularity for any branch.

COROLLARY. We have the theorem, originally due to Cauchy, as an inference from the whole investigation:—

*The roots $w$ of an equation $f(w, z) = 0$, which is polynomial in $w$ and uniform in $z$, are continuous functions of $z$.*

It follows at once from the two relations

$$z - a = \zeta^q, \qquad w - \alpha = \zeta^p S(\zeta).$$

---

\* Such is the case for the equation

$$w^6 - 15w^4 z - 2w^3 z + 15w^2 z^2 + 6wz^2 + z^2 - z^3 = 0.$$

*Note.* If $v_1$ be a multiple root of its equation, the form

$$z - a = \zeta^q, \qquad w - \alpha = \zeta^p S(\zeta),$$

is still valid: but $p$ and $q$ are then not necessarily prime to each other. (The equation represented by

$$z - a = \zeta^{30}, \qquad w - \alpha = \sum_{n=2}^{\infty} a_n \zeta^n,$$

is an example.) The condition is that, if the indices in the expression for $w - \alpha$ have a common factor $f$, then $f$ is not a factor of $q$.

**98.** There is one case of considerable importance which, though limited in character, is made the basis of Clebsch and Gordan's investigations[*] in the theory of Abelian functions—the results being, of course, restricted by the initial limitations. It is assumed that *all the branch-points are simple*, that is, are such that only one pair of branches of $w$ are interchanged by a circuit of the variable round the point; and it is assumed that the equation $f = 0$ is polynomial not merely in $w$ but also in $z$. The equation $f = 0$ can then be regarded as the generalised form of the equation of a curve of the $n$th order, the generalisation consisting in replacing the usual coordinates by complex variables; and it is further assumed, in order to simplify the analysis, that all the multiple points on the curve are (real or imaginary) double-points. But, even with the limitations, the results are of great value in themselves; and the theory of birational transformation (§§ 245—252) brings them within the range of unrestricted generality. It is therefore desirable to establish the results that belong to the present section of the subject.

We assume, therefore, that the branch-points are such that only one pair of branches of $w$ are interchanged by a small closed circuit round any one of the points. The branch-points are among the values of $z$ determined by the equations

$$f(w, z) = 0, \qquad \frac{\partial f(w, z)}{\partial w} = 0.$$

When $f = 0$ has the most general form consistent with the assigned limitations, $f(w, z)$ is of the $n$th degree in $z$; the values of $z$ are determined by the eliminant of the two equations which is of degree $n(n-1)$, and there are, therefore, $n(n-1)$ values of $z$ which must be examined.

First, suppose that $\dfrac{\partial f(w, z)}{\partial z}$ does not vanish for a value of $z$, thus obtained, and the corresponding value of $w$; then we have the first case in the preceding investigation. And, on the hypothesis adopted in the present instance, $m = 2$; so that *each such point $z$ is a branch-point.*

* Clebsch und Gordan, *Theorie der Abel'schen Functionen*, (Leipzig, Teubner, 1866). It will be proved hereafter (§ 252) that any algebraical equation can be transformed birationally into an equation of the kind indicated. The actual transformations, however, tend to become extremely complicated; and, in particular instances, detailed results would be obtained more simply by proceeding directly from the original equation.

Next, suppose that $\dfrac{\partial f\,(w,\,z)}{\partial z}$ vanishes for some of the $n\,(n-1)$ values of $z$; the value of $m$ is still 2, owing to the hypothesis. The case will now be still further limited by assuming that $\dfrac{\partial^2 f\,(w,\,z)}{\partial z^2}$ does not vanish for the value of $z$ and the corresponding value of $w$; and thus in the vicinity of $z=a$, $w=\alpha$ we have an equation

$$0 = Az'^2 + 2Bz'w' + Cw'^2 + \text{terms of the third degree} + \ldots\ldots,$$

where $A$, $B$, $C$ are the values of $\dfrac{\partial^2 f}{\partial z^2},\ \dfrac{\partial^2 f}{\partial z\,\partial w},\ \dfrac{\partial^2 f}{\partial w^2}$ for $z=a$, $w=\alpha$.

If $B^2 \gtrless AC$, this equation leads to the solution

$$Cw + Bz' \propto \text{uniform function of } z'.$$

The point $z=a$, $w=\alpha$ is *not* a branch-point; the values of $w$, equal at the point, are functionally distinct. Moreover, such a point $z$ occurs doubly in the eliminant; so that, if there be $\delta$ such points, they account for $2\delta$ in the eliminant of degree $n\,(n-1)$; and therefore, on their score, the number $n\,(n-1)$ must be diminished by $2\delta$. The case is, reverting to the generalisation of the geometry, that of a double point where the tangents are not coincident.

If, however, $B^2 = AC$, the equation leads to the solution

$$Cw' + Bz' = Lz'^{\frac{3}{2}} + Mz'^2 + Nz'^{\frac{5}{2}} + \ldots\ldots$$

The point $z=a$, $w=\alpha$ is a point where the two values of $z$ interchange. Now such a point $z$ occurs triply in the eliminant; so that, if there be $\kappa$ such points, they account for $3\kappa$ of the degree of the equation. Each of them provides only one branch-point, and the aggregate therefore provides $\kappa$ branch-points; hence, in counting the branch-points of this type as derived through the degree of the eliminant, the degree must be diminished by $2\kappa$. The case is, reverting to the generalisation of the geometry, that of a double point (real or imaginary) where the tangents are coincident.

It is assumed that all the $n\,(n-1)$ points $z$ are accounted for under the three classes considered. Hence *the number of branch-points of the equation is*

$$\Omega = n\,(n-1) - 2\delta - 2\kappa,$$

where $n$ is the degree of the equation, $\delta$ is the number of double points (in the generalised geometrical sense) at which tangents to the curve do not coincide, and $\kappa$ is the number of double points at which tangents to the curve do coincide.

And at each of these branch-points, $\Omega$ in number, two branches of the function are equal and, for a small circuit round it, interchange.

**99.** The following theorem is a combined converse of many of the theorems which have been proved:—

*A function $w$, which has $n$ (and only $n$) values for each value of $z$, and which has a finite number of infinities and of branch-points in any part of the plane, is a root of an equation in $w$ of degree $n$, the coefficients of which are uniform functions of $z$ in that part of the plane.*

We shall first prove that every integral symmetric function of the $n$ values is a uniform function in the part of the plane under consideration.

Let $S_k$ denote $\sum\limits_{i=1}^{n} w_i{}^k$, where $k$ is a positive integer. At an ordinary point of the plane, $S_k$ is evidently a one-valued function and that value is finite; $S_k$ is continuous; and therefore the function $S_k$ is uniform in the immediate vicinity of an ordinary point of the plane.

For a point $a$, which is a branch-point of the function $w$, we know that the branches can be arranged in cyclical systems. Let $w_1, \ldots, w_\mu$ be such a system. Then these branches interchange in cyclical order for a description of a small circuit round $a$; and, if $z - a = Z^\mu$, it is known (§ 93) that, in the vicinity of $Z = 0$, a branch $w$ is a uniform function of $Z$, say

$$w = G\left(\frac{1}{Z}\right) + P(Z).$$

Therefore 
$$w^k = G_k\left(\frac{1}{Z}\right) + P_k(Z),$$

in the vicinity of $Z = 0$; say

$$w_1{}^k = A_k + \sum_{m=1} B_{k,m} Z^{-m} + \sum_{m=1} C_{k,m} Z^m.$$

Now the other branches of the function, which are equal at $a$, are derivable from any one of them by taking the successive values which that one acquires as the variable describes successive circuits round $a$. A circuit of $w$ round $a$ changes the argument of $z - a$ by $2\pi$, and therefore gives $Z$ reproduced but multiplied by a factor which is a primitive $\mu$th root of unity, say by a factor $\alpha$; a second circuit will reproduce $Z$ with a factor $\alpha^2$; and so on. Hence

$$w_2{}^k = A_k + \sum_{m=1} B_{k,m} \alpha^{-m} Z^{-m} + \sum_{m=1} C_{k,m} \alpha^m Z^m,$$

$$\cdots\cdots\cdots\cdots\cdots \vdots \cdots\cdots\cdots\cdots\cdots$$

$$w_{r+1}{}^k = A_k + \sum_{m=1} B_{k,m} \alpha^{-rm} Z^{-m} + \sum_{m=1} C_{k,m} \alpha^{rm} Z^m,$$

$$\cdots\cdots\cdots\cdots\cdots \vdots \cdots\cdots\cdots\cdots\cdots$$

and therefore

$$\sum_{r=1}^{\mu} w_r^k = \mu A_k + \sum_{m=1} B_{km} Z^{-m} (1 + \alpha^{-m} + \alpha^{-2m} + \ldots + \alpha^{-m\mu+m})$$

$$+ \sum_{m=1} C_{km} Z^m (1 + \alpha^m + \alpha^{2m} + \ldots + \alpha^{m\mu-m}).$$

Now, since $\alpha$ is a primitive $\mu$th root of unity,

$$1 + \alpha^s + \alpha^{2s} + \ldots + \alpha^{s(\mu-1)}$$

is zero for all integral values of $s$ which are not integral multiples of $\mu$, and it is $\mu$ for those values of $s$ which are integral values of $\mu$; hence

$$\frac{1}{\mu} \sum_{r=1}^{\mu} w_r^k = A_k + B_{k,\mu} Z^{-\mu} + B_{k,2\mu} Z^{-2\mu} + B_{k,3\mu} Z^{-3\mu} + \ldots$$

$$+ C_{k,\mu} Z^{\mu} + C_{k,2\mu} Z^{2\mu} + C_{k,3\mu} Z^{3\mu} + \ldots$$

$$= A_k + B'_{k,1} (z-a)^{-1} + B'_{k,2} (z-a)^{-2} + B'_{k,3} (z-a)^{-3} + \ldots$$

$$+ C'_{k,1} (z-a) + C'_{k,2} (z-a)^2 + C'_{k,3} (z-a)^3 + \ldots.$$

Hence the point $z = a$ may be a singularity of $\sum_{r=1}^{\mu} w_r^k$ but it is not a branch-point of the function; and therefore in the immediate vicinity of $z = a$ the quantity $\sum_{r=1}^{\mu} w_r^k$ is a uniform function.

The point $a$ is an essential singularity of this uniform function, if the order of the infinity of $w$ at $a$ be infinite: it is an accidental singularity, if that order be finite.

This result is evidently valid for all the cyclical systems at $a$, as well as for the individual branches which may happen to be one-valued at $a$. Hence $S_k$, being the sum of sums of the form $\sum_{r=1}^{\mu} w_r^k$ each of which is a uniform function of $z$ in the vicinity of $a$, is itself a uniform function of $z$ in that vicinity. Also $a$ is an essential singularity of $S_k$, if the order of the infinity at $z = a$ for any one of the branches of $w$ be infinite; and it is an accidental singularity of $S_k$, if the order of the infinity at $z = a$ for all the branches of $w$ be finite. Lastly, it is an ordinary point of $S_k$, if there be no branch of $w$ for which it is an infinity. Similarly for each of the branch-points.

Again, let $c$ be a regular singularity of any one (or more) of the branches of $w$; then $c$ is a regular singularity of every power of each of those branches, the singularities being simultaneously accidental or simultaneously essential. Hence $c$ is a singularity of $S_k$: and therefore in the vicinity of $c$, $S_k$ is a uniform function, having $c$ for an accidental singularity if it be so for each of the branches $w$ affected by it, and having $c$ for an essential singularity if it be so for any one of the branches $w$.

It thus appears that in the part of the plane under consideration the function $S_k$ is one-valued; and it is continuous and finite, except at certain isolated points each of which is a singularity. It is therefore a uniform function in that part of the plane; and the singularity of the function at any point is essential, if the order of the infinity for any one of the branches $w$ at that point be infinite, but it is accidental, if the order of the infinity for all the branches $w$ there be finite. And the number of these singularities is finite, being not greater than the combined number of the infinities of the function $w$, whether regular singularities or branch-points.

Since the sums of the $k$th powers for all positive values of the integer $k$ are uniform functions, and since any integral symmetric function of the $n$ values is a rational integral function of the sums of the powers, it follows that any integral symmetric function of the $n$ values is a uniform function of $z$ in the part of the plane under consideration; and every infinity of a branch $w$ leads to a singularity of the symmetric function, which is essential or accidental according as the orders of infinity of the various branches are not all finite or are all finite.

Since $w$ has $n$ (and only $n$) values $w_1, \ldots, w_n$ for each value of $z$, the equation which determines $w$ is

$$(w - w_1)(w - w_2) \ldots (w - w_n) = 0.$$

The coefficients of the various powers of $w$ are symmetric functions of the branches $w_1, \ldots, w_n$; and therefore they are uniform functions of $z$ in the part of the plane under consideration. They possess a finite number of singularities, which are accidental or essential according to the character of the infinities of the branches at the same points.

COROLLARY. *If all the infinities of the branches in the finite part of the whole plane be of finite order, then the finite singularities of all the coefficients of the powers of $w$ in the equation satisfied by $w$ are all accidental; and the coefficients themselves then take the form of a quotient of an integral uniform function (which may be either transcendental or merely polynomial, in the sense of § 47) by another function of a similar character.*

If $z = \infty$ be an essential singularity for at least one of the coefficients, through being an infinity of unlimited order for a branch of $w$, then one or both of the functions in the quotient-form of one at least of the coefficients must be transcendental.

If $z = \infty$ be an accidental singularity or an ordinary point for all the coefficients, through being either an infinity of finite order or an ordinary point for the branches of $w$, then all the functions which occur in all the coefficients are rational expressions. When the equation is multiplied throughout by the least common multiple of the denominators of the coefficients, it takes the form

$$w^n h_0(z) + w^{n-1} h_1(z) + \ldots + w h_{n-1}(z) + h_n(z) = 0,$$

where the functions $h_0(z), h_1(z), \ldots, h_n(z)$ are polynomials in $z$.

A knowledge of the number of infinities of $w$ gives an upper limit of the degree of the equation in $z$ in the last form. Thus, let $a_i$ be a regular singularity of the function; and let $\alpha_i, \beta_i, \gamma_i, \ldots$ be the orders of the infinities of the branches at $a_i$; then

$$w_1 w_2 \ldots w_n (z - a_i)^{\lambda_i},$$

where $\lambda_i$ denotes $\alpha_i + \beta_i + \gamma_i + \ldots$, is finite (but not zero) for $z = a_i$.

Let $c_i$ be a branch-point, which is an infinity; and let $\mu$ branches $w$ form a system for $c_i$, such that $w (z - c_i)^{\frac{\theta_i}{\mu}}$ is finite (but not zero) at the point; then

$$w_1 w_2 \ldots w_\mu (z - c_i)^{\theta_i}$$

is finite (but not zero) at the point, and therefore also

$$w_1 \ldots w_n (z - c_i)^{\theta_i + \phi_i + \psi_i + \ldots}$$

is finite, where $\theta_i$, $\phi_i$, $\psi_i$, $\ldots$ are numbers belonging to the various systems; or, if $\epsilon_i$ denote $\theta_i + \phi_i + \psi_i + \ldots$, then

$$w_1 \ldots w_n (z - c_i)^{\epsilon_i}$$

is finite for $z = c_i$. Similarly for other symmetric functions of $w$.

Hence, if $a_1, a_2, \ldots$ be the regular singularities with numbers $\lambda_1, \lambda_2, \ldots$ defined as above, and if $c_1, c_2, \ldots$ be the branch-points, that are also infinities, with numbers $\epsilon_1, \epsilon_2, \ldots$ defined as above, then the product

$$(w - w_1) \ldots\ldots (w - w_n) \prod_{i=1} (z - a_i)^{\lambda_i} \prod_{i=1} (z - c_i)^{\epsilon_i}$$

is finite at all the points $a_i$ and at all the points $c_i$. The points $a$ and the points $c$ are the only points in the finite part of the plane that can make the product infinite: hence it is finite everywhere in the finite part of the plane, and it is therefore polynomial in $z$.

Lastly, let $\rho$ be the number for $z = \infty$ corresponding to $\lambda_i$ for $a_i$ or to $\epsilon_i$ for $c_i$, so that for the coefficient of any power of $w$ in $(w - w_1) \ldots (w - w_n)$ the greatest difference in degree between the numerator and the denominator is $\rho$ in favour of the excess of the former.

Then the preceding product is of order

$$\rho + \Sigma \lambda_i + \Sigma \epsilon_i,$$

which is therefore the degree of the equation in $z$ when it is expressed in a holomorphic form.

# CHAPTER IX.

## PERIODS OF DEFINITE INTEGRALS, AND PERIODIC FUNCTIONS IN GENERAL.

**100.** INSTANCES have already occurred in which the value of a function of $z$ is not dependent solely upon the value of $z$ but depends also on the course of variation by which $z$ obtains that value; for example, integrals of uniform functions, and multiform functions. And it may be expected that, *a fortiori*, the value of an integral connected with a multiform function will depend upon the course of variation of the variable $z$. Now as integrals which arise in this way through multiform functions and, generally, integrals connected with differential equations are a fruitful source of new functions, it is desirable that the effects on the value of an integral caused by variations of a $z$-path be assigned so that, within the limits of algebraic possibility, the expression of the integral may be made completely determinate.

There are two methods which, more easily than others, secure this result; one of them is substantially due to Cauchy, the other to Riemann.

The consideration of Riemann's method, both for multiform functions and for integrals of such functions, will be undertaken later, in Chapters XV., XVI. Cauchy's method has already been used in preceding sections relating to uniform functions, and it can be extended to multiform functions. Its characteristic feature is the isolation of critical points, whether regular singularities or branch-points, by means of small curves each containing one and only one critical point.

Over the rest of the plane the variable $z$ ranges freely and, under certain conditions, any path of variation of $z$ from one point to another can, as will be proved immediately, be deformed without causing any change in the value of the integral, provided that the path does not meet any of the small curves in the course of the deformation. Further, from a knowledge of the relation of any point thus isolated to the function, it is possible to calculate the change caused by a deformation of the $z$-path over such a point; and thus, for defined deformations, the value of the integral can be assigned precisely.

The properties proved in Chapter II. are useful in the consideration of the integrals of uniform functions; it is now necessary to establish the propositions which give the effects of deformation of path on the integrals of multiform functions. The most important of these propositions is the following :—

*If $w$ be a multiform function, the value of $\int_a^b wdz$, taken between two ordinary points, is unaltered for a deformation of the path, provided that the initial branch of $w$ be the same and that no branch-point or infinity be crossed in the deformation.*

Consider two paths $acb$, $adb$, (fig. 16, p. 181), satisfying the conditions specified in the proposition. Then in the area between them the branch $w$ has no infinity and no point of discontinuity; and there is no branch-point in that area. Hence, by § 90, Corollary VI., the branch $w$ is a uniform monogenic function for that area; it is continuous and finite everywhere within it and, by the same Corollary, we may treat $w$ as a uniform, monogenic, finite and continuous function. Hence, by § 17, we have

$$(c) \int_a^b wdz + (d) \int_b^a wdz = 0,$$

the first integral being taken along $acb$ and the second along $bda$; and therefore

$$(c) \int_a^b wdz = -(d) \int_b^a wdz = (d) \int_a^b wdz,$$

shewing that the values of the integral along the two paths are the same under the specified conditions.

It is evident that, if some critical point be crossed in the deformation, the branch $w$ cannot be declared uniform and finite in the area, and the theorem of § 17 cannot then be applied.

COROLLARY I. *The integral round a closed curve containing no critical point is zero.*

COROLLARY II. *A curve round a branch-point, containing no other critical point of the function, can be deformed into a loop without altering the value of $\int wdz$;* for the deformation satisfies the condition of the proposition. Hence, when the value of the integral for the loop is known, the value of the integral is known for the curve.

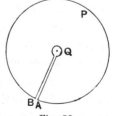

Fig. 22.

COROLLARY III. From the proposition it is possible to infer conditions, under which *the integral $\int wdz$ round the whole of any curve remains unchanged, when the whole curve is deformed,* without leaving an infinitesimal arc common as in Corollary II.

Let $CDC'$, $ABA'$ be the curves: join two consecutive points $AA'$ to two consecutive points $CC'$. Then if the area $CABA'C'DC$ enclose no critical point of the function $w$, the value of $\int wdz$ along $CDC'$ is by the proposition the same as its value along $CABA'C'$. The latter is made up of the value along $CA$, the value along $ABA'$, and the value along $A'C'$, say

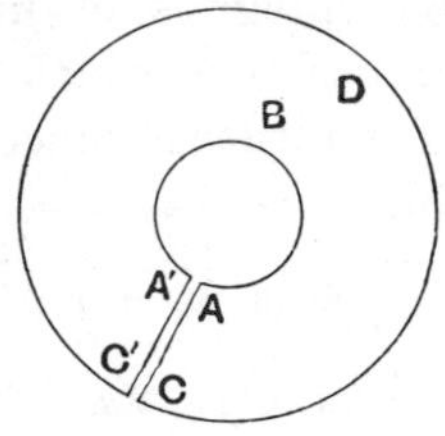

$$\int_C^A wdz + \int_B wdz + \int_{A'}^{C'} w'dz,$$

where $w'$ is the changed value of $w$ consequent on the description of a simple curve reducible to $B$ (§ 90, Cor. II.).

Fig. 23.

Now since $w$ is finite everywhere, the difference between the values of $w$ at $A$ and at $A'$ consequent on the description of $ABA'$ is finite: hence as $A'A$ is infinitesimal the value of $\int wdz$ necessary to complete the value for the whole curve $B$ is infinitesimal and therefore the complete value can be taken as the foregoing integral $\int_{B.} wdz$. Similarly for the complete value along the curve $D$: and therefore the difference of the integrals round $B$ and round $D$ is

$$\int_C^A wdz + \int_{A'}^{C'} w'dz,$$

say

$$\int_C^A (w - w')dz.$$

In general this integral is not zero, so that the values of the integral round $B$ and round $D$ are not equal to one another: and therefore the curve $D$ cannot be deformed into the curve $B$ without affecting the value of $\int wdz$ round the whole curve, even when the deformation does not cause the curve to pass over a critical point of the function.

But in special cases it may vanish. The most important and, as a matter of fact, the one of most frequent occurrence is that in which the description of the curve $B$ restores at $A'$ the initial value of $w$ at $A$. It easily follows, by the use of § 90, Cor. II., that the description of $D$ (assuming that the area between $B$ and $D$ includes no critical point) restores at $C'$ the initial value of $w$ at $C$. In such a case, $w = w'$ for corresponding points on $AC$ and $A'C'$, and the integral, which expresses the difference, is zero: the value of the integral for the curve $B$ is then the same as that for $D$. Hence we have the proposition :—

*If a curve be such that the description of it by the independent variable restores the initial value of a multiform function $w$, then the value of $\int wdz$ taken round the curve is unaltered when the curve is deformed into any other curve, provided that no branch-point or point of discontinuity of $w$ is crossed in the course of deformation.*

This is the generalisation of the proposition of § 19 which has thus far been used only for uniform functions.

*Note.*  Two particular cases, which are very simple, may be mentioned here: special examples will be given immediately.

The first is that in which the curve $B$, and therefore also $D$, encloses no branch-point or infinity; the initial value of $w$ is restored after a description of either curve, and it is easy to see (by reducing $B$ to a point, as may be done) that the value of the integral is zero.

The second is that in which the curve encloses more than one branch-point, the enclosed branch-points being such that a circuit of all the loops, into which (by Corollary V., § 90) the curve can be deformed, restores the initial branch of $w$.  This case is of especial importance when $w$ is two-valued: the curves then enclose an even number of branch-points.

**101.**  It is important to know the value of the integral of a multiform function round a small curve enclosing a branch-point.

Let $c$ be a point at which $m$ branches of an algebraic function are equal and interchange in a single cycle; and let $c$, if an infinity, be of only finite order, say $k/m$.  Then in the vicinity of $c$, any of the branches $w$ can be expressed in the form

$$w = \sum_{s=-k}^{\infty} g_s (z-c)^{\frac{s}{m}},$$

where $k$ is a finite integer.

The value of $\int w dz$ taken round a small curve enclosing $c$ is the sum of the integrals

$$g_s \int (z-c)^{\frac{s}{m}} dz,$$

the value of which, taken once round the curve and beginning at a point $z_1$, is

$$\frac{m g_s}{m+s} (z_1 - c)^{\frac{s}{m}+1} [\alpha^s - 1],$$

where $\alpha$ is a primitive $m$th root of unity, provided $m+s$ is not zero.  If then $m+s$ be positive, the value is zero in the limit when the curve is infinitesimal: if $m+s$ be negative, the value is $\infty$ in the limit.

But, if $m+s$ be zero, the value is $2\pi i g_s$.

Hence we have the proposition: *If, in the vicinity of a branch-point $c$, where $m$ branches $w$ are equal to one another and interchange cyclically, the expression of one of the branches be*

$$g_k (z-c)^{-\frac{k}{m}} + g_{k-1} (z-c)^{-\frac{k-1}{m}} + \ldots\ldots$$

*then $\int w dz$, taken once round a small curve enclosing $c$, is zero, if $k < m$; is infinite, if $k > m$; and is $2\pi i g_k$, if $k = m$.*

It is easy to see that, if the integral be taken $m$ times round the small curve enclosing $c$, then the value of the integral is $2m\pi i g_m$ when $k$ is greater than $m$, so that the integral vanishes unless there be a term involving $(z-c)^{-1}$ in the expansion of a branch $w$ in the vicinity of the point. The reason that the integral, which can furnish an infinite value for a single circuit, ceases to do so for $m$ circuits, is that the quantity $(z_1-c)^{-\frac{\lambda}{m}}$, which becomes indefinitely great in the limit, is multiplied for a single circuit by $\alpha^\lambda - 1$, for a second circuit by $\alpha^{2\lambda} - \alpha^\lambda$, and so on, and for the $m$th circuit by $\alpha^{m\lambda} - \alpha^{(m-1)\lambda}$, the sum of all of which coefficients is zero.

*Ex.* The integral $\int \{(z-a)(z-b)\dots(z-f)\}^{-\frac{1}{2}} dz$ taken round an indefinitely small curve enclosing $a$ is zero, provided no one of the quantities $b, \dots, f$ is equal to $a$.

**102.** Some illustrations have already been given in Chapter II., but they relate solely to definite, not to indefinite, integrals of uniform functions. The whole theory will not be considered at this stage; we shall merely give some additional illustrations, which will shew how the method can be applied to indefinite integrals of uniform functions and to integrals of multiform functions, and which will also form a simple and convenient introduction to the theory of periodic functions of a single variable.

We shall first consider indefinite integrals of uniform functions.

*Ex.* 1.   Consider the integral $\int \dfrac{dz}{z}$, and denote* it by $f(z)$.

The function to be integrated is uniform, and it has an accidental singularity of the first order at the origin, which is its only singularity. The value of $\int z^{-1} dz$ taken positively along a small curve round the origin, say round a circle with the origin as centre, is $2\pi i$; but the value of the integral is zero when taken along any closed curve which does not include the origin.

Taking $z=1$ as the lower limit of the integral, and any point $z$ as the upper limit, we consider the possible paths from 1 to $z$. Any path from 1 to $z$ can be deformed, without crossing the origin, into a path which circumscribes the origin positively some number of times, say $m_1$, and negatively some number of times, say $m_2$, all in any order, and then leads in a straight line from 1 to $z$. For this path the value of the integral is equal to

$$(2\pi i)\, m_1 + (-2\pi i)\, m_2 + \int_1^z \frac{dz}{z},$$

that is, to

$$2m\pi i + \int_1^z \frac{dz}{z},$$

where $m$ is an integer, and in the last integral the variation of $z$ is along a straight line from 1 to $z$. Let the last integral be denoted by $u$; then

$$f(z) = u + 2m\pi i,$$

and therefore, inverting the function and denoting $f^{-1}$ by $\phi$, we have

$$z = \phi(u + 2m\pi i).$$

Hence the general integral is a function of $z$ with an infinite number of values; and $z$ is a periodic function of the integral, the period being $2\pi i$.

* See Chrystal, ii, pp. 288—297, for the elementary properties of the function and its inverse, when the variable is complex.

*Ex.* 2.   Consider the function $\int \dfrac{dz}{1+z^2}$; and again denote it by $f(z)$.

The one-valued function to be integrated has two accidental singularities $\pm i$, each of the first order.   The value of the integral taken positively along a small curve round $i$ is $\pi$, and along a small curve round $-i$ is $-\pi$.

We take the origin $O$ as the lower limit and any point $z$ as the upper limit.   Any path from $O$ to $z$ can be deformed, without crossing either of the singularities and therefore without changing the value of the integral, into

(i)   any numbers of positive $(m_1, m_2)$ and of negative $(m_1', m_2')$ circuits round $i$ and round $-i$, in any order, and

(ii)   a straight line from $O$ to $z$.

Then we have

$$f(z)=m_1\pi + m_1'(-\pi)+m_2(-\pi)+m_2'\{-(-\pi)\}+\int_0^z \frac{dz}{1+z^2}$$
$$=n\pi +\int_0^z \frac{dz}{1+z^2}$$
$$=n\pi + u,$$

where $n$ is an integer and the integral on the right-hand side is taken along a straight line from $O$ to $z$.

Inverting the function and denoting $f^{-1}$ by $\phi$, we have

$$z=\phi(u+n\pi).$$

The integral, as before, is a function of $z$ with an infinite number of values; and $z$ is a periodic function of the integral, the period being $\pi$.

*Ex.* 3.   Denoting by $I$ the value of the integral

$$\frac{1}{2\pi i}\int_{z_0}^z \frac{f(z)}{(z-a)(z-b)(z-c)}\,dz,$$

taken along a straight line from $z_0$ to $z$ on which no one of the points $a$, $b$, $c$ lies, find the general value of the integral for a path from $z_0$ that goes $l$ times round $a$, $m$ times round $b$, $n$ times round $c$.

What is the form of the result, when $a$ and $b$ coincide ?

**103.**   Before passing to the integrals of multiform functions, it is convenient to consider the method in which Hermite* discusses the multiplicity in value of a definite integral of a uniform function.

Taking a simple case, let      $\phi(z)=\int_0^z \dfrac{dZ}{1+Z}$

and introduce a new variable $t$ such that $Z=zt$; then

$$\phi(z)=\int_0^1 \frac{zdt}{1+zt}.$$

When the path of $t$ is assigned, the integral is definite, finite and unique in value for all points of the plane except for those for which $1+zt=0$; and, according to the path of variation of $t$ from 0 to 1, there will be a $z$-curve which is a curve of discontinuity for the subject of integration.   Suppose the

* *Crelle*, t. xci, (1881), pp. 62—77; *Cours à la Faculté des Sciences*, 4ème éd. (1891), pp. 76—79, 154—164, and elsewhere.

path of $t$ to be the straight line from 0 to 1; then the curve of discontinuity is the axis of $x$ between $-1$ and $-\infty$. In this curve let any point $-\xi$ be taken where $\xi > 1$; and consider a point $z_1 = -\xi + i\epsilon$ and a point $z_2 = -\xi - i\epsilon$, respectively on the positive and the negative sides of the axis of $x$, both being ultimately taken as infinitesimally near the point $-\xi$. Then

$$\phi(z_1) - \phi(z_2) = \int_0^1 \left( \frac{-\xi + i\epsilon}{1 - \xi t + i\epsilon t} + \frac{\xi + i\epsilon}{1 - \xi t - i\epsilon t} \right) dt$$

$$= \int_0^1 \frac{2i\epsilon}{(1 - \xi t)^2 + \epsilon^2 t^2} \, dt = \int_1^\infty \frac{2i\epsilon}{(t - \xi)^2 + \epsilon^2} \, dt$$

$$= 2i \left[ \tan^{-1} \frac{t - \xi}{\epsilon} \right]_1^\infty.$$

Let $\epsilon$ become infinitesimal; then, when $t$ is infinite, we have

$$\tan^{-1} \frac{t - \xi}{\epsilon} = \tfrac{1}{2}\pi,$$

for $\epsilon$ is positive; and, when $t$ is unity, we have

$$\tan^{-1} \frac{t - \xi}{\epsilon} = -\tfrac{1}{2}\pi,$$

for $\xi$ is $> 1$.   Hence          $\phi(z_1) - \phi(z_2) = 2\pi i.$

The part of the axis of $x$ from $-1$ to $-\infty$ is therefore a line of discontinuity in value of $\phi(z)$, such that there is a sudden change in passing from one edge of it to the other. If the plane be cut along this line so that it cannot be crossed by the variable which may not pass out of the plane, then the integral is everywhere finite and uniform in the modified surface. If the plane be not cut along the line, it is evident that a single passage across the line from one edge to the other makes a difference of $2\pi i$ in the value, and consequently any number of passages across will give rise to the multiplicity in value of the integral.

Such a line is called a *section** by Hermite, after Riemann who, in a different manner, introduces these lines of singularity into his method of representing the variable on surfaces†.

When we take the general integral of a uniform function of $Z$ and make the substitution $Z = zt$, the integral that arises for consideration is of the form

$$\Phi(z) = \int_{t_0}^{t_1} \frac{F(t, z)}{G(t, z)} \, dt.$$

We shall suppose that the path of variation of $t$ is the axis of real quantities: and the subject of integration will be taken to be a general function of $t$ and $z$, without special regard to its derivation from a uniform function of $Z$.

* *Coupure;* see *Crelle*, t. xci, p. 62.               † See Chapter XV.

It is easy, after the special example, to see that $\Phi$ is a continuous function of $z$ in any space that does not include a $z$-point which, for values of $t$ included within the range of integration, would satisfy the equation

$$G\,(t,\,z) = 0.$$

But in the vicinity of a $z$-point, say $\zeta$, corresponding to the value $t = \theta$ in the range of integration, there will be discontinuity in the subject of integration and also, as will now be proved, in the value of the integral.

Let $Z$ be the point $\zeta$, and draw the curve through $Z$ corresponding to $t = $ real constant; let $N_1$ be a point on the positive side and $N_2$ a point on the negative side of this curve positively described, both points being on the normal at $Z$; and let $ZN_1 = ZN_2 = \epsilon'$, supposed small.   Then for $N_1$ we have

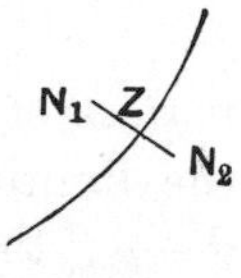

$$x_1 = \xi - \epsilon' \sin \psi, \qquad y_1 = \eta + \epsilon' \cos \psi,$$

so that $\qquad\qquad z_1 = \zeta + i\epsilon' \,(\cos \psi + i \sin \psi),$

Fig. 24.

where $\psi$ is the inclination of the tangent to the axis of real quantities.   But, if $d\sigma$ be an arc of the curve at $Z$,

$$\frac{d\sigma}{dt}\,(\cos \psi + i \sin \psi) = \frac{d\xi}{dt} + i\,\frac{d\eta}{dt} = \frac{d\zeta}{dt}$$

for variations along the tangent at $Z$, that is,

$$\frac{d\sigma}{dt}\,(\cos \psi + i \sin \psi) = -\frac{\dfrac{\partial}{\partial \theta}\,G\,(\theta,\,\zeta)}{\dfrac{\partial}{\partial \zeta}\,G\,(\theta,\,\zeta)}.$$

Thus, since $\dfrac{d\sigma}{dt}$ may be taken as finite on the supposition that $Z$ is an ordinary point of the curve, we have

$$z_1 = \zeta - i\epsilon\,\frac{P}{Q},$$

where $\qquad \epsilon = \epsilon'\,\dfrac{dt}{d\sigma}, \qquad P = \dfrac{\partial}{\partial \theta}\,G\,(\theta,\,\zeta), \qquad Q = \dfrac{\partial}{\partial \zeta}\,G\,(\theta,\,\zeta).$

Similarly $\qquad\qquad\qquad z_2 = \zeta + i\epsilon\,\dfrac{P}{Q}.$

Hence $\qquad \Phi\,(z_1) = \displaystyle\int_{t_0}^{t_1} \frac{F\,(t,\,z_1)}{G\,(t,\,z_1)}\,dt$

$$= \int_{t_0}^{t_1} \frac{F\,(t,\,\zeta) - i\epsilon \left\{\dfrac{\partial}{\partial \zeta} F\,(t,\,\zeta)\right\} \dfrac{P}{Q}}{G\,(t,\,\zeta) - i\epsilon \left\{\dfrac{\partial}{\partial \zeta} G\,(t,\,\zeta)\right\} \dfrac{P}{Q}}\,dt,$$

with a similar expression for $\Phi(z_2)$; and therefore

$$\Phi(z_1) - \Phi(z_2) = 2i \int_{t_0}^{t_1} \epsilon \frac{F(t,\zeta)\frac{\partial}{\partial\zeta}\{G(t,\zeta)\}\frac{P}{Q} - G(t,\zeta)\frac{\partial}{\partial\zeta}\{F(t,\zeta)\}\frac{P}{Q}}{G^2(t,\zeta) + \epsilon^2 \frac{P^2}{Q^2}\left\{\frac{\partial}{\partial\zeta}G(t,\zeta)\right\}^2} dt.$$

The subject of integration is infinitesimal, except in the immediate vicinity of $t = \theta$; and there

$$G(t,\zeta) = (t-\theta)P, \quad F(t,\zeta) = F(\theta,\zeta),$$

$$\frac{\partial}{\partial\zeta}\{G(t,\zeta)\} = Q, \qquad \frac{\partial}{\partial\zeta}\{F(t,\zeta)\} = \frac{\partial}{\partial\zeta}\{F(\theta,\zeta)\},$$

powers of small quantities other than those retained being negligible. Let the limiting values of $t$, that need be retained, be denoted by $\theta + \nu$ and $\theta - \mu$; then, after reduction, we have

$$\Phi(z_1) - \Phi(z_2) = 2i \int_{\theta-\mu}^{\theta+\nu} \frac{F(\theta,\zeta)}{P} \frac{\epsilon dt}{(t-\theta)^2 + \epsilon^2}$$

$$= 2\pi i \frac{F(\theta,\zeta)}{\frac{\partial}{\partial\theta}\{G(\theta,\zeta)\}},$$

in the limit when $\epsilon$ is made infinitesimal.

Hence a line of discontinuity of the subject of integration is a section for the integral; and the preceding expression is the magnitude, by numerical multiples of which the values of the integral differ*.

*Ex.* 1. Consider the integral

$$\Phi(z) = \int \frac{dZ}{1+Z^2}$$

$$= \int \frac{z dt}{1+z^2t^2}.$$

We have

$$\frac{F(\theta,\zeta)}{\frac{\partial}{\partial\theta}\{G(\theta,\zeta)\}} = \frac{\zeta}{2\zeta^2\theta} = \frac{1}{2\zeta\theta} = \frac{1}{2i},$$

so that $\pi$ is the period for the above integral.

*Ex.* 2. Shew that the sections for the integral

$$\int_0^\infty \frac{t^a \sin z}{1 + 2t\cos z + t^2} dt,$$

where $a$ is positive and less than 1, are the straight lines $x = (2k+1)\pi$, where $k$ assumes all integral values; and that the period of the integral at any section at a distance $\eta$ from the axis of real quantities is $2\pi \cosh(a\eta)$.                    (Hermite.)

* The memoir and the *Cours d'Analyse* of Hermite should be consulted for further developments; and, in reference to the integral treated above, Jordan, *Cours d'Analyse*, t. ii, pp. 293—296, may be consulted with advantage. See also, generally, for functions defined by definite integrals, Goursat, *Acta Math.*, t. ii, (1883), pp. 1—70, and ib., t. v, (1884), pp. 97—120; and Pochhammer, *Math. Ann.*, t. xxxv, (1890), pp. 470—494, 495—526. Goursat also discusses double integrals.

*Ex.* 3.  Prove that the function defined by

$$1 + x + \frac{x^2}{2^2} + \frac{x^3}{3^2} + \cdots\cdots$$

has a logarithmic singularity at $x=1$ and no other finite singularity.  If the plane be divided by a cut extending along the positive part of the real axis extending from 1 to $\infty$, shew that in the divided plane the function defined by the above series and its continuations is one-valued, and that, at corresponding points on opposite sides of the cut, its values differ by $2\pi i \log x$.                    (Math. Trip., Part II., 1899.)

*Ex.* 4.  Shew that the integral

$$\int_0^1 u^{\beta-1}(1-u)^{\gamma-\beta-1}(1-zu)^{-\alpha}du,$$

where the real parts of $\beta$ and $\gamma-\beta$ are positive, has the part of the axis of real quantities between 1 and $+\infty$ for a section.

Shew also that the integral

$$\phi(z) = \int_0^{\frac{1}{z}} u^{\beta-1}(1-u)^{\gamma-\beta-1}(1-zu)^{-\alpha}du,$$

where the real parts of $\beta$ and $1-a$ are positive, has the part of the axis of real quantities between 0 and 1 for a section: but that, in order to render $\phi(z)$ a uniform function of $z$, it is necessary to prevent the variable from crossing, not merely the section, but also the part of the axis of real quantities between 1 and $+\infty$.                    (Goursat.)

(The latter line is called a section of the *second* kind.)

*Ex.* 5.  Discuss generally the effect of changing the path of $t$ on a section of the integral; and, in particular, obtain the section for $\int_0^z \dfrac{dZ}{1+Z}$ when, after the substitution $Z=zt$, the path of $t$ is made a semi-circle on the line joining 0 and 1 as diameter.

*Ex.* 6.  Shew that, for the function $f(z)$ defined by the definite integral

$$f(z) = \int_{-\infty}^{\infty} \frac{e^{2n\pi z i} + e^{-2n\pi z i}}{e^{2n\pi t} + e^{-2n\pi t}} \, \frac{i^{n+1} i^n \, e^{-2\pi t}}{e^{-2\pi t} - e^{2\pi z i}} \, dt,$$

where $n$ is a positive integer and the integration is for real values of $t$, while $z=x+iy$, the sections are the lines

$$x=0, \ \pm 1, \ \pm 2, \ldots,$$

and that the increment of $f(z)$ in crossing the section $x=0$ in the positive direction is $z^n$.
                                                                              (Appell.)

*Note.*  It is manifestly impossible to discuss all the important bearings of theorems and principles, which arise from time to time in our subject; we can do no more than mention the subject of those definite integrals involving complex variables, which first occur as solutions of the better-known linear differential equations of the second order.

Thus for the definite integral connected with the hypergeometric series, memoirs by Jacobi* and Goursat† should be consulted; for the definite integral connected with Bessel's functions, memoirs by Hankel‡ and Weber§ should be consulted; and Heine's *Handbuch der Kugelfunctionen* for the definite integrals connected with Legendre's functions.

---

* *Crelle*, t. lvi, (1859), pp. 149—165; the memoir was not published until after his death.

† *Sur l'équation différentielle linéaire qui admet pour intégrale la série hypergéométrique*, (Thèse, Gauthier-Villars, Paris, 1881).

‡ *Math. Ann.*, t. i, (1869), pp. 467—501.

§ *Math. Ann.*, t. xxxvii, (1890), pp. 404—416.

**104.**   We shall now consider integrals of multiform functions.

*Ex.* 1.   To find the integral of a multiform function round one loop; and round a number of loops.

Let the function be          $w = \{(z-a_1)(z-a_2)\dots(z-a_n)\}^{\frac{1}{m}},$

where $m$ may be a negative or a positive integer, and the quantities $a$ are unequal to one another; and let the loop be from the origin round the point $a_1$.   Then, if $I$ be the value of the integral with an assigned initial branch $w$, we have

$$I = \int_0^{a_1} w\,dz + \int_c w\,dz + \int_{a_1}^0 aw\,dz,$$

where $a$ is $e^{\frac{2\pi i}{m}}$ and the middle integral is taken round the circle at $a_1$ of infinitesimal radius. But, since the limit of $(z-a_1)w$ when $z=a_1$ is zero, the middle integral vanishes by § 101; and therefore

$$I_{a_1} = (1-a)\int_0^{a_1} w\,dz,$$

where the integral may, if convenient, be considered as taken along the straight line from $O$ to $a_1$.

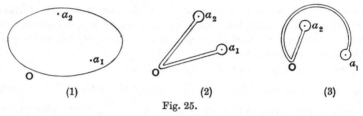

(1)                    (2)                    (3)

Fig. 25.

Next, consider a circuit for an integral of $w$ which (fig. 25) encloses two branch-points, say $a_1$ and $a_2$, but no others; the circuit in (1) can be deformed into that in (2) or into that in (3) as well as into other forms.   Hence the integral round all the three circuits must be the same.   Beginning with the same branch as in the first case, we have

$$(1-a)\int_0^{a_1} w\,dz,$$

as the integral after the first loop in (2).   And the branch with which the second loop begins is $aw$, so that the integral described as in the second loop is

$$(1-a)\int_0^{a_2} aw\,dz;$$

and therefore, for the circuit as in (2), the integral is

$$I = (1-a)\int_0^{a_1} w\,dz + a(1-a)\int_0^{a_2} w\,dz.$$

Proceeding similarly with the integral for the circuit in (3), we find that its expression is

$$I = (1-a)\int_0^{a_2} w\,dz + a(1-a)\int_0^{a_1} w\,dz,$$

and these two values must be equal.

But the integrals denoted by the same symbols are not the same in the two cases; the function $\int_0^{a_1} w\,dz$ is different in the second value of $I$ from that in the first, for the deformation of path necessary to change from the one to the other passes over the branch-point $a_2$. In fact, the equality of the two values of $I$ really determines the value of the integral for the loop $Oa_1$ in (3).

And, in general, equations thus obtained by varied deformations do not give relations among loop-integrals; they define the values of those loop-integrals for the deformed paths.

We therefore take that deformation of the circuit into loops which gives the simplest path. Usually *the path is changed into a group of loops round the branch-points as they occur, taken in order in a trigonometrically positive direction.*

The value of the integral round a circuit, equivalent to any number of loops, is obvious.

*Ex.* 2. *To find the value of $\int w\,dz$, taken round a simple curve which includes all the branch-points of $w$ and all the infinities.*

If $z = \infty$ be a branch-point or an infinity, then all the branch-points and all the infinities of $w$ lie on what is usually regarded as the exterior of the curve, or the curve may in one sense be said to exclude all these points. The integral round the curve is then the integral of a function round a curve, such that over the area included by it the function is uniform, finite and continuous; hence the integral is zero.

If $z = \infty$ be neither a branch-point nor an infinity, the curve can be deformed until it is a circle, centre the origin and of very great radius. If then the limit of $zw$, when $|z|$ is infinitely great, be zero, the value of the integral again is zero, by II., § 24.

Another method of considering the integral, is to use Neumann's sphere for the representation of the variable. Any simple closed curve divides the area of the sphere into two parts; when the curve is defined as above, one of those parts is such that the function is uniform, finite and continuous throughout, and therefore its integral round the curve, regarded as the boundary of that part, is zero. (See Corollary III., § 90.)

*Ex.* 3. To find the general value of $\int (1 - z^2)^{-\frac{1}{2}} dz$. The function to be integrated is two-valued: the two values interchange round each of the branch-points $\pm 1$, which are the only branch-points of the function.

Let $I$ be the value of the integral for a loop from the origin round $+1$, beginning with the branch which has the value $+1$ at the origin; and let $I'$ be the corresponding value for the loop from the origin round $-1$, beginning with the same branch. Then, by Ex. 1,

$$I = 2\int_0^1 (1 - z^2)^{-\frac{1}{2}} dz, \qquad I' = 2\int_0^{-1} (1 - z^2)^{-\frac{1}{2}} dz$$
$$= -I,$$

the last equality being easily obtained by changing variables.

Now consider the integral when taken round a circle, centre the origin and of indefinitely great radius $R$; then by § 24, II., if the limit of $zw$ for $z = \infty$ be $k$, the value of $\int w\,dz$ round this circle is $2\pi ik$. In the present case $w = (1 - z^2)^{-\frac{1}{2}}$ so that the limit of $zw$ is $+\frac{1}{i}$; hence

$$\int (1 - z^2)^{-\frac{1}{2}} dz = 2\pi,$$

the integral being taken round the circle. But since a description of the circle restores the initial value, it can be deformed into the two loops from $O$ to $A$ and from $O$ to $A'$. The value round the first is $I$; and the branch with which the second begins to be described has the value $-1$ at the origin, so that the consequent value round the second is $-I'$; hence

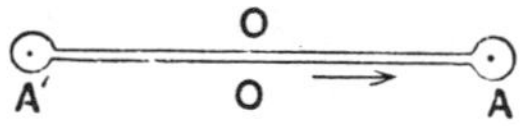

Fig. 26.

$$I - I' = 2\pi*,$$
and therefore
$$I = -I' = \pi,$$
verifying the ordinary result that

$$\int_0^1 (1 - z^2)^{-\frac{1}{2}} dz = \tfrac{1}{2}\pi,$$

when the integral is taken along a straight line.

* It is interesting to obtain this equation when $O'$ is taken as the initial point, instead of $O$.

To find the general value of $u$ for any path of variation between $O$ and $z$, we proceed as follows. Let $\Omega$ be any circuit which restores the initial branch of $(1-z^2)^{-\frac{1}{2}}$. Then by § 100, Corollary II., $\Omega$ may be composed of

    (i) a set of double circuits round $+1$, say $m'$ in number,

    (ii) a set of double circuits round $-1$, say $m''$ in number,

and   (iii) a set of circuits round $+1$ and $-1$ ;

and these may come in any order and each may be described in either direction. Now for a double circuit positively described, the value of the integral for the first description is $I$ and for the second description, which begins with the branch $-(1-z^2)^{-\frac{1}{2}}$, it is $-I$; hence for the double circuit it is zero when positively described, and therefore it is zero also when negatively described. Hence each of the $m'$ double circuits yields zero as its nett contribution to the integral.

Similarly, each of the $m''$ double circuits round $-1$ yields zero as its nett contribution to the integral.

For a circuit round $+1$ and $-1$ described positively, the value of the integral has just been proved to be $I-I'$, and therefore when described negatively it is $I'-I$. Hence, if there be $n_1$ positive descriptions and $n_2$ negative descriptions, the nett contribution of all these circuits to the value of the integral is $(n_1-n_2)(I-I')$, that is, $2n\pi$ where $n$ is an integer.

Hence the complete value for the circuit $\Omega$ is $2n\pi$.

Now any path from $O$ to $z$ can be resolved into a circuit $\Omega$, which restores the initial branch of $(1-z^2)^{-\frac{1}{2}}$, chosen to have the value $+1$ at the origin, and either (i) a straight line $Oz$ ;

    or (ii) the path $OACz$, viz., a loop round $+1$ and the line $Oz$ ;

    or (iii) the path $OA'Cz$, viz., a loop round $-1$ and the line $Oz$.

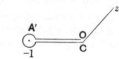

Fig. 27.

Let $u$ denote the value for the line $Oz$, so that

$$u = \int_0^z (1-z^2)^{-\frac{1}{2}}\, dz.$$

Hence, for case (i), the general value of the integral is

$$2n\pi + u.$$

For the path $OACz$, the value is $I$ for the loop $OAC$, and is $(-u)$ for the line $Cz$, the negative sign occurring because, after the loop, the branch of the function for integration along the line is $-(1-z^2)^{-\frac{1}{2}}$; this value is $I-u$, that is, it is $\pi-u$. Hence, for case (ii), the value of the integral is

$$2n\pi + \pi - u.$$

For the path $OA'Cz$, the value is similarly found to be $-\pi-u$; and therefore, for case (iii), the value of the integral is

$$2n\pi - \pi - u.$$

If $f(z)$ denote the general value of the integral, we have either

$$f(z) = 2n\pi + u,$$

or

$$f(z) = (2m+1)\pi - u,$$

where $n$ and $m$ are any integers, so that $f(z)$ is a function with two infinite series of values.

Lastly, if $z = \phi(\theta)$ be the inverse of $f(z) = \theta$, then the relation between $u$ and $z$ given by

$$u = \int_0^z (1 - z^2)^{-\frac{1}{2}} \, dz$$

can be represented in the form

$$\left. \begin{array}{l} \phi(u) = z = \phi(2n\pi + u) \\ \phi(u) = z = \phi(2m\pi + \pi - u) \end{array} \right\},$$

and

both equations being necessary for the full representation. Evidently $z$ is a simply-periodic function of $u$, the period being $2\pi$; and from the definition it is easily seen to be an odd function.

Let $y = (1 - z^2)^{\frac{1}{2}} = \chi(u)$, so that $y$ is an even function of $u$; from the consideration of the various paths from $O$ to $z$, it is easy to prove that

$$\left. \begin{array}{l} \chi(u) = \chi(2n\pi + u) \\ \quad = -\chi(2m\pi + \pi - u) \end{array} \right\}.$$

*Ex.* 4. To find the general value of $\int \{(1 - z^2)(1 - k^2 z^2)\}^{-\frac{1}{2}} \, dz$. It will be convenient to regard this integral as a special case of

$$Z = \int \{(z - a)(z - b)(z - c)(z - d)\}^{-\frac{1}{2}} \, dz = \int w \, dz.$$

The two-valued function to be integrated has $a$, $b$, $c$, $d$ (but not $\infty$) as the complete system of branch-points; and the two values interchange at each of them. We proceed as in the last example, omitting mere re-statements of reasons there given that are applicable also to the present example.

Any circuit $\Omega$, which restores an initial branch of $w$, can be made up of

    (i)   sets of double circuits round each of the branch-points,

and   (ii)   sets of circuits round any two of the branch-points.

The value of $\int w \, dz$ for a loop from the origin to a branch-point $k$ (where $k = a$, $b$, $c$, or $d$) is

$$2 \int_0^k w \, dz \, ;$$

and this may be denoted by $K$, where $K = A$, $B$, $C$, or $D$.

The value of the integral for a double circuit round a branch-point is zero. Hence the amount contributed to the value of the integral by all the sets in (i) as this part of $\Omega$ is zero.

The value of the integral for a circuit round $a$ and $b$ taken positively is $A - B$; for one round $b$ and $c$ is $B - C$; for one round $c$ and $d$ is $C - D$; for one round $a$ and $c$ is $A - C$, which is the sum of $A - B$ and $B - C$; and similarly for circuits round $a$ and $d$, and round $b$ and $d$. There are therefore three distinct values, say $A - B$, $B - C$, $C - D$, the values for circuits round $a$ and $b$, $b$ and $c$, $c$ and $d$ respectively; the values for circuits round any other pair can be expressed linearly in terms of these values. Suppose then that the part of $\Omega$ represented by (ii), when thus resolved, is the nett equivalent of the description of $m'$ circuits round $a$ and $b$, of $n'$ circuits round $b$ and $c$, and of $l'$ circuits round $c$ and $d$. Then the value of the integral contributed by this part of $\Omega$ is

$$m'(A - B) + n'(B - C) + l'(C - D),$$

which is therefore the whole value of the integral for $\Omega$.

But the values of $A$, $B$, $C$, $D$ are not independent*. Let a circle with centre the origin and very great radius be drawn; then since the limit of $zw$ for $|z| = \infty$ is zero and since

---

* For a purely analytical proof of the following relation, see Greenhill's *Elliptic Functions*, Chapter II.

$z = \infty$ is not a branch-point, the value of $\int w\, dz$ round this circle is zero (Ex. 2). The circle can be deformed into four loops round $a$, $b$, $c$, $d$ respectively in order; and therefore the value of the integral is $A - B + C - D$, that is,

$$A - B + C - D = 0.$$

Hence the value of the integral for the circuit $\Omega$ is

$$m\,(A - B) + n\,(B - C),$$

where $m$ and $n$ denote $m' - l'$ and $n'$ respectively.

Now any path from the origin to $z$ can be resolved into $\Omega$, together with either

    (i)   a straight line from $O$ to $z$,

or   (ii)   a loop round $a$ and then a straight line to $z$.

It might appear that another resolution would be given by a combination of $\Omega$ with, say, a loop round $b$ and then a straight line to $z$; but it is resoluble into the second of the above combinations. For at $C$, after the description of the loop $B$, introduce a double description of the loop $A$, which adds nothing to the value of the integral and does not in the end affect the branch of $w$ at $C$; then the new path can be regarded as made up of $(a)$ the circuit constituted by the loop round $b$ and the first loop round $a$, $(\beta)$ the second loop round $a$, which begins with the initial branch of $w$, followed by a straight path to $z$. Of these $(a)$ can be absorbed into $\Omega$, and $(\beta)$ is the same as (ii); hence the path is not essentially new. Similarly for the other points.

Let $u$ denote the value of the integral with a straight path from $O$ to $z$; then the whole value of the integral for the combination of $\Omega$ with (i) is of the form

$$m\,(A - B) + n\,(B - C) + u.$$

For the combination of $\Omega$ with (ii), the value of the integral for the part (ii) of the path is $A$, for the loop round $a$, $+(-u)$, for the straight path which, owing to the description of the loop round $a$, begins with $-w$; hence the whole value of the integral is of the form

$$m\,(A - B) + n\,(B - C) + A - u^{*}.$$

Hence, if $f(z)$ denote the general value of the integral, it has two systems of values, each containing a doubly-infinite number of terms; and, if $z = \phi(u)$ denote the inverse of $u = f(z)$, we have

$$\phi(u) = \phi\{m\,(A - B) + n\,(B - C) + u\}$$
$$= \phi\{m\,(A - B) + n\,(B - C) + A - u\},$$

where $m$ and $n$ are any integers. Evidently $z$ is a doubly-periodic function of $u$, with periods $A - B$ and $B - C$.

    *Ex.* 5.   The case of the foregoing integral which most frequently occurs is the elliptic integral in the form used by Legendre and Jacobi, viz. :

$$u = \int\{(1 - z^{2})\,(1 - k^{2}z^{2})\}^{-\frac{1}{2}}\, dz = \int w\, dz,$$

where $k$ is real. The branch-points of the function to be integrated are $1$, $-1$, $\dfrac{1}{k}$,

---

   * The value for a loop round $b$ and then a straight line to $z$, just considered, is $B - u$,

$$= -(A - B) + A - u,$$

giving the value in the text with $m$ changed to $m - 1$.

and $-\frac{1}{k}$, and the values of the integral for the corresponding loops from the origin are

$$2 \int_0^1 wdz,$$

$$2 \int_0^{-1} wdz = -2 \int_0^1 wdz,$$

$$2 \int_0^{\frac{1}{k}} wdz,$$

and
$$2 \int_0^{-\frac{1}{k}} wdz = -2 \int_0^{\frac{1}{k}} wdz.$$

Now the values for the loops are connected by the equation

$$A - B + C - D = 0,$$

and so it will be convenient that, as all the points lie on the axis of real variables, we arrange the order of the loops so that this relation is identically satisfied. Otherwise, the relation will, after Ex. 1, be a definition of the paths of integration chosen for the loops.

Among the methods of arrangement, which secure the identical satisfaction of the

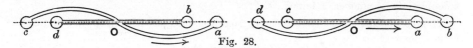

Fig. 28.

relation, the two in the figure are the simplest, the curved lines being taken straight in the limit; for, by the first arrangement when $k < 1$, we have

$$\left\{ 2 \int_0^{\frac{1}{k}} - 2 \int_0^1 + 2 \int_0^{-\frac{1}{k}} - 2 \int_0^{-1} \right\} wdz = 0,$$

and, by the second when $k > 1$, we have

$$\left\{ 2 \int_0^1 - 2 \int_0^{\frac{1}{k}} + 2 \int_0^{-1} - 2 \int_0^{-\frac{1}{k}} \right\} wdz = 0,$$

both of which are identically satisfied. We may therefore take either of them; let the former be adopted.

The periods are $A - B$, $B - C$, (and $C - D$, which is equal to $B - A$), and any linear combination of these is a period: we shall take $A - B$, and $B - D$. The latter, $B - D$, is equal to

$$2 \int_0^1 wdz - 2 \int_0^{-1} wdz,$$

which, being denoted by $4K$, gives

$$4K = 4 \int_0^1 \frac{dz}{\{(1 - z^2)(1 - k^2 z^2)\}^{\frac{1}{2}}}$$

as one period. The former, $A - B$, is equal to

$$2 \int_0^{\frac{1}{k}} wdz - 2 \int_0^1 wdz,$$

which is
$$2 \int_1^{\frac{1}{k}} wdz;$$

this, being denoted by $2iK'$, gives

$$2iK' = 2\int_1^{\frac{1}{k}} \frac{dz}{\{(1-z^2)(1-k^2z^2)\}^{\frac{1}{2}}}$$

$$= 2i\int_0^1 \frac{dz'}{\{(1-z'^2)(1-k'^2z'^2)\}^{\frac{1}{2}}},$$

where $k'^2 + k^2 = 1$, and the relation between the variables of the integrals is $k^2z^2 + k'^2z'^2 = 1$.

Hence the periods of the integral are $4K$ and $2iK'$. Moreover, $A$ is $2\int_0^{\frac{1}{k}} w\,dz$, which is

$$2\int_0^1 w\,dz + 2\int_1^{\frac{1}{k}} w\,dz = 2K + 2iK'.$$

Hence the general value of $\int_0^z \{(1-z^2)(1-k^2z^2)\}^{-\frac{1}{2}} dz$ is either

$$u + 4mK + 2niK',$$

or

$$2K + 2iK' - u + 4mK + 2niK',$$

that is,

$$2K - u + 4mK + 2niK',$$

where $u$ is the integral taken from $O$ to $z$ along an assigned path, often taken to be a straight line; so that there are two systems of values for the integral, each containing a doubly-infinite number of terms.

If $z$ be denoted by $\phi(u)$—evidently, from the integral definition, an odd function of $u$—, then

$$\phi(u) = \phi(u + 4mK + 2niK')$$

$$= \phi(2K - u + 4mK + 2niK'),$$

so that $z$ is a doubly-periodic function of $u$, the periods being $4K$ and $2iK'$.

Now consider the function $z_1 = (1-z^2)^{\frac{1}{2}}$. A $z$-path round $\frac{1}{k}$ does not affect $z_1$ by way of change, provided the curve does not include the point 1; hence, if $z_1 = \chi(u)$, we have

$$\chi(u) = \chi(u + 2K + 2iK').$$

But a $z$-path round the point 1 does change $z_1$ into $-z_1$; so that

$$\chi(u) = -\chi(u + 2K).$$

Hence $\chi(u)$, which is an even function, has two periods, viz., $4K$ and $2K + 2iK'$, whence

$$\chi(u) = \chi(u + 4mK + 2nK + 2niK').$$

Similarly, taking $z_2 = (1 - k^2z^2)^{\frac{1}{2}} = \psi(u)$, it is easy to see that

$$\psi(u) = \psi(u + 2K),$$

$$-\psi(u) = \psi(u + 2K + 2iK') = \psi(u + 2iK'),$$

so that $\psi(u)$, which is an even function, has two periods, viz., $2K$ and $4iK'$; whence

$$\psi(u) = \psi(u + 2mK + 4niK').$$

The functions $\phi(u)$, $\chi(u)$, $\psi(u)$ are of course sn $u$, cn $u$, dn $u$ respectively.

*Ex.* 6. If in a single infinite sheet, representing the values of $z$, three cuts be made along the real axis joining respectively $\left(-\infty, -\frac{1}{k}\right)$, $(-1, 1)$, $\left(\frac{1}{k}, \infty\right)$, shew that the integral (in the notation of elliptic functions, $0 < k < 1$, $\sqrt{z^2-1} = +i\sqrt{1-z^2}$)

$$u = \int_0^z \frac{K - E - k^2Kx^2}{\{(1-x^2)(1-k^2x^2)\}^{\frac{1}{2}}} dx$$

becomes a one-valued function of $z$. And shew that $z$ is a uniform function of $u$ for the values of $u$ which arise.

If the cut joining $(-1, 1)$ do not lie along the real axis, describe the values of $z$ as a function of $u$.                                                             (Math. Trip., Part II., 1894.)

*Ex.* 7. To find the general value of the integral*

$$\int_z^\infty \{4\,(z-e_1)\,(z-e_2)\,(z-e_3)\}^{-\frac{1}{2}}\,dz = w.$$

The function to be integrated has $e_1$, $e_2$, $e_3$, and $\infty$ for its branch-points; and for paths round each of them the two branches interchange.

A circuit $\Omega$, which restores the initial branch of the function to be integrated, can be resolved into:—

(i) Sets of double circuits round each of the branch-points alone: as before, the value of the integral for each of these double circuits is zero.

(ii) Sets of circuits, each enclosing two of the branch-points: it is convenient to retain circuits including $\infty$ and $e_1$, $\infty$ and $e_2$, $\infty$ and $e_3$, the other three combinations being reducible to these.

The values of the integral for these three retained are respectively

$$E_1 = 2\int_{e_1}^\infty \{4\,(z-e_1)\,(z-e_2)\,(z-e_3)\}^{-\frac{1}{2}}\,dz = 2\omega_1,$$

$$E_2 = 2\int_{e_2}^\infty \{4\,(z-e_1)\,(z-e_2)\,(z-e_3)\}^{-\frac{1}{2}}\,dz = 2\omega_2,$$

$$E_3 = 2\int_{e_3}^\infty \{4\,(z-e_1)\,(z-e_2)\,(z-e_3)\}^{-\frac{1}{2}}\,dz = 2\omega_3,$$

and therefore the value of the integral for the circuit $\Omega$ is of the form

$$m'E_1 + n'E_2 + l'E_3.$$

But $E_1$, $E_2$, $E_3$ are not linearly independent. The integral of the function round any curve in the finite part of the plane, which does not include $e_1$, $e_2$ or $e_3$ within its boundary, is zero, by Ex. 2; and this curve can be deformed to the shape in the figure, until it becomes infinitely large, without changing the value of the integral.

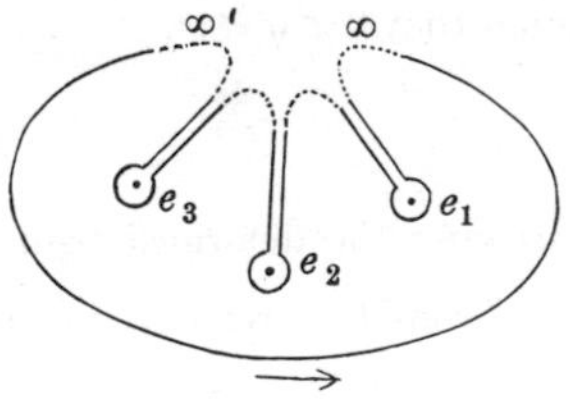

Fig. 29.

Since the limit of $zw$ for $|z| = \infty$ is zero, the value of the integral from $\infty'$ to $\infty$ is zero, by § 24, II.; and if the description begin with a branch $w$, the branch at $\infty$ is $-w$. The rest of the integral consists of the sum of the values round the loops, which is

$$-E_1 + E_2 - E_3,$$

because a path round a loop changes the branch of $w$ and the last branch after describing the loop round $e_3$ is $+w$ at $\infty'$, the proper value (§ 90, III.). Hence, as the whole integral is zero, we have

$$-E_1 + E_2 - E_3 = 0,$$

or say                                    $$E_2 = E_1 + E_3.$$

---

* The choice of $\infty$ for the upper limit is made on a ground which will subsequently be considered, viz., that, when the integral is zero, $z$ is infinite.

Thus the value of the integral for any circuit $\Omega$, which restores the initial branch of $w$, can be expressed in any of the equivalent forms $mE_1 + nE_3$, $m'E_1 + n'E_2$, $m''E_2 + n''E_3$, where the $m$'s and $n$'s are integers.

Now any path from $\infty$ to $z$ can be resolved into a circuit $\Omega$, which restores at $\infty$ the initial branch of $w$, combined with either

    (i) a straight path from $\infty$ to $z$,

or   (ii) a loop between $\infty$ and $e_1$, together with a straight path from $\infty$ to $z$.

(The apparently distinct alternatives, of a loop between $\infty$ and $e_2$, together with a straight path from $\infty$ to $z$, and of a similar path round $e_3$, are inclusible in the second alternative above; the reasons are similar to those in Ex. 5.)

If $u$ denote $\int_z^\infty \{4 (z - e_1) (z - e_2) (z - e_3)\}^{-\frac{1}{2}} dz$ when the integral is taken in a straight line, then the value of the integral for part (i) of a path is $u$; and the value of the integral for part (ii) of a path is $E_1 - u$, the initial branch in each case for these parts being the initial branch of $w$ for the whole path. Hence the most general value of the integral for any path is either

$$2m\omega_1 + 2n\omega_3 + u,$$

or
$$2m\omega_1 + 2n\omega_3 + 2\omega_1 - u,$$

the two being evidently included in the form

$$2m\omega_1 + 2n\omega_3 \pm u.$$

If, then, we denote by $z = \wp(u)$ the relation which is inverse to

$$u = \int_z^\infty \{4 (z - e_1) (z - e_2) (z - e_3)\}^{-\frac{1}{2}} dz,$$

we have
$$\wp(u) = \wp(2m\omega_1 + 2n\omega_3 \pm u).$$

In the same way as in the preceding example, it follows that

$$\wp'(u) = \wp'(2m\omega_1 + 2n\omega_3 + u) = -\wp'(2m\omega_1 + 2n\omega_3 - u),$$

where $\wp'(u)$ is $-\{4 (z - e_1) (z - e_2) (z - e_3)\}^{\frac{1}{2}}$.

*Ex.* 8. Prove that, when $m$ is a positive integer $\geq 2$, and when $q$ is a positive quantity such that $0 < q < m$,

$$\int_0^\infty \frac{y^{q-1}}{1 + y^m} dy = \frac{\pi}{m} \frac{1}{\sin \pi \dfrac{q}{m}},$$

drawing the deformed figure of the loops.

From this relation, deduce the results

    (i) $\int_0^\infty \dfrac{(\log z)^2}{1 + z^2} dz = \tfrac{1}{8}\pi^3$,     (ii) $\int_0^\infty \dfrac{(\log z)^4}{1 + z^2} dz = \tfrac{5}{32}\pi^5$,

    (iii) $\int_0^\infty \dfrac{(Ay + B) \log y}{1 + y^3} dy = \tfrac{2}{27}\pi^2 (A - B)$,

where $A$ and $B$ are constants.

Shew also how to deduce the value of

$$\int_0^\infty \frac{P(y)\, Q(\log y)}{1 + y^m} dy,$$

where $Q(\log y)$ is any polynomial in $\log y$, and $P(y)$ is a polynomial in $y$ of degree not greater than $m - 2$.

The foregoing simple examples are sufficient illustrations of the multiplicity of value of an integral of a uniform function or of a multiform function, when branch-points or discontinuities occur in the part of the plane in which the path of integration lies. They also shew one of the modes in which singly-periodic and doubly-periodic functions arise, the periodicity consisting in the addition of arithmetical multiples of constant quantities to the argument.

To the properties of such periodic functions, especially of uniform periodic functions, we shall return in Chapter X. It will there appear that each of the special functions, which have been considered in the preceding examples 3, 4, 5, 7, expresses $z$ as a uniform function of its argument.

Meanwhile, it is not difficult to prove directly that the functions of $u$ in Ex. 5 and of $w$ in Ex. 7 are uniform functions of their arguments.

Consider the quantity $z$ and the integral $u$ connected by the relation

$$u = \int_0^z \{(1-z^2)(1-k^2z^2)\}^{-\frac{1}{2}} dz,$$

or by the differential equation

$$\left(\frac{dz}{du}\right)^2 = (1-z^2)(1-k^2z^2),$$

with the condition that $u = 0$ when $z = 0$ and the further property as to the periods of $u$. Evidently the vicinities of the respective critical points $1, -1, 1/k, -1/k$ must be taken into account; likewise the vicinity of any other finite value of $z$; likewise very large values of $z$. We take them in turn.

In the vicinity of $z = 1$, let $z = 1 + \zeta$. At $z = 1$, we can take $u = K$ (subject to periods); so

$$u - K = \int_0^\zeta (-2t + t^2)^{-\frac{1}{2}} (k'^2 - 2k^2t - k^2t^2)^{-\frac{1}{2}} dt$$

$$= \int_0^\zeta (-2k'^2)^{-\frac{1}{2}} t^{-\frac{1}{2}} P(t)\, dt,$$

where $P(t)$ is a regular function of $t$ in the vicinity of $t = 0$ such that $P(0) = 1$. Thus

$$u - K = \frac{1}{k'}(-2)^{\frac{1}{2}} \zeta^{\frac{1}{2}} R(\zeta),$$

where $R(\zeta)$ is a regular function of $\zeta$ such that $R(0) = 1$. Consequently,

$$z - 1 = \zeta = -\tfrac{1}{2} k'^2 (u-K)^2 S(u-K),$$

where $S(u-K)$ is a regular function of $(u-K)^2$, such that $S(0) = 1$. Clearly $z$ is a regular function of $u$ in the vicinity of the place $z = 1$.

Exactly similar analysis shews that $z$ is a regular function of $u$ in the vicinity of the place $z = -1$, the substitution being $z = -1 + \zeta$; we find

$$z + 1 = -\tfrac{1}{2} k'^2 (u + K)^2 S(u + K),$$

where $S(u + K)$ is a regular function of $(u + K)^2$, such that $S(0) = 1$.

Again, for the vicinity of $z = 1/k$, we take $z - 1/k = \zeta'$; we find

$$z - \frac{1}{k} = \zeta' = \frac{k'^2}{4k} (u - K - iK')^2 S(u - K - iK')^2,$$

where $S$ is a regular function of its argument such that $S(0) = 1$.

For the vicinity of $z = -1/k$, we find

$$z + \frac{1}{k} = \frac{k'^2}{4k} (u + K + iK')^2 S(u + K + iK')^2,$$

where again $S$ is a regular function of its argument such that $S(0) = 1$.

Next, for a value of $|z| < 1$, we have

$$u = \int_0^z \{(1 - t^2)(1 - k^2 t^2)\}^{-\frac{1}{2}} dt$$
$$= z P(z),$$

where $P(z)$ is a regular even function of $z$ such that $P(0) = 1$. Consequently $z$ is a regular function and an uneven function of $u$ for values of $|z| < 1$.

For any ordinary place for $z$, given by $z = a$, let a value of $u$ be $\alpha$. Taking $z = a + Z$, we have

$$u - \alpha = \int_a^{a+Z} \{(1 - t^2)(1 - k^2 t^2)\}^{-\frac{1}{2}} dt$$
$$= \frac{Z}{\{(1 - a^2)(1 - k^2 a^2)\}^{-\frac{1}{2}}} R(Z),$$

where $R(Z)$ is a regular function of $Z$ such that $R(0) = 1$. As before, $Z$ is a regular function of $u - \alpha$ in the vicinity; that is, $z$ is a regular function of $u$ in the vicinity of any ordinary place.

Finally, for large values of $z$, say $z'$, we have

$$u = \int_0^{\frac{1}{k}} + \int_{\frac{1}{k}}^{z'} \{(1 - t^2)(1 - k^2 t^2)\}^{-\frac{1}{2}} dt.$$

In the integral, write $$kt = \frac{1}{t'};$$

then $$u = \int_0^{\frac{1}{k}} + \int_{\frac{1}{kz'}}^1$$

$$= \int_1^{\frac{1}{k}} + \int_0^{\frac{1}{kz'}} \{(1 - t'^2)(1 - k^2 t'^2)\}^{-\frac{1}{2}} dt'$$

$$= iK' + \int_0^{\frac{1}{kz'}} \{(1 - t'^2)(1 - k^2 t'^2)\}^{-\frac{1}{2}} dt'.$$

Thus $\dfrac{1}{kz'}$ is a regular function of $u$ in the vicinity of $u = iK'$ and it vanishes to the first order at that place. Therefore $z$ is a uniform function of $u$ in the vicinity of $u = iK'$; and it has a simple pole at that value.

Hence, in every case, $z$ is a uniform function of $u$; and this uniform function has simple poles at $u = iK'$ and at all places reducible to this place by multiples of $2K$ and $2iK'$.

As already stated, we shall give full references at a later stage to the cases when a differential equation

$$f\left(\frac{dz}{du}, u\right) = 0$$

defines $z$ as a uniform function of $u$.

*Ex.* 9. Shew that, for the relation just discussed, the functions $(1 - z^2)^{\frac{1}{2}}$ and $(1 - k^2 z^2)^{\frac{1}{2}}$ are uniform functions of $u$.

*Ex.* 10. Shew that, when $u$ and $z$ are connected by the relation

$$u = \int_z^\infty \{4 (z - e_1) (z - e_2) (z - e_3)\}^{-\frac{1}{2}} dz$$

of Ex. 7, when we denote $z$ as a function of $u$ by $\wp(u)$, each of the functions

$$\wp(u), \quad \{\wp(u) - e_1\}^{\frac{1}{2}}, \quad \{\wp(u) - e_2\}^{\frac{1}{2}}, \quad \{\wp(u) - e_3\}^{\frac{1}{2}}$$

is a uniform function of $u$.

**105.** We proceed to the theory of uniform periodic functions, some special examples of which have just been considered; and limitation will be made here to periodicity of the linear additive type, which is only a very special form of periodicity.

A function $f(z)$ is said to be periodic when there is a quantity $\omega$ such that the equation

$$f(z + \omega) = f(z)$$

is an identity for all values of $z$. Then $f(z + n\omega) = f(z)$, where $n$ is any integer positive or negative; and it is assumed that $\omega$ is the smallest quantity for which the equation holds, that is, that no submultiple of $\omega$ will satisfy the equation. The quantity $\omega$ is called a *period* of the function.

A function is said to be *simply-periodic* when there is only a single period: to be *doubly-periodic* when there are two periods; and so on, the periodicity being for the present limited to additive modification of the argument. Moreover, we exclude the possibility of periods that can be made less than any finite quantity, however small. If such infinitesimal periods were admissible for a uniform function, then within a finite region (however small) round any point the function would acquire the same value an unlimited number of times. Then the uniform function would either be constant everywhere within that finite region and so would be constant

everywhere : or it would possess an unlimited number of constant values
within that region : or an unlimited number of infinities within the region.
In the second case, its derivative would possess an unlimited number of zeros
in the region, which is any small region round any point: as at the end of
§ 37, the point would be an essential singularity. Similarly, in the third case,
the point would be an essential singularity. Each of the alternatives, consequent upon the possession of an infinitesimal period, is to be excluded : hence
we also exclude the possibility of infinitesimal periods.

It is convenient to have a graphical representation of the periodicity of a
function.

(i)   For simply-periodic functions, we
take a series of points $O$, $A_1$, $A_2$, ... ,
$A_{-1}$, $A_{-2}$, ... representing $0$, $\omega$, $2\omega$, ... ,
$-\omega$, $-2\omega$, ... ; and through these points
we draw a series of parallel lines, dividing
the plane into bands. Let $P$ be any
point $z$ in the band between the lines
through $O$ and through $A_1$; through $P$
draw a line parallel to $OA_1$ and measure
off $PP_1 = P_1P_2 = ... = PP_{-1} = P_{-1}P_{-2} = ...$,
each equal to $OA_1$; then all the points
$P_1$, $P_2$, ... , $P_{-1}$, $P_{-2}$, ... are represented

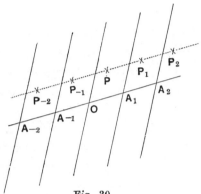

Fig. 30.

by $z + n\omega$ for positive and negative integral values of $n$. But $f(z + n\omega) = f(z)$;
and therefore the value of the function at a point $P_n$ in any of the bands is
the same as the value at $P$. Moreover, to a point in any of the bands there
corresponds a point in any other of the bands; and therefore, owing to the
periodic resumption of the value at the points corresponding to each point $P$,
it is sufficient to consider the variation of the function for points within one
band, say the band between the lines through $O$ and through $A_1$. A point $P$
within the band is sometimes called irreducible, the corresponding points $P$
in the other bands reducible.

If it were convenient, the boundary lines of the bands could be taken
through points other than $A_1$, $A_2$, ... ; for example, through points $(m + \frac{1}{2})\omega$
for positive and negative integral values of $m$. Moreover, they need not be
straight lines. The essential feature of the graphic representation is the
division of the plane into bands.

(ii)   For doubly-periodic functions a similar method is adopted. Let $\omega$
and $\omega'$ be the two periods of such a function $f(z)$, so that

$$f(z + \omega) = f(z) = f(z + \omega');$$

then                    $$f(z + n\omega + n'\omega') = f(z),$$

where $n$ and $n'$ are any integers positive or negative.

For graphic purposes, we take points $O, A_1, A_2, ..., A_{-1}, A_{-2}, ...$ representing $0, \omega, 2\omega, ..., -\omega, -2\omega, ...$ ; and we take another series $O, B_1, B_2, ..., B_{-1}, B_{-2}, ...$ representing $0, \omega', 2\omega', .., -\omega', -2\omega', ...$; through the points $A$ we draw lines parallel to the line of points $B$, and through the points $B$ we draw lines parallel to the line of points $A$. The intersection of the lines through $A_n$ and $B_{n'}$ is evidently the point $n\omega + n'\omega'$, that is, the angular points of the parallelograms into which the plane is divided represent the points $n\omega + n'\omega'$ for the values of $n$ and $n'$.

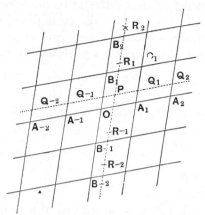

Fig. 31.

Let $P$ be any point $z$ in the parallelogram $OA_1C_1B_1$; on lines through $P$, parallel to the sides of the parallelogram, take points $Q_1, Q_2, ..., Q_{-1}, Q_{-2}, ...$ such that $PQ_1 = Q_1Q_2 = ... = \omega$, and points $R_1, R_2, ..., R_{-1}, R_{-2}, ...$ such that $PR_1 = R_1R_2 = ... = \omega'$; and through these new points draw lines parallel to the sides of the parallelogram. Then the variables of the points in which these lines intersect are all represented by $z + m\omega + m'\omega'$ for positive and negative integral values of $m$ and $m'$; and the point represented by $z + m\omega + m'\omega'$ is situated in the parallelogram, the angular points of which are $m\omega + m'\omega'$, $(m + 1)\omega + m'\omega'$, $m\omega + (m' + 1)\omega'$, and $(m + 1)\omega + (m' + 1)\omega'$, exactly as $P$ is situated in $OA_1C_1B_1$. But

$$f(z + m\omega + m'\omega') = f(z),$$

and therefore the value of the function at such a point is the same as the value at $P$. Since the parallelograms are all equal and similarly situated, to any point in any of them there corresponds a point in $OA_1C_1B_1$; and the value of the function at the two points is the same. Hence *it is sufficient to consider the variation of the function for points within one parallelogram*, say, that which has $0, \omega, \omega + \omega', \omega'$ for its angular points. A point $P$ within this parallelogram is sometimes called *irreducible*, the corresponding points within the other parallelograms *reducible* to $P$; the whole aggregate of the points thus reducible to any one are called *homologous* points. And the parallelogram to which the reduction is made is called the parallelogram of periods.

As in the case of simply-periodic functions, it may prove convenient to choose the position of the *fundamental parallelogram* so that the origin is not on its boundary; thus it might be the parallelogram the middle points of whose sides are $\pm \frac{1}{2}\omega, \pm \frac{1}{2}\omega'$.

*Ex.* Shew how to reduce a given point numerically; for instance, find the irreducible point homologous to $730 + 482i$ for periods $1 + 9i$, $3 + 2i$.

**106.** In the preceding representation it has been assumed that the line of points $A$ is different in direction from the line of points $B$. If $\omega = u + iv$ and $\omega' = u' + iv'$, this assumption implies that $v'/u'$ is unequal to $v/u$, and therefore that the real part of $\omega'/i\omega$ does not vanish. The justification of this assumption is established by the proposition, due to Jacobi[*] :—

*The ratio of the periods of a uniform doubly-periodic function cannot be real.*

Let $f(z)$ be a function, having $\omega$ and $\omega'$ as its periods. If the ratio $\omega'/\omega$ be real, it must be either commensurable or incommensurable.

If it be commensurable, let it be equal to $n'/n$, where $n$ and $n'$ are integers, neither of which is unity owing to the definition of the periods $\omega$ and $\omega'$.

Let $n'/n$ be developed as a continued fraction, and let $m'/m$ be the last convergent before $n'/n$, where $m$ and $m'$ are integers. Then

$$\frac{n'}{n} \sim \frac{m'}{m} = \frac{1}{mn},$$

that is,
$$mn' \sim m'n = 1,$$

so that
$$m'\omega \sim m\omega' = \frac{\omega}{n}(m'n \sim mn') = \frac{\omega}{n}.$$

Therefore
$$f(z) = f(z + m'\omega \sim m\omega'),$$

since $m$ and $m'$ are integers; so that

$$f(z) = f\left(z + \frac{\omega}{n}\right),$$

contravening the definition of $\omega$ as a period, viz., that no submultiple of $\omega$ is a period. Hence the ratio of the periods is not a commensurable real quantity.

If it be incommensurable, we express $\omega'/\omega$ as a continued fraction. Let $p/q$ and $p'/q'$ be two consecutive convergents: their values are separated by the value of $\omega'/\omega$, so that we may write

$$\frac{\omega'}{\omega} = \frac{p}{q} + h\left(\frac{p'}{q'} - \frac{p}{q}\right),$$

where
$$1 > h > 0.$$

Now $pq' \sim p'q = 1$, so that

$$\frac{\omega'}{\omega} = \frac{p}{q} + \frac{\epsilon}{qq'},$$

where $\epsilon$ is real and $|\epsilon| < 1$; hence

$$q\omega' - p\omega = \frac{\epsilon}{q'}\omega.$$

---

[*] *Ges. Werke*, t. ii, pp. 25, 26.

Therefore $\qquad f(z) = f(z + q\omega' - p\omega),$

since $p$ and $q$ are integers; so that

$$f(z) = f\left(z + \frac{\epsilon}{q'}\,\omega\right).$$

Now since $\omega'/\omega$ is incommensurable, the continued fraction is unending. We therefore can take an advanced convergent, so that $q'$ is very large; and we choose it so that $\left|\dfrac{\epsilon}{q'}\,\omega\right|$ is less than any assigned positive quantity, however small. But $\dfrac{\epsilon}{q'}\,\omega$ is equal to $q\omega' - p\omega$, where $q$ and $p$ are integers, and it therefore is a period of the function $f(z)$. Hence, on the assumption that $\omega'/\omega$ is real and incommensurable, it follows that the function possesses an infinitesimal period: the possibility of which was initially excluded (§ 105).

The ratio of the periods is thus not an incommensurable real quantity.

We therefore infer Jacobi's theorem that the ratio of the periods cannot be real. In general, the ratio is a complex quantity; it may, however, be a pure imaginary*.

COROLLARY. If a uniform function have two periods $\omega_1$ and $\omega_2$, such that a relation

$$m_1\omega_1 + m_2\omega_2 = 0$$

exists for integral values of $m_1$ and $m_2$, the function is only simply-periodic. And such a relation cannot exist between two periods of a simply-periodic function, if $m_1$ and $m_2$ be real and incommensurable; for then the function would have an infinitesimal period.

Similarly, if a uniform function have three periods $\omega_1$, $\omega_2$, $\omega_3$, connected by two relations

$$m_1\omega_1 + m_2\omega_2 + m_3\omega_3 = 0,$$
$$n_1\omega_1 + n_2\omega_2 + n_3\omega_3 = 0,$$

where the coefficients $m$ and $n$ are integers, then the function is only simply-periodic.

**107.** The two following propositions, also due to Jacobi†, are important in the theory of uniform periodic functions of a single variable:—

*If a uniform function have three periods $\omega_1$, $\omega_2$, $\omega_3$, such that a relation*

$$m_1\omega_1 + m_2\omega_2 + m_3\omega_3 = 0$$

*is satisfied for integral values of $m_1$, $m_2$, $m_3$, then the function is only a doubly-periodic function.*

---

* It was proved, in Ex. 5 and Ex. 7 of § 104, that certain uniform functions are doubly-periodic. A direct proof, that the ratio of the distinct periods of the functions there obtained is not a real quantity, is given by Falk, *Acta Math.*, t. vii, (1885), pp. 197—200, and by Pringsheim, *Math. Ann.*, t. xxvii, (1886), pp. 151—157.

† *Ges. Werke*, t. ii, pp. 27—32.

What has to be proved, in order to establish this proposition, is that two periods exist of which $\omega_1$, $\omega_2$, $\omega_3$ are integral multiple combinations.

Evidently we may assume that $m_1$, $m_2$, $m_3$ have no common factor: let $f$ be the common factor (if any) of $m_2$ and $m_3$, which is prime to $m_1$. Then since

$$\frac{m_1}{f}\,\omega_1 = -\,\frac{m_2}{f}\,\omega_2 - \frac{m_3}{f}\,\omega_3$$

and the right-hand side is an integral combination of periods, it follows that $\dfrac{m_1}{f}\,\omega_1$ is a period.

Now $\dfrac{m_1}{f}$ is a fraction in its lowest terms. Change it into a continued fraction and let $\dfrac{p}{q}$ be the last convergent before the proper value; then

$$\frac{m_1}{f} - \frac{p}{q} = \pm\,\frac{1}{fq}$$

so that

$$q\,\frac{m_1}{f} - p = \pm\,\frac{1}{f}.$$

But $\omega_1$ is a period and $\dfrac{m_1}{f}\,\omega_1$ is a period; therefore $q\,\dfrac{m_1}{f}\,\omega_1 - p\omega_1$ is a period, or $\omega_1/f$ is a period, $=\omega_1'$ say.

Let $m_2/f = m_2'$, $m_3/f = m_3'$, so that $m_1\omega_1' + m_2'\omega_2 + m_3'\omega_3 = 0$. Change $m_2'/m_3'$ into a continued fraction, taking $\dfrac{r}{s}$ to be the last convergent before the proper value, so that

$$\frac{m_2'}{m_3'} - \frac{r}{s} = \pm\,\frac{1}{sm_3'}.$$

Then $r\omega_2 + s\omega_3$, being an integral combination of periods, is a period. But

$$\pm\,\omega_2 = \omega_2\,(sm_2' - rm_3')$$
$$= -\,r\omega_2 m_3' - s\,(m_1\omega_1' + m_3'\omega_3)$$
$$= -\,m_1 s\omega_1' - m_3'\,(r\omega_2 + s\omega_3)\,;$$

also

$$\pm\,\omega_3 = \omega_3\,(sm_2' - rm_3')$$
$$= sm_2'\omega_3 + r\,(m_1\omega_1' + m_2'\omega_2)$$
$$= m_1 r\omega_1' + m_2'\,(r\omega_2 + s\omega_3)\,;$$

and

$$\omega_1 = f\omega_1'.$$

Hence two periods $\omega_1'$ and $r\omega_2 + s\omega_3$ exist of which $\omega_1$, $\omega_2$, $\omega_3$ are integral multiple combinations; and therefore all the periods are equivalent to $\omega_1'$ and $r\omega_2 + s\omega_3$, that is, the function is only doubly-periodic.

COROLLARY. If a function have four periods $\omega_1$, $\omega_2$, $\omega_3$, $\omega_4$ connected by two relations

$$m_1\omega_1 + m_2\omega_2 + m_3\omega_3 + m_4\omega_4 = 0,$$

$$n_1\omega_1 + n_2\omega_2 + n_3\omega_3 + n_4\omega_4 = 0,$$

where the coefficients $m$ and $n$ are integers, the function is only doubly-periodic.

**108.** *If a uniform function of one variable have three periods* $\omega_1$, $\omega_2$, $\omega_3$, *then a relation of the form*

$$m_1\omega_1 + m_2\omega_2 + m_3\omega_3 = 0$$

*must be satisfied for some integral values of* $m_1$, $m_2$, $m_3$.

Let $\omega_r = \alpha_r + i\beta_r$, for $r = 1, 2, 3$; in consequence of § 106, we shall assume that no one of the ratios of $\omega_1$, $\omega_2$, $\omega_3$ in pairs is real, for, otherwise, either the three periods reduce to two immediately, or the function has an infinitesimal period. Then, determining two quantities $\lambda$ and $\mu$ by the equations

$$\alpha_3 = \lambda\alpha_1 + \mu\alpha_2, \quad \beta_3 = \lambda\beta_1 + \mu\beta_2,$$

so that $\lambda$ and $\mu$ are real quantities and neither zero nor infinity, we have

$$\omega_3 = \lambda\omega_1 + \mu\omega_2,$$

for real values of $\lambda$ and $\mu$.

Then, first, if either $\lambda$ or $\mu$ be commensurable, the other is also commensurable. Let $\lambda = a/b$, where $a$ and $b$ are integers; then

$$b\mu\omega_2 = b\omega_3 - b\lambda\omega_1$$

$$= b\omega_3 - a\omega_1,$$

so that $b\mu\omega_2$ is a period. Now, if $b\mu$ be not commensurable, change it into a continued fraction, and let $p/q$, $p'/q'$ be two consecutive convergents, so that, as in § 106,

$$b\mu = \frac{p}{q} + \frac{x}{qq'},$$

where $1 > x > -1$. Then $\dfrac{p}{q}\omega_2 + \dfrac{x\omega_2}{qq'}$ is a period, and so is $\omega_2$; hence

$$q\left(\frac{p}{q}\omega_2 + \frac{x\omega_2}{qq'}\right) - p\omega_2$$

is a period, that is, $\dfrac{x}{q}\omega_2$ is a period. We may take $q'$ indefinitely large, and then the function has an infinitesimal quantity for a period, which has been excluded by our initial argument. Hence $b\mu$ (and therefore $\mu$) cannot be incommensurable, if $\lambda$ be commensurable; and thus $\lambda$ and $\mu$ are simultaneously commensurable or simultaneously incommensurable.

If $\lambda$ and $\mu$ be simultaneously commensurable, let $\lambda = \dfrac{a}{b}$, $\mu = \dfrac{c}{d}$, so that

$$\omega_3 = \frac{a}{b}\,\omega_1 + \frac{c}{d}\,\omega_2,$$

and therefore $\qquad\qquad bd\omega_3 = ad\omega_1 + bc\omega_2,$

a relation of the kind required.

If $\lambda$ and $\mu$ be simultaneously incommensurable, express $\lambda$ as a continued fraction; then by taking any convergent $r/s$, we have

$$\lambda - \frac{r}{s} = \frac{x}{s^2},$$

where $1 > x > -1$, so that $\qquad s\lambda - r = \dfrac{x}{s};$

by taking the convergent sufficiently advanced the right-hand side can be made infinitesimal.

Let $r_1$ be the nearest integer to the value of $s\mu$, so that, if

$$s\mu - r_1 = \Delta,$$

we have $\Delta$ numerically not greater than $\frac{1}{2}$. Then

$$s\omega_3 - r\omega_1 - r_1\omega_2 = \frac{x}{s}\,\omega_1 + \Delta\omega_2,$$

and the quantity $\dfrac{x}{s}\,\omega_1$ can be made so small as to be negligible. Hence integers $r$, $r_1$, $s$ can be chosen so as to give a new period $\omega_2{}'\ (= \Delta\omega_2)$, such that $|\,\omega_2{}'\,| \leqslant \frac{1}{2}\,|\,\omega_2\,|$.

We now take $\omega_1$, $\omega_2{}'$, $\omega_3$: they will be connected by a relation of the form

$$\omega_3 = \lambda'\omega_1 + \mu'\omega_2{}',$$

and $\lambda'$ and $\mu'$ must be incommensurable: for otherwise the substitution for $\omega_2{}'$ of its value just obtained would lead to a relation among $\omega_1$, $\omega_2$, $\omega_3$ that would imply commensurability of $\lambda$ and of $\mu$.

Proceeding just as before, we may similarly obtain a new period $\omega_2{}''$ such that $|\,\omega_2{}''\,| \leqslant \frac{1}{2}\,|\,\omega_2{}'\,|$; and so on in succession. Hence we shall obtain, after $n$ such processes, a period $\omega_2{}^{(n)}$ such that $|\,\omega_2{}^{(n)}\,| \leqslant \dfrac{1}{2^n}\,|\,\omega_2\,|$, so that by making $n$ sufficiently large we shall ultimately obtain a period less than any assigned quantity. Such a period is infinitesimal; and infinitesimal periods were initially excluded (§ 105) for reasons there given. Thus $\lambda$ and $\mu$ cannot be simultaneously incommensurable.

Hence the only constructive result is that $\lambda$ and $\mu$ are simultaneously commensurable; and then there is a period-equation of the form

$$m_1\omega_1 + m_2\omega_2 + m_3\omega_3 = 0,$$

where $m_1$, $m_2$, $m_3$ are integers.

The foregoing proof is substantially due to Jacobi (l.c.). The result can be obtained from geometrical considerations by shewing that the infinite number of points, at which the function resumes its value, along a line through $z$ parallel to the $\omega_3$-line will, unless the condition be satisfied, reduce to an infinite number of points in the $\omega_1$, $\omega_2$ parallelogram which will form either a continuous line or a continuous area, in either of which cases the function would be a constant; or there will be an unlimited number condensed in any region round $z$, however small, thus making the point an essential singularity, which is impossible for every point $z$. But, if the condition be satisfied, then the points along the line through $z$ reduce to only a finite number of points*.

COROLLARY I. Uniform functions of a single variable cannot have three independent periods; in other words, *triply-periodic uniform functions of a single variable do not exist*†; *and, a fortiori, uniform functions of a single variable with a number of independent periods greater than two do not exist.*

But functions involving more than one variable can have more than two periods, e.g., Abelian transcendents; and a function of one variable, having more than two periods, is not uniform.

COROLLARY II. *All the periods of a uniform periodic function of a single variable reduce either to integral multiples of one period or to linear combinations of integral multiples of two periods whose ratio is not a real quantity.*

**109**. It is desirable to have the parallelogram, in which a doubly-periodic function is considered, as small as possible. If in the parallelogram (supposed, for convenience, to have the origin for an angular point) there be a point $\omega''$, such that

$$f(z + \omega'') = f(z)$$

for all values of $z$, then the parallelogram can be replaced by another.

It is evident that $\omega''$ is a period of the function; hence (§ 108) we must have

$$\omega'' = \lambda\omega + \mu\omega';$$

and both $\lambda$ and $\mu$, which are commensurable quantities, are less than unity since the point is within the parallelogram. Moreover, $\omega + \omega' - \omega''$, which is equal to $(1 - \lambda)\omega + (1 - \mu)\omega'$, is another point within the parallelogram; and

$$f(z + \omega + \omega' - \omega'') = f(z),$$

since $\omega$, $\omega'$, $\omega''$ are periods. Thus there cannot be only one such point unless

$$\lambda = \tfrac{1}{2} = \mu.$$

* For another proof, see Goursat, *Cours d'analyse mathématique*, t. ii, § 324.
† This theorem is also due to Jacobi, (l.c., p. 239, note).

But the number of such points within the parallelogram must be finite. If there were an infinite number, they would form a continuous line or a continuous area where the uniform function had an unvarying value, and the function would have a constant value everywhere; or they would condense within any region (however small) round any point, and so would make the point an essential singularity, a result to be excluded as in § 37.

To construct a new parallelogram when all the points are known, we first choose the series of points parallel to the $\omega$-line through the origin $O$, and of that series we choose the point nearest $O$, say $A_1$. We similarly choose the point, nearest the origin, of the series of points parallel to the $\omega$-line and nearest to it after the series that includes $A_1$, say $B_1$: we take $OA_1$, $OB_1$ as adjacent sides of the parallelogram, and these lines as the vectorial representations of the periods. No point lies within this parallelogram where the function has the same value as at $O$; hence the angular points of the original parallelograms coincide with angular points of the new parallelograms.

When a parallelogram has thus been obtained, containing no internal point $\Omega$ such that the function can satisfy the equation

$$f(z + \Omega) = f(z)$$

for all values of $z$, it is called a *fundamental*, or a *primitive, parallelogram*. The parallelogram of reference in subsequent investigations will be assumed to be of a fundamental character.

But *a fundamental parallelogram is not unique.*

Let $\omega$ and $\omega'$ be the periods for a given fundamental parallelogram, so that every other period $\omega''$ is of the form $\lambda\omega + \mu\omega'$, where $\lambda$ and $\mu$ are integers. Take any four integers $a$, $b$, $c$, $d$ such that $ad - bc = \pm 1$, as may be done in an infinite variety of ways; and adopt two new periods $\omega_1$ and $\omega_2$, such that

$$\omega_1 = a\omega + b\omega', \qquad \omega_2 = c\omega + d\omega'.$$

Then the parallelogram with $\omega_1$ and $\omega_2$ for adjacent sides is fundamental. For we have

$$\pm \omega = d\omega_1 - b\omega_2, \qquad \pm \omega' = -c\omega_1 + a\omega_2,$$

and therefore any period $\omega''$

$$= \lambda\omega + \mu\omega'$$

$$= (\lambda d - \mu c)\, \omega_1 + (-\lambda b + \mu a)\, \omega_2, \text{ save as to signs of } \lambda \text{ and } \mu.$$

The coefficients of $\omega_1$ and $\omega_2$ are integers, that is, the point $\omega''$ lies outside the new parallelogram of reference; there is therefore no point in it such that

$$f(z + \omega'') = f(z),$$

and hence the parallelogram is fundamental.

COROLLARY. *The aggregate of the angular points in one division of the plane into fundamental parallelograms coincides with their aggregate in any other division into fundamental parallelograms; and all fundamental parallelograms for a given function are of the same area.*

The method suggested above for the construction of a fundamental parallelogram is geometrical, and it assumes a knowledge of all the points $\omega''$ within a given parallelogram for which the equation $f(z+\omega'')=f(z)$ is satisfied.

Such a point $\omega_3$ within the $\omega_1$, $\omega_2$ parallelogram is given by

$$\omega_3=\frac{m_1}{m_3}\omega_1+\frac{m_2}{m_3}\omega_2,$$

where $m_1$, $m_2$, $m_3$ are integers. We may assume that no two of these three integers have a common factor; were it otherwise, say for $m_1$ and $m_2$, then, as in § 107, a submultiple of $\omega_3$ would be a period—a result which may be considered as excluded. Evidently all the points in the parallelogram are the reduced points homologous with $\omega_3$, $2\omega_3$, ......, $(m_3-1)\omega_3$; when these are obtained, the geometrical construction is possible.

The following is a simple and practicable analytical method for the construction.

Change $m_1/m_3$ and $m_2/m_3$ into continued fractions; and let $p/q$ and $r/s$ be the last convergents before the respective proper values, so that

$$\frac{m_1}{m_3}-\frac{p}{q}=\frac{\epsilon}{qm_3},\qquad \frac{m_2}{m_3}-\frac{r}{s}=\frac{\epsilon'}{sm_3},$$

where $\epsilon$ and $\epsilon'$ are each of them $\pm1$. Let

$$q\frac{m_2}{m_3}=\theta+\frac{\mu}{m_3},\qquad s\frac{m_1}{m_3}=\phi+\frac{\lambda}{m_3},$$

where $\lambda$ and $\mu$ are taken to be less than $m_3$, but they do not vanish because $q$ and $s$ are less than $m_3$. Then

$$q\omega_3-p\omega_1-\theta\omega_2=\frac{1}{m_3}(\mu\omega_2+\epsilon\omega_1),\qquad s\omega_3-r\omega_2-\phi\omega_1=\frac{1}{m_3}(\lambda\omega_1+\epsilon'\omega_2);$$

the left-hand sides are periods, say $\Omega_1$ and $\Omega_2$ respectively, and since $\mu+\epsilon$ is not $>m_3$ and $\lambda+\epsilon'$ is not $>m_3$, the points $\Omega_1$ and $\Omega_2$ determine a parallelogram smaller than the initial parallelogram.

Thus $\qquad\qquad\epsilon\omega_1+\mu\omega_2=m_3\Omega_1,\qquad \lambda\omega_1+\epsilon'\omega_2=m_3\Omega_2,$

are equations defining new periods $\Omega_1$, $\Omega_2$. Moreover

$$\phi+\frac{\lambda}{m_3}=s\frac{m_1}{m_3}=s\frac{p}{q}+\frac{\epsilon s}{qm_3},\qquad \theta+\frac{\mu}{m_3}=q\frac{m_2}{m_3}=q\frac{r}{s}+\frac{\epsilon'q}{sm_3}:$$

so that, multiplying the right-hand sides together and likewise the left-hand sides, we at once see that $\lambda\mu-\epsilon\epsilon'$ is divisible by $m_3$ if it be not zero: let

$$\lambda\mu-\epsilon\epsilon'=m_3\Delta.$$

Then, as $\lambda$ and $\mu$ are less than $m_3$, they are greater than $\Delta$; and they are prime to it, because $\epsilon\epsilon'$ is $\pm1$. Hence we have

$$\Delta\omega_1=\mu\Omega_2-\epsilon'\Omega_1,\qquad \Delta\omega_2=\lambda\Omega_1-\epsilon\Omega_2.$$

Since $\lambda$ and $\mu$ are both greater than $\Delta$, let

$$\lambda = \lambda_1 \Delta + \lambda', \qquad \mu = \mu_1 \Delta + \mu',$$

where $\lambda'$ and $\mu'$ are $< \Delta$. Then $\lambda'\mu' - \epsilon\epsilon'$ is divisible by $\Delta$ if it be not zero, say

$$\lambda'\mu' - \epsilon\epsilon' = \Delta\Delta';$$

then $\lambda'$ and $\mu'$ are $> \Delta'$ and are prime to it. And now

$$\Delta(\omega_1 - \mu_1\Omega_2) = \mu'\Omega_2 - \epsilon'\Omega_1, \qquad \Delta(\omega_2 - \lambda_1\Omega_1) = \lambda'\Omega_1 - \epsilon\Omega_2;$$

thus, if $\omega_1 - \mu_1\Omega_2 = \Omega_3$, $\omega_2 - \lambda_1\Omega_1 = \Omega_4$, which are periods, we have

$$\Delta\Omega_3 = \mu'\Omega_2 - \epsilon'\Omega_1, \qquad \Delta\Omega_4 = \lambda'\Omega_1 - \epsilon\Omega_2.$$

With $\Omega_3$ and $\Omega_4$ we can construct a parallelogram smaller than that constructed with $\Omega_1$ and $\Omega_2$. We now have

$$\Delta'\Omega_1 = \epsilon\Omega_3 + \mu'\Omega_4, \qquad \Delta'\Omega_2 = \lambda'\Omega_3 + \epsilon'\Omega_4,$$

that is, equations of the same form as before. We proceed thus in successive stages: each quantity $\Delta$ thus obtained is distinctly less than the preceding $\Delta$, and so finally we shall reach a stage when the succeeding $\Delta$ would be unity, that is, the solution of the pair of equations then leads to periods that determine a fundamental parallelogram. It is not difficult to prove that $\omega_1$, $\omega_2$, $\omega_3$ are combinations of integral multiples of these periods.

If one of the quantities, such as $\lambda'\mu' - \epsilon\epsilon'$, be zero, then $\lambda' = \mu' = 1$, $\epsilon = \epsilon' = \pm 1$; and then $\Omega_3$ and $\Omega_4$ are identical. If $\epsilon = \epsilon' = +1$, then $\Delta\Omega_3 = \Omega_2 - \Omega_1$, and the fundamental parallelogram is determined by

$$\Omega_3' = \Omega_1 + \frac{1}{\Delta}(\Omega_2 - \Omega_1), \qquad \Omega_4' = \Omega_2 - \frac{1}{\Delta}(\Omega_2 - \Omega_1).$$

If $\epsilon = \epsilon' = -1$, then $\Delta\Omega_3 = \Omega_2 + \Omega_1$, so that, as $\Delta$ is not unity in this case, the fundamental parallelogram is determined by $\Omega_2$ and $\Omega_3$.

*Ex.* If a function be periodic in $\omega_1$, $\omega_2$, and also in $\omega_3$ where

$$29\omega_3 = 17\omega_1 + 11\omega_2,$$

periods for a fundamental parallelogram are

$$\Omega_1' = 5\omega_1 + 3\omega_2 - 8\omega_3, \qquad \Omega_2' = 3\omega_1 + 2\omega_2 - 5\omega_3,$$

and the values of $\omega_1$, $\omega_2$, $\omega_3$ in terms of $\Omega_1'$ and $\Omega_2'$ are

$$\omega_1 = \Omega_2' + 3\Omega_1', \qquad \omega_2 = 9\Omega_2' - 2\Omega_1', \qquad \omega_3 = 4\Omega_2' + \Omega_1'.$$

Further discussion relating to the transformation of periods and of fundamental parallelograms will be found in Briot and Bouquet's *Théorie des fonctions elliptiques*, pp. 234, 235, 268—272.

**110.** It has been proved that uniform periodic functions of a single variable cannot have more than two periods, independent in the sense that their ratio is not a real quantity. If then a function exist, which has two periods with a real incommensurable ratio or has more than two independent periods, either it is not uniform or it is a function (whether uniform or multiform) of more variables than one.

When restriction is made to uniform functions, the only alternative is that the function should depend on more than one variable.

In the case when three periods $\omega_1$, $\omega_2$, $\omega_3$ (each of the form $\alpha + i\beta$) were assigned, it was proved that the necessary condition for the existence of a uniform function of a single variable is that finite integers $m_1$, $m_2$, $m_3$ can be found such that

$$m_1 \alpha_1 + m_2 \alpha_2 + m_3 \alpha_3 = 0,$$

$$m_1 \beta_1 + m_2 \beta_2 + m_3 \beta_3 = 0 \,;$$

and that, if these conditions be not satisfied, then finite integers $m_1$, $m_2$, $m_3$ can be found such that both $\Sigma m\alpha$ and $\Sigma m\beta$ become infinitesimally small.

This theorem is purely algebraical, and is only a special case of a more general theorem as follows :—

*Let* $\alpha_{11}$, $\alpha_{12}$, $\ldots$, $\alpha_{1,r+1}$; $\alpha_{21}$, $\alpha_{22}$, $\ldots$, $\alpha_{2,r+1}$; $\ldots$; $\alpha_{r1}$, $\alpha_{r2}$, $\ldots$, $\alpha_{r,r+1}$ *be* $r$ *sets of real quantities such that a relation of the form*

$$n_1 \alpha_{s1} + n_2 \alpha_{s2} + \ldots + n_{r+1} \alpha_{s,r+1} = 0$$

*is not satisfied among any one set. Then finite integers* $m_1$, $\ldots$, $m_{r+1}$ *can be determined such that each of the sums*

$$m_1 \alpha_{s1} + m_2 \alpha_{s2} + \ldots + m_{r+1} \alpha_{s,r+1}$$

(*for* $s = 1$, $2$, $\ldots$, $r$) *can be made less than any assigned quantity, however small.* And, *a fortiori*, if fewer than $r$ sets, each containing $r + 1$ quantities be given, the $r + 1$ integers can be determined so as to lead to the result enunciated; all that is necessary for the purpose being an arbitrary assignment of sets of real quantities necessary to make the number of sets equal to $r$. But the result is not true if more than $r$ sets be given.

We shall not give a proof of this general theorem[*]; it would follow the lines of the proof in the limited case, as given in § 108. But the theorem can be used to indicate how the value of an integral with more than two periods is affected by the periodicity.

Let $I$ be the value of the integral taken along some assigned path from an initial point $z_0$ to a final point $z$; and let the periods be $\omega_1$, $\omega_2$, $\ldots$, $\omega_r$, (where $r > 2$), so that the general value is

$$I + m_1 \omega_1 + m_2 \omega_2 + \ldots + m_r \omega_r,$$

where $m_1$, $m_2$, $\ldots$, $m_r$ are integers. Now if $\omega_s = \alpha_s + i\beta_s$, for $s = 1$, $2$, $\ldots$, $r$, when it is divided into its real and its imaginary parts, then finite integers $n_1$, $n_2$, $\ldots$, $n_r$ can be determined such that

$$n_1 \alpha_1 + n_2 \alpha_2 + \ldots + n_r \alpha_r$$

$$n_1 \beta_1 + n_2 \beta_2 + \ldots + n_r \beta_r$$

* A proof will be found in Clebsch and Gordan's *Theorie der Abel'schen Functionen*, § 38. See also Baker's *Abelian Functions*, chapters ix, xix, where full references will be found.

can be made infinitesimal, that is, less than any assigned quantity, however small; and then $\left| \sum\limits_{s=1}^{r} n_s \omega_s \right|$ is infinitesimal. But the addition of $\sum\limits_{s=1}^{r} n_s \omega_s$ still gives a value of the integral; hence the value can be modified by infinitesimal quantities, and the modification can be repeated indefinitely. The modifications of the value correspond to modifications of the path from $z_0$ to $z$; and hence the integral, regarded as depending on a single variable, can be made, by modifications of the path of the variable, to assume any value. The integral, in fact, has not a definite value dependent solely upon the final value of the variable; to make the value definite, the path by which the variable passes from the lower to the upper limit must be specified.

It will subsequently (§ 239) be shewn how this limitation is avoided by making the integral, regarded as a function, depend upon a proper number of independent variables—the number being greater than unity.

*Ex.* 1. If $V_0$ be the value of $\int_0^z \dfrac{dz}{(1-z^n)^{\frac{1}{2}}}$, ($n$ integral), taken along an assigned path, and if

$$P = 2 \int_0^1 \frac{dx}{(1-x^n)^{\frac{1}{2}}} \quad (x \text{ real}),$$

then the general value of the integral is

$$(-1)^q V_0 + P \left[ \tfrac{1}{2}\{1 - (-1)^q\} + \sum_{p=1}^{n} m_p e^{\frac{2p\pi i}{n}} \right],$$

where $q$ is any integer and $m_p$ any positive or negative integer such that $\sum\limits_{p=1}^{n} m_p = 0$.

(Math. Trip., Part II., 1889.)

*Ex.* 2. If, in an integration in regard to the complex variable $z$, $(a_r b_s \ldots)$ denote a contour enclosing the "critical" points $a_r, b_s, \ldots$; and, for two points, $(a_r ; b_s)$ denote the triple contour $(a_r b_s)(a_r)^{-1}(b_s)^{-1}$, prove that in the integrals

$$y_1 = \int_{(x;0)} z^{p-1}(z-1)^{q-1}(z-x)^{r-1}\, dz, \qquad y_2 = \int_{(x;1)} z^{p-1}(z-1)^{q-1}(z-x)^{r-1}\, dz,$$

where $p, q, r$ are not rational integers, if $x$ describe a closed curve round $z=0$, the $z$-loops being deformed so as not to be intersected by this $x$-closed curve, the new values of $y_1, y_2$ are

$$y_1' = e^{2\pi i(p+r)} y_1, \qquad y_2' = e^{2\pi i r} (e^{2\pi i q} - 1) y_1 + y_2 :$$

and determine the similar changes in $y_1, y_2$ when $x$ moves round $z=1$.

Deduce without direct calculation, that if $p+r$ be a rational integer, $y_1$ is uniform in the neighbourhood of $x=0$, and, also in this neighbourhood,

$$y_2 = \phi(x) + \frac{e^{2\pi i r}(e^{2\pi i q} - 1)}{2\pi i} y_1 \log x,$$

$\phi(x)$ being also uniform in this neighbourhood.

Calculate $y_1$ and $\phi(x)$ from the integrals, as ordinary power-series in $x$, when $p = q = r = \tfrac{1}{2}$.

(Math. Trip., Part II., 1893.)

*Ex.* 3.   Prove that $v = \int_0^z u\,dz$, where

$$u^3 - 3zu + z^3 = 0,$$

is an algebraic function satisfying the equation

$$8\,(v + \tfrac{3}{2})^3 - 12\,(v + \tfrac{3}{2})^2 - 12z^3\,(v + \tfrac{3}{2}) + z^6 + 16z^3 = 0\,;$$

and obtain the conditions necessary and sufficient to ensure that

$$v = \int u\,dz$$

should be an algebraic function, when $u$ is an algebraic function satisfying an equation

$$f(z,\, u) = 0.$$

(Liouville, Briot and Bouquet.)

# CHAPTER X.

## Uniform Simply-Periodic and Doubly-Periodic Functions.

**111.** Only a few of the properties of simply-periodic functions will be given[*], partly because some of them are connected with Fourier's series the detailed discussion of which lies beyond our limits, and partly because, as will shortly be explained, many of them can at once be changed into properties of uniform non-periodic functions which have already been considered.

When we use the graphical method of § 105, it is evident that we need consider the variation of the function within only a single band. Within that band any function must have at least one infinity, for, if it had not, it would not have an infinity anywhere in the plane and so would be a constant; and it must have at least one zero, for, if it had not, its reciprocal, also a simply-periodic function, would not have an infinity in the band. The infinities may, of course, be accidental or essential: their character is reproduced at the homologous points in all the bands.

For purposes of analytical representation, it is convenient to use a relation

$$Z = e^{\frac{2\pi i}{\omega} z},$$

so that, if the point $Z$ in its plane have $R$ and $\Theta$ for polar coordinates,

$$z = \frac{\omega}{2\pi i} \log R + \frac{\Theta}{2\pi} \omega.$$

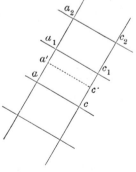

Fig. 32.

If we take any point $A$ in the $Z$-plane and a corresponding point $a$ in the $z$-plane, then, as $Z$ describes a complete circle through $A$ with the origin as centre, $z$ moves along a line $aa_1$, where $a_1$ is $a + \omega$. A second description of the circle makes $z$ move from $a_1$ to $a_2$, where $a_2 = a_1 + \omega$; and so on in succession.

---

[*] For a fuller discussion, see Chessin, *Amer. Journ. Math.*, t. xix, (1897), pp. 217—258.

For various descriptions, positive and negative, the point $a$ describes a line, the inclination of which to the axis of real quantities is the argument of $\omega$.

Instead of making $Z$ describe a circle through $A$, let us make it describe a part of the straight line from the origin through $A$, say from $A$, where $OA = R$, to $C$, where $OC = R'$. Then $z$ describes a line through $a$ perpendicular to $aa_1$, and it moves to $c$ where

$$c - a = \frac{\omega}{2\pi i}(\log R' - \log R).$$

Similarly, if any point $A'$ on the former circumference move radially to a point $C$ at a distance $R'$ from the $Z$-origin, the corresponding $z$-point $a'$ moves through a distance $a'c'$, parallel and equal to $ac$: and all the points $c'$ lie on a line parallel to $aa_1$. Repeated description of a $Z$-circumference with the origin as centre makes $z$ describe the whole line $cc_1c_2$.

If then a function be simply-periodic in $\omega$, we may conveniently take any point $a$, and another point $a_1 = a + \omega$, through $a$ and $a_1$ draw straight lines perpendicular to $aa_1$, and then consider the function within this band. The aggregate of points within this band is obtained by taking

(i)   all points along a straight line, perpendicular to a boundary of the band, as $aa_1$;

(ii)   the points along all straight lines, which are drawn through the points of (i) parallel to a boundary of the band.

In (i), the value of $z$ varies from 0 to $\omega$ in an expression $a + z$, that is, in the $Z$-plane for a given value of $R$, the angle $\Theta$ varies from 0 to $2\pi$.

In (ii), the value of $\log R$ varies from $-\infty$ to $+\infty$ in an expression $\frac{\omega}{2\pi i}\log R + \frac{\Theta}{2\pi}\omega$, that is, the radius $R$ must vary from 0 to $\infty$.

Hence the band in the $z$-plane and the whole of the $Z$-plane are made equivalent to one another by the transformation

$$Z = e^{\frac{2\pi i}{\omega}z}.$$

Now let $z_0$ be any special point in the finite part of the band for a given simply-periodic function, and let $Z_0$ be the corresponding point in the $Z$-plane. Then for points $z$ in the immediate vicinity of $z_0$ and for points $Z$ which are consequently in the immediate vicinity of $Z_0$, we have

$$Z - Z_0 = e^{\frac{2\pi i}{\omega}z} - e^{\frac{2\pi i}{\omega}z_0}$$

$$= e^{\frac{2\pi i}{\omega}z_0}\{e^{\frac{2\pi i}{\omega}(z-z_0)} - 1\}$$

$$= \lambda\frac{2\pi i}{\omega}e^{\frac{2\pi i z_0}{\omega}}(z - z_0),$$

where $|\lambda|$ differs from unity only by an infinitesimal quantity.

If then $w$, a function of $z$, be changed into $W$ a function of $Z$, the following relations subsist :—

When a point $z_0$ is a zero of $w$, the corresponding point $Z_0$ is a zero of $W$.

When a point $z_0$ is an accidental singularity of $w$, the corresponding point $Z_0$ is an accidental singularity of $W$.

When a point $z_0$ is an essential singularity of $w$, the corresponding point $Z_0$ is an essential singularity of $W$.

When a point $z_0$ is a branch-point of any order for a function $w$, the corresponding point $Z_0$ is a branch-point of the same order for $W$.

And the converses of these relations also hold.

Since the character of any finite critical point for $w$ is thus unchanged by the transformation, it is often convenient to change the variable to $Z$ so as to let the variable range over the whole plane, in which case the theorems already proved in the preceding chapters are applicable. But special account must be taken of the point $z = \infty$.

**112.** We can now apply Laurent's theorem to deduce what is practically Fourier's series, as follows.

*Let $f(z)$ be a simply-periodic function having $\omega$ as its period, and suppose that in a portion of the z-plane bounded by any two parallel lines, the inclination of which to the axis of real quantities is equal to the argument of $\omega$, the function is uniform and has no singularities; then, at points within that portion of the plane, the function can be expressed in the form of a converging series of positive and of negative integral powers of $e^{\frac{2\pi z i}{\omega}}$.*

In figure 32, let $aa_1a_2...$ and $cc_1c_2...$ be the two lines which bound the portion of the plane: the variations of the function will all take place within that part of the portion of the plane which lies within one of the representative bands, say within the band bounded by $...ac...$ and $...a_1c_1...$: that is, we may consider the function within the rectangle $acc_1a_1a$, where it has no singularities and is uniform.

Now the rectangle $acc_1a_1a$ in the $z$-plane corresponds to a portion of the $Z$-plane which, after the preceding explanation, is bounded by two circles with the origin for common centre and of radii $\left| e^{\frac{2\pi i}{\omega} z_a} \right|$ and $\left| e^{\frac{2\pi i}{\omega} z_c} \right|$; and the variations of the function within the rectangle are given by the variations of a transformed function within the circular ring. The characteristics of the one function at points in the rectangle are the same as the characteristics of the other at points in the circular ring: and therefore, from the character of the assigned function, the transformed function has no singularities and it is uniform within the circular ring. Hence, by Laurent's Theorem (§ 28), the transformed function is expressible in the form

$$F(Z) = \sum_{n=-\infty}^{n=+\infty} a_n Z^n,$$

a series which converges within the ring: and the value of the coefficient $a_n$ is given by

$$\frac{1}{2\pi i} \int \frac{F(Z)}{Z^{n+1}} dZ,$$

taken along any circle in the ring concentric with the boundaries.

Retransforming to the variable $z$, the expression for the original function is

$$f(z) = \sum_{n=-\infty}^{n=+\infty} a_n e^{\frac{2n\pi i z}{\omega}}$$

The series converges for points within the rectangle and therefore, as it is periodic, it converges within the portion of the plane assigned. And the value of $a_n$ is

$$a_n = \frac{1}{\omega} \int f(z) e^{-\frac{2n\pi i z}{\omega}} dz,$$

taken along a path which is the equivalent of any circle in the ring concentric with the boundaries, that is, along any line perpendicular to $ac$ and $a_1 c_1$, and therefore parallel to the lines which bound the assigned portion of the plane.

The expression of the function can evidently be changed into the form

$$f(z) = \frac{1}{\omega} \int \sum_{n=-\infty}^{n=\infty} e^{\frac{2n\pi i}{\omega}(z-\zeta)} f(\zeta) d\zeta,$$

where the integral is taken along the piece of a line, perpendicular to the boundaries and intercepted between them.

If one of the boundaries of the portion of the plane be at infinity, (so that the periodic function has no singularities within one part of the plane), then the corresponding portion of the $Z$-plane is either the part within or the part without a circle, centre the origin, according as the one or the other of the boundaries is at $\infty$. In the former case, the terms with negative indices $n$ are absent; in the latter, the terms with positive indices are absent.

**113.** On account of the consequences of the relation subsisting between the variables $z$ and $Z$, many of the propositions relating to general uniform functions, as well as of those relating to multiform functions, can be changed, merely by the transformation of the variables, into propositions relating to simply-periodic functions. One such proposition occurs in the preceding section; the following are a few others, the full development being unnecessary here, in consequence of the foregoing remark  The band of reference for the simply-periodic functions considered will be supposed to include the origin: and, when any point is spoken of, it is that one of the series of homologous points in the plane, which lies in the band.

We know that, if a uniform function of $Z$ have no essential singularity, then it is a rational function, which is integral if $Z = \infty$ be the only accidental singularity and is meromorphic if there be accidental singularities in the finite part of the plane; and every such function has as many zeros as it has accidental singularities.

Hence *a uniform simply-periodic function with* $z = \infty$ *as its sole essential singularity has as many zeros as it has infinities in each band of the plane; the number of points at which it assumes a given value is equal to the number of its zeros; if this common number be finite, and if the period be* $\omega$*, the function is a rational function of* $e^{\frac{2\pi i z}{\omega}}$ *, which is integral if all the singularities be at an infinite distance and is meromorphic if some (or all) of them be in a finite part of the plane.* (But any number of zeros and any number of infinities may be absorbed in the essential singularity at $z = \infty$.)

The simplest function of $Z$, thus restricted to have the same number of zeros as of infinities, is one which has a single zero and a single infinity in the finite part of the plane; the possession of a single zero and a single infinity will therefore characterise the most elementary simply-periodic function. Now, bearing in mind the relation

$$Z = e^{\frac{2\pi i z}{\omega}},$$

the simplest $z$-point to choose for a zero is the origin, so that $Z = 1$; and then the simplest $z$-point to choose for an infinity at a finite distance is $\frac{1}{2}\omega$, (being half the period), so that $Z = -1$. The expression of the function in the $Z$-plane with 1 for a zero and $-1$ for an accidental singularity is

$$A\frac{Z-1}{Z+1},$$

and therefore assuming as the most elementary simply-periodic function that which in the plane has a series of zeros and a series of accidental singularities all of the first order, the points of the one being midway between those of the other, its expression is

$$A\frac{e^{\frac{2\pi i z}{\omega}}-1}{e^{\frac{2\pi i z}{\omega}}+1},$$

which is a constant multiple of $\tan\frac{\pi z}{\omega}$. Since $e^{\frac{2\pi i z}{\omega}}$ is a rational fractional function of $\tan\frac{\pi z}{\omega}$, part of the foregoing theorem can be re-stated as follows:—

*If the period of the function be* $\omega$*, the function is a rational function of* $\tan\frac{\pi z}{\omega}$.

Moreover, in the general theory of uniform functions, it was found convenient to have a simple element for the construction of products, there (§ 53) called a *primary factor*: it was of the type

$$\frac{Z-a}{Z-c}\,e^{\,G\left(\frac{1}{Z-c}\right)},$$

where the function $G\left(\dfrac{1}{Z-c}\right)$ could be a constant; and it had only one infinity and one zero.

Hence for simply-periodic functions we may regard $\tan\dfrac{\pi z}{\omega}$ as a typical primary factor when the number of irreducible zeros and the (equal) number of irreducible accidental singularities are finite. If these numbers should tend to an infinite limit, then an exponential factor might have to be associated with $\tan\dfrac{\pi z}{\omega}$; and the function in that case might have essential singularities elsewhere than at $z=\infty$.

*Ex.* Prove that a rational function of $z$ cannot be simply-periodic.

**114.** We can now prove that *every uniform function, which has no essential singularities in the finite part of the plane and is such that all its accidental singularities and its zeros are arranged in groups equal and finite in number at equal distances along directions parallel to a given direction, is a simply-periodic function, save as to a possible factor of the form $e^{g(z)}$, where $g(z)$ is a uniform function of $z$ regular everywhere in the finite part of the plane.*

Let $\omega$ be the common period of the groups of zeros and of singularities: and let the plane be divided into bands by parallel lines, perpendicular to any line representing $\omega$. Let $a, b, \dots$ be the zeros, $\alpha, \beta, \dots$ the singularities in any one band.

Take a uniform function $\phi(z)$, simply-periodic in $\omega$, and having a single zero and a single singularity in the band: we might take $\tan\dfrac{\pi z}{\omega}$ as a value of $\phi(z)$. Then

$$\frac{\phi(z)-\phi(a)}{\phi(z)-\phi(\alpha)}$$

is a simply-periodic function having only a single zero, viz., $z=a$ and a single singularity, viz., $z=\alpha$; for as $\phi(z)$ has only a single zero, there is only a single point for which $\phi(z)=\phi(a)$, and a single point for which $\phi(z)=\phi(\alpha)$. Hence

$$\frac{\{\phi(z)-\phi(a)\}\,\{\phi(z)-\phi(b)\}\dots}{\{\phi(z)-\phi(\alpha)\}\,\{\phi(z)-\phi(\beta)\}\dots}$$

is a simply-periodic function with all the zeros and with all the infinities of
the given function within the band.   But on account of its periodicity it has
all the zeros and all the infinities of the given function over the whole plane;
hence its quotient by the given function has no zero and no singularity over
the whole plane.   Hence, by Corollary I. in § 52, this quotient is of the form
$e^{\bar{g}(z)}$, where $\bar{g}(z)$ is a uniform function of $z$, finite everywhere in the finite
part of the plane: and it may be a constant.   Consequently, the expression
for the given function is known.   It is thus a simply-periodic function, save
as to the factor specified; and this factor may be a constant, in which case
the function is actually simply-periodic.

This method can evidently be used to construct simply-periodic functions, having
assigned zeros and assigned singularities.   Thus if a function have $a + m\omega$ as its zeros and
$c + m'\omega$ as its singularities, where $m$ and $m'$ have all integral values from $-\infty$ to $+\infty$,
the simplest form is obtained by taking a constant multiple of

$$\frac{\tan \dfrac{\pi z}{\omega} - \tan \dfrac{\pi a}{\omega}}{\tan \dfrac{\pi z}{\omega} - \tan \dfrac{\pi c}{\omega}}.$$

*Ex.*   Construct a function, simply-periodic in $\omega$, having zeros given by $(m+\frac{1}{2})\omega$ and
$(m+\frac{3}{4})\omega$ and singularities by $(m+\frac{1}{3})\omega$ and $(m+\frac{2}{3})\omega$.

The irreducible zeros are $\frac{1}{2}\omega$ and $\frac{3}{4}\omega$; the irreducible singularities are $\frac{1}{3}\omega$ and $\frac{2}{3}\omega$.   Now

$$A' \frac{\left(\tan \dfrac{\pi z}{\omega} - \tan \tfrac{1}{2}\pi\right) \left(\tan \dfrac{\pi z}{\omega} - \tan \tfrac{3}{4}\pi\right)}{\left(\tan \dfrac{\pi z}{\omega} - \tan \tfrac{1}{3}\pi\right) \left(\tan \dfrac{\pi z}{\omega} - \tan \tfrac{2}{3}\pi\right)}$$

is evidently a function, initially satisfying the required conditions.   But, as $\tan \frac{1}{2}\pi$ is
infinite, we divide out by it and absorb it into $A'$ as a factor; the function then takes
the form

$$A \frac{1 + \tan \dfrac{\pi z}{\omega}}{3 - \tan^2 \dfrac{\pi z}{\omega}}.$$

We shall not consider simply-periodic functions, which have essential
singularities elsewhere than at $z = \infty$; adequate investigation will be found
in the second part of Guichard's memoir, (l.c., p. 176).   But before leaving
the consideration of the present class of functions, one remark may be made.
It was proved, in our earlier investigations, that uniform functions can be
expressed as infinite series of functions of the variable and also as infinite
products of functions of the variable.   This general result is true when the
functions in the series and in the products are simply-periodic in the same
period.   But the function, so represented, though periodic in that common
period, may also have another period: and, in fact, many doubly-periodic
functions of different kinds (§ 136) are often conveniently expressed as infinite
converging series or infinite converging products of simply-periodic functions.

Any detailed illustration of this remark belongs to the theory of elliptic functions: one simple example must suffice.

Let the real part of $\dfrac{i\pi\omega'}{\omega}$ be negative, and let $q$ denote $e^{\frac{i\pi\omega'}{\omega}}$ ; then the function

$$\theta(z) = \sum_{n=-\infty}^{n=\infty} (-1)^n q^{n^2} e^{\frac{2ni\pi z}{\omega}},$$

being an infinite converging series of powers of the simply-periodic function $e^{\frac{2i\pi z}{\omega}}$, is finite everywhere in the plane. Evidently $\theta(z)$ is periodic in $\omega$, so that

$$\theta(z+\omega) = \theta(z).$$

Again, $$\theta(z+\omega') = \sum_{n=-\infty}^{n=\infty} (-1)^n q^{n^2} e^{\frac{2ni\pi(z+\omega')}{\omega}}$$

$$= \sum_{n=-\infty}^{n=\infty} (-1)^n q^{n^2} e^{\frac{2ni\pi z}{\omega}} q^{2n}$$

$$= -\frac{1}{q} e^{-\frac{2i\pi z}{\omega}} \sum_{n=-\infty}^{n=\infty} \left\{ (-1)^{n+1} q^{(n+1)^2} e^{\frac{2(n+1)i\pi z}{\omega}} \right\}$$

$$= -\frac{1}{q} e^{-\frac{2i\pi z}{\omega}} \theta(z),$$

the change in the summation so as to give $\theta(z)$ being permissible, because the convergence of $\theta(z)$ is absolute on account of the assumption with regard to $q$. There is thus a pseudo-periodicity for $\theta(z)$ in a period $\omega'$.

Similarly, if $$\theta_3(z) = \sum_{n=-\infty}^{n=\infty} q^{n^2} e^{\frac{2ni\pi z}{\omega}},$$

we can prove that $$\theta_3(z+\omega) = \theta(z),$$

$$\theta_3(z+\omega') = \frac{1}{q} e^{-\frac{2i\pi z}{\omega}} \theta(z).$$

Then $\theta_3(z) \div \theta(z)$ is doubly-periodic in $\omega$ and $2\omega'$, though constructed only from functions simply-periodic in $\omega$: it is a function with an infinite number of irreducible accidental singularities in a band.

**115.** We now pass to doubly-periodic functions of a single variable, the periodicity being additive. The properties, characteristic of this important class of functions, will be given in the form either of new theorems or appropriate modifications of theorems, already established; and the development adopted will follow, in a general manner, the theory given by Liouville*. It will be assumed that the functions are *uniform*, unless multiformity be explicitly stated, and that all the singularities in the finite part of the plane are accidental†.

* In his lectures of 1847, edited by Borchardt and published in *Crelle*, t. lxxxviii, (1880), pp. 277—310. They are the basis of the researches of Briot and Bouquet, the most complete exposition of which will be found in their *Théorie des fonctions elliptiques*, (2nd ed.), pp. 239—280.

† For doubly-periodic functions, which have essential singularities, reference should be made to Guichard's memoir, (the introductory remarks and the third part), already quoted on p. 176, *note*.

The geometrical representation of double-periodicity, explained in § 105, will be used concurrently with the analysis; and the parallelogram of periods, to which the variable argument of the function is referred, is a fundamental parallelogram (§ 109) with periods* $2\omega$ and $2\omega'$. An angular point $z_0$ for the parallelogram of reference can be chosen so that neither a zero nor a pole of the function lies on the perimeter; for the number of zeros and the number of poles in any finite area must be finite, as otherwise they would form a continuous line or a continuous area, or they would be in the vicinity of an essential singularity. This choice will, in general, be made; but, in particular cases, it is convenient to have the origin as an angular point of the parallelogram and then it not infrequently occurs that a zero or a pole lies on a side or at a corner. If such a point lie on a side, the homologous point on the opposite side is assigned to the parallelogram which has that opposite side as homologous; and if it be at an angular point, the remaining angular points are assigned to the parallelograms which have them as homologous corners.

The parallelogram of reference will therefore, in general, have $z_0$, $z_0 + 2\omega$, $z_0 + 2\omega'$, $z_0 + 2\omega + 2\omega'$ for its angular points; but occasionally it is desirable to take an equivalent parallelogram having $z_0 \pm \omega \pm \omega'$ as its angular points.

When the function is denoted by $\phi(z)$, the equations indicating the periodicity are

$$\phi(z + 2\omega) = \phi(z) = \phi(z + 2\omega').$$

**116.** We now proceed to the fundamental propositions relating to doubly-periodic functions.

I. *Every doubly-periodic function must have zeros and infinities within the fundamental parallelogram.*

For the function, not being a constant, has zeros somewhere in the plane and it has infinities somewhere in the plane; and, being doubly-periodic, it experiences within the parallelogram all the variations that it can have over the plane.

COROLLARY. *The function cannot be a rational function of z.*

A rational function of $z$ possesses only a limited number of zeros in the plane. Within the fundamental parallelogram, a doubly-periodic function possesses zeros: and therefore the number of zeros which it possesses in the plane is unlimited. The two functions therefore cannot be equivalent.

An analytical form for $\phi(z)$ can be obtained which will put its singularities in evidence. Let $a$ be such a pole, of multiplicity $n$; then we know that, as the function is uniform, coefficients $A$ can be determined so that the function

$$\phi(z) - \frac{A_n}{(z-a)^n} - \frac{A_{n-1}}{(z-a)^{n-1}} - \cdots - \frac{A_2}{(z-a)^2} - \frac{A_1}{z-a}$$

* The factor 2 is introduced merely for the sake of convenience.

is finite in the vicinity of $a$; but the remaining poles of $\phi(z)$ are singularities of this modified function. Proceeding similarly with the other singularities $b, c, \ldots$, which are finite in number and each of which is finite in degree, we have coefficients $A, B, C, \ldots$ determined so that

$$\phi(z) - \sum_{\kappa = a, b, \ldots} \left\{ \sum_{r=1}^{n_\kappa} \frac{K_r}{(z - \kappa)^r} \right\}$$

is finite in the vicinity of every pole of $\phi(z)$ within the parallelogram and therefore is finite everywhere within the parallelogram. Let its value be $\chi(z)$; then for points lying within the parallelogram, the function $\phi(z)$ is expressed in the form

$$\chi(z) + \frac{A_1}{z - a} + \frac{A_2}{(z - a)^2} + \ldots + \frac{A_n}{(z - a)^n}$$

$$+ \frac{B_1}{z - b} + \frac{B_2}{(z - b)^2} + \ldots + \frac{B_m}{(z - b)^m}$$

$$+ \ldots\ldots\ldots\ldots\ldots\ldots\ldots\ldots$$

$$+ \frac{H_1}{z - h} + \frac{H_2}{(z - h)^2} + \ldots + \frac{H_l}{(z - h)^l}.$$

But though $\phi(z)$ is periodic, $\chi(z)$ is not periodic. It has the property of being finite everywhere within the parallelogram; if it were periodic, it would be finite everywhere, and therefore could have only a constant value; and then $\phi(z)$ would be a rational meromorphic function, which is not periodic. The sum of the fractions in $\phi(z)$ may be called the fractional part of the function: owing to the meromorphic character of the function, it cannot be evanescent.

The analytical expression can be put in the form

$$(z - a)^{-n} (z - b)^{-m} \ldots (z - h)^{-l} F(z),$$

where $F(z)$ is finite everywhere within the parallelogram. If $\alpha, \beta, \ldots, \eta$ be all the zeros, of degrees $\nu, \mu, \ldots, \lambda$, within the parallelogram, then

$$F(z) = (z - \alpha)^\nu (z - \beta)^\mu \ldots (z - \eta)^\lambda G(z),$$

where $G(z)$ has no zero within the parallelogram; and so the function can be expressed in the form

$$\frac{(z - \alpha)^\nu (z - \beta)^\mu \ldots (z - \eta)^\lambda}{(z - a)^n (z - b)^m \ldots (z - h)^l} G(z),$$

where $G(z)$ has no zero and no infinity within the parallelogram or on its boundary; and $G(z)$ is not periodic.

The *order* of a doubly-periodic function is the sum of the multiplicities of all the poles which the function has within a fundamental parallelogram;

and, the sum being $n$, the function is said to be of the $n$th order. All these singularities are, as already assumed, accidental; it is convenient to speak of any particular singularity as simple, double, ... according to its multiplicity.

If two doubly-periodic functions $u$ and $v$ be such that an equation

$$Au + Bv + C = 0$$

is satisfied for constant values of $A$, $B$, $C$, the functions are said to be *equivalent* to one another. Equivalent functions evidently have the same accidental singularities in the same multiplicity.

II.  *The integral of a doubly-periodic function round the boundary of a fundamental parallelogram is zero.*

Let $ABCD$ be a fundamental parallelogram, the boundary of it being taken so as to pass through no pole of the function. Let $A$ be $z_0$, $B$ be $z_0 + 2\omega$, and* $D$ be $z_0 + 2\omega'$; then any point in $AB$ is

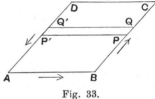

Fig. 33.

$$z_0 + 2\omega t,$$

where $t$ is a real quantity lying between 0 and 1; and therefore the integral along $AB$ is

$$\int_0^1 \phi (z_0 + 2\omega t)\, 2\omega dt.$$

Any point in $BC$ is $z_0 + 2\omega + 2\omega' t$, where $t$ is a real quantity lying between 0 and 1; therefore the integral along $BC$ is

$$\int_0^1 \phi (z_0 + 2\omega + 2\omega' t)\, 2\omega' dt$$

$$= \int_0^1 \phi (z_0 + 2\omega' t)\, 2\omega' dt,$$

since $\phi$ is periodic in $2\omega$.

Any point in $DC$ is $z_0 + 2\omega' + 2\omega t$, where $t$ is a real quantity lying between 0 and 1; therefore the integral along $CD$ is

$$\int_1^0 \phi (z_0 + 2\omega' + 2\omega t)\, 2\omega dt$$

$$= \int_1^0 \phi (z_0 + 2\omega t)\, 2\omega dt$$

$$= - \int_0^1 \phi (z_0 + 2\omega t)\, 2\omega dt.$$

* The figure implies that the argument of $\omega'$ is greater than the argument of $\omega$, a hypothesis which, though unimportant for the present proposition, must be taken account of hereafter (e.g., § 129).

Similarly, the integral along $DA$ is

$$= -\int_0^1 \phi\,(z_0 + 2\omega't)\,2\omega'dt.$$

Hence the complete value of the integral, taken round the parallelogram, is

$$= \int_0^1 \phi\,(z_0 + 2\omega t)\,2\omega dt + \int_0^1 \phi\,(z_0 + 2\omega't)\,2\omega'dt$$

$$- \int_0^1 \phi\,(z_0 + 2\omega t)\,2\omega dt - \int_0^1 \phi\,(z_0 + 2\omega't)\,2\omega'dt,$$

which is manifestly zero, since each of the integrals is the integral of a continuous function.

COROLLARY. Let $\psi\,(z)$ be any uniform function of $z$, not necessarily doubly-periodic, but without singularities on the boundary. Then the integral $\int\psi\,(z)\,dz$ taken round the parallelogram of periods is easily seen to be

$$\int_0^1 \psi\,(z_0 + 2\omega t)\,2\omega dt + \int_0^1 \psi\,(z_0 + 2\omega + 2\omega't)\,2\omega'dt$$

$$- \int_0^1 \psi\,(z_0 + 2\omega' + 2\omega t)\,2\omega dt - \int_0^1 \psi\,(z_0 + 2\omega't)\,2\omega'dt;$$

or, if we write
$$\psi\,(\zeta + 2\omega) - \psi\,(\zeta) = \psi_1\,(\zeta),$$
$$\psi\,(\zeta + 2\omega') - \psi\,(\zeta) = \psi_2\,(\zeta),$$

then
$$\int\psi\,(z)\,dz = \int_0^1 \psi_1\,(z_0 + 2\omega't)\,2\omega'dt - \int_0^1 \psi_2\,(z_0 + 2\omega t)\,2\omega dt,$$

where on the left-hand side the integral is taken positively round the boundary of the parallelogram and on the right-hand side the variable $t$ in the integrals is real.

The result may also be written in the form

$$\int\psi\,(z)\,dz = \int_A^D \psi_1\,(z)\,dz - \int_A^B \psi_2\,(z)\,dz,$$

the integrals on the right-hand side being taken along the straight lines $AD$ and $AB$ respectively.

Evidently the foregoing main proposition is established, when $\psi_1\,(\zeta)$ and $\psi_2\,(\zeta)$ vanish for all values of $\zeta$.

III. *If a doubly-periodic function* $\phi\,(z)$ *have infinities* $a_1, a_2, \dots$ *within the parallelogram, and if* $A_1, A_2, \dots$ *be the coefficients of* $(z - a_1)^{-1}, (z - a_2)^{-1}, \dots$ *respectively in the fractional part of* $\phi\,(z)$ *when it is expanded in the parallelogram, then*

$$A_1 + A_2 + \dots = 0.$$

As the function $\phi(z)$ is uniform, the integral $\int\phi(z)\,dz$ is, by § 19, II., the sum of the integrals round a number of curves each including one and only one of the infinities within that parallelogram.

Taking the expression for $\phi(z)$ on p. 259, the integral $A_m\int(z-a)^{-m}\,dz$ round the curve enclosing $a$ is 0, if $m$ be not unity, and is $2\pi i A_1$, if $m$ be unity; the integral $K_m\int(z-\kappa)^{-m}\,dz$ round that curve is 0 for all values of $m$ and for all points $\kappa$ other than $a$; and the integral $\int\chi(z)\,dz$ round the curve is zero, since $\chi(z)$ is uniform and finite everywhere in the vicinity of $a$. Hence the integral of $\phi(z)$ round a curve enclosing $a_1$ alone of all the infinities is $2\pi i A_1$.

Similarly the integral round a curve enclosing $a_2$ alone is $2\pi i A_2$; and so on, for each of the curves in succession.

Hence the value of the integral round the parallelogram is

$$2\pi i \Sigma A.$$

But by the preceding proposition, the value of $\int\phi(z)\,dz$ round the parallelogram is zero; and therefore

$$A_1 + A_2 + \ldots = 0.$$

This result can be expressed in the form that *the sum of the residues\* of a doubly-periodic function relative to a fundamental parallelogram of periods is zero.*

COROLLARY 1. *A doubly-periodic function of the first order does not exist.*

Let such a function have $a$ for its single simple infinity. Then an expression for the function within the parallelogram is

$$\frac{A}{z-a} + \chi(z),$$

where $\chi(z)$ is everywhere finite in the parallelogram. By the above proposition, $A$ vanishes; and so the function has no infinity in the parallelogram. It therefore has no infinity anywhere in the plane, and so is merely a constant: that is, quà function of a variable, it does not exist.

COROLLARY 2. *Doubly-periodic functions of the second order are of two classes.*

As the function is of the second order, the sum of the degrees of the infinities is two. There may thus be either a single infinity of the second degree or two simple infinities.

In the former case, the analytical expression of the function is

$$\phi(z) = \frac{A_1}{z-a} + \frac{A_2}{(z-a)^2} + \chi(z),$$

* See p. 48.

where $a$ is the infinity of the second degree and $\chi(z)$ is holomorphic within the parallelogram. But, by the preceding proposition, $A_1 = 0$; hence the analytical expression for a doubly-periodic function with a single irreducible infinity $a$ of the second degree is

$$\frac{A_2}{(z-a)^2} + \chi(z)$$

within the parallelogram. Such functions of the second order, which have only a single irreducible infinity, may be called the first class.

In the latter case, the analytical expression of the function is

$$\phi(z) = \frac{C_1}{z-c_1} + \frac{C_2}{z-c_2} + \chi(z),$$

where $c_1$ and $c_2$ are the two simple infinities and $\chi(z)$ is finite within the parallelogram. Then

$$C_1 + C_2 = 0;$$

so that, if $C_1 = -C_2 = C$, the analytical expression for a doubly-periodic function with two simple irreducible infinities $a_1$ and $a_2$ is

$$C\left(\frac{1}{z-a_1} - \frac{1}{z-a_2}\right) + \chi(z)$$

within the parallelogram. Such functions of the second order, which have two irreducible infinities, may be called the second class.

COROLLARY 3. *If within any parallelogram of periods a function is only of the second order, the parallelogram is fundamental.*

COROLLARY 4. *A similar division of doubly-periodic functions of any order into classes can be effected according to the variety in the constitution of the order, the number of classes being the number of partitions of the order.*

The simplest class of functions of the $n$th order is that in which the functions have only a single irreducible infinity of the $n$th degree. Evidently the analytical expression of the function within the parallelogram is

$$\frac{G_2}{(z-a)^2} + \frac{G_3}{(z-a)^3} + \dots + \frac{G_n}{(z-a)^n} + \chi(z),$$

where $\chi(z)$ is holomorphic within the parallelogram. Some of the coefficients $G$ may vanish; but all may not vanish, for the function would then be finite everywhere in the parallelogram.

It will however be seen, from the next succeeding propositions, that the division into classes is of most importance for functions of the second order.

IV. *Two functions, which are doubly-periodic in the same periods\*, and which have the same zeros and the same infinities each in the same degrees respectively, are in a constant ratio.*

\* Such functions will be called *homoperiodic*.

Let $\phi$ and $\psi$ be the functions, having the same periods; let $\alpha$ of degree $\nu$, $\beta$ of degree $\mu$, ... be all the irreducible zeros of $\phi$ and $\psi$; and let $a$ of degree $n$, $b$ of degree $m$, ... be all the irreducible infinities of $\phi$ and of $\psi$. Then a function $G(z)$, without zeros or infinities within the parallelogram, exists such that

$$\phi(z) = \frac{(z-\alpha)^\nu (z-\beta)^\mu \ldots}{(z-a)^n (z-b)^m \ldots} G(z);$$

and another function $H(z)$, without zeros or infinities within the parallelogram, exists such that

$$\psi(z) = \frac{(z-\alpha)^\nu (z-\beta)^\mu \ldots}{(z-a)^n (z-b)^m \ldots} H(z).$$

Hence

$$\frac{\phi(z)}{\psi(z)} = \frac{G(z)}{H(z)}.$$

Now the function on the right-hand side has no zeros in the parallelogram, for $G$ has no zeros and $H$ has no infinities; and it has no infinities in the parallelogram, for $G$ has no infinities and $H$ has no zeros: hence it has neither zeros nor infinities in the parallelogram. Since it is equal to the function on the left-hand side, which is a doubly-periodic function, it has no zeros and no infinities in the whole plane; it is therefore a constant, say $A$. Thus[*]

$$\phi(z) = A\psi(z).$$

V. *Two functions of the second order, doubly-periodic in the same periods and having the same infinities, are equivalent to one another.*

If one of the functions be of the first class in the second order, it has one irreducible double infinity, say at $a$; so that we have

$$\phi(z) = \frac{G}{(z-a)^2} + \chi(z),$$

where $\chi(z)$ is finite everywhere within the parallelogram. Then the other function also has $z = a$ for its sole irreducible infinity and that infinity is of the second degree; therefore we have

$$\psi(z) = \frac{H}{(z-a)^2} + \chi_1(z),$$

where $\chi_1(z)$ is finite everywhere within the parallelogram. Hence

$$H\phi(z) - G\psi(z) = H\chi(z) - G\chi_1(z).$$

Now $\chi$ and $\chi_1$ are finite everywhere within the parallelogram, and therefore so is $H\chi - G\chi_1$. But $H\chi - G\chi_1$, being equal to the doubly-periodic function $H\phi - G\psi$, is therefore doubly-periodic; as it has no infinities within the

---

[*] This proposition is the modified form of the proposition of § 52, when the generalising exponential factor has been determined so as to admit of the periodicity.

parallelogram, it consequently can have none over the plane and therefore it is a constant, say $I$. Thus

$$H\phi(z) - G\psi(z) = I,$$

proving that the functions $\phi$ and $\psi$ are equivalent.

If on the other hand one of the functions be of the second class in the second order, it has two irreducible simple infinities, say at $b$ and $c$, so that we have

$$\phi(z) = C\left(\frac{1}{z-b} - \frac{1}{z-c}\right) + \theta(z),$$

where $\theta(z)$ is finite everywhere within the parallelogram. Then the other function also has $z=b$ and $z=c$ for its irreducible infinities, each of them being simple; therefore we have

$$\psi(z) = D\left(\frac{1}{z-b} - \frac{1}{z-c}\right) + \theta_1(z),$$

where $\theta_1(z)$ is finite everywhere within the parallelogram. Hence

$$D\phi(z) - C\psi(z) = D\theta(z) - C\theta_1(z).$$

The right-hand side, being finite everywhere in the parallelogram, and equal to the left-hand side which is a doubly-periodic function, is finite everywhere in the plane; it is therefore a constant, say $B$, so that

$$D\phi(z) - C\psi(z) = B,$$

proving that $\phi$ and $\psi$ are equivalent to one another.

It thus appears that in considering doubly-periodic functions of the second order, homoperiodic functions of the same class are equivalent to one another if they have the same infinities; so that, practically, it is by their infinities that homoperiodic functions of the second order and the same class are discriminated.

COROLLARY 1. *If two equivalent functions of the second order have one zero the same, all their zeros are the same.*

For in the one class the constant $I$, and in the other class the constant $B$, is seen to vanish on substituting for $z$ the common zero; and then the two functions always vanish together.

COROLLARY 2. *If two functions, doubly-periodic in the same periods but not necessarily of the second order, have the same infinities occurring in such a way that the fractional parts of the two functions are the same except as to a constant factor, the functions are equivalent to one another. And if, in addition, they have one zero common, then all their zeros are common, so that the functions are then in a constant ratio.*

Corollary 3. *If two functions of the second order, doubly-periodic in the same periods, have their zeros the same, and one infinity common, they are in a constant ratio.*

VI. *Every doubly-periodic function has as many irreducible zeros as it has irreducible infinities.*

Let $\phi(z)$ be such a function. Then

$$\frac{\phi(z+h) - \phi(z)}{z+h-z}$$

is a doubly-periodic function for any value of $h$, for the numerator is doubly-periodic and the denominator does not involve $z$; so that, in the limit when $h = 0$, the function is doubly-periodic, that is, $\phi'(z)$ is doubly-periodic.

Now suppose $\phi(z)$ has irreducible zeros of degree $m_1$ at $a_1$, $m_2$ at $a_2, \ldots$, and has irreducible infinities of degree $\mu_1$ at $\alpha_1$, $\mu_2$ at $\alpha_2, \ldots$; so that the number of irreducible zeros is $m_1 + m_2 + \ldots$, and the number of irreducible infinities is $\mu_1 + \mu_2 + \ldots$, both of these numbers being finite. It has been shewn that $\phi(z)$ can be expressed in the form

$$\frac{(z-a_1)^{m_1}(z-a_2)^{m_2}\ldots}{(z-\alpha_1)^{\mu_1}(z-\alpha_2)^{\mu_2}\ldots} F(z),$$

where $F(z)$ has neither a zero nor an infinity within, or on the boundary of, the parallelogram of reference.

Since $F(z)$ has a value, which is finite, continuous and different from zero everywhere within the parallelogram or on its boundary, the function $\frac{F'(z)}{F(z)}$ is not infinite within the same limits. Hence we have

$$\frac{\phi'(z)}{\phi(z)} = g(z) + \frac{m_1}{z-a_1} + \frac{m_2}{z-a_2} + \ldots$$

$$+ \frac{-\mu_1}{z-\alpha_1} + \frac{-\mu_2}{z-\alpha_2} + \ldots,$$

where $g(z)$ has no infinities within, or on the boundary of, the parallelogram of reference. But, because $\phi'(z)$ and $\phi(z)$ are doubly-periodic, their quotient is also doubly-periodic; and therefore, applying Prop. II., we have

$$m_1 + m_2 + \ldots - \mu_1 - \mu_2 - \ldots = 0,$$

that is,       $$m_1 + m_2 + \ldots = \mu_1 + \mu_2 + \ldots,$$

or the number of irreducible zeros is equal to the number of irreducible infinities.

Corollary 1. *The number of irreducible points for which a doubly-periodic function assumes a given value is equal to the number of irreducible zeros.*

For if the value be $A$, every infinity of $\phi(z)$ is an infinity of the doubly-periodic function $\phi(z) - A$; hence the number of the irreducible zeros of the latter is equal to the number of its irreducible infinities, which is the same as the number for $\phi(z)$ and therefore the same as the number of irreducible zeros of $\phi(z)$. And every irreducible zero of $\phi(z) - A$ is an irreducible point, for which $\phi(z)$ assumes the value $A$.

COROLLARY 2. *A doubly-periodic function with only a single zero does not exist; a doubly-periodic function of the second order has two zeros; and, generally, the order of a function can be measured by its number of irreducible zeros.*

*Note.* It may here be remarked that the doubly-periodic functions (§ 115), that have only accidental singularities in the finite part of the plane, have $z = \infty$ for an essential singularity. It is evident that for infinite values of $z$, the finite magnitude of the parallelogram of periods is not recognisable; and thus for $z = \infty$ the function can have any value, shewing that $z = \infty$ is an essential singularity.

VII. *Let $a_1$, $a_2$, ... be the irreducible zeros' of a function of degrees $m_1$, $m_2$, ... respectively; $\alpha_1$, $\alpha_2$, ... its irreducible infinities of degrees $\mu_1$, $\mu_2$, ... respectively; and $z_1$, $z_2$, ... the irreducible points where it assumes a value $c$, which is neither zero nor infinity, their degrees being $M_1$, $M_2$, ... respectively. Then, except possibly as to additive multiples of the periods, the quantities $\sum\limits_{r=1} m_r a_r$, $\sum\limits_{r=1} \mu_r \alpha_r$ and $\sum\limits_{r=1} M_r z_r$ are equal to one another, so that*

$$\sum_{r=1} m_r a_r \equiv \sum_{r=1} M_r z_r \equiv \sum_{r=1} \mu_r \alpha_r \ (\text{mod. } 2\omega, 2\omega').$$

Let $\phi(z)$ be the function. Then the quantities which occur are the sums of the zeros, the assigned values, and the infinities, the degree of each being taken account of when there is multiple occurrence; and by the last proposition these degrees satisfy the relations

$$\Sigma m_r = \Sigma M_r = \Sigma \mu_r.$$

The function $\phi(z) - c$ is doubly-periodic in $2\omega$ and $2\omega'$; its zeros are $z_1$, $z_2$, ... of degrees $M_1$, $M_2$, ... respectively; and its infinities are $\alpha_1$, $\alpha_2$, ... of degrees $\mu_1$, $\mu_2$, ..., being the same as those of $\phi(z)$. Hence there exists a function $G(z)$, without either a zero or an infinity lying in the parallelogram or on its boundary, such that $\phi(z) - c$ can be expressed in the form

$$\frac{(z - z_1)^{M_1} (z - z_2)^{M_2} \cdots}{(z - \alpha_1)^{\mu_1} (z - \alpha_2)^{\mu_2} \cdots} G(z)$$

for all points not outside the parallelogram; and therefore, for points in that region

$$\frac{\phi'(z)}{\phi(z) - c} = \sum_{r=1} \frac{M_r}{z - z_r} - \Sigma \frac{\mu_r}{z - \alpha_r} + \frac{G'(z)}{G(z)}.$$

Hence

$$\frac{z\phi'(z)}{\phi(z)-c} = \sum_{r=1} \frac{M_r z}{z-z_r} - \sum \frac{\mu_r z}{z-\alpha_r} + \frac{zG'(z)}{G(z)}$$

$$= \sum_{r=1} M_r + \sum_{r=1} \frac{M_r z_r}{z-z_r} - \sum_{r=1} \mu_r - \sum \frac{\mu_r \alpha_r}{z-\alpha_r} + \frac{zG'(z)}{G(z)}$$

$$= \sum_{r=1} \frac{M_r z_r}{z-z_r} - \sum \frac{\mu_r \alpha_r}{z-\alpha_r} + \frac{zG'(z)}{G(z)},$$

because

$$\sum_{r=1} M_r = \sum_{r=1} \mu_r.$$

Integrate both sides round the boundary of the fundamental parallelogram. Because $G(z)$ has no zero and no infinity in the included region and does not vanish along the curve, the integral

$$\int \frac{zG'(z)}{G(z)} \, dz$$

vanishes. But the points $z_i$ and $\alpha_i$ are enclosed in the area; and therefore the value of the right-hand side is

$$2\pi i \Sigma M_r z_r - 2\pi i \Sigma \mu_r \alpha_r,$$

so that

$$2\pi i \left(\Sigma M_r z_r - \Sigma \mu_r \alpha_r\right) = \int \frac{z\phi'(z)}{\phi(z)-c} \, dz,$$

the integral being extended round the parallelogram.

Denoting the subject of integration $\dfrac{z\phi'(z)}{\phi(z)-c}$ by $f(z)$, we have

$$f(z+2\omega) - f(z) = 2\omega \frac{\phi'(z)}{\phi(z)-c},$$

$$f(z+2\omega') - f(z) = 2\omega' \frac{\phi'(z)}{\phi(z)-c};$$

and therefore, by the Corollary to Prop. II., the value of the foregoing integral is

$$2\omega \int_A^D \frac{\phi'(z)}{\phi(z)-c} \, dz - 2\omega' \int_A^B \frac{\phi'(z)}{\phi(z)-c} \, dz,$$

the integrals being taken along the straight lines $AD$ and $AB$ respectively (fig. 33, p. 260).

Let $w = \phi(z) - c$; then, as $z$ describes a path, $w$ will also describe a single path as it is a uniform function of $z$. When $z$ moves from $A$ to $D$, $w$ moves from $\phi(A) - c$ by some path to $\phi(D) - c$, that is, it returns to its initial position since $\phi(D) = \phi(A)$; hence, as $z$ describes $AD$, $w$ describes a simple closed path, the area included by which may or may not contain zeros and infinities of $w$. Now

$$dw = \phi'(z) \, dz,$$

and therefore the integral $\displaystyle\int_A^D \frac{\phi'(z)}{\phi(z) - c}\, dz$ is equal to

$$\int \frac{dw}{w},$$

taken in some direction round the corresponding closed path for $w$. This integral vanishes, if no $w$-zero or $w$-infinity be included within the area bounded by the path; it is $\pm 2m'\pi i$, if $m'$ be the excess of the number of included zeros over the number of included infinities, the $+$ or $-$ sign being taken with a positive or a negative description: hence we have

$$\int_A^D \frac{\phi'(z)}{\phi(z) - c}\, dz = 2m\pi i,$$

where $m$ is some positive or negative integer and may be zero. Similarly

$$\int_A^B \frac{\phi'(z)}{\phi(z) - c}\, dz = 2n\pi i,$$

where $n$ is some positive or negative integer and may be zero.

Thus $\qquad 2\pi i\,(\Sigma M_r z_r - \Sigma \mu_r a_r) = 2\omega\,.\,2m\pi i - 2\omega'\,.\,2n\pi i,$

and therefore $\qquad \Sigma M_r z_r - \Sigma \mu_r a_r = 2m\omega - 2n\omega'$

$$\equiv 0 \ (\text{mod. } 2\omega,\ 2\omega').$$

Finally, since $\Sigma M_r z_r \equiv \Sigma \mu_r a_r$ whatever be the value of $c$, for the right-hand side is independent of $c$, we may assign to $c$ any value we please. Let the value zero be assigned; then $\Sigma M_r z_r$ becomes $\Sigma m_r a_r$, so that

$$\Sigma m_r a_r \equiv \Sigma \mu_r a_r \ (\text{mod. } 2\omega,\ 2\omega').$$

The combination of these results leads to the required theorem[*], expressed by the congruences

$$\sum_{r=1} m_r a_r \equiv \sum_{r=1} M_r z_r \equiv \sum_{r=1} \mu_r a_r \ (\text{mod. } 2\omega,\ 2\omega').$$

*Note.* Any point within the parallelogram can be represented in the form $z_0 + a2\omega + b2\omega'$, where $a$ and $b$ are real positive quantities less than unity. Hence

$$\Sigma M_r z_r = A_z 2\omega + B_z 2\omega' + z_0 \Sigma M_r,$$

where $A$ and $B$ are real positive quantities each less than $\Sigma M_r$, that is, less than the order of the function.

In particular, for functions of the second order, we have

$$z_1 + z_2 = A_z 2\omega + B_z 2\omega' + 2z_0,$$

---

* The foregoing proof is suggested by Königsberger, *Theorie der elliptischen Functionen*, t. i, p. 342; other proofs are given by Briot and Bouquet and by Liouville, to whom the adopted form of the theorem is due. The theorem is substantially contained in one of Abel's general theorems in the comparison of transcendents.

where $A_z$ and $B_z$ are positive quantities each less than 2. Similarly, if $a$ and $b$ be the zeros,

$$a + b = A_a 2\omega + B_a 2\omega' + 2z_0,$$

where $A_a$ and $B_a$ are each less than 2; hence, if

$$z_1 + z_2 - a - b = m2\omega + m'2\omega',$$

then $m$ may have any one of the three values $-1, 0, 1$, and so may $m'$, the simultaneous values not being necessarily the same.

Let $\alpha$ and $\beta$ be the infinities of a function of the second class; then

$$\alpha + \beta - a - b = n2\omega + n'2\omega',$$

where $n$ and $n'$ may each have any one of the three values $-1, 0, 1$. By changing the origin of the fundamental parallelogram, so as to obtain a different set of irreducible points, we can secure that $n$ and $n'$ are zero, and then

$$\alpha + \beta = a + b.$$

Thus, if $n$ be 1 with an initial parallelogram, so that

$$\alpha + \beta = a + b + 2\omega,$$

we should take either $\beta - 2\omega = \beta'$, or $\alpha - 2\omega = \alpha'$, according to the position of $\alpha$ and $\beta$, and then have a new parallelogram such that

$$\alpha + \beta' = a + b, \quad \text{or} \quad \alpha' + \beta = a + b.$$

The case of exception is when the function is of the first class and has a repeated zero.

VIII. *Let $\phi(z)$ be a doubly-periodic function of the second order. If $\gamma$ be the one double infinity when the function is of the first class, and if $\alpha$ and $\beta$ be the two simple infinities when the function is of the second class, then in the former case*

$$\phi(z) = \phi(2\gamma - z),$$

*and in the latter case* $\quad \phi(z) = \phi(\alpha + \beta - z).$

Since the function is of the second order, so that it has two irreducible infinities, there are two (and only two) irreducible points in a fundamental parallelogram at which the function can assume any the same value: let them be $z$ and $z'$.

Then, for the first class of functions, we have

$$z + z' \equiv 2\gamma$$
$$= 2\gamma + 2m\omega + 2n\omega',$$

where $m$ and $n$ are integers; and then, since $\phi(z) = \phi(z')$ by definition of $z$ and $z'$, we have

$$\phi(z) = \phi(2\gamma - z + 2m\omega + 2n\omega')$$
$$= \phi(2\gamma - z).$$

For the second class of functions, we have

$$z + z' \equiv \alpha + \beta$$

$$= \alpha + \beta + 2m\omega + 2n\omega';$$

so that, as before,

$$\phi(z) = \phi(\alpha + \beta - z + 2m\omega + 2n\omega')$$

$$= \phi(\alpha + \beta - z).$$

**117.** Among the functions which have the same periodicity as a given function $\phi(z)$, the one which is most closely related to it is its derivative $\phi'(z)$. We proceed to find *the zeros and the infinities of the derivative of a function, in particular, of a function of the second order.*

Since $\phi(z)$ is uniform, an irreducible infinity of degree $n$ for $\phi(z)$ is an irreducible infinity of degree $n+1$ for $\phi'(z)$. Moreover $\phi'(z)$, being uniform, has no infinity which is not an infinity of $\phi(z)$; thus the order of $\phi'(z)$ is $\Sigma(n+1)$, or its order is greater than that of $\phi(z)$ by an integer which represents the number of distinct irreducible infinities of $\phi(z)$, no account being taken of their degree. If, then, a function be of order $m$, the order of its derivative is not less than $m+1$ and is not greater than $2m$.

Functions of the second order either possess one double infinity, so that within the parallelogram they take the form

$$\phi(z) = \frac{A}{(z-\gamma)^2} + \chi(z),$$

and then

$$\phi'(z) = \frac{-2A}{(z-\gamma)^3} + \chi'(z),$$

that is, the infinity of $\phi(z)$ is the single infinity of $\phi'(z)$ and it is of the third degree, so that $\phi'(z)$ is of the third order; or they possess two simple infinities, so that within the parallelogram they take the form

$$\phi(z) = C\left(\frac{1}{z-\alpha_1} - \frac{1}{z-\alpha_2}\right) + \chi(z),$$

and then

$$\phi'(z) = -C\left\{\frac{1}{(z-\alpha_1)^2} - \frac{1}{(z-\alpha_2)^2}\right\} + \chi'(z),$$

that is, each of the simple infinities of $\phi(z)$ is an infinity for $\phi'(z)$ of the second degree, so that $\phi'(z)$ is of the fourth order.

It is of importance (as will be seen presently) to know the zeros of the derivative of a function of the second order.

For a function of the first class, let $\gamma$ be the irreducible infinity of the second degree; then we have

$$\phi(z) = \phi(2\gamma - z),$$

and therefore

$$\phi'(z) = -\phi'(2\gamma - z).$$

Now $\phi'(z)$ is of the third order, having $\gamma$ for its irreducible infinity in the third degree: hence it has three irreducible zeros.

In the foregoing equation, take $z = \gamma$: then

$$\phi'(\gamma) = -\phi'(\gamma),$$

shewing that $\gamma$ is either a zero or an infinity. It is known to be the only infinity of $\phi'(z)$.

Next, take $z = \gamma + \omega$; then

$$\phi'(\gamma + \omega) = -\phi'(\gamma - \omega)$$
$$= -\phi'(\gamma - \omega + 2\omega)$$
$$= -\phi'(\gamma + \omega),$$

shewing that $\gamma + \omega$ is either a zero or an infinity. It is known not to be an infinity; hence it is a zero.

Similarly $\gamma + \omega'$ and $\gamma + \omega + \omega'$ are zeros. Thus three zeros are obtained, distinct from one another; and only three zeros are required; if they be not within the parallelogram, we take the irreducible points homologous with them. Hence :—

IX. *The three zeros of the derivative of a function, doubly-periodic in $2\omega$ and $2\omega'$ and having $\gamma$ for its double (and only) irreducible infinity, are*

$$\gamma + \omega, \quad \gamma + \omega', \quad \gamma + \omega + \omega'.$$

For a function of the second class, let $\alpha$ and $\beta$ be the two simple irreducible infinities; then we have

$$\phi(z) = \phi(\alpha + \beta - z),$$

and therefore $\qquad \phi'(z) = -\phi'(\alpha + \beta - z).$

Now $\phi'(z)$ is of the fourth order, having $\alpha$ and $\beta$ as its irreducible infinities each in the second degree; hence it must have four irreducible zeros.

In the foregoing equation, take $z = \frac{1}{2}(\alpha + \beta)$; then

$$\phi'\{\tfrac{1}{2}(\alpha + \beta)\} = -\phi'\{\tfrac{1}{2}(\alpha + \beta)\},$$

shewing that $\frac{1}{2}(\alpha + \beta)$ is either a zero or an infinity. It is known not to be an infinity; hence it is a zero.

Next, take $z = \frac{1}{2}(\alpha + \beta) + \omega$; then

$$\phi'\{\tfrac{1}{2}(\alpha + \beta) + \omega\} = -\phi'\{\tfrac{1}{2}(\alpha + \beta) - \omega\}$$
$$= -\phi'\{\tfrac{1}{2}(\alpha + \beta) - \omega + 2\omega\}$$
$$= -\phi'\{\tfrac{1}{2}(\alpha + \beta) + \omega\},$$

shewing that $\frac{1}{2}(\alpha + \beta) + \omega$ is either a zero or an infinity. As before, it is a zero.

Similarly $\frac{1}{2}(\alpha + \beta) + \omega'$ and $\frac{1}{2}(\alpha + \beta) + \omega + \omega'$ are zeros. Four zeros are thus obtained, distinct from one another; and only four zeros are required. Hence :—

X.  *The four zeros of the derivative of a function, doubly-periodic in $2\omega$ and $2\omega'$ and having $\alpha$ and $\beta$ for its simple (and only) irreducible infinities, are*

$$\tfrac{1}{2}(\alpha + \beta), \quad \tfrac{1}{2}(\alpha + \beta) + \omega, \quad \tfrac{1}{2}(\alpha + \beta) + \omega', \quad \tfrac{1}{2}(\alpha + \beta) + \omega + \omega'.$$

The verification in each of these two cases of Prop. VII., that the sum of the zeros of the doubly-periodic function $\phi'(z)$ is congruent with the sum of its infinities, is immediate.

Lastly, it may be noted that, *if $z_1$ and $z_2$ be the two irreducible points for which a doubly-periodic function of the second order assumes a given value, then the values of its derivative for $z_1$ and for $z_2$ are equal and opposite.* For

$$\phi(z) = \phi(\alpha + \beta - z) = \phi(z_1 + z_2 - z),$$

since $z_1 + z_2 \equiv \alpha + \beta$; and therefore

$$\phi'(z) = -\phi'(z_1 + z_2 - z),$$

that is,
$$\phi'(z_1) = -\phi'(z_2),$$

which proves the statement.

**118.**  We now come to a different class of theorems.

XI.  *Any doubly-periodic function of the second order can be expressed rationally in terms of an assigned doubly-periodic function of the second order, if the periods be the same.*

The theorem will be sufficiently illustrated and the line of proof sufficiently indicated, if we express a function $\phi(z)$ of the second class, with irreducible infinities $\alpha$, $\beta$ and irreducible zeros $a$, $b$ such that $\alpha + \beta = a + b$, in terms of a function $\Phi$ of the first class with $\gamma$ as its irreducible double infinity.

Consider a function    $\dfrac{\Phi(z + h) - \Phi(h')}{\Phi(z + h) - \Phi(h'')}.$

A zero of $\Phi(z + h)$ is neither a zero nor an infinity of this function; nor is an infinity of $\Phi(z + h)$ a zero or an infinity of the function. It will have $a$ and $b$ for its irreducible zeros, if

$$a + h = h',$$
$$b + h + h' = 2\gamma;$$

and these will be the only zeros, for $\Phi$ is of the second order. It will have $\alpha$ and $\beta$ for its irreducible infinities, if

$$\alpha + h = h'',$$
$$\beta + h + h'' = 2\gamma;$$

and these will be the only infinities, for $\Phi$ is of the second order. These equations are satisfied by

$$h'' = \tfrac{1}{2}(2\gamma - \beta + \alpha),$$
$$h' = \tfrac{1}{2}(2\gamma - b + a),$$
$$h = \tfrac{1}{2}(2\gamma - \alpha - \beta) = \tfrac{1}{2}(2\gamma - a - b).$$

Hence the assigned function, with these values of $h$, has the same zeros and the same infinities as $\phi(z)$; and it is doubly-periodic in the same periods. The ratio of the two functions is therefore a constant, by Prop. IV., so that

$$\phi(z) = A \frac{\Phi(z+h) - \Phi(h')}{\Phi(z+h) - \Phi(h'')}.$$

If the expression be required in terms of $\Phi(z)$ alone and constants, then $\Phi(z+h)$ must be expressed in terms of $\Phi(z)$ and constants which are values of $\Phi(z)$ for special values of $z$. This will be effected later.

The preceding proposition is a special case of a more general theorem which will be considered later; the following is another special case of that theorem: viz. :—

XII. *A doubly-periodic function with any number of simple infinities can be expressed either as a sum or as a product, of functions of the second order and the second class which are doubly-periodic in the same periods.*

Let $\alpha_1$, $\alpha_2$, ..., $\alpha_n$ be the irreducible infinities of the function $\Phi$, and suppose that the fractional part of $\Phi(z)$ is

$$\frac{A_1}{z - \alpha_1} + \frac{A_2}{z - \alpha_2} + \cdots + \frac{A_n}{z - \alpha_n},$$

with the condition $A_1 + A_2 + \cdots + A_n = 0$. Let $\phi_{ij}(z)$ be a function, doubly-periodic in the same periods, with $\alpha_i$, $\alpha_j$ as its only irreducible infinities, supposed simple; where $i$ has the values $1, \ldots, n-1$, and $j = i + 1$. Then the fractional parts of the functions $\phi_{12}(z)$, $\phi_{23}(z)$, ... are

$$G_1 \left( \frac{1}{z - \alpha_1} - \frac{1}{z - \alpha_2} \right),$$

$$G_2 \left( \frac{1}{z - \alpha_2} - \frac{1}{z - \alpha_3} \right),$$

$$\vdots$$

respectively; and therefore the fractional part of

$$\frac{A_1}{G_1} \phi_{12}(z) + \frac{A_1 + A_2}{G_2} \phi_{23}(z) + \cdots + \frac{A_1 + A_2 + \cdots + A_{n-1}}{G_{n-1}} \phi_{n-1, n}(z)$$

is

$$\frac{A_1}{z - \alpha_1} + \frac{A_2}{z - \alpha_2} + \cdots + \frac{A_{n-1}}{z - \alpha_{n-1}} - \frac{A_1 + A_2 + \cdots + A_{n-1}}{z - \alpha_n}$$

$$= \frac{A_1}{z - \alpha_1} + \cdots + \frac{A_{n-1}}{z - \alpha_{n-1}} + \frac{A_n}{z - \alpha_n},$$

since $\overset{n}{\underset{i=1}{\Sigma}} A_i = 0$. This is the same as the fractional part of $\Phi(z)$; and therefore

$$\Phi(z) - \frac{A_1}{G_1}\phi_{12}(z) - \frac{A_1 + A_2}{G_2}\phi_{23}(z) - \ldots - \frac{A_1 + \ldots + A_{n-1}}{G_{n-1}}\phi_{n-1,n}(z)$$

has no fractional part. It thus has no infinity within the parallelogram; it is a doubly-periodic function and therefore has no infinity anywhere in the plane; and it is therefore merely a constant, say $B$. Hence, changing the constants, we have

$$\Phi(z) - B_1\phi_{12}(z) - B_2\phi_{23}(z) - \ldots - B_{n-1}\phi_{n-1,n}(z) = B,$$

giving an expression for $\Phi(z)$ as a linear combination of functions of the second order and the second class. But as the assignment of the infinities is arbitrary, the expression is not unique.

For the expression in the form of a product, we may denote the $n$ irreducible zeros, supposed simple, by $a_1, \ldots, a_n$. We determine $n-2$ new irreducible quantities $c$, such that

$$c_1 \equiv a_1 + a_2 - a_1,$$

$$c_2 \equiv a_3 + c_1 - a_2,$$

$$c_3 \equiv a_4 + c_2 - a_3,$$

$$\vdots$$

$$c_{n-2} \equiv a_{n-1} + c_{n-3} - a_{n-2},$$

$$a_n \equiv a_n \quad + c_{n-2} - a_{n-1},$$

this being possible because $\overset{n}{\underset{r=1}{\Sigma}} a_r \equiv \overset{n}{\underset{r=1}{\Sigma}} a_r$; and we denote by $\phi(z; \alpha, \beta; e, f)$ a function of $z$, which is doubly-periodic in the periods of the given function, has $\alpha$ and $\beta$ for simple irreducible infinities, and has $e$ and $f$ for simple irreducible zeros. Then the function

$$\phi(z; \alpha_1, \alpha_2; a_1, c_1)\phi(z; \alpha_3, c_1; a_2, c_2) \ldots \phi(z; \alpha_n, c_{n-2}; a_{n-1}, a_n)$$

has neither a zero nor an infinity at $c_1$, at $c_2$, ..., and at $c_{n-2}$; it has simple infinities at $\alpha_1, \alpha_2, \ldots, \alpha_n$, and simple zeros at $a_1, a_2, \ldots, a_{n-1}, a_n$. Hence it has the same irreducible infinities and the same irreducible zeros in the same degree as the given function $\Phi(z)$; and therefore, by Prop. IV., $\Phi(z)$ is a mere constant multiple of the foregoing product.

The theorem is thus completely proved.

Other developments for functions, the infinities of which are not simple, are possible; but they are relatively unimportant in view of a theorem, Prop. XV., about to be proved, which expresses any periodic function in terms of a single function of the second order and its derivative.

XIII.  *If two doubly-periodic functions have the same periods, they are connected by an algebraic equation.*

Let $u$ be one of the functions, having $n$ irreducible infinities, and $v$ be the other, having $m$ irreducible infinities.

By Prop. VI., Corollary 1, there are $n$ irreducible values of $z$ for a value of $u$; and to each irreducible value of $z$ there is a doubly-infinite series of values of $z$ over the plane.  The function $v$ has the same value for all the points in any one series, so that a single value of $v$ can be associated uniquely with each of the irreducible values of $z$, that is, there are $n$ values of $v$ for each value of $u$.  Hence (§ 99) $v$ is a root of an algebraic equation of the $n$th degree, the coefficients of which are functions of $u$.

Similarly $u$ is a root of an algebraic equation of the $m$th degree, the coefficients of which are functions of $v$.

Hence, combining these results, we have an algebraic equation between $u$ and $v$ of the $n$th degree in $v$ and the $m$th in $u$, where $m$ and $n$ are the respective orders of $v$ and $u$.

COROLLARY 1.  *If both the functions be even functions of $z$; then $n$ and $m$ are even integers; and the algebraic relation between $u$ and $v$ is of degree $\frac{1}{2}n$ in $v$ and of degree $\frac{1}{2}m$ in $u$.*

COROLLARY 2.  *If a function $u$ be doubly-periodic in $\omega$ and $\omega'$, and a function $v$ be doubly-periodic in $\Omega$ and $\Omega'$, where*

$$\Omega = m\omega + n\omega', \quad \Omega' = m'\omega + n'\omega',$$

*$m$, $n$, $m'$, $n'$ being integers, then there is an algebraic relation between $u$ and $v$.*

**119.**  It has been proved that, if a doubly-periodic function $u$ be of order $m$, then its derivative $du/dz$ is doubly-periodic in the same periods and is of an order $n$, which is not less than $m+1$ and not greater than $2m$.  Hence, by Prop. XIII., there subsists between $u$ and $u'$ an algebraic equation of order $m$ in $u'$ and of order $n$ in $u$; let it be arranged in powers of $u'$, so that it takes the form

$$U_0 u'^m + U_1 u'^{m-1} + \ldots + U_{m-2} u'^2 + U_{m-1} u' + U_m = 0,$$

where $U_0, U_1, \ldots, U_m$ are rational integral functions of $u$ one at least of which must be of degree $n$.

Because the only distinct infinities of $u'$ are infinities of $u$, it is impossible that $u'$ should become infinite for finite values of $u$: hence $U_0 = 0$ can have no finite roots for $u$, that is, it is a constant and so it may be taken as unity.

And because the $m$ values of $z$, for which $u$ assumes a given value, have their sum constant save as to integral multiples of the periods, we have

$$\delta z_1 + \delta z_2 + \ldots + \delta z_m = 0$$

corresponding to a variation $\delta u$; or

$$\frac{dz_1}{du} + \frac{dz_2}{du} + \ldots + \frac{dz_m}{du} = 0.$$

Now $\dfrac{du}{dz_1}$ is one of the values of $u'$ corresponding to the value of $u$, and so for the others; hence

$$\sum_{r=1}^{m} \frac{1}{u_r'} = 0,$$

that is, by the foregoing equation,

$$\frac{U_{m-1}}{U_m} = 0,$$

and therefore $U_{m-1}$ vanishes.  Hence :—

XIV.  *There is a relation, between a uniform doubly-periodic function u of order m and its derivative, of the form*

$$u'^m + U_1 u'^{m-1} + \ldots + U_{m-2} u'^2 + U_m = 0,$$

*where $U_1, \ldots, U_{m-2}, U_m$ are rational integral functions of u, at least one of which must be of degree n, the order of the derivative, and n is not less than $m+1$ and not greater than $2m$.*

Further, by taking $v = \dfrac{1}{u}$, which is a function of order $m$ because it has the $m$ irreducible zeros of $u$ for its infinities, and substituting, we have

$$v'^m - v^2 U_1 v'^{m-1} + v^4 U_2 v'^{m-2} - \ldots \pm v^{2m-4} U_{m-2} v'^2 \mp v^{2m} U_m = 0$$

The coefficients of this equation must be integral functions of $v$; hence the *degree of $U_r$ in u cannot be greater than 2r\**.

Corollary.  The foregoing equation becomes very simple in the case of doubly-periodic functions of the second order.

Then                                        $m = 2.$

If the function have one infinity of the second degree, its derivative has that infinity in the third degree, and is of the third order, so that $n = 3$; and the equation is

$$\left(\frac{du}{dz}\right)^2 = \lambda u^3 + 3\mu u^2 + 3\nu u + \rho,$$

where $\lambda, \mu, \nu, \rho$ are constants.  If $\theta$ be the infinity, so that

$$u = \phi(z) = \frac{A}{(z-\theta)^2} + \chi(z),$$

where $\chi(z)$ is everywhere finite in the parallelogram, then $\dfrac{1}{\lambda} = \tfrac{1}{4}A$; and the zeros of $\dfrac{du}{dz}$ are $\theta + \omega,\ \theta + \omega',\ \theta + \omega + \omega'$; so that

$$\tfrac{1}{4} A \left(\frac{d\phi}{dz}\right)^2 = \{\phi(z) - \phi(\theta+\omega)\}\{\phi(z) - \phi(\theta+\omega')\}\{\phi(z) - \phi(\theta+\omega+\omega')\}.$$

This is *the general differential equation of Weierstrass's elliptic functions.*

* For a converse proposition, see the *Note on differential equations of the first order having uniform integrals*, at the end of this chapter.

If the function have two simple infinities $\alpha$ and $\beta$, its derivative has each of them as an infinity of the second degree, and is of the fourth order, so that $n = 4$; and the equation is

$$\left(\frac{du}{dz}\right)^2 = c_0 u^4 + 4c_1 u^3 + 6c_2 u^2 + 4c_3 u + c_4,$$

where $c_0$, $c_1$, $c_2$, $c_3$, $c_4$ are constants.   Moreover

$$u = \phi(z) = G\left(\frac{1}{z-\alpha} - \frac{1}{z-\beta}\right) + \chi(z),$$

where $\chi(z)$ is finite everywhere in the parallelogram.   Then $c_0 = G^{-2}$; and the zeros of $\dfrac{du}{dz}$ are $\frac{1}{2}(\alpha+\beta)$, $\frac{1}{2}(\alpha+\beta)+\omega$, $\frac{1}{2}(\alpha+\beta)+\omega'$, $\frac{1}{2}(\alpha+\beta)+\omega+\omega'$, so that the equation is

$$G^2\left(\frac{d\phi}{dz}\right)^2 = [\phi(z) - \phi\{\tfrac{1}{2}(\alpha+\beta)\}][\phi(z) - \phi\{\tfrac{1}{2}(\alpha+\beta)+\omega\}]$$
$$\times [\phi(z) - \phi\{\tfrac{1}{2}(\alpha+\beta)+\omega'\}][\phi(z) - \phi\{\tfrac{1}{2}(\alpha+\beta)+\omega+\omega'\}].$$

This is *the general differential equation of Jacobi's elliptic functions.*

The canonical forms of both of these equations will be obtained in Chapter XI., where some properties of the functions are investigated as special illustrations of the general theorems.

*Note.*   All the derivatives of a doubly-periodic function are doubly-periodic in the same periods, and have the same infinities as the function but in different degrees.   In the case of a function of the second order, which must satisfy one or other of the two foregoing equations, it is easy to see that a derivative of even rank is a rational integral function of $u$, and that a derivative of odd rank is the product of a rational integral function of $u$ by the first derivative of $u$.

It may be remarked that the form of these equations confirms the result at the end of § 117, by giving two values of $u'$ for one value of $u$, the two values being equal and opposite.

*Ex.* 1.   If $u$ be a doubly-periodic function having a single irreducible infinity of the third degree so as to be expressible in the form

$$-\frac{2}{z^3} + \frac{\theta}{z^2} + \text{integral function of } z$$

within the parallelogram of periods, then the differential equation of the first order which determines $u$ is

$$u'^3 + (a + 3\theta u) u'^2 = U_4,$$

where $U_4$ is a quartic function of $u$ and where $a$ is a constant which does not vanish with $\theta$.

(Math. Trip., Part II., 1889.)

*Ex.* 2.   A doubly-periodic function $u$ has three irreducible poles $a_1$, $a_2$, $a_3$, such that in the immediate vicinity of each

$$u = \frac{\lambda_s}{z - a_s} + v_s(z - a_s) + \text{powers of } z - a_s,$$

for $s = 1, 2, 3$.   Prove that
$$u'^3 + Uu'^2 + V = 0,$$
where
$$U = \left(\frac{1}{\lambda_1} + \frac{1}{\lambda_2} + \frac{1}{\lambda_3}\right) u^2 - 3\,\frac{\Sigma v_1\,(\lambda_1 - \lambda_2)\,(\lambda_1 - \lambda_3)}{\lambda_1\lambda_2 + \lambda_2\lambda_3 + \lambda_3\lambda_1}\,,$$
and $V$ is a sextic polynomial in $u$ of which the highest terms are
$$\frac{1}{\lambda_1\lambda_2\lambda_3}\left\{u^6 - \frac{u^4}{\lambda_1\lambda_2\lambda_3}\,\Sigma v_1\lambda_1{}^2\,(\lambda_1 - \lambda_2)\,(\lambda_1 - \lambda_3)\right\}.$$

(Math. Trip., Part II., 1895.)

XV.   *Every doubly-periodic function can be expressed rationally in terms of a function of the second order, doubly-periodic in the same periods, and its derivative.*

Let $u$ be a function of the second order and the second class, having the same two periods as $v$, a function of the $m$th order; then, by Prop. XIII., there is an algebraic relation between $u$ and $v$ which, being of the second degree in $v$ and the $m$th degree in $u$, may be taken in the form
$$Lv^2 - 2Mv + P = 0,$$
where the quantities $L, M, P$ are rational integral functions of $u$ and at least one of them is of degree $m$.   Taking
$$Lv - M = w,$$
we have
$$w^2 = M^2 - LP,$$
a rational integral function of $u$ of degree not higher than $2m$.

Thus $w$ cannot be infinite for any finite value of $u$: an infinite value of $u$ makes $w$ infinite, of finite multiplicity.   To each value of $u$ there correspond two values of $w$ equal to one another but opposite in sign.

Moreover $w$, being equal to $Lv - M$, is a uniform function of $z$, say $F(z)$, while it is a two-valued function of $u$.   A value of $u$ gives two distinct values of $z$, say $z_1$ and $z_2$; hence the values of $w$, which arise from an assigned value of $u$, are values of $w$ arising as uniform functions of the two distinct values of $z$.   Hence as the two values of $w$ are equal in magnitude and opposite in sign, we have
$$F(z_1) + F(z_2) = 0,$$
that is, since $z_1 + z_2 \equiv \alpha + \beta$ where $\alpha$ and $\beta$ are the irreducible infinities of $u$,
$$F(z_1) + F(\alpha + \beta - z_1) = 0,$$
so that $\frac{1}{2}(\alpha + \beta)$, $\frac{1}{2}(\alpha + \beta) + \omega$, $\frac{1}{2}(\alpha + \beta) + \omega'$, and $\frac{1}{2}(\alpha + \beta) + \omega + \omega'$ are either zeros or infinities of $w$.   They are known not to be infinities of $u$, and $w$ is infinite only for infinite values of $u$; hence the four points are zeros of $w$.

But these are all the irreducible zeros of $u'$; hence the zeros of $u'$ are included among the zeros of $w$.

Now consider the function $w/u'$. The numerator has two values equal and opposite for an assigned value of $u$; so also has the denominator. Hence $w/u'$ is a uniform function of $u$.

This uniform function of $u$ may become infinite for

    (i)    infinities of the numerator,

    (ii)    zeros of the denominator.

But, so far as concerns (ii), we know that the four irreducible zeros of the denominator are all simple zeros of $u'$ and each of them is a zero of $w$; hence $w/u'$ does not become infinite for any of the points in (ii). And, so far as concerns (i), we know that all of them are infinities of $u$. Hence $w/u'$, a uniform function of $u$, can become infinite only for an infinite value of $u$, and its multiplicity for such a value is finite; hence it is a rational integral function of $u$, say $N$, so that

$$w = Nu'.$$

Moreover, because $w^2$ is of degree in $u$ not higher than $2m$, and $u'^2$ is of the fourth degree in $u$, it follows that $N$ *is of degree not higher than* $m - 2$.

We thus have
$$Lv - M = Nu',$$

or
$$v = \frac{M + Nu'}{L} = \frac{M}{L} + \frac{N}{L}u',$$

where $L$, $M$, $N$ are rational integral functions of $u$; the degrees of $L$ and $M$ are not higher than $m$, and that of $N$ is not higher than $m - 2$.

*Note* 1.    The function $u$, which has been considered in the preceding proof, is of the second order and the second class. If a function $u$ of the second order and the first class, having a double irreducible infinity, be chosen, the course of proof is similar; the function $w$ has the three irreducible zeros of $u'$ among its zeros and the result, as before, is

$$w = Nu'.$$

But, now, $w^2$ is of degree in $u$ not higher than $2m$ and $u'^2$ is of the third degree in $u$; hence $N$ is of degree not higher than $m - 2$, and the degree of $w^2$ in $u$ cannot be higher than $2m - 1$.

Hence, if $L$, $M$, $P$ be all of degree $m$, the terms of degree $2m$ in $LP - M^2$ disappear. If all of them be not of degree $m$, the degree of $M$ must not be higher than $m - 1$; the degree of either $L$ or $P$ must be $m$, but the degree of the other must not be greater than $m - 1$, for otherwise the algebraic equation between $u$ and $v$ would not be of degree $m$ in $u$.

We thus have
$$Lv^2 - 2Mv + P = 0, \quad Lv - M = Nu',$$

where the degree of $N$ in $u$ is not higher than $m-2$. If the degree of $L$ be less than $m$, the degree of $M$ is not higher than $m-1$ and the degree of $P$ is $m$. If the degree of $L$ be $m$, the degree of $M$ may also be $m$ provided that the degree of $P$ be $m$ and that the highest terms be such that the coefficient of $u^{2m}$ in $LP - M^2$ vanishes.

*Note* 2. The theorem expresses a function $v$ rationally in terms of $u$ and $u'$ : but $u'$ is an irrational function of $u$, so that $v$ is not expressed rationally in terms of $u$ alone.

But, in Propositions XI. and XII., it was indicated that a function such as $v$ could be rationally expressed in terms of a doubly-periodic function, such as $u$. The apparent contradiction is explained by the fact that, in the earlier propositions, the arguments of the function $u$ in the rational expression and of the function $v$ are not the same ; whereas, in the later proposition whereby $v$ is expressed in general irrationally in terms of $u$, the arguments are the same. The transition from the first (which is the less useful form) to the second is made by expressing the functions of those different arguments in terms of functions of the same argument when (as will appear subsequently, in § 121, in proving the so-called addition-theorem) the irrational function of $u$, represented by the derivative $u'$, is introduced.

*Note* 3. The theorem of this section, usually called Liouville's theorem, is valid only when there are no essential singularities in the finite part of the plane. The limitation arises in that part of the proof, where the irreducible zeros and the irreducible poles are considered : it is there assumed that their number is finite, which cannot be the case when essential singularities exist in the finite part of the plane and when therefore there are irreducible essential singularities. Hence Liouville's theorem is true only for those uniform doubly-periodic functions which have their essential singularities at infinity.

In illustration of this remark, it may be noted that $e^{\operatorname{sn} u}$, though a uniform doubly-periodic function of $u$, is not expressible rationally in terms of $\operatorname{sn} u$ and $\operatorname{sn}' u$.

*Ex.* If $f(u)$ be a doubly-periodic function of the third order with poles at $c_1, c_2, c_3$ ; and if $\phi(u)$ be a doubly-periodic function of the second order, with the same periods, and with poles at $a, \beta$, its value in the neighbourhood of $u = a$ being

$$\phi(u) = \frac{\lambda}{u-a} + \lambda_1(u-a) + \lambda_2(u-a)^2 + \dots ;$$

prove

$$\tfrac{1}{2}\lambda^2 \{f''(a) - f''(\beta)\} - \lambda\{f'(a) - f'(\beta)\} \sum_1^3 \phi(c_1) + \{f(a) - f(\beta)\}\{3\lambda\lambda_1 + \sum_1^3 \phi(c_2)\phi(c_3)\} = 0.$$

COROLLARY 1. Let $\Omega$ denote the sum of the irreducible infinities or of the irreducible zeros of the function $u$ of the second order, so that $\Omega \equiv 2\gamma$ for functions of the first class, and $\Omega \equiv a + \beta$ for functions of the second class.

Let $u$ be represented by $\phi(z)$ and $v$ by $\psi(z)$, when the argument must be put in evidence.   Then

$$\phi(\Omega - z) = \phi(z),$$

$$-\phi'(\Omega - z) = \phi'(z),$$

so that $\qquad \psi(\Omega - z) = \dfrac{M + N\phi'(\Omega - z)}{L} = \dfrac{M}{L} - \dfrac{N}{L}\,\phi'(z).$

Hence $\qquad \psi(z) + \psi(\Omega - z) = 2\,\dfrac{M}{L} = 2R,$

$$\psi(z) - \psi(\Omega - z) = 2\,\frac{N}{L}\,\phi'(z) = 2S\phi'(z).$$

First, if $\psi(z) = \psi(\Omega - z)$, then $S = 0$ and $\psi(z) = R$ : that is, *a function $\psi(z)$, which satisfies the equation*

$$\psi(z) = \psi(\Omega - z),$$

*can be expressed as a rational meromorphic function of $\phi(z)$ of the second order, doubly-periodic in the same periods and having the sum of its irreducible infinities congruent with $\Omega$.*

Second, if $\psi(z) = -\psi(\Omega - z)$, then $R = 0$ and $\psi(z) = S\phi'(z)$; that is, *a function $\psi(z)$, which satisfies the equation*

$$\psi(z) = -\psi(\Omega - z),$$

*can be expressed as a rational meromorphic function of $\phi(z)$, multiplied by $\phi'(z)$, where $\phi(z)$ is doubly-periodic in the same periods, is of the second order, and has the sum of its irreducible infinities congruent with $\Omega$.*

Third, if $\psi(z)$ have no infinities except those of $u$, it cannot become infinite for finite values of $u$; hence $L = 0$ has no roots, that is, $L$ is a constant which may be taken to be unity.   Then $\psi(z)$ a function of order $m$ can be expressed in the form

$$M + N\phi'(z),$$

where, if the function $\phi(z)$ be of the second class, the degree of $M$ is not higher than $m$; but, if it be of the first class, the degree of $M$ is not higher than $m - 1$; and in each case the degree of $N$ is not higher than $m - 2$.

It will be found in practice, with functions of the first class, that these upper limits for degrees can be considerably reduced by counting the degrees of the infinities in

$$M + N\phi'(z).$$

Thus, if the degree of $M$ in $u$ be $\mu$ and of $N$ be $\lambda$, the highest degree of an infinity is either $2\mu$ or $2\lambda + 3$; so that, if the order of $\psi(z)$ be $m$, we should have

$$m = 2\mu \quad \text{or} \quad m = 2\lambda + 3,$$

according as $m$ is even or odd.

When functions of the second class are used to represent a function $\psi(z)$, which has two infinities $\alpha$ and $\beta$ each of degree $n$, then it is easy to see that $M$ is of degree $n$ and $N$ of degree $n-2$; and so for other cases.

COROLLARY 2. *Any doubly-periodic function can be expressed rationally in terms of any other function $u$ of any order $n$, doubly-periodic in the same periods, and of its derivative; and this rational expression can always be taken in the form*

$$U_0 + U_1 u' + U_2 u'^2 + \ldots + U_{n-1} u'^{n-1},$$

*where $U_0, \ldots, U_{n-1}$ are rational meromorphic functions of $u$.*

COROLLARY 3. *If $\phi$ be a doubly-periodic function, then $\phi(u+v)$ can be expressed in the form*

$$\frac{A + B\psi'(u) + C\psi'(v) + D\psi'(u)\psi'(v)}{E},$$

*where $\psi$ is a doubly-periodic function in the same periods and of the second order: each of the functions $A, D, E$ is a symmetric function of $\psi(u)$ and $\psi(v)$, and $B$ is the same function of $\psi(v)$ and $\psi(u)$ as $C$ is of $\psi(u)$ and $\psi(v)$.*

The degrees of $A$ and $E$ are not greater than $m$ in $\psi(u)$ and than $m$ in $\psi(v)$, where $m$ is the order of $\phi$; the degree of $D$ is not greater than $m-2$ in $\psi(u)$ and than $m-2$ in $\psi(v)$; the degree of $B$ is not greater than $m-2$ in $\psi(u)$ and than $m$ in $\psi(v)$, and the degree of $C$ is not greater than $m-2$ in $\psi(v)$ and than $m$ in $\psi(u)$.

## Note on Differential Equations of the First Order having Uniform Integrals.

The relation given in Proposition XIV., § 119, immediately suggests a converse question as follows:—

Under what conditions does an equation

$$u'^m + u'^{m-1} f_1(u) + \ldots + f_m(u) = 0$$

possess integrals expressing $u$ as a uniform function of $z$? Further, we should expect, after the proposition which has just been mentioned, that under fitting conditions the uniform function could be doubly-periodic; and we have already seen (in § 104) that the integral of the equation

$$u'^2 = (1 - u^2)(1 - k^2 u^2)$$

is a uniform doubly-periodic function of $z$. But it might happen (and it does happen) that other classes of uniform functions are integrals of differential equations of the same form.

The full investigation belongs to the theory of differential equations; an account is given in Chapter X., Part II. (vol. ii.) of my *Theory of Differential Equations*. The following statement of results, which are established there, may be useful for reference.

The differential equation is to be regarded as irreducible. We shall need the equation satisfied by $1/u$; so we shall take $v = 1/u$ and denote its derivative by $v'$.

I.  In order that the equation

$$F(u', u) = u'^m + u'^{m-1} f_1(u) + \ldots + f_m(u) = 0$$

may have a uniform function for its integral, the coefficients $f_1(u), \ldots, f_m(u)$ must be polynomials in $u$ of degrees not higher than $2, \ldots, 2m$ respectively; and the condition is then satisfied for the equation

$$G(v', v) = v'^m - v'^{m-1} f_1(v) + \ldots + (-1)^m f_m(v) = 0.$$

II.  If any finite value of $u$ is a branch-point of $u'$ determined as a function of $u$ by the equation $F(u', u) = 0$, all the affected values of $u'$ must be zero for that value of $u$; and likewise for the value $v = 0$ in connection with the equation $G(v', v) = 0$.  (The latter condition covers an infinite value of $u$ as a branch-point of $u'$.)

III.  If there is a multiple root $u'$ of $F(u', u) = 0$, which is zero for $n$ branches for the branch-place $u$, then the term of lowest degree in the expansion of each of those $n$ branches in the vicinity of that branch-place $u$ is of degree either $1 - \dfrac{1}{n}$, $1$, or $1 + \dfrac{1}{n}$; and likewise for the value $v = 0$ for the equation $G(v', v) = 0$.  The number $1 - \dfrac{1}{n}$, $1$, or $1 + \dfrac{1}{n}$, is called the index-degree.

IV.  The genus of the equation $F(u', u) = 0$, regarded as an equation in $u'$, is either zero or unity—as is therefore also the genus of the associated Riemann surface (see Chapter XV., *post*).

V.  When the index-degree of $u'$, for any finite value or for an infinite value of $u$ as a branch value for $u'$, is less than unity, being then necessarily of the form $1 - \dfrac{1}{n}$ for each branch value, though $n$ need not be the same for all the different branch-places, $u$ is a uniform *doubly-periodic* function of $z$.

VI.  If for some one value of $u$ there is a single set of multiple zero roots $u'$ of index-degree equal to unity, and if for other values of $u$ (finite or infinite) all the multiple zero roots $u'$ are of index-degree less than unity and therefore necessarily of the form $1 - \dfrac{1}{n}$, then $u$ is a uniform *singly-periodic* function of $z$.

VII.  If for some one value of $u$ there is a single set of multiple zero roots $u'$ of index-degree greater than unity and therefore necessarily of the form $1 + \dfrac{1}{n}$, and for other values of $u$ (finite or infinite) all the multiple zero roots $u'$ are of index-degree less than unity and therefore necessarily of the form $1 - \dfrac{1}{n}$, then $u$ is a *rational* function of $z$.

VIII.  When these conditions are applied to the binomial equation

$$\left(\frac{du}{dz}\right)^s = f(u),$$

where $f(u)$ is a polynomial in $u$ of degree not greater than $2s$, so as to obtain integrals $u$ which are uniform functions of $z$, the results are as follows:—

(A)  Equations, having uniform integrals which are rational functions of $z$,

$$\left(\frac{du}{dz}\right)^s = \mu (u - a)^{s-1},$$

$$\left(\frac{du}{dz}\right)^s = \mu (u - a)^{s+1},$$

$$\left(\frac{du}{dz}\right)^s = \mu (u - a)^{s-1} (u - b)^{s+1},$$

where $\mu$ is a constant in each case;

(B)  Equations, having uniform integrals which are simply-periodic functions of $z$,

$$\frac{du}{dz} = \mu\,(u - a),$$

$$\frac{du}{dz} = \mu\,(u - a)\,(u - b),$$

$$\left(\frac{du}{dz}\right)^2 = \mu\,(u - a)\,(u - b),$$

$$\left(\frac{du}{dz}\right)^2 = \mu\,(u - a)^2\,(u - b),$$

$$\left(\frac{du}{dz}\right)^2 = \mu\,(u - a)^2\,(u - b)\,(u - c),$$

where $\mu$ is a constant in each case;

(C)  Equations, having uniform integrals which are doubly-periodic functions of $z$,

$$\left(\frac{du}{dz}\right)^6 = \mu\,(u - a)^4\,(u - b)^5,$$

$$\left(\frac{du}{dz}\right)^6 = \mu\,(u - a)^3\,(u - b)^5,$$

$$\left(\frac{du}{dz}\right)^6 = \mu\,(u - a)^3\,(u - b)^4,$$

$$\left(\frac{du}{dz}\right)^4 = \mu\,(u - a)^3\,(u - b)^3,$$

$$\left(\frac{du}{dz}\right)^4 = \mu\,(u - a)^2\,(u - b)^3,$$

$$\left(\frac{du}{dz}\right)^3 = \mu\,(u - a)^2\,(u - b)^2,$$

$$\left(\frac{du}{dz}\right)^6 = \mu\,(u - a)^3\,(u - b)^4\,(u - c)^5,$$

$$\left(\frac{du}{dz}\right)^4 = \mu\,(u - a)^2\,(u - b)^3\,(u - c)^3,$$

$$\left(\frac{du}{dz}\right)^3 = \mu\,(u - a)^2\,(u - b)^2\,(u - c)^2,$$

$$\left(\frac{du}{dz}\right)^2 = \mu\,(u - a)\,(u - b)\,(u - c),$$

$$\left(\frac{du}{dz}\right)^2 = \mu\,(u - a)\,(u - b)\,(u - c)\,(u - d).$$

# CHAPTER XI.

## Doubly-Periodic Functions of the Second Order.

THE present chapter will be devoted, in illustration of the preceding theorems, to the establishment of some of the fundamental formulæ relating to doubly-periodic functions of the second order which, as has already (in § 119, Cor. to Prop. XIV.) been indicated, are substantially elliptic functions : but for any development of their properties, recourse must be had to treatises on elliptic functions.

It may be remarked that, in dealing with doubly-periodic functions, we may restrict ourselves to a discussion of even functions and of odd functions. For, if $\phi(z)$ be any function, then $\frac{1}{2}\{\phi(z) + \phi(-z)\}$ is an even function, and $\frac{1}{2}\{\phi(z) - \phi(-z)\}$ is an odd function. both of them being doubly-periodic in the periods of $\phi(z)$; and the new functions would, in general, be of order double that of $\phi(z)$. We shall practically limit the discussion to even functions and odd functions of the second order.

**120.** Consider a function $\phi(z)$, doubly-periodic in $2\omega$ and $2\omega'$; and let it be an odd function of the second class, with $\alpha$ and $\beta$ as its irreducible infinities, and $a$ and $b$ as its irreducible zeros*.

Then we have
$$\phi(z) = \phi(\alpha + \beta - z),$$

which always holds; and
$$\phi(-z) = -\phi(z),$$

which holds because $\phi(z)$ is an odd function. Hence

$$\phi(\alpha + \beta + z) = \phi(-z)$$
$$= -\phi(z),$$

so that $\alpha + \beta$ is not a period; and

$$\phi(\alpha + \beta + \alpha + \beta + z) = -\phi(\alpha + \beta + z)$$
$$= \phi(z),$$

---

* To fix the ideas, it will be convenient to compare it with sn $z$, for which $2\omega = 4K$, $2\omega' = 2iK'$, $\alpha = iK'$, $\beta = iK' + 2K$, $a = 0$, and $b = 2K$.

whence $2(\alpha + \beta)$ is a period. Since $\alpha + \beta$ is not a period, we take $\alpha + \beta \equiv \omega$, or $\equiv \omega'$, or $\equiv \omega + \omega'$; the first two alternatives merely interchange $\omega$ and $\omega'$, so that we have either

$$\alpha + \beta \equiv \omega,$$

or

$$\alpha + \beta \equiv \omega + \omega'.$$

And we know that, in general,

$$a + b \equiv \alpha + \beta.$$

First, for the zeros: we have

$$\phi(0) = -\phi(-0) = -\phi(0),$$

so that $\phi(0)$ is either zero or infinite. The choice is at our disposal; for $\frac{1}{\phi(z)}$ satisfies all the equations which have been satisfied by $\phi(z)$ and an infinity of either is a zero of the other. We therefore take

$$\phi(0) = 0,$$

so that we have

$$a = 0,$$
$$b = \omega \quad \text{or} \quad \omega + \omega'.$$

Next, for the infinities: we have

$$\phi(z) = -\phi(-z)$$

and therefore

$$\phi(-\alpha) = -\phi(\alpha) = \infty.$$

The only infinities of $\phi$ are $\alpha$ and $\beta$, so that either

$$-\alpha \equiv \alpha,$$

or

$$-\alpha \equiv \beta.$$

The latter cannot hold, because it would give $\alpha + \beta \equiv 0$ whereas $\alpha + \beta \equiv \omega$ or $\equiv \omega + \omega'$; hence

$$2\alpha \equiv 0,$$

which must be associated with $\alpha + \beta \equiv \omega$ or with $\alpha + \beta \equiv \omega + \omega'$.

Hence $\alpha$, being a point inside the fundamental parallelogram, is either 0, $\omega$, $\omega'$, or $\omega + \omega'$.

It cannot be 0 in any case, for that is a zero.

If $\alpha + \beta \equiv \omega$, then $\alpha$ cannot be $\omega$, because that value would give $\beta = 0$, which is a zero, not an infinity. Hence either $\alpha = \omega'$, and then $\beta = \omega' + \omega$; or $\alpha = \omega' + \omega$, and then $\beta = \omega'$. These are effectively one solution; so that, if $\alpha + \beta \equiv \omega$, we have

$$\left.\begin{array}{l} \alpha, \beta = \omega', \omega' + \omega \\ a, b = 0, \omega \end{array}\right\}.$$

and

If $\alpha + \beta \equiv \omega + \omega'$, then $\alpha$ cannot be $\omega + \omega'$, because that value would give $\beta = 0$, which is a zero, not an infinity. Hence either $\alpha = \omega$ and then $\beta = \omega'$, or $\alpha = \omega'$ and then $\beta = \omega$. These again are effectively one solution; so that, if $\alpha + \beta \equiv \omega + \omega'$, we have

$$\left.\begin{array}{l} \alpha, \beta = \omega, \omega' \\ a, b = 0, \omega + \omega' \end{array}\right\}.$$

and

This combination can, by a change of fundamental parallelogram, be made the same as the former; for, taking as new periods

$$2\omega' = 2\omega', \qquad 2\Omega = 2\omega + 2\omega',$$

which give a new fundamental parallelogram, we have $\alpha + \beta \equiv \Omega$, and

$$\alpha, \ \beta = \omega', \ \Omega - \omega', \text{ that is, } \omega', \ \Omega - \omega' + 2\omega',$$

so that                    $\alpha, \ \beta = \omega', \ \Omega + \omega' \ \Big\}$

and                        $a, \ b = 0, \ \Omega \quad \Big\} \ ,$

being the same as the former with $\Omega$ instead of $\omega$.    Hence it is sufficient to retain the first solution alone : and therefore

$$\alpha = \omega', \qquad \beta = \omega' + \omega,$$

$$a = 0, \qquad b = \omega.$$

Hence, by § 116, I., we have

$$\phi(z) = \frac{z(z - \omega)}{(z - \omega')(z - \omega - \omega')} F(z),$$

where $F(z)$ is finite everywhere within the parallelogram.

Again, $\phi(z + \omega')$ has $z = 0$ and $z = \omega$ as its irreducible infinities, and it has $z = \omega'$ and $z = \omega + \omega'$ as its irreducible zeros, within the parallelogram of $\phi(z)$; hence

$$\phi(z + \omega') = \frac{(z - \omega')(z - \omega - \omega')}{z(z - \omega)} F_1(z),$$

where $F_1(z)$ is finite everywhere within the parallelogram.    Thus

$$\phi(z) \, \phi(z + \omega') = F(z) \, F_1(z),$$

a function which is finite everywhere within the parallelogram ; since it is doubly-periodic, it is finite everywhere in the plane and it is therefore a constant and equal to the value at any point.    Taking $-\tfrac{1}{2}\omega'$ as the point (which is neither a zero nor an infinity) and remembering that $\phi$ is an odd function, we have

$$\phi(z) \, \phi(z + \omega') = - \{\phi(\tfrac{1}{2}\omega')\}^2 = \frac{1}{k},$$

$k$ being a constant used to represent the value of $-\{\phi(\tfrac{1}{2}\omega')\}^{-2}$.

Also                  $\phi(z + \omega) = \phi(z + \alpha + \beta - 2\omega')$

$$= \phi(z + \alpha + \beta) = - \phi(z),$$

and therefore also        $\phi(\omega - z) = \phi(z).$

The irreducible zeros of $\phi'(z)$ were obtained in § 117, X.    In the present example, those points are $\omega' + \tfrac{1}{2}\omega$, $\omega' + \tfrac{3}{2}\omega$, $\tfrac{1}{2}\omega$, $\tfrac{3}{2}\omega$; so that, as there, we have

$$K\{\phi'(z)\}^2 = \{\phi(z) - \phi(\tfrac{1}{2}\omega)\}\{\phi(z) - \phi(\tfrac{3}{2}\omega)\}\{\phi(z) - \phi(\omega' + \tfrac{1}{2}\omega)\}\{\phi(z) - \phi(\omega' + \tfrac{3}{2}\omega)\},$$

where $K$ is a constant.    But

$$\phi(\tfrac{3}{2}\omega) = \phi(2\omega - \tfrac{1}{2}\omega) = \phi(-\tfrac{1}{2}\omega) = - \phi(\tfrac{1}{2}\omega);$$

and
$$\phi\left(\tfrac{3}{2}\omega + \omega'\right) = \phi\left(2\omega + 2\omega' - \tfrac{1}{2}\omega - \omega'\right)$$
$$= \phi\left(-\tfrac{1}{2}\omega - \omega'\right)$$
$$= -\phi\left(\tfrac{1}{2}\omega + \omega'\right);$$

so that
$$\{\phi'(z)\}^2 = A\left[1 - \left\{\frac{\phi(z)}{\phi\left(\tfrac{1}{2}\omega\right)}\right\}^2\right]\left[1 - \left\{\frac{\phi(z)}{\phi\left(\tfrac{1}{2}\omega + \omega'\right)}\right\}^2\right],$$

where $A$ is a new constant, evidently equal to $\{\phi'(0)\}^2$. Now, as we know the periods, the irreducible zeros and the irreducible infinities of the function $\phi(z)$, it is completely determinate save as to a constant factor. To determine this factor we need only know the value of $\phi(z)$ for any particular finite value of $z$. Let the factor be determined by the condition

$$\phi\left(\tfrac{1}{2}\omega\right) = 1;$$

then, since
$$\phi\left(\tfrac{1}{2}\omega\right)\phi\left(\tfrac{1}{2}\omega + \omega'\right) = \frac{1}{k}$$

by a preceding equation, we have

$$\phi\left(\tfrac{1}{2}\omega + \omega'\right) = \frac{1}{k};$$

and then
$$\{\phi'(z)\}^2 = \{\phi'(0)\}^2[1 - \{\phi(z)\}^2][1 - k^2\{\phi(z)\}^2]$$
$$= \mu^2[1 - \{\phi(z)\}^2][1 - k^2\{\phi(z)\}^2].$$

Hence, since $\phi(z)$ is an odd function, we have

$$\phi(z) = \operatorname{sn}(\mu z).$$

Evidently $2\mu\omega$, $2\mu\omega' = 4K$, $2iK'$, where $K$ and $K'$ have the ordinary significations. The simplest case arises when $\mu = 1$.

**121.** Before proceeding to the deduction of the properties of even functions of $z$ which are doubly-periodic, it is desirable to obtain the addition-theorem for $\phi$, that is, the expression of $\phi(y + z)$ in terms of functions of $y$ alone and $z$ alone.

When $\phi(y + z)$ is regarded as a function of $z$, which is necessarily of the second order, it is (§ 119, XV.) of the form

$$\frac{M + N\phi'(z)}{L},$$

where $M$ and $L$ are of degree in $\phi(z)$ not higher than 2 and $N$ is independent of $z$. Moreover $y + z = \alpha$ and $y + z = \beta$ are the irreducible simple infinities of $\phi(y + z)$; so that $L$, as a function of $z$, may be expressed in the form

$$\{\phi(z) - \phi(\alpha - y)\}\{\phi(z) - \phi(\beta - y)\},$$

and therefore
$$\phi(y + z) = \frac{P + Q\phi(z) + R\{\phi(z)\}^2 + S\phi'(z)}{\{\phi(z) - \phi(\alpha - y)\}\{\phi(z) - \phi(\beta - y)\}},$$

where $P$, $Q$, $R$, $S$ are independent of $z$ but they may be functions of $y$. Now

$$\phi\,(a-y)=\phi\,(\omega'-y)=-\frac{1}{k\phi\,(y)},$$

and

$$\phi\,(\beta-y)=\phi\,(\omega'+\omega-y)=\frac{1}{k\phi\,(\omega-y)}=\frac{1}{k\phi\,(y)};$$

so that the denominator of the expression for $\phi\,(y+z)$ is

$$\{\phi\,(z)\}^2-\frac{1}{k^2\,\{\phi\,(y)\}^2}.$$

Since $\phi\,(z)$ is an odd function, $\phi'\,(z)$ is even; hence

$$\phi\,(y-z)=\frac{P-Q\phi\,(z)+R\,\{\phi\,(z)\}^2+S\phi'\,(z)}{\{\phi\,(z)\}^2-\dfrac{1}{k^2\,\{\phi\,(y)\}^2}},$$

and therefore

$$\phi\,(y+z)-\phi\,(y-z)=\frac{2Q\phi\,(z)}{\{\phi\,(z)\}^2-\dfrac{1}{k^2\,\{\phi\,(y)\}^2}}.$$

Differentiating with regard to $z$ and then making $z=0$, we have

$$2\phi'\,(y)=\frac{2Q\phi'\,(0)}{-\dfrac{1}{k^2\,\{\phi\,(y)\}^2}},$$

so that, substituting for $Q$ we have

$$\phi\,(y+z)-\phi\,(y-z)=\frac{1}{\phi'\,(0)}\frac{2\phi\,(z)\,\phi'\,(y)}{1-k^2\,\{\phi\,(y)\}^2\,\{\phi\,(z)\}^2}.$$

Interchanging $y$ and $z$ and noting that $\phi\,(y-z)=-\phi\,(z-y)$, we have

$$\phi\,(y+z)+\phi\,(y-z)=\frac{1}{\phi'\,(0)}\frac{2\phi\,(y)\,\phi'\,(z)}{1-k^2\,\{\phi\,(y)\}^2\,\{\phi\,(z)\}^2},$$

and therefore

$$\phi\,(y+z)\,\phi'\,(0)=\frac{\phi\,(z)\,\phi'\,(y)+\phi\,(y)\,\phi'\,(z)}{1-k^2\,\{\phi\,(y)\}^2\,\{\phi\,(z)\}^2},$$

which is the addition-theorem required.

*Ex.* If $f\,(u)$ be a doubly-periodic function of the second order with infinities $b_1$, $b_2$, and $\phi\,(u)$ a doubly-periodic function of the second order with infinities $a_1$, $a_2$ such that, in the vicinity of $a_i$ (for $i=1$, 2), we have

$$\phi\,(u)=\frac{(-1)^i\lambda}{u-a_i}+p_i+q_i\,(u-a_i)+\ldots\ldots+k_i\,(u-a_i)^n+\ldots\ldots,$$

then

$$\frac{f'\,(a_1)+f'\,(a_2)}{f\,(a_1)-f\,(a_2)}=-\frac{1}{\lambda}\{\phi\,(b_1)+\phi\,(b_2)-p_1-p_2\},$$

the periods being the same for both functions. Verify the theorem when the functions are sn $u$ and sn $(u+v)$.

Prove also that $k_1=(-1)^n\,k_2$.                    (Math. Trip., Part II., 1891.)

**122.** The preceding discussion of uneven doubly-periodic functions having two simple irreducible infinities is a sufficient illustration of the method of procedure. That, which now follows, relates to doubly-periodic functions with one irreducible infinity of the second degree; and it will be used to deduce some of the leading properties of Weierstrass's $\sigma$-function (of § 57) and of functions which arise from it.

The definition of the $\sigma$-function is

$$\sigma(z) = z \prod_{-\infty}^{\infty} \prod_{-\infty}^{\infty} \left\{ \left(1 - \frac{z}{\Omega}\right) e^{\frac{z}{\Omega} + \frac{1}{2}\frac{z^2}{\Omega^2}} \right\},$$

where $\Omega = 2m\omega + 2m'\omega'$, the ratio of $\omega' : \omega$ not being purely real; and the infinite product is extended over all terms that are given by assigning to $m$ and to $m'$ all positive and negative integral values from $+\infty$ to $-\infty$, excepting only simultaneous zero values. It has been proved (and it is easy to verify quite independently) that, when $\sigma(z)$ is regarded as the product of the primary factors

$$\left(1 - \frac{z}{\Omega}\right) e^{\frac{z}{\Omega} + \frac{1}{2}\frac{z^2}{\Omega^2}},$$

the doubly-infinite product converges uniformly and unconditionally for all values of $z$ in the finite part of the plane; therefore the function which it represents can, in the vicinity of any point $c$ in the plane, be expanded in a converging series of positive powers of $z - c$, but the series will only express the function in the domain of $c$. The series, however, can be continued over the whole plane.

It is at once evident that $\sigma(z)$ is not a doubly-periodic function, for it has no infinity in any finite part of the plane.

It is also evident that $\sigma(z)$ is an odd function. For a change of sign in $z$ in a primary factor only interchanges that factor with the one which has equal and opposite values of $m$ and of $m'$, so that the product of the two factors is unaltered. Hence the product of all the primary factors, being independent of the nature of the infinite limits, is an even function; when $z$ is associated as a factor, the function becomes uneven and it is $\sigma(z)$.

The first derivative, $\sigma'(z)$, is therefore an even function; and it is not infinite for any point in the finite part of the plane.

It will appear that, though $\sigma(z)$ is not periodic, it is connected with functions that have $2\omega$ and $2\omega'$ for periods; and therefore the plane will be divided up into parallelograms. When the whole plane is divided up, as in § 105, into parallelograms, the adjacent sides of which are vectorial representations of $2\omega$ and $2\omega'$, the function $\sigma(z)$ has one, and only one, zero in each parallelogram; each such zero is simple, and their aggregate is given by $z = \Omega$. The parallelogram of reference can be chosen so that a zero of

$\sigma(z)$ does not lie upon its boundary; and, except where explicit account is taken of the alternative, we shall assume that the argument of $\omega'$ is greater than the argument of $\omega$, so that the real part* of $\omega'/i\omega$ is positive.

Before proceeding further, it is convenient to establish some propositions relating to series which will be used almost immediately.

We have seen that the series $\Sigma\Omega_{m,m'}^{-3}$, where $\Omega_{m,m'}$ denotes $2m\omega + 2m'\omega'$ for all positive and negative integers $m$ and $m'$ ranging independently from $-\infty$ to $+\infty$ (only the simultaneous zero values being excepted), converges absolutely. Now consider the series

$$\Sigma\frac{1}{(\Omega_{m,m'}-z)^3},$$

for the same range of summation; and assume that $z$ can have any value except a quantity $\Omega_{m,m'}$, when there is obviously an infinite term of order three. From the series, we temporarily exclude all the terms for which

$$|z| \geqslant \tfrac{1}{2}|\Omega_{m,m}|;$$

as $|z|$ is finite, these terms are finite in number and their sum does not affect the convergence of the series.

For all the remaining terms, we have

$$|z| < \tfrac{1}{2}|\Omega|.$$

Now

$$|\Omega - z| > |\Omega| - |z|,$$

so that

$$\frac{|\Omega - z|}{|\Omega|} > 1 - \frac{|z|}{|\Omega|}$$

$$> \tfrac{1}{2}.$$

Hence

$$\frac{1}{|\Omega - z|^3} < 8\,\frac{1}{|\Omega|^3};$$

consequently the series

$$\Sigma\frac{1}{(\Omega - z)^3}$$

converges absolutely for all finite values of $z$ except the isolated values given by $z=\Omega$; and, by Weierstrass's $M$-test†, the same inequality shews that the series converges uniformly.

It is a known property (p. 22) of uniformly converging series that they can be integrated term by term within a finite range and the resulting series will also converge uniformly. Now

$$\int_0^z \frac{dz}{(\Omega - z)^3} = \frac{1}{2}\left\{\frac{1}{(\Omega - z)^2} - \frac{1}{\Omega^2}\right\},$$

choosing the path of integration merely to avoid a possible infinity of the subject of integration—a choice that does not affect the result in this case. Hence dropping the factor $\tfrac{1}{2}$, we see that the series

$$\Sigma\left\{\frac{1}{(\Omega - z)^2} - \frac{1}{\Omega^2}\right\}$$

is a series that converges uniformly for all finite values of $z$, except the isolated values given by $z=\Omega$.

* This quantity is often denoted by $\Re\left(\dfrac{\omega'}{i\omega}\right)$.

† Bromwich, *Theory of Infinite Series*, § 81.

As this series converges uniformly, it also can be integrated term by term within a finite range and the resulting series will also converge uniformly. Now

$$\int_0^z \left\{\frac{1}{(\Omega - z)^2} - \frac{1}{\Omega^2}\right\} dz = \frac{1}{\Omega - z} - \frac{1}{\Omega} - \frac{z}{\Omega^2} ;$$

hence

$$\Sigma \left\{\frac{1}{\Omega} + \frac{z}{\Omega^2} + \frac{1}{z - \Omega}\right\}$$

is a series which converges uniformly for all finite values of $z$, except the isolated values given by $z = \Omega$.

Again integrating within the finite range from 0 to $z$, we have

$$\int_0^z \left\{\frac{1}{\Omega} + \frac{z}{\Omega^2} + \frac{1}{z - \Omega}\right\} dz = \frac{z}{\Omega} + \frac{1}{2}\frac{z^2}{\Omega^2} + \log\left(1 - \frac{z}{\Omega}\right) ;$$

hence

$$\Sigma \left\{\frac{z}{\Omega} + \frac{1}{2}\frac{z^2}{\Omega^2} + \log\left(1 - \frac{z}{\Omega}\right)\right\}$$

is a series which converges uniformly for all finite values of $z$, except the isolated values given by $z = \Omega$.

**123.** We now proceed to obtain other expressions for $\sigma(z)$, and particularly, in the knowledge that it can be represented by a converging series in the vicinity of any point, to obtain a useful expression in the form of a series, converging in the vicinity of the origin.

Since $\sigma(z)$ is represented by an infinite product that converges uniformly and unconditionally for all finite values of $z$, its logarithm is equal to the sum of the logarithms of its factors, so that

$$\log \sigma(z) = \log z + \sum_{-\infty}^{\infty} \sum_{-\infty}^{\infty} \left\{\frac{z}{\Omega} + \frac{1}{2}\frac{z^2}{\Omega^2} + \log\left(1 - \frac{z}{\Omega}\right)\right\},$$

where the series on the right-hand side extends to the same combinations of $m$ and $m'$ as the infinite product for $z$. When it is regarded as a sum of functions $\frac{z}{\Omega} + \frac{1}{2}\frac{z^2}{\Omega^2} + \log\left(1 - \frac{z}{\Omega}\right)$, the series converges uniformly and unconditionally, except for points $z = \Omega$. This expression is valid for $\log \sigma(z)$ over the whole plane.

Now let these additive functions be expanded, as in § 82. In the immediate vicinity of the origin, we have

$$\frac{z}{\Omega} + \frac{1}{2}\frac{z^2}{\Omega^2} + \log\left(1 - \frac{z}{\Omega}\right)$$

$$= -\frac{1}{3}\frac{z^3}{\Omega^3} - \frac{1}{4}\frac{z^4}{\Omega^4} - \frac{1}{5}\frac{z^5}{\Omega^5} - \cdots,$$

a series which by itself converges uniformly and unconditionally in that vicinity. When this expression is substituted in the right-hand side of the foregoing expression for $\log \sigma(z)$, we have a triple series

$$-\sum_{-\infty}^{\infty} \sum_{-\infty}^{\infty} \left\{\sum_{r=3}^{\infty} \frac{1}{r}\frac{z^r}{\Omega^r}\right\}.$$

It is easy to see that this triple series converges uniformly for the values of $z$ considered. As in the lemma at the end of § 122, we omit temporarily all the terms for which $|z| \geqslant \frac{1}{2}|\Omega|$; they are finite in number for finite values of $z$, and their omission does not affect the convergence of the series. Now the modulus of the remainder

$$< \sum_{-\infty}^{\infty} \sum_{-\infty}^{\infty} \sum_{r=3}^{\infty} \frac{1}{r} \frac{|z|^r}{|\Omega|^r}$$

$$< \frac{1}{3} \sum_{-\infty}^{\infty} \sum_{-\infty}^{\infty} \sum_{r=3}^{\infty} \frac{|z|^r}{|\Omega|^r}$$

$$< \frac{1}{3} \sum_{-\infty}^{\infty} \sum_{-\infty}^{\infty} \frac{|z|^3}{|\Omega|^3} \frac{1}{1 - \left|\dfrac{z}{\Omega}\right|}.$$

But for each of these terms $|z| < \frac{1}{2}|\Omega|$; and therefore

$$\frac{1}{1 - \left|\dfrac{z}{\Omega}\right|} < 2,$$

so that the modulus is less than

$$\tfrac{2}{3}|z|^3 \sum_{-\infty}^{\infty} \sum_{-\infty}^{\infty} |\Omega^{-3}|,$$

a finite quantity. Hence the whole triple series converges uniformly and absolutely for the values of $z$ considered; and so we may take it in the form

$$- \sum_{r=3}^{\infty} \frac{z^r}{r} \left\{ \sum_{-\infty}^{\infty} \sum_{-\infty}^{\infty} \Omega^{-r} \right\}.$$

In § 56, it was proved that each of the coefficients

$$\sum_{-\infty}^{\infty} \sum_{-\infty}^{\infty} \Omega^{-r},$$

for $r = 3, 4, \ldots$, is finite, and has a value independent of the nature of the infinite limits in the summation. When we make the positive infinite limit for $m$ numerically equal to the negative infinite limit for $m$, and likewise for $m'$, then each of these coefficients determined by an odd index $r$ vanishes, and therefore it vanishes in general. We then have

$$\log \sigma (z) = \log z - \tfrac{1}{4} z^4 \Sigma\Sigma\Omega^{-4} - \tfrac{1}{6} z^6 \Sigma\Sigma\Omega^{-6} - \tfrac{1}{8} z^8 \Sigma\Sigma\Omega^{-8} - \ldots,$$

a series which converges uniformly and unconditionally in the vicinity of the origin.

The coefficients, which occur, involve $\omega$ and $\omega'$, two independent constants. It is convenient to introduce two other magnitudes, $g_2$ and $g_3$, defined by the equations

$$g_2 = 60\Sigma\Sigma\Omega^{-4}, \quad g_3 = 140\Sigma\Sigma\Omega^{-6},$$

so that $g_2$ and $g_3$ are evidently independent of one another; then all the remaining coefficients are functions* of $g_2$ and $g_3$. We thus have

$$\log \sigma (z) = \log z - \frac{1}{240} g_2 z^4 - \frac{1}{840} g_3 z^6 - \ldots - \frac{1}{2n} z^{2n} \Sigma\Sigma\Omega^{-2n} - \ldots,$$

and therefore                    $\sigma (z) = z e^{-\frac{1}{240} g_2 z^4 - \frac{1}{840} g_3 z^6 - \ldots}$,

where the series in the index, containing only even powers of $z$, converges uniformly and unconditionally in the vicinity of the origin.

It is sufficiently evident that this expression for $\sigma (z)$ is an effective representation only in the vicinity of the origin; for points in the vicinity of any other zero of $\sigma (z)$, say $c$, a similar expression in powers of $z - c$ instead of in powers of $z$ would be obtained.

**124.** From the first form of the expression for $\log \sigma (z)$, we have

$$\frac{\sigma' (z)}{\sigma (z)} = \frac{1}{z} + \sum_{-\infty}^{\infty} \sum_{-\infty}^{\infty} \left( \frac{1}{\Omega} + \frac{z}{\Omega^2} + \frac{1}{z - \Omega} \right),$$

where the quantity in the bracket on the right-hand side is to be regarded as an element of summation, being derived from the primary factor in the product-expression for $\sigma (z)$. We have seen (p. 293) that this double series converges uniformly for the values of $z$ concerned, except of course the isolated values $\Omega$.

We write                    $\zeta (z) = \dfrac{\sigma' (z)}{\sigma (z)}$,

so that $\zeta (z)$ is, by § 122, an odd function, a result also easily derived from the foregoing equation; and so

$$\zeta (z) = \frac{1}{z} + \Sigma\Sigma \left( \frac{1}{\Omega} + \frac{z}{\Omega^2} + \frac{1}{z - \Omega} \right).$$

This expression for $\zeta (z)$ is valid over the whole plane.

Evidently $\zeta (z)$ has simple infinities given by

$$z = \Omega,$$

for all values of $m$ and of $m'$ between $+ \infty$ and $- \infty$, including simultaneous zeros. There is only one infinity in each parallelogram, and it is simple; for the function is the logarithmic derivative of $\sigma (z)$, which has no infinity and only one zero (a simple zero) in the parallelogram. Hence $\zeta (z)$ is not a doubly-periodic function.

For points, which are in the immediate vicinity of the origin, we have

$$\zeta (z) = \frac{d}{dz} \left[ \log z - \frac{1}{240} g_2 z^4 - \frac{1}{840} g_3 z^6 - \ldots - \frac{1}{2n} z^{2n} \Sigma\Sigma\Omega^{-2n} - \ldots \right]$$

$$= \frac{1}{z} - \frac{1}{60} g_2 z^3 - \frac{1}{140} g_3 z^5 - \ldots - z^{2n-1} \Sigma\Sigma\Omega^{-2n} - \ldots;$$

---

* See *Quart. Journ.*, vol. xxii, pp. 4, 5. The magnitudes $g_2$ and $g_3$ are often called the *invariants*.

but, as in the case of $\sigma(z)$, this is an effective representation of $\zeta(z)$ only in the vicinity of the origin; and a different expression would be used for points in the vicinity of any other pole.

We again introduce a new function $\wp(z)$ defined by the equation

$$\wp(z) = -\frac{d\zeta(z)}{dz} = -\frac{d^2}{dz^2}\{\log \sigma(z)\}.$$

Because $\zeta$ is an odd function, $\wp(z)$ is an even function; and

$$\wp(z) = \frac{1}{z^2} - \sum_{-\infty}^{\infty}\sum_{-\infty}^{\infty}\left\{\frac{1}{\Omega^2} - \frac{1}{(z-\Omega)^2}\right\} = \frac{1}{z^2} + \sum_{-\infty}^{\infty}\sum_{-\infty}^{\infty}\left\{\frac{1}{(z-\Omega)^2} - \frac{1}{\Omega^2}\right\},$$

where the quantity in the bracket is to be regarded as an element of summation. We have seen (p. 293) that this double series converges uniformly for the values of $z$ concerned, except of course the isolated values $\Omega$. Thus the expression for $\wp(z)$ is valid over the whole plane. Evidently $\wp(z)$ has infinities, each of the second degree, given by $z = \Omega$, for all values of $m$ and of $m'$ between $+\infty$ and $-\infty$, including simultaneous zeros; and there is one, and only one, of these infinities in each parallelogram. One of these infinities is the origin; using the expression which represents $\log \sigma(z)$ in the immediate vicinity of the origin, we have

$$\wp(z) = -\frac{d^2}{dz^2}\left[\log z - \frac{1}{240}g_2 z^4 - \frac{1}{840}g_3 z^6 - \cdots\right]$$

$$= \frac{1}{z^2} + \frac{1}{20}g_2 z^2 + \frac{1}{28}g_3 z^4 + \cdots + (2n-1)z^{2n-2}\Sigma\Sigma\Omega^{-2n} + \cdots,$$

for points $z$ in the immediate vicinity of the origin.

A corresponding expression exists for $\wp(z)$ in the vicinity of any other pole.

**125.** The importance of this function $\wp(z)$ lies in its periodic character; and the importance of the functions $\sigma(z)$ and $\zeta(z)$ partly lies in their pseudo-periodic character. To establish the necessary properties, we use the derivative of $\wp(z)$; we differentiate term by term the series in the expression

$$\wp(z) = \frac{1}{z^2} + \sum_{-\infty}^{\infty}\sum_{-\infty}^{\infty}\left\{\frac{1}{(z-\Omega)^2} - \frac{1}{\Omega^2}\right\},$$

and we have

$$\wp'(z) = -\frac{2}{z^3} - 2\sum_{-\infty}^{\infty}\sum_{-\infty}^{\infty}{}'\frac{1}{(z-\Omega)^3}$$

$$= -2\sum_{-\infty}^{\infty}\sum_{-\infty}^{\infty}\frac{1}{(z-\Omega)^3},$$

where the double summation no longer excludes the simultaneous zero values of $m$ and $m'$ in the expression of $\Omega$. The series on the right-hand side converges uniformly and absolutely (p. 292) for all values of $z$ except the isolated places given by $z = \Omega$; and so this expression for $\wp'(z)$ is valid over the whole plane.

Evidently $\wp'(z)$ has infinities, each of the third degree, given by $z = \Omega$ for all values of $m$ and $m'$ within the range from $+\infty$ to $-\infty$, including the simultaneous zero values; and there is one, and only one, of these infinities within each parallelogram. Using the expression for $\wp(z)$ in the vicinity of $z = 0$, we have

$$\wp' = \wp'(z) = -\frac{2}{z^3} + \frac{1}{10} g_2 z + \frac{1}{7} g_3 z^3 + \ldots.$$

Clearly $\wp'$ is an odd function of $z$.

The periodicity of $\wp'(z)$ can be deduced at once. We have

$$\wp'(z) = -2\Sigma\Sigma \frac{1}{(z - \Omega)^3} = -2\Sigma\Sigma \frac{1}{(z - 2m\omega - 2m'\omega')^3};$$

and therefore

$$\wp'(z + 2\omega) = -2\Sigma\Sigma \frac{1}{\{z - 2(m-1)\omega - 2m'\omega'\}^3}.$$

Now the series $\Sigma\Sigma(z - \Omega)^{-3}$ converges absolutely; and so (p. 21) its sum does not depend upon the order in which the terms are taken. The series in $\wp'(z + 2\omega)$ differs from the series in $\wp'(z)$ merely in taking the terms in the order of values of $m - 1$ from $-\infty$ to $+\infty$ instead of the terms in the order of values of $m$ from $-\infty$ to $+\infty$; this negative unit derangement in the summation for $m$ is permissible under the convergence; and so we have

$$\wp'(z + 2\omega) = \wp'(z).$$

Similarly we have

$$\wp'(z + 2\omega') = \wp(z),$$

equations which shew the double periodicity of $\wp'(z)$. Further, we have

$$\wp'(z + 2\omega + 2\omega') = \wp'(z + 2\omega') = \wp'(z);$$

or writing

$$\omega'' = \omega + \omega',$$

we have

$$\wp'(z + 2\omega'') = \wp'(z).$$

Integrating these equations respectively, we have

$$\wp(z + 2\omega) = \wp(z) + A, \qquad \wp(z + 2\omega') = \wp(z) + B,$$

where $A$ and $B$ are constants. To determine these constants, take $z = -\omega$ in the former equation and $z = -\omega'$ in the latter; we have

$$\wp(\omega) = \wp(-\omega) + A, \qquad \wp(\omega') = \wp(-\omega') + B.$$

Neither $\omega$ nor $\omega'$ is a pole of $\wp(z)$, for the isolated poles of $\wp(z)$ are given by $z = 2m\omega + 2m'\omega'$, for integer values of $m$ and $m'$; and $\wp(z)$ is an even function. Thus $A = 0$, $B = 0$; and so we have

$$\wp(z + 2\omega) = \wp(z), \qquad \wp(z + 2\omega') = \wp(z),$$

and therefore also

$$\wp(z + 2\omega'') = \wp(z),$$

equations which shew the double periodicity of $\wp(z)$.

The poles of $\wp(z)$ are given by $z = \Omega$, and each is of order 2. Thus in any parallelogram whose adjacent sides are $2\omega$ and $2\omega'$, there is one (and there is only one) pole, and it is of order 2. Hence by § 116, Prop. III., Cor. 3, $2\omega$ and $2\omega'$ determine a primitive parallelogram for $\wp(z)$. Consequently our function $\wp(z)$ is of the first class and the second order.

We shall assume that the parallelogram of reference is so chosen as to include the origin in its interior.

**126.** In the preceding chapter, we have seen (§ 119) that there exists an algebraical relation between $\wp(z)$ and $\wp'(z)$. Owing to the order of $\wp(z)$, this must have the form

$$\wp'^2(z) = A\wp^3(z) + B\wp^2(z) + C\wp(z) + D,$$

where $A$, $B$, $C$, $D$ are constants.

The only irreducible infinity of $\wp'(z)$ is of the third order, being the origin; and the function $\wp'(z)$ is odd. As

$$\wp'(z + 2\omega) = \wp'(z) = \wp'(z + 2\omega') = \wp'(z + 2\omega''),$$

we have

$$\wp'(\omega) = -\wp'(\omega), \qquad \wp'(\omega') = -\wp'(\omega'), \qquad \wp'(\omega'') = -\wp'(\omega''),$$

so that the irreducible zeros of $\wp'(z)$ are $\omega$, $\omega'$, $\omega''$. We write

$$\wp(\omega) = e_1, \qquad \wp(\omega'') = e_2, \qquad \wp(\omega') = e_3, \qquad \wp(z) = \wp, \qquad \wp'(z) = \wp';$$

and then the foregoing relation becomes

$$\wp'^2 = A\ (\wp - e_1)(\wp - e_2)(\wp - e_3),$$

where $A$ is some constant. To determine the equation more exactly, we substitute the expression of $\wp$ in the vicinity of the origin. Then

$$\wp = \frac{1}{z^2} + \frac{1}{20} g_2 z^2 + \frac{1}{28} g_3 z^4 + \cdots$$

so that

$$\wp' = -\frac{2}{z^3} + \frac{1}{10} g_2 z + \frac{1}{7} g_3 z^3 + \cdots.$$

When substitution is made, it is necessary to retain in the expansion all terms up to $z^0$ inclusive. We then have, for $\wp'^2$, the expression

$$\frac{4}{z^6} - \frac{2}{5} \frac{g_2}{z^2} - \frac{4}{7} g_3 + \cdots;$$

and for $A\ (\wp - e_1)(\wp - e_2)(\wp - e_3)$, the expression

$$A \left[ \frac{1}{z^6} + \frac{3}{20} \frac{g_2}{z^2} + \frac{3}{28} g_3 + \cdots \right.$$
$$\left. - (e_1 + e_2 + e_3) \left( \frac{1}{z^4} + \frac{1}{10} g_2 + \cdots \right) + (e_1 e_2 + e_2 e_3 + e_3 e_1) \left( \frac{1}{z^2} + \cdots \right) - e_1 e_2 e_3 \right].$$

When we equate coefficients in these two expressions, we find

$$A = 4,$$

$$e_1 + e_2 + e_3 = 0, \qquad e_1 e_2 + e_2 e_3 + e_3 e_1 = -\tfrac{1}{4} g_2, \qquad e_1 e_2 e_3 = \tfrac{1}{4} g_3;$$

therefore the differential equation satisfied by $\wp$ is

$$\wp'^2 = 4 (\wp - e_1)(\wp - e_2)(\wp - e_3)$$
$$= 4\wp^3 - g_2\wp - g_3.$$

Evidently
$$\wp'' = 6\wp^2 - \tfrac{1}{2}g_2,$$
$$\wp''' = 12\wp\wp',$$

and so on; it is easy to verify that the $2n$th derivative of $\wp$ is a rational integral function of $\wp$ of degree $n + 1$, and that the $(2n + 1)$th derivative of $\wp$ is the product of $\wp'$ by a rational integral function of $\wp$ of degree $n$.

The differential equation can be otherwise obtained, by dependence on Cor. 2, Prop. V. of § 116. We have, by differentiation of $\wp'$,

$$\wp'' = \frac{6}{z^4} + \frac{1}{10} g_2 + \frac{3}{7} g_3 z^2 + \dots$$

for points in the vicinity of the origin; and also

$$\wp^2 = \frac{1}{z^4} + \frac{1}{10} g_2 + \frac{1}{14} g_3 z^2 + \dots.$$

Hence $\wp''$ and $\wp^2$ have the same irreducible infinities in the same degree and their fractional parts are essentially the same: they are homoperiodic and therefore they are equivalent to one another. It is easy to see that $\wp'' - 6\wp^2$ is equal to a function which, being finite in the vicinity of the origin, is finite in the parallelogram of reference and therefore, as it is doubly-periodic, is finite over the whole plane. It therefore has a constant value, which can be obtained by taking the value at any point; the value of the function for $z = 0$ is $-\tfrac{1}{2}g_2$ and therefore

$$\wp'' - 6\wp^2 = -\tfrac{1}{2}g_2,$$

so that
$$\wp'' = 6\wp^2 - \tfrac{1}{2}g_2,$$

the integration of which, with determination of the constant of integration, leads to the former equation.

This form, involving the second derivative, is a convenient one by which to determine a few more terms of the expansion in the vicinity of the origin: and it is easy to shew that

$$\wp = \frac{1}{z^2} + \frac{1}{20} g_2 z^2 + \frac{1}{28} g_3 z^4 + \frac{1}{1200} g_2^2 z^6 + \frac{1}{6160} g_2 g_3 z^8 + \dots,$$

from which some theorems relating to the sums $\Sigma\Sigma\Omega^{-2n}$ can be deduced*.

*Ex.* If $c_n$ be the coefficient of $z^{2n-2}$ in the expansion of $\wp(z)$ in the vicinity of the origin, then

$$c_n = \frac{3}{(2n+1)(n-3)} \sum_{r=2}^{r=n-2} c_r c_{n-r}. \qquad \text{(Weierstrass.)}$$

* See a paper by the author, *Quart. Journ.*, vol. xxii, (1887), pp. 1—43, where other references are given and other applications of the general theorems are made.

We have $$\wp'^2 = 4\wp^3 - g_2\wp - g_3;$$

the function $\wp'$ is odd, and in the vicinity of the origin we have

$$\wp' = -\frac{2}{z^3} + \dots;$$

hence, representing by $-(4\wp^3 - g_2\wp - g_3)^{\frac{1}{2}}$ that branch of the function which is negative for large real values, we have

$$\frac{d\wp}{dz} = -(4\wp^3 - g_2\wp - g_3)^{\frac{1}{2}},$$

and therefore

$$z = \int_\wp \frac{d\wp}{(4\wp^3 - g_2\wp - g_3)^{\frac{1}{2}}}.$$

The upper limit is determined by the fact that when $z = 0$, $\wp = \infty$; so that

$$z = \int_\wp^\infty \frac{d\wp}{(4\wp^3 - g_2\wp - g_3)^{\frac{1}{2}}}$$

$$= \int_\wp^\infty \frac{d\wp}{\{4(\wp - e_1)(\wp - e_2)(\wp - e_3)\}^{\frac{1}{2}}}.$$

This is, as it should be, an integral with a doubly-infinite series of values. We have, by Ex. 7 of § 104,

$$\omega_1 = \omega \ = \int_{e_1}^\infty \frac{d\wp}{(4\wp^3 - g_2\wp - g_3)^{\frac{1}{2}}},$$

$$\omega_2 = \omega'' = \int_{e_2}^\infty \frac{d\wp}{(4\wp^3 - g_2\wp - g_3)^{\frac{1}{2}}},$$

$$\omega_3 = \omega' \ = \int_{e_3}^\infty \frac{d\wp}{(4\wp^3 - g_2\wp - g_3)^{\frac{1}{2}}},$$

with the relation $$\omega'' = \omega + \omega'.$$

**127.** We have seen (§ 125) that $\wp(z)$ is doubly-periodic, so that

$$\wp(z + 2\omega) = \wp(z),$$

and therefore

$$\frac{d\zeta(z + 2\omega)}{dz} = \frac{d\zeta(z)}{dz};$$

hence integrating

$$\zeta(z + 2\omega) = \zeta(z) + A.$$

Now $\zeta$ is an odd function; hence, taking $z = -\omega$ which is not an infinity of $\zeta$, we have

$$A = 2\zeta(\omega) = 2\eta$$

say, where $\eta$ denotes $\zeta(\omega)$; and therefore

$$\zeta(z + 2\omega) - \zeta(z) = 2\eta,$$

which is a constant.

Similarly $$\zeta(z + 2\omega') - \zeta(z) = 2\eta',$$

where $\eta' = \zeta(\omega')$ and is constant.

Similarly
$$\zeta(z + 2\omega'') - \zeta(z) = 2\eta'',$$
where $\eta'' = \zeta(\omega'')$ and is constant. Moreover,
$$\zeta(z + 2\omega'') = \zeta(z + 2\omega + 2\omega')$$
$$= \zeta(z + 2\omega) + 2\eta'$$
$$= \zeta(z) + 2\eta + 2\eta',$$
and therefore
$$\eta'' = \eta + \eta',$$
a relation which merely expresses $\zeta(\omega + \omega')$ as the sum of $\zeta(\omega)$ and $\zeta(\omega')$.

Combining the results, we have
$$\zeta(z + 2m\omega + 2m'\omega') - \zeta(z) = 2m\eta + 2m'\eta',$$
where $m$ and $m'$ are any integers.

It is evident that $\eta$ and $\eta'$ cannot be absorbed into $\zeta$; so that $\zeta$ is not a periodic function, a result confirmatory of the statement in § 124.

There is, however, a *pseudo-periodicity* of the function $\zeta$: its characteristic is the reproduction of the function with an added constant for an added period. This form is only one of several simple forms of pseudo-periodicity which will be considered in the next chapter.

**128.** But, though $\zeta(z)$ is not periodic, functions which are periodic can be constructed by its means.

Thus, if $\quad \phi(z) = A\,\zeta(z - a) + B\,\zeta(z - b) + C\,\zeta(z - c) + \ldots,$

then $\quad \phi(z + 2\omega) - \phi(z) = \Sigma A\,\{\zeta(z - a + 2\omega) - \zeta(z - a)\}$
$$= 2\eta\,(A + B + C + \ldots),$$
and $\quad \phi(z + 2\omega') - \phi(z) = 2\eta'\,(A + B + C + \ldots),$

so that, subject to the condition
$$A + B + C + \ldots = 0,$$
$\phi(z)$ is a doubly-periodic function.

Again, we know that, within the fundamental parallelogram, $\zeta$ has a single irreducible infinity and that the infinity is simple; hence the irreducible infinities of the function $\phi(z)$ are $z = a, b, c, \ldots$, and each is a simple infinity. The condition $A + B + C + \ldots = 0$ is merely the condition of Prop. III., § 116, that the 'integral residue' of the function is zero.

Conversely, a doubly-periodic function with $m$ assigned infinities can be expressed in terms of $\zeta$ and its derivatives. Let $a_1$ be an irreducible infinity of $\Phi$ of degree $n$, and suppose that the fractional part of $\Phi$ for expansion in the immediate vicinity of $a_1$ is
$$\frac{A_1}{z - a_1} + \frac{B_1}{(z - a_1)^2} + \ldots + \frac{K_1}{(z - a_1)^n}.$$

Then

$$\Phi(z) - \left[ A_1 \zeta(z-a_1) - B_1 \zeta'(z-a_1) + \frac{C_1}{2\,!}\,\zeta''(z-a_1) - \ldots \right.$$

$$\left. + (-1)^n \frac{K_1}{(n-1)\,!} \frac{d^{n-1}}{dz^{n-1}} \zeta(z-a_1) \right]$$

is not infinite for $z = a_1$.

Proceeding similarly for each of the irreducible infinities, we have a function

$$\Phi(z) - \sum_{r=1}^{m} \left[ A_r \zeta(z-a_r) - B_r \zeta'(z-a_r) + \frac{C_r}{2\,!}\,\zeta''(z-a_r) - \ldots \right],$$

which is not infinite for any of the points $z = a_1, a_2, \ldots$. But because $\Phi(z)$ is doubly-periodic, we have

$$A_1 + A_2 + \ldots + A_n = 0,$$

and therefore the function

$$\sum_{r=1}^{m} A_r \zeta(z-a_r)$$

is doubly-periodic. Moreover, all the derivatives of any order of each of the functions $\zeta$ are doubly-periodic; hence the foregoing function is doubly-periodic.

The function has been shewn to be not infinite at the points $a_1, a_2, \ldots$, and therefore it has no infinities in the fundamental parallelogram; consequently, being doubly-periodic, it has no infinities in the plane and it is a constant, say $C$. Hence we have

$$\Phi(z) = C + \sum_{r=1}^{m} A_r \zeta(z-a_r) - \sum_{r=1}^{m} B_r \frac{d\zeta(z-a_r)}{dz} + \frac{1}{2\,!} \sum_{r=1}^{m} C_r \frac{d^2\zeta(z-a_r)}{dz^2} - \ldots,$$

with the condition $\sum_{r=1}^{m} A_r = 0$, which is satisfied because $\Phi(z)$ is doubly-periodic.

This is the required expression* for $\Phi(z)$ in terms of the function $\zeta$ and its derivatives; it is evidently of especial importance when the indefinite integral of a doubly-periodic function is required.

**129.** Constants $\eta$ and $\eta'$, connected with $\omega$ and $\omega'$, have been introduced by the pseudo-periodicity of $\zeta(z)$; the relation, contained in the following proposition, is necessary and useful:—

*The constants $\eta$, $\eta'$, $\omega$, $\omega'$ are connected by the relation*

$$\eta\omega' - \eta'\omega = \pm \tfrac{1}{2}\pi i,$$

*the* + *or* − *sign being taken according as the real part of $\omega'/\omega i$ is positive or negative.*

* See Hermite, *Ann. de Toulouse*, t. ii, (1888), C, pp. 1—12.

A fundamental parallelogram having an angular point at $z_0$ is either of the form (i) in fig. 34, in which case $\Re\left(\dfrac{\omega'}{\omega i}\right)$ is positive; or of the form (ii), in which case $\Re\left(\dfrac{\omega'}{\omega i}\right)$ is negative.   Evidently a description of the parallelogram $ABCD$ in (i) will give for an integral the same result (but with an opposite sign) as a description of the parallelogram in (ii) for the same integral in the direction $ABCD$ in that figure.

We choose the fundamental parallelogram, so that it may contain the origin in the included area.   The origin is the only infinity of $\zeta$ which can lie within the area: along the boundary $\zeta$ is always finite.

Now since

$$\zeta(z + 2\omega) - \zeta(z) = 2\eta,$$
$$\zeta(z + 2\omega') - \zeta(z) = 2\eta',$$

the integral of $\zeta(z)$ round $ABCD$ in (i), fig. 34, is (§ 116, Prop. II., Cor.)

$$\int_A^D 2\eta\,dz - \int_A^B 2\eta'\,dz,$$

the integrals being along the lines $AD$ and $AB$ respectively, that is, the integral is

$$4\,(\eta\omega' - \eta'\omega).$$

But as the origin is the only infinity within the parallelogram, the path of integration $ABCDA$ can be deformed so as to be merely a small curve round the origin.   In the vicinity of the origin, we have

$$\zeta(z) = \frac{1}{z} - \frac{1}{60}\,g_2 z^3 - \frac{1}{140}\,g_3 z^5 - \dots,$$

and therefore, as the integrals of all terms except the first vanish when taken round this curve, we have

$$\int \zeta(z)\,dz = \int \frac{dz}{z}$$

$$= 2\pi i.$$

Hence                          $4\,(\eta\omega' - \eta'\omega) = 2\pi i,$

and therefore                  $\eta\omega' - \eta'\omega = \tfrac{1}{2}\pi i.$

This is the result as derived from (i), fig. 34, that is, when $\Re\left(\dfrac{\omega'}{i\omega}\right)$ is positive.

When (ii), fig. 34, is taken account of, the result is the same except that, when the circuit passes from $z_0$ to $z_0 + 2\omega$, then to $z_0 + 2\omega + 2\omega'$, then to $z_0 + 2\omega'$ and then to $z_0$, it passes in the negative direction round the parallelogram. The value of the integral along the path $ABCDA$ is the same as before, viz., $4(\eta\omega' - \eta'\omega)$; when the path is deformed into a small curve round the origin, the value of the integral is $\int \dfrac{dz}{z}$ taken negatively, and therefore it is $-2\pi i$: hence

$$\eta\omega' - \eta'\omega = -\tfrac{1}{2}\pi i.$$

Combining the results, we have

$$\eta\omega' - \eta'\omega = \pm \tfrac{1}{2}\pi i,$$

according as $\Re\left(\dfrac{\omega'}{\omega i}\right)$ is positive or negative.

COROLLARY. If there be a change to any other fundamental parallelogram, determined by $2\Omega$ and $2\Omega'$, where

$$\Omega = p\omega + q\omega', \qquad \Omega' = p'\omega + q'\omega',$$

$p, q, p', q'$ being integers such that $pq' - p'q = \pm 1$, and if $H, H'$ denote $\zeta(\Omega)$, $\zeta(\Omega')$, then

$$H = p\eta + q\eta', \qquad H' = p'\eta + q'\eta';$$

therefore

$$H\Omega' - H'\Omega = \pm \tfrac{1}{2}\pi i,$$

according as the real part of $\dfrac{\Omega'}{i\Omega}$ is positive or negative.

**130.** It has been seen that $\zeta(z)$ is pseudo-periodic; there is also a pseudo-periodicity for $\sigma(z)$, but of a different kind. We have

$$\zeta(z + 2\omega) = \zeta(z) + 2\eta,$$

that is,

$$\frac{\sigma'(z + 2\omega)}{\sigma(z + 2\omega)} = \frac{\sigma'(z)}{\sigma(z)} + 2\eta,$$

and therefore

$$\sigma(z + 2\omega) = A e^{2\eta z}\, \sigma(z),$$

where $A$ is a constant. To determine $A$, we make $z = -\omega$, which is not a zero or an infinity of $\sigma(z)$; then, since $\sigma(z)$ is an odd function, we have

$$-A e^{-2\eta\omega} = 1,$$

so that

$$\sigma(z + 2\omega) = -e^{2\eta(z+\omega)}\, \sigma(z).$$

Hence

$$\sigma(z + 4\omega) = -e^{2\eta(z+3\omega)}\, \sigma(z + 2\omega)$$

$$= e^{2\eta(2z+4\omega)}\, \sigma(z);$$

and similarly

$$\sigma(z + 2m\omega) = (-1)^m\, e^{2\eta(mz+m^2\omega)}\, \sigma(z).$$

Proceeding in the same way from

$$\zeta(z + 2\omega') = \zeta(z) + 2\eta',$$

we find

$$\sigma(z + 2m'\omega') = (-1)^{m'}\, e^{2\eta'(m'z+m'^2\omega')}\, \sigma(z).$$

Then

$$\sigma(z + 2m\omega + 2m'\omega') = (-1)^m\, e^{2\eta(mz+m^2\omega+2mm'\omega')}\, \sigma(z + 2m'\omega')$$

$$= (-1)^{m+m'}\, e^{2z(m\eta+m'\eta')+2\eta m^2\omega+4\eta mm'\omega'+2\eta'm'^2\omega'}\, \sigma(z)$$

$$= (-1)^{m+m'}\, e^{2(m\eta+m'\eta')(z+m\omega+m'\omega')+2mm'(\eta\omega'-\eta'\omega)}\, \sigma(z).$$

But
$$\eta\omega' - \eta'\omega = \pm \tfrac{1}{2}\pi i,$$
so that
$$e^{2mm'(\eta\omega'-\eta'\omega)} = e^{\pm mm'\pi i} = (-1)^{mm'};$$
and therefore
$$\sigma(z + 2m\omega + 2m'\omega') = (-1)^{mm'+m+m'} e^{2(m\eta+m'\eta')(z+m\omega+m'\omega')} \sigma(z),$$
which is the law of change of $\sigma(z)$ for increase of $z$ by integral multiples of the periods.

Evidently $\sigma(z)$ is not a periodic function, a result confirmatory of the statement in § 122. But there is a pseudo-periodicity the characteristic of which is the reproduction, for an added period, of the function with an exponential factor, the index being linear in the variable. This is another of the forms of pseudo-periodicity which will be considered in the next chapter.

**131.** But though $\sigma(z)$ is not periodic, we can by its means construct functions which are periodic in the pseudo-periods of $\sigma(z)$.

By the result in the last section, we have
$$\frac{\sigma(z - \alpha + 2m\omega + 2m'\omega')}{\sigma(z - \beta + 2m\omega + 2m'\omega')} = \frac{\sigma(z - \alpha)}{\sigma(z-\beta)} e^{2(m\eta+m'\eta')(\beta-\alpha)};$$
and therefore, if $\phi(z)$ denote
$$\frac{\sigma(z-\alpha_1)\,\sigma(z-\alpha_2)\,\ldots\ldots\,\sigma(z-\alpha_n)}{\sigma(z-\beta_1)\,\sigma(z-\beta_2)\,\ldots\ldots\,\sigma(z-\beta_n)},$$
then
$$\phi(z + 2m\omega + 2m'\omega') = e^{2(m\eta+m'\eta')(\Sigma\beta_r-\Sigma\alpha_r)} \phi(z),$$
so that $\phi(z)$ is doubly-periodic in $2\omega$ and $2\omega'$ provided
$$\Sigma\beta_r - \Sigma\alpha_r = 0.$$

Now the zeros of $\phi(z)$, regarded as a product of $\sigma$-functions, are $\alpha_1, \alpha_2, \ldots, \alpha_n$ and the points homologous with them; and the infinities are $\beta_1, \beta_2, \ldots, \beta_n$ and the points homologous with them. It may happen that not all the points $\alpha$ and $\beta$ are in the parallelogram of reference; if the irreducible points homologous with them be $a_1, \ldots, a_n$ and $b_1, \ldots, b_n$, then
$$\Sigma a_r \equiv \Sigma b_r \,(\text{mod. } 2\omega, 2\omega'),$$
and the new points are the irreducible zeros and the irreducible infinities of $\phi(z)$. This result, we know from Prop. III., § 116, must be satisfied.

It is naturally assumed that no one of the points $\alpha$ is the same as, or is homologous with, any one of the points $\beta$: the order of the doubly-periodic function would otherwise be diminished by 1.

If any $\alpha$ be repeated, then that point is a repeated zero of $\phi(z)$; similarly if any $\beta$ be repeated, then that point is a repeated infinity of $\phi(z)$. In every case, the sum of the irreducible zeros must be congruent with the sum of the irreducible infinities in order that the above expression for $\phi(z)$ may be doubly-periodic.

Conversely, if a doubly-periodic function $\phi(z)$ be required with $m$ assigned irreducible zeros $a$ and $m$ assigned irreducible infinities $b$, which are subject to the congruence

$$\Sigma a \equiv \Sigma b \ (\text{mod. } 2\omega, 2\omega'),$$

we first find points $\alpha$ and $\beta$ homologous with $a$ and with $b$ respectively such that

$$\Sigma \alpha = \Sigma \beta.$$

Then the function $\dfrac{\sigma(z-\alpha_1)\ \ldots\ldots\ \sigma(z-\alpha_m)}{\sigma(z-\beta_1)\ \ldots\ldots\ \sigma(z-\beta_m)}$

has the same zeros and the same infinities as $\phi(z)$, and is homoperiodic with it; and therefore, by § 116, IV.,

$$\phi(z) = A\frac{\sigma(z-\alpha_1)\ \ldots\ldots\ \sigma(z-\alpha_m)}{\sigma(z-\beta_1)\ \ldots\ldots\ \sigma(z-\beta_m)},$$

where $A$ is a quantity independent of $z$.

*Ex.* 1. Consider $\wp'(z)$. It has the origin for an infinity of the third degree and all the remaining infinities are reducible to the origin; and its three irreducible zeros are $\omega, \omega', \omega''$. Moreover, since $\omega'' = \omega' + \omega$, we have $\omega + \omega' + \omega''$ congruent with but not equal to zero. We therefore choose other points so that the sum of the zeros may be actually the same as the sum of the infinities, which is zero; the simplest choice is to take $\omega, \omega', -\omega''$. Hence

$$\wp'(z) = A\frac{\sigma(z-\omega)\sigma(z-\omega')\sigma(z+\omega'')}{\sigma^3(z)},$$

where $A$ is a constant. To determine $A$, consider the expansions in the immediate vicinity of the origin; then

$$-\frac{2}{z^3} + \ldots\ldots = A\frac{\sigma(-\omega)\sigma(-\omega')\sigma(\omega'')}{z^3} + \ldots\ldots,$$

so that $\qquad \wp'(z) = -2\dfrac{\sigma(z-\omega)\sigma(z-\omega')\sigma(z+\omega'')}{\sigma(\omega)\sigma(\omega')\sigma(\omega'')\sigma^3(z)}.$

Another method of arranging zeros, so that their sum is equal to that of the infinities, is to take $-\omega, -\omega', \omega''$; and then we should find

$$\wp'(z) = 2\frac{\sigma(z+\omega)\sigma(z+\omega')\sigma(z-\omega'')}{\sigma(\omega)\sigma(\omega')\sigma(\omega'')\sigma^3(z)}.$$

This result can, however, be deduced from the preceding form merely by changing the sign of $z$.

*Ex.* 2. Consider the function

$$A\frac{\sigma(u+v)\sigma(u-v)}{\sigma^2(u)},$$

where $v$ is any quantity and $A$ is independent of $u$. It is, quà function of $u$, doubly-periodic; and it has $u=0$ as an infinity of the second degree, all the infinities being homologous with the origin. Hence the function is homoperiodic with $\wp(u)$ and it has the same infinities as $\wp(u)$: thus the two are equivalent, so that

$$A\frac{\sigma(u+v)\sigma(u-v)}{\sigma^2(u)} = B\wp(u) - C,$$

where $B$ and $C$ are independent of $u$. The left-hand side vanishes if $u=v$; hence $C=B\wp(v)$, and therefore

$$A'\frac{\sigma(u+v)\,\sigma(u-v)}{\sigma^2(u)}=\wp(u)-\wp(v),$$

where $A'$ is a new quantity independent of $u$. To determine $A'$ we consider the expansions in the vicinity of $u=0$; we have

$$\frac{A'\sigma(v)\,\sigma(-v)}{u^2}+\cdots\cdots=\frac{1}{u^2}+\cdots\cdots,$$

so that                                     $-A'\sigma^2(v)=1,$

and therefore           $\dfrac{\sigma(u+v)\,\sigma(u-v)}{\sigma^2(u)\,\sigma^2(v)}=\wp(v)-\wp(u),$

a formula of very great importance.

*Ex.* 3.  Taking logarithmic derivatives with regard to $u$ of the two sides of the last equation, we have

$$\zeta(u+v)+\zeta(u-v)-2\zeta(u)=-\frac{\wp'(u)}{\wp(v)-\wp(u)};$$

and, similarly, taking them with regard to $v$, we have

$$\zeta(u+v)-\zeta(u-v)-2\zeta(v)=\frac{\wp'(v)}{\wp(v)-\wp(u)};$$

whence           $\zeta(u+v)-\zeta(u)-\zeta(v)=\frac{1}{2}\dfrac{\wp'(v)-\wp'(u)}{\wp(v)-\wp(u)},$

giving the special value of the left-hand side as (§ 128) a doubly-periodic function.  It is also the addition-theorem, so far as there is an addition-theorem, for the $\zeta$-function.

*Ex.* 4.  We can, by differentiation, at once deduce the addition-theorem for $\wp(u+v)$. Evidently

$$\wp(u+v)=\wp(u)-\frac{1}{2}\frac{d}{du}\left\{\frac{\wp'(v)-\wp'(u)}{\wp(v)-\wp(u)}\right\},$$

which is only one of many forms: one of the most useful is

$$\wp(u+v)=-\wp(u)-\wp(v)+\frac{1}{4}\left\{\frac{\wp'(u)-\wp'(v)}{\wp(u)-\wp(v)}\right\}^2,$$

which can be deduced from the preceding form.

The result can be used to modify the expression for a general doubly-periodic function $\Phi(z)$ obtained in § 128.   We have

$$\sum_{r=1}^{m}A_r\zeta(z-a_r)=\sum_{r=1}^{m}A_r\left\{\zeta(z)-\zeta(a_r)-\frac{1}{2}\frac{\wp'(a_r)+\wp'(z)}{\wp(a_r)-\wp(z)}\right\}$$

$$=\left(\sum_{r=1}^{m}A_r\right)\zeta(z)-\sum_{r=1}^{m}A_r\zeta(a_r)+\frac{1}{2}\sum_{r=1}^{m}A_r\frac{\wp'(z)+\wp'(a_r)}{\wp(z)-\wp(a_r)}$$

$$=-\sum_{r=1}^{m}A_r\zeta(a_r)+\frac{1}{2}\sum_{r=1}^{m}A_r\frac{\wp'(z)+\wp'(a_r)}{\wp(z)-\wp(a_r)}.$$

Each derivative of $\zeta$ can be expressed either as a polynomial function of $\wp(z-a_r)$ or as the product of $\wp'(z-a_r)$ by such a function; and by the use of the addition-theorem, these can be expressed in the form

$$\frac{M+N\wp'(z)}{L},$$

where $L$, $M$, $N$ are rational integral functions of $\wp(z)$. Hence the function $\Phi(z)$ can be expressed in the same form. The simplest case arises when all its infinities are simple, and then

$$\Phi(z) = C + \sum_{r=1}^{m} A_r \zeta(z-a_r)$$

$$= C - \sum_{r=1}^{m} A_r \zeta(a_r) + \tfrac{1}{2} \sum_{r=1}^{m} A_r \frac{\wp'(z) + \wp'(a_r)}{\wp(z) - \wp(a_r)}$$

$$= B + \tfrac{1}{2} \sum_{r=1}^{m} A_r \frac{\wp'(z) + \wp'(a_r)}{\wp(z) - \wp(a_r)},$$

with the condition $\sum_{r=1}^{m} A_r = 0$.

*Ex.* 5. The function $\wp(z) - e_1$ is an even function, doubly-periodic in $2\omega$ and $2\omega'$ and having $z = 0$ for an infinity of the second degree; it has only a single infinity of the second degree in a fundamental parallelogram.

Again, $z = \omega$ is a zero of the function; and, since $\wp'(\omega) = 0$ but $\wp''(\omega)$ is not zero, $z = \omega$ is a double zero of $\wp(z) - e_1$. All the zeros are therefore reducible to $z = \omega$; and the function has only a single zero of the second degree in a fundamental parallelogram.

Taking then the parallelogram of reference so as to include the points $z = 0$ and $z = \omega$, we have

$$\wp(z) - e_1 = \frac{(z-\omega)^2}{z^2} Q(z),$$

where $Q(z)$ has no zero and no infinity for points within the parallelogram.

Again, for $\wp(z+\omega) - e_1$, the irreducible zero of the second degree within the parallelogram is given by $z + \omega \equiv \omega$, that is, it is $z = 0$; and the irreducible infinity of the second degree within the parallelogram is given by $z + \omega \equiv 0$, that is, it is $z = \omega$. Hence we have

$$\wp(z+\omega) - e_1 = \frac{z^2}{(z-\omega)^2} Q_1(z),$$

where $Q_1(z)$ has no zero and no infinity for points within the parallelogram.

Hence              $\{\wp(z) - e_1\}\{\wp(z+\omega) - e_1\} = Q(z) Q_1(z)$;

that is, the function on the left-hand side has no zero and no infinity for points within the parallelogram of reference. Being doubly-periodic, it therefore has no zero and no infinity anywhere in the plane; it consequently is a constant, which is the value for any point. Taking the special value $z = \omega'$, we have $\wp(\omega') = e_3$, and $\wp(\omega' + \omega) = e_2$; and therefore

$$\{\wp(z) - e_1\}\{\wp(z+\omega) - e_1\} = (e_3 - e_1)(e_2 - e_1).$$

Similarly              $\{\wp(z) - e_2\}\{\wp(z+\omega'') - e_2\} = (e_1 - e_2)(e_3 - e_2),$

and              $\{\wp(z) - e_3\}\{\wp(z+\omega') - e_3\} = (e_2 - e_3)(e_1 - e_3).$

It is possible to derive at once from these equations the values of the $\wp$-function for the quarter-periods.

*Note.* In the preceding chapter some theorems were given which indicated that functions, which are doubly-periodic in the same periods, can be expressed in terms of one another: in particular cases, care has occasionally to be exercised to be certain that the periods of the functions are the same, especially when transformations of the variables are effected. For instance, since $\wp(z)$ has the origin for an infinity and sn $u$ has it for a zero, it is natural to express the one in terms of the other. Now $\wp(z)$ is an even function, and sn $u$ is an odd function; hence the relation to be obtained will be expected to be one between $\wp(z)$ and $\text{sn}^2 u$. But one of the periods of $\text{sn}^2 u$ is only one-half of the corresponding period of sn $u$; and so the period-parallelogram is changed. The actual relation* is

$$\wp(z) - e_3 = (e_1 - e_3)\, \mathrm{sn}^{-2} u,$$

where $u = (e_1 - e_3)^{\frac{1}{2}} z$ and $k^2 = (e_2 - e_3)/(e_1 - e_3)$.

Again, with the ordinary notation of Jacobian elliptic functions, the periods of sn $z$ are $4K$ and $2iK'$, those of dn $z$ are $2K$ and $4iK'$, and those of cn $z$ are $4K$ and $2K + 2iK'$. The squares of these three functions are homoperiodic in $2K$ and $2iK'$; they are each of the second order, and they have the same infinities. Hence $\mathrm{sn}^2 z$, $\mathrm{cn}^2 z$, $\mathrm{dn}^2 z$ are equivalent to one another (§ 116, V.).

But such cases belong to the detailed development of the theory of particular classes of functions, rather than to what are merely illustrations of the general propositions.

*Ex.* 6.   Prove that

$$g(u) = \frac{\sigma(u + u_1)\, \sigma(u + u_2)\, \sigma(u + u_3)\, \sigma(u + u_4)}{\sigma[2u + \frac{1}{2}(u_1 + u_2 + u_3 + u_4)]}$$

is a doubly-periodic function of $u$, such that, with the ordinary notation,

$$g(u) + g(u + \omega) + g(u + \omega') + g(u + \omega + \omega')$$

$$= -2\sigma\left(\frac{u_2 + u_3 - u_1 - u_4}{2}\right)\sigma\left(\frac{u_3 + u_1 - u_2 - u_4}{2}\right)\sigma\left(\frac{u_1 + u_2 - u_3 - u_4}{2}\right).$$

Prove further that, if $S$ denote the substitution

$$\tfrac{1}{2}\begin{pmatrix} -1 & 1 & 1 & 1 \\ 1 & -1 & 1 & 1 \\ 1 & 1 & -1 & 1 \\ 1 & 1 & 1 & -1 \end{pmatrix},$$

and $(U_1,\ U_2,\ U_3,\ U_4) = S(u_1,\ u_2,\ u_3,\ u_4)$ and $G(u)$ denote what $g(u)$ becomes when, therein, $U_1,\ U_2,\ U_3,\ U_4$ are written for $u_1,\ u_2,\ u_3,\ u_4$ respectively, then also

$$(-G(u),\ -G(u + \omega),\ -G(u + \omega'),\ -G(u + \omega + \omega'))$$

$$= S(g(u),\ g(u + \omega),\ g(u + \omega'),\ g(u + \omega + \omega')).$$

(Math. Trip., Part II., 1893.)

*Ex.* 7.   All the zeros of a function, doubly-periodic in the periods of $\wp(z)$, are simple and are given by $p\omega + q\omega'$, where $p$ and $q$ are integers such that $p + q$ is odd; all its infinities are simple and are given by $p\omega + q\omega'$, where $p$ and $q$ are integers such that $p + q$ is even.   Shew that the function is a constant multiple of

$$\frac{\wp'(z)}{\wp(z) - e_2}.$$     (Trinity Fellowship, 1896.)

*Ex.* 8.   Construct the differential equation of the first order, satisfied by

$$\zeta(z - a) - \zeta(z - b).$$

(Trinity Fellowship, 1899.)

**132.**   As a last illustration giving properties of the functions just considered, the derivatives of an elliptic function with regard to the periods will be obtained.

Let $\phi(z)$ be any function, doubly-periodic in $2\omega$ and $2\omega'$ so that

$$\phi(z + 2m\omega + 2m'\omega') = \phi(z).$$

* Halphen, *Fonctions Elliptiques*, t. i, pp. 23—25.

The coefficients in $\phi$ implicitly involve $\omega$ and $\omega'$. Let $\phi_1$, $\phi_2$, and $\phi'$ respectively denote $\partial\phi/\partial\omega$, $\partial\phi/\partial\omega'$, $\partial\phi/\partial z$; then

$$\phi_1(z + 2m\omega + 2m'\omega') + 2m\phi'(z + 2m\omega + 2m'\omega') = \phi_1(z),$$
$$\phi_2(z + 2m\omega + 2m'\omega') + 2m'\phi'(z + 2m\omega + 2m'\omega') = \phi_2(z),$$
$$\phi'(z + 2m\omega + 2m'\omega') = \phi'(z).$$

Multiplying by $\omega$, $\omega'$, $z$ respectively and adding, we have

$$\omega\phi_1(z + 2m\omega + 2m'\omega') + \omega'\phi_2(z + 2m\omega + 2m'\omega')$$
$$+ (z + 2m\omega + 2m'\omega')\phi'(z + 2m\omega + 2m'\omega')$$
$$= \omega\phi_1(z) + \omega'\phi_2(z) + z\phi'(z).$$

Hence, *if* $$f(z) = \omega\phi_1(z) + \omega'\phi_2(z) + z\phi'(z),$$

then $f(z)$ *is a function doubly-periodic in the periods of* $\phi$.

Again, multiplying by $\eta$, $\eta'$, $\zeta(z)$, adding, and remembering that

$$\zeta(z + 2m\omega + 2m'\omega') = \zeta(z) + 2m\eta + 2m'\eta',$$

we have

$$\eta\phi_1(z + 2m\omega + 2m'\omega') + \eta'\phi_2(z + 2m\omega + 2m'\omega')$$
$$+ \zeta(z + 2m\omega + 2m'\omega')\phi'(z + 2m\omega + 2m'\omega')$$
$$= \eta\phi_1(z) + \eta'\phi_2(z) + \zeta(z)\phi'(z).$$

Hence, *if* $$g(z) = \eta\phi_1(z) + \eta'\phi_2(z) + \zeta(z)\phi'(z),$$

then $g(z)$ *is a function doubly-periodic in the periods of* $\phi$.

In what precedes, the function $\phi(z)$ is any function, doubly-periodic in $2\omega$, $2\omega'$; one simple and useful case occurs when $\phi(z)$ is taken to be the function $\wp(z)$. Now

$$\wp(z) = \frac{1}{z^2} + \frac{1}{20}g_2 z^2 + \frac{1}{28}g_3 z^4 + \frac{1}{1200}g_2^2 z^6 + \dots,$$

and $$\zeta(z) = \frac{1}{z} - \frac{1}{60}g_2 z^3 - \frac{1}{140}g_3 z^5 - \frac{1}{8400}g_2^2 z^7 - \dots;$$

hence, in the vicinity of the origin, we have

$$\omega\frac{\partial\wp}{\partial\omega} + \omega'\frac{\partial\wp}{\partial\omega'} + z\frac{\partial\wp}{\partial z} = -\frac{2}{z^2} + \text{even integral powers of } z^2$$
$$= -2\wp,$$

since both functions are doubly-periodic and the terms independent of $z$ vanish for both functions. It is easy to see that this equation merely expresses the fact that $\wp$, which is equal to

$$\frac{1}{z^2} + \Sigma\Sigma'\left\{\frac{1}{(z-\Omega)^2} - \frac{1}{\Omega^2}\right\},$$

is homogeneous of degree $-2$ in $z$, $\omega$, $\omega'$.

Similarly

$$\eta \frac{\partial \wp}{\partial \omega} + \eta' \frac{\partial \wp}{\partial \omega'} + \zeta(z) \frac{\partial \wp}{\partial z} = -\frac{2}{z^4} + \frac{2}{15} g_2 + \text{even integral powers of } z.$$

But, in the vicinity of the origin,

$$\frac{\partial^2 \wp}{\partial z^2} = \frac{6}{z^4} + \frac{1}{10} g_2 + \text{even integral powers of } z,$$

so that

$$\eta \frac{\partial \wp}{\partial \omega} + \eta' \frac{\partial \wp}{\partial \omega'} + \zeta(z) \frac{\partial \wp}{\partial z} + \frac{1}{3} \frac{\partial^2 \wp}{\partial z^2} = \frac{1}{6} g_2 + \text{even integral powers of } z.$$

The function on the left-hand side is doubly-periodic: it has no infinity at the origin and therefore none in the fundamental parallelogram; it therefore has no infinities in the plane. It is thus constant and equal to its value anywhere, say at the origin. This value is $\frac{1}{6} g_2$, and therefore

$$\eta \frac{\partial \wp}{\partial \omega} + \eta' \frac{\partial \wp}{\partial \omega'} + \zeta(z) \frac{\partial \wp}{\partial z} = -\frac{1}{3} \frac{\partial^2 \wp}{\partial z^2} + \frac{1}{6} g_2$$

$$= -2\wp^2 + \frac{1}{3} g_2.$$

*This equation, when combined with*

$$\omega \frac{\partial \wp}{\partial \omega} + \omega' \frac{\partial \wp}{\partial \omega'} + z \frac{\partial \wp}{\partial z} = -2\wp,$$

*gives the value of* $\dfrac{\partial \wp}{\partial \omega}$ *and* $\dfrac{\partial \wp}{\partial \omega'}$.

The equations are identically satisfied. Equating the coefficients of $z^2$ in the expansions, which are valid in the vicinity of the origin, we have

$$\left. \begin{aligned} \omega \frac{\partial g_2}{\partial \omega} + \omega' \frac{\partial g_2}{\partial \omega'} &= -4g_2 \\ \eta \frac{\partial g_2}{\partial \omega} + \eta' \frac{\partial g_2}{\partial \omega'} &= -6g_3 \end{aligned} \right\};$$

and equating the coefficients of $z^4$ in the same expansions, we have

$$\left. \begin{aligned} \omega \frac{\partial g_3}{\partial \omega} + \omega' \frac{\partial g_3}{\partial \omega'} &= -6g_3 \\ \eta \frac{\partial g_3}{\partial \omega} + \eta' \frac{\partial g_3}{\partial \omega'} &= -\frac{1}{3} g_2^{\,2} \end{aligned} \right\}.$$

Hence for any function $u$, which involves $\omega$ and $\omega'$ and therefore implicitly involves $g_2$ and $g_3$, we have

$$\omega \frac{\partial u}{\partial \omega} + \omega' \frac{\partial u}{\partial \omega'} = -\left( 4g_2 \frac{\partial u}{\partial g_2} + 6g_3 \frac{\partial u}{\partial g_3} \right),$$

$$\eta \frac{\partial u}{\partial \omega} + \eta' \frac{\partial u}{\partial \omega'} = -\frac{1}{2} \left( 12g_3 \frac{\partial u}{\partial g_2} + \frac{2}{3} g_2^{\,2} \frac{\partial u}{\partial g_3} \right).$$

Since $\wp$ is such a function, we have

$$4g_2 \frac{\partial \wp}{\partial g_2} + 6g_3 \frac{\partial \wp}{\partial g_3} - z \frac{\partial \wp}{\partial z} = 2\wp,$$

$$12g_3 \frac{\partial \wp}{\partial g_2} + \frac{2}{3} g_2{}^2 \frac{\partial \wp}{\partial g_3} - 2\zeta(z) \frac{\partial \wp}{\partial z} = 4\wp^2 - \frac{2}{3} g_2,$$

being *the equations which determine the derivatives of $\wp$ with regard to the invariants $g_2$ and $g_3$.*

The latter equation, integrated twice, leads to

$$\frac{\partial^2 \sigma}{\partial z^2} - 12g_3 \frac{\partial \sigma}{\partial g_2} - \frac{2}{3} g_2{}^2 \frac{\partial \sigma}{\partial g_3} + \frac{1}{12} g_2 z^2 \sigma = 0,$$

a differential equation\* satisfied by $\sigma(z)$.

**133.** The foregoing investigations give some of the properties of doubly-periodic functions of the second order, whether they be uneven and have two simple irreducible infinities, or even and have one double irreducible infinity.

If a function $U$ of the second order have a repeated infinity at $z = \gamma$, then it is determined by an equation of the form

$$U'^2 = 4a^2 \left[ (U - \lambda)(U - \mu)(U - \nu) \right],$$

or, taking $U - \frac{1}{3}(\lambda + \mu + \nu) = Q$, the equation is

$$Q'^2 = 4a^2 \left[ (Q - e_1)(Q - e_2)(Q - e_3) \right],$$

where $e_1 + e_2 + e_3 = 0$. Taking account of the infinities, we have

$$Q = \wp(az - a\gamma);$$

and therefore $\quad U - \frac{1}{3}(\lambda + \mu + \nu) = \wp(az - a\gamma)$

$$= -\wp(az) - \wp(a\gamma) + \frac{1}{4} \left\{ \frac{\wp'(az) + \wp'(a\gamma)}{\wp(az) - \wp(a\gamma)} \right\}^2,$$

by Ex. 4, p. 308. The right-hand side cannot be an odd function; hence *an odd function of the second order cannot have a repeated infinity.* Similarly, by taking reciprocals of the functions, it follows that *an odd function of the second order cannot have a repeated zero.*

It thus appears that the investigations in §§ 120, 121 are sufficient for the included range of properties of odd functions. We now proceed to obtain the general equations of even functions. Every such function can (by § 118, XIII., Cor. 1) be expressed in the form $\{a\wp(z) + b\} \div \{c\wp(z) + d\}$, and its equations could thence be deduced from those of $\wp(z)$; but, partly for uniformity, we shall adopt the same method as in § 120 for odd functions. And, as already stated (p. 286), the separate class of functions of the second order that are neither even nor odd, will not be discussed.

---

\* For this and other deductions from these equations, see Frobenius und Stickelberger, *Crelle*, t. xcii, (1882), pp. 311—327; Halphen, *Traité des fonctions elliptiques*, t. i, (1886), chap. IX.; and a memoir by the author, quoted on p. 299, note.

**134.** Let, then, $\phi(z)$ denote an even doubly-periodic function of the second order (it may be either of the first class or of the second class) and let $2\omega$, $2\omega'$ be its periods; and denote $2\omega + 2\omega'$ by $2\omega''$. Then

$$\phi(z) = \phi(-z),$$

since the function is even; and since

$$\phi(\omega + z) = \phi(-\omega - z)$$
$$= \phi(2\omega - \omega - z)$$
$$= \phi(\omega - z),$$

it follows that $\phi(\omega + z)$ is an even function. Similarly, $\phi(\omega' + z)$ and $\phi(\omega'' + z)$ are even functions.

Now $\phi(\omega + z)$, an even function, has two irreducible infinities, and is periodic in $2\omega$, $2\omega'$; also $\phi(z)$, an even function, has two irreducible infinities and is periodic in $2\omega$, $2\omega'$. There is therefore a relation between $\phi(z)$ and $\phi(\omega + z)$, which, by § 118, Prop. XIII., Cor. 1, is of the first degree in $\phi(z)$ and of the first degree in $\phi(\omega + z)$; thus it must be included in

$$B\phi(z)\phi(\omega + z) - C\phi(z) - C'\phi(\omega + z) + A = 0.$$

But $\phi(z)$ is periodic in $2\omega$; hence, on writing $z + \omega$ for $z$ in the equation, it becomes

$$B\phi(\omega + z)\phi(z) - C\phi(\omega + z) - C'\phi(z) + A = 0;$$

thus　　　　　　　　　　　　$C = C'$.

If $B$ be zero, then $C$ may not be zero, for the relation cannot become evanescent: it is of the form

$$\phi(z) + \phi(\omega + z) = A' \quad\dots\dots\dots\dots\dots(1).$$

If $B$ be not zero, then the relation is

$$\phi(\omega + z) = \frac{C\phi(z) - A}{B\phi(z) - C} \quad\dots\dots\dots\dots\dots(2).$$

Treating $\phi(\omega' + z)$ in the same way, we find that the relation between it and $\phi(z)$ is

$$F\phi(z)\phi(\omega' + z) - D\phi(z) - D\phi(\omega' + z) + E = 0,$$

so that, if $F$ be zero, the relation is of the form

$$\phi(z) + \phi(\omega' + z) = E' \quad\dots\dots\dots\dots\dots(1)',$$

and, if $F$ be not zero, the relation is of the form

$$\phi(\omega' + z) = \frac{D\phi(z) - E}{F\phi(z) - D} \quad\dots\dots\dots\dots\dots(2)'.$$

Four cases thus arise, viz., the coexistence of (1) with (1)', of (1) with (2)', of (2) with (1)', and of (2) with (2)'. These will be taken in order.

I. : the coexistence of (1) with (1)′. From (1) we have

$$\phi(\omega' + z) + \phi(\omega'' + z) = A',$$

so that $\qquad \phi(z) + \phi(\omega + z) + \phi(\omega' + z) + \phi(\omega'' + z) = 2A'.$

Similarly, from (1)′,

$$\phi(z) + \phi(\omega' + z) + \phi(\omega + z) + \phi(\omega'' + z) = 2E';$$

so that $A' = E'$, and then

$$\phi(\omega + z) = \phi(\omega' + z),$$

whence $\omega \sim \omega'$ is a period, contrary to the initial hypothesis that $2\omega$ and $2\omega$ determine a fundamental parallelogram. Hence equations (1) and (1)′ cannot coexist.

II. : the coexistence of (1) with (2)′. From (1) we have

$$\phi(\omega'' + z) = A' - \phi(\omega' + z)$$
$$= \frac{(A'F - D)\phi(z) - (A'D - E)}{F\phi(z) - D},$$

on substitution from (2)′. From (2)′ we have

$$\phi(\omega'' + z) = \frac{D\phi(\omega + z) - E}{F\phi(\omega + z) - D}$$
$$= \frac{(A'D - E) - D\phi(z)}{A'F - D - F\phi(z)},$$

on substitution from (1). The two values of $\phi(\omega'' + z)$ must be the same, whence

$$A'F - D = D,$$

which relation establishes the periodicity of $\phi(z)$ in $2\omega''$, when it is considered as given by either of the two expressions which have been obtained. We thus have

$$A'F = 2D;$$

and then, by (1), we have

$$\phi(z) - \frac{D}{F} + \phi(\omega + z) - \frac{D}{F} = 0;$$

and, by (2)′, we have

$$\left\{\phi(z) - \frac{D}{F}\right\}\left\{\phi(\omega' + z) - \frac{D}{F}\right\} = \frac{D^2 - EF}{F^2}.$$

If a new even function be introduced, doubly-periodic in the same periods having the same infinities and defined by the equation

$$\phi_1(z) = \phi(z) - \frac{D}{F},$$

the equations satisfied by $\phi_1(z)$ are

$$\left.\begin{array}{l} \phi_1(\omega + z) + \phi_1(z) = 0 \\ \phi_1(\omega' + z)\,\phi_1(z) = \text{constant} \end{array}\right\}.$$

To the detailed properties of such functions we shall return later; meanwhile it may be noticed that these equations are, in form, the same as those satisfied by an odd function of the second order.

III.: the coexistence of (2) with (1)′. This case is similar to II., with the result that, if an even function be introduced, doubly-periodic in the same periods having the same infinities and defined by the equation

$$\phi_2(z) = \phi(z) - \frac{C}{B},$$

the equations satisfied by $\phi_2(z)$ are

$$\left.\begin{array}{l} \phi_2(\omega' + z) + \phi_2(z) = 0 \\ \phi_2(\omega + z)\, \phi_2(z) = \text{constant} \end{array}\right\}.$$

It is, in fact, merely the previous case with the periods interchanged.

IV.: the coexistence of (2) with (2)′. From (2) we have

$$\phi(\omega'' + z) = \frac{C\phi(\omega' + z) - A}{B\phi(\omega' + z) - C}$$

$$= \frac{(CD - AF)\,\phi(z) - (CE - AD)}{(BD - CF)\,\phi(z) - (BE - CD)},$$

on substitution from (2)′. Similarly from (2)′, after substitution from (2), we have

$$\phi(\omega'' + z) = \frac{(CD - BE)\,\phi(z) + (CE - AD)}{(CF - BD)\,\phi(z) + (CD - AF)}.$$

The two values must be the same; hence

$$CD - AF = -(CD - BE),$$

which indeed is the condition that each of the expressions for $\phi(\omega'' + z)$ should give a function periodic in $2\omega''$. Thus

$$AF + BE = 2CD.$$

One sub-case may be at once considered and removed, viz. if $C$ and $D$ vanish together. Then since, by the hypothesis of the existence of (2) and of (2)′, neither $B$ nor $F$ vanishes, we have

$$\frac{A}{B} = -\frac{E}{F},$$

so that 
$$\phi(\omega + z) = -\frac{A}{B\phi(z)} = \frac{E}{F\phi(z)} = -\phi(\omega' + z),$$

and then the relations are $\phi(\omega + z) + \phi(\omega' + z) = 0,$

or, what is the same thing, 
and
$$\left.\begin{array}{l} \phi(z) + \phi(\omega'' + z) = 0 \\ \phi(z)\, \phi(\omega + z) = \text{constant} \end{array}\right\}.$$

The sub-case is substantially the same as that of II. and III., arising merely from a modification (§ 109) of the fundamental parallelogram, into one whose sides are determined by $2\omega$ and $2\omega''$.

Hence we may have (2) coexistent with (2)′, provided

$$AF + BE = 2CD;$$

$C$ and $D$ do not both vanish, and neither $B$ nor $F$ vanishes.

IV. (1).   Let neither $C$ nor $D$ vanish; and for brevity write

$$\phi(\omega + z) = \phi_1, \quad \phi(\omega'' + z) = \phi_2, \quad \phi(\omega' + z) = \phi_3, \quad \phi(z) = \phi.$$

Then the equations in IV. are

$$B\phi\phi_1 - C(\phi + \phi_1) + A = 0,$$
$$F\phi\phi_3 - D(\phi + \phi_3) + E = 0.$$

Now a doubly-periodic function, with given zeros and given infinities, is determinate save as to an arbitrary constant factor.   We therefore introduce an arbitrary factor $\lambda$, so that

$$\phi = \lambda\psi,$$

and then taking

$$\frac{C}{B\lambda} = c_1, \quad \frac{D}{F\lambda} = c_3,$$

we have

$$(\psi - c_1)(\psi_1 - c_1) = c_1^2 - \frac{A}{B\lambda^2},$$

$$(\psi - c_3)(\psi_3 - c_3) = c_3^2 - \frac{E}{F\lambda^2}.$$

The arbitrary quantity $\lambda$ is at our disposal: we introduce a new quantity $c_2$, defined by the equation

$$\frac{A}{B\lambda^2} = c_1(c_2 + c_3) - c_2 c_3,$$

and therefore at our disposal.   But since

$$AF + BE = 2CD,$$

we have

$$\frac{A}{B\lambda^2} + \frac{E}{F\lambda^2} = 2\,\frac{C}{B\lambda}\,\frac{D}{F\lambda} = 2c_1 c_3,$$

and therefore

$$\frac{E}{F\lambda^2} = c_3(c_1 + c_2) - c_1 c_2.$$

Hence the foregoing equations are

$$(\psi - c_1)(\psi_1 - c_1) = (c_1 - c_2)(c_1 - c_3),$$
$$(\psi - c_3)(\psi_3 - c_3) = (c_3 - c_1)(c_3 - c_2).$$

The equation for $\phi_2$, which is $\phi(\omega'' + z)$, is

$$\phi_2 = \frac{L\phi - M}{N\phi - L},$$

where   $L = CD - BE = AF - CD, \quad M = AD - CE, \quad N = CF - BD,$

so that                          $AN + BM = 2CL.$

As before, one particular sub-case may be considered and removed. If $N$ be zero, so that

$$\frac{C}{B} = \frac{D}{F} = \alpha,$$

say, and

$$\frac{A}{B} + \frac{E}{F} = 2\frac{CD}{BF} = 2\alpha^2,$$

then we find

$$\phi + \phi_2 = \phi_1 + \phi_3 = 2\alpha,$$

or taking a function

$$\chi = \phi - \alpha,$$

the equation becomes

$$\chi(z) + \chi(\omega'' + z) = 0.$$

The other equations then become

$$\chi(z)\,\chi(\omega + z) = \alpha^2 - \frac{A}{B} \left.\right\},$$

$$\chi(z)\,\chi(\omega' + z) = \alpha^2 - \frac{E}{F}$$

and therefore they are similar to those in Cases II. and III.

If $N$ be not zero, then it is easy to shew that

$$N = BF\lambda\,(c_1 - c_3),$$

$$L = BF\lambda^2\,(c_1 - c_3)\,c_2,$$

$$M = BF\lambda^3\,(c_1 - c_3)\,(c_2 c_1 + c_2 c_3 - c_1 c_3);$$

and then the equation connecting $\phi$ and $\phi_2$ changes to

$$(\psi - c_2)\,(\psi_2 - c_2) = (c_2 - c_1)\,(c_2 - c_3) \left.\right\}$$

which, with

$$(\psi - c_1)\,(\psi_1 - c_1) = (c_1 - c_2)\,(c_1 - c_3) \left.\right\},$$

$$(\psi - c_3)\,(\psi_3 - c_3) = (c_3 - c_1)\,(c_3 - c_2)$$

are relations between $\psi$, $\psi_1$, $\psi_2$, $\psi_3$, where the quantity $c_2$ is at our disposal.

IV. (2). These equations have been obtained on the supposition that neither $C$ nor $D$ is zero. If either vanish, let it be $C$: then $D$ does not vanish; and the equations can be expressed in the form

$$\phi\phi_1 = \frac{E}{F},$$

$$\left(\phi - \frac{D}{F}\right)\left(\phi_3 - \frac{D}{F}\right) = \frac{D^2 - EF}{F^2},$$

$$\left(\phi - \frac{E}{D}\right)\left(\phi_2 - \frac{E}{D}\right) = -\frac{E\,(D^2 - EF)}{FD^2}.$$

We therefore obtain the following theorem :—

*If $\phi$ be an even function doubly-periodic in $2\omega$ and $2\omega'$ and of the second order, and if all functions equivalent to $\phi$ in the form $R\phi + S$ (where $R$ and*

*S are constants*) *be regarded as the same as* $\phi$, *then either the function satisfies the system of equations*

$$\left.\begin{aligned} \phi(z) + \phi(\omega + z) &= 0 \\ \phi(z) \quad \phi(\omega' + z) &= H \\ \phi(z) \quad \phi(\omega'' + z) &= -H \end{aligned}\right\} \quad \dots\dots\dots\dots\dots(I)^*,$$

*where H is a constant; or it satisfies the system of equations*

$$\left.\begin{aligned} \{\phi(z) - c_1\}\{\phi(\omega + z) - c_1\} &= (c_1 - c_2)(c_1 - c_3) \\ \{\phi(z) - c_3\}\{\phi(\omega' + z) - c_3\} &= (c_3 - c_1)(c_3 - c_2) \\ \{\phi(z) - c_2\}\{\phi(\omega'' + z) - c_2\} &= (c_2 - c_1)(c_2 - c_3) \end{aligned}\right\} \quad \dots\dots\dots(II),$$

*where of the three constants* $c_1$, $c_2$, $c_3$ *one can be arbitrarily assigned.*

We shall now very briefly consider these in turn.

**135.** So far as concerns the former class of equations satisfied by an even doubly-periodic function, viz.,

$$\left.\begin{aligned} \phi(z) + \phi(\omega + z) &= 0 \\ \phi(z) \quad \phi(\omega' + z) &= H \end{aligned}\right\},$$

we proceed initially as in (§ 120) the case of an odd function. We have the further equations

$$\phi(z) = \phi(-z),$$

$$\phi(\omega + z) = \phi(\omega - z), \qquad \phi(\omega' + z) = \phi(\omega' - z).$$

Taking $z = -\tfrac{1}{2}\omega$, the first gives

$$\phi(\tfrac{1}{2}\omega) + \phi(\tfrac{1}{2}\omega) = 0,$$

so that $\tfrac{1}{2}\omega$ is either a zero or an infinity.

If $\tfrac{1}{2}\omega$ be a zero, then

$$\phi(\tfrac{3}{2}\omega) = \phi(\omega + \tfrac{1}{2}\omega) = -\phi(\tfrac{1}{2}\omega) \text{ by the first equation}$$
$$= 0,$$

so that $\tfrac{1}{2}\omega$ and $\tfrac{3}{2}\omega$ are zeros. And then, by the second equation,

$$\omega' + \tfrac{1}{2}\omega, \qquad \omega' + \tfrac{3}{2}\omega$$

are infinities.

If $\tfrac{1}{2}\omega$ be an infinity, then in the same way $\tfrac{3}{2}\omega$ is also an infinity; and then $\omega' + \tfrac{1}{2}\omega$, $\omega' + \tfrac{3}{2}\omega$ are zeros. Since these amount merely to interchanging zeros and infinities, which is the same functionally as taking the reciprocal of the function, we may choose either arrangement. We shall take that which gives $\tfrac{1}{2}\omega$, $\tfrac{3}{2}\omega$ as the zeros; and $\omega' + \tfrac{1}{2}\omega$, $\omega' + \tfrac{3}{2}\omega$ as the infinities.

The function $\phi$ is evidently of the second class, in that it has two distinct simple irreducible infinities.

---

* The systems obtained by the interchange of $\omega$, $\omega'$, $\omega''$ among one another in the equations are not substantially distinct from the form adopted for the system I.; the apparent difference can be removed by an appropriate corresponding interchange of the periods.

Because $\omega' + \tfrac{1}{2}\omega$, $\omega' + \tfrac{3}{2}\omega$ are the irreducible infinities of $\phi(z)$, the four zeros of $\phi'(z)$ are, by § 117, the irreducible points homologous with $\omega''$, $\omega'' + \omega$, $\omega'' + \omega'$, $\omega'' + \omega''$, that is, the irreducible zeros of $\phi'(z)$ are $0, \omega, \omega', \omega''$. Moreover

$$\phi(0) + \phi(\omega) = 0,$$

$$\phi(\omega') + \phi(\omega'') = 0,$$

by the first of the equations of the system; hence the relation between $\phi(z)$ and $\phi'(z)$ is

$$\phi'^2(z) = A \left\{\phi(z) - \phi(0)\right\} \left\{\phi(z) - \phi(\omega)\right\} \left\{\phi(z) - \phi(\omega')\right\} \left\{\phi(z) - \phi(\omega'')\right\}$$

$$= A \left\{\phi^2(0) - \phi^2(z)\right\} \left\{\phi^2(\omega') - \phi^2(z)\right\}.$$

Since the origin is neither a zero nor an infinity of $\phi(z)$, let

$$\phi(z) = \phi(0) \phi_1(z),$$

so that $\phi_1(0)$ is unity and $\phi_1'(0)$ is zero; then

$$\phi_1'^2(z) = \lambda^2 \left\{1 - \phi_1^2(z)\right\} \left\{\mu - \phi_1^2(z)\right\}$$

the differential equation determining $\phi_1(z)$.

The character of the function depends upon the value of $\mu$ and the constant of integration. The function may be compared with $\operatorname{cn} u$, by taking $2\omega$, $2\omega' = 4K$, $2K + 2iK'$; and with $\dfrac{1}{\operatorname{dn} u}$, by taking $2\omega$, $2\omega' = 2K$, $4iK'$, which (§ 131, note) are the periods of these (even) Jacobian elliptic functions.

We may deal even more briefly with the even function characterised by the second class of equations in § 134. One of the quantities $c_1$, $c_2$, $c_3$ being at our disposal, we choose it so that

$$c_1 + c_2 + c_3 = 0;$$

and then the analogy with the equations of Weierstrass's $\wp$-function is complete (see § 133).

# CHAPTER XII.

## PSEUDO-PERIODIC FUNCTIONS.

**136.** Most of the functions in the last two chapters are of the type called doubly-periodic, that is, they are reproduced when their arguments are increased by integral multiples of two distinct periods. But, in §§ 127, 130, functions of only a pseudo-periodic type have arisen: thus the $\zeta$-function satisfies the equation

$$\zeta(z + m2\omega + m'2\omega') = \zeta(z) + m2\eta + m'2\eta',$$

and the $\sigma$-function the equation

$$\sigma(z + m2\omega + m'2\omega') = (-1)^{mm'+m+m'} e^{2(m\eta+m'\eta')(z+m\omega+m'\omega')} \sigma(z).$$

These are instances of the most important classes: and the distinction between the two can be made even less by considering the function $e^{\zeta(z)} = \xi(z)$, when we have

$$\xi(z + m2\omega + m'2\omega') = e^{2m\eta} e^{2m'\eta'} \xi(z).$$

In the case of the $\xi$-function, an increase of the argument by a period leads to the reproduction of the function multiplied by an exponential factor that is constant. In the case of the $\sigma$-function, a similar change of the argument leads to the reproduction of the function multiplied by an exponential factor having its index of the form $az + b$.

Hence, when an argument is subject to periodic increase, there are three simple classes of functions of that argument.

First, if a function $f(z)$ satisfy the equations

$$f(z + 2\omega) = f(z), \qquad f(z + 2\omega') = f(z),$$

it is strictly periodic: it is sometimes called *a doubly-periodic function of the first kind*. The general properties of such functions have already been considered.

Secondly, if a function $F(z)$ satisfy the equations

$$F(z + 2\omega) = \mu F(z), \qquad F(z + 2\omega') = \mu' F(z),$$

where $\mu$ and $\mu'$ are constants, it is pseudo-periodic: it is called *a doubly-periodic function of the second kind*. The first derivative of the logarithm of such a function is a doubly-periodic function of the first kind.

Thirdly, if a function $\phi(z)$ satisfy the equations

$$\phi(z+2\omega) = e^{az+b}\,\phi(z), \qquad \phi(z+2\omega') = e^{a'z+b'}\,\phi(z),$$

where $a$, $b$, $a'$, $b'$ are constants, it is pseudo-periodic: it is called *a doubly-periodic function of the third kind*. The second derivative of the logarithm of such a function is a doubly-periodic function of the first kind.

The equations of definition for functions of the third kind can be modified. We have

$$\phi(z+2\omega+2\omega') = e^{a(z+2\omega')+b+a'z+b'}\,\phi(z)$$
$$= e^{a'(z+2\omega)+b'+az+b}\,\phi(z),$$

whence
$$a'\omega - a\omega' = -m\pi i,$$

where $m$ is an integer. Let a new function $E(z)$ be introduced, defined by the equation

$$E(z) = e^{\lambda z^2 + \mu z}\,\phi(z);$$

then $\lambda$ and $\mu$ can be chosen so that $E(z)$ satisfies the equations

$$E(z+2\omega) = E(z), \qquad E(z+2\omega') = e^{Az+B}\,E(z).$$

From the last equations, we have

$$E(z+2\omega+2\omega') = e^{A(z+2\omega)+B}\,E(z)$$
$$= e^{Az+B}\,E(z),$$

so that $2A\omega$ is an integral multiple of $2\pi i$.

Also we have
$$E(z+2\omega) = e^{\lambda(z+2\omega)^2 + \mu(z+2\omega)}\,\phi(z+2\omega)$$
$$= e^{4\lambda z\omega + 4\lambda\omega^2 + 2\mu\omega + az + b}\,E(z),$$

so that
$$4\lambda\omega + a = 0,$$

and
$$4\lambda\omega^2 + 2\mu\omega + b \equiv 0 \ (\text{mod. } 2\pi i).$$

Similarly,
$$E(z+2\omega') = e^{\lambda(z+2\omega')^2 + \mu(z+2\omega')}\,\phi(z+2\omega')$$
$$= e^{4\lambda z\omega' + 4\lambda\omega'^2 + 2\mu\omega' + a'z + b'}\,E(z),$$

so that
$$4\lambda\omega' + a' = A,$$

and
$$4\lambda\omega'^2 + 2\mu\omega' + b' \equiv B \,(\text{mod. } 2\pi i).$$

From the two equations, which involve $\lambda$ and not $\mu$, we have

$$A\omega = a'\omega - a\omega'$$
$$= -m\pi i,$$

agreeing with the result that $2A\omega$ is an integral multiple of $2\pi i$.

And from the two equations, which involve $\mu$, we have, on the elimination of $\mu$ and on substitution for $\lambda$,

$$b'\omega - b\omega' - a\omega'(\omega' - \omega) \equiv B\omega \,(\text{mod. } 2\pi i).$$

If $A$ be zero, then $E(z)$ is a doubly-periodic function of the first kind when $e^B$ is unity, and it is a doubly-periodic function of the second kind when $e^B$ is not unity. Hence $A$, and therefore $m$, may be assumed to be different from zero for functions of the third kind. Take a new function $\Phi(z)$, such that

$$\Phi(z) = E\left(z - \frac{B}{A}\right) = E\left(z + \frac{B\omega}{m\pi i}\right);$$

then $\Phi(z)$ satisfies the equations

$$\Phi(z + 2\omega) = \Phi(z), \qquad \Phi(z + 2\omega') = e^{-\frac{m\pi i}{\omega}z}\,\Phi(z),$$

which will be taken as the *canonical equations defining a doubly-periodic function of the third kind*.

*Ex.* Obtain the values of $\lambda$, $\mu$, $A$, $B$ for the Weierstrassian function $\sigma(z)$.

We proceed to obtain some properties of these two classes of functions which, for brevity, will be called *secondary-periodic* functions and *tertiary-periodic* functions respectively.

### Doubly-Periodic Functions of the Second Kind.

For the secondary-periodic functions the chief sources of information are :—

Hermite, *Comptes Rendus*, t. liii, (1861), pp. 214—228, ib., t. lv, (1862), pp. 11—18, 85—91; *Sur quelques applications des fonctions elliptiques*, §§ i—iii, separate reprint (1885) from *Comptes Rendus*; "Note sur la théorie des fonctions elliptiques" in Lacroix, vol. ii, (6th edition, 1885), pp. 484—491; *Cours d'Analyse*, (4me éd.), pp. 227—234.

Mittag-Leffler, *Comptes Rendus*, t. xc, (1880), pp. 177—180.

Frobenius, *Crelle*, t. xciii, (1882), pp. 53—68.

Brioschi, *Comptes Rendus*, t. xcii, (1881), pp. 325—328.

Halphen, *Traité des fonctions elliptiques*, t. i, pp. 225—238, 411—426, 438—442, 463.

**137.** In the case of the periodic functions of the first kind it was proved that they can be expressed by means of functions of the second order in the same period—these being the simplest of such functions. It will now be proved that a similar result holds for secondary-periodic functions, defined by the equations

$$F(z + 2\omega) = \mu F(z), \qquad F(z + 2\omega') = \mu' F(z).$$

Take a function $\qquad\qquad G(z) = \dfrac{\sigma(z + a)}{\sigma(z)\,\sigma(a)}\, e^{\lambda z};$

then we have $\qquad\qquad G(z + 2\omega) = \dfrac{\sigma(z + a + 2\omega)}{\sigma(a)\,\sigma(z + 2\omega)}\, e^{\lambda z + 2\lambda\omega}$

$$= e^{2\eta a + 2\lambda\omega}\, G(z),$$

and $\qquad\qquad\qquad G(z + 2\omega') = e^{2\eta' a + 2\lambda\omega'}\, G(z).$

The quantities $a$ and $\lambda$ being unrestricted, we choose them so that

$$\mu = e^{2\eta a + 2\lambda\omega}, \qquad \mu' = e^{2\eta' a + 2\lambda\omega'};$$

and then $G(z)$, a known function, satisfies the same equation as $F(z)$.

Let $u$ denote a quantity independent of $z$, and consider the function
$$f(z) = F(z)\, G(u-z).$$
We have
$$f(z + 2\omega) = F(z + 2\omega)\, G(u - z - 2\omega)$$
$$= \mu F(z)\, \frac{1}{\mu}\, G(u-z)$$
$$= f(z);$$
and similarly
$$f(z + 2\omega') = f(z),$$
so that $f(z)$ is a doubly-periodic function of the first kind with $2\omega$ and $2\omega'$ for its periods.

The sum of the residues of $f(z)$ is therefore zero. To express this sum, we must obtain the fractional part of the function for expansion in the vicinity of each of the (accidental) singularities of $f(z)$, that lie within the parallelogram of periods. The singularities of $f(z)$ are those of $G(u-z)$ and those of $F(z)$.

Choosing the parallelogram of reference so that it may contain $u$, we have $z = u$ as the only singularity of $G(u-z)$ and it is of the first order, so that, since
$$G(\zeta) = \frac{1}{\zeta} + \text{positive integral powers of } \zeta$$
in the vicinity of $\zeta = 0$, we have, in the vicinity of $u$,
$$f(z) = \{F(u) + \text{positive integral powers of } u - z\} \left\{ \frac{1}{u - z} + \text{positive powers} \right\}$$
$$= -\frac{F(u)}{z - u} + \text{positive integral powers of } z - u;$$
hence the residue of $f(z)$ for $u$ is $-F(u)$.

Let $z = c$ be a pole of $F(z)$ in the parallelogram of order $n + 1$; and, in the vicinity of $c$, let
$$F(z) = \frac{C_1}{z - c} + C_2 \frac{d}{dz}\left(\frac{1}{z - c}\right) + \dots + C_{n+1} \frac{d^n}{dz^n}\left(\frac{1}{z - c}\right) + \text{positive integral powers.}$$
Then in that vicinity
$$G(u - z) = G(u - c) - (z - c)\frac{d}{du} G(u - c) + \frac{(z - c)^2}{2!} \frac{d^2}{du^2} G(u - c) - \dots,$$
and therefore the coefficient of $\dfrac{1}{z - c}$ in the expansion of $f(z)$ for points in the vicinity of $c$ is
$$C_1 G(u - c) + C_2 \frac{d}{du} G(u - c) + C_3 \frac{d^2}{du^2} G(u - c) + \dots + C_{n+1} \frac{d^n}{du^n} G(u - c),$$
which is therefore the residue of $f(z)$ for $c$.

This being the form of the residue of $f(z)$ for each of the poles of $F(z)$, then, since the sum of the residues is zero, we have
$$- F(u) + \Sigma \left[ C_1 G(u - c) + C_2 \frac{d}{du} G(u - c) + \dots + C_{n+1} \frac{d^n}{du^n} G(u - c) \right] = 0,$$

or, changing the variable,

$$F(z) = \Sigma \left[ C_1 G(z-c) + C_2 \frac{d}{dz} G(z-c) + \dots + C_{n+1} \frac{d^n}{dz^n} G(z-c) \right],$$

where the summation extends over all the poles of $F(z)$ within that parallelogram of periods in which $z$ lies. This result is due to Hermite.

**138.** It has been assumed that $a$ and $\lambda$, parameters in $G$, are determinate, an assumption that requires $\mu$ and $\mu'$ to be general constants: their values are given by

$$\eta a + \omega \lambda = \tfrac{1}{2} \log \mu, \quad \eta' a + \omega' \lambda = \tfrac{1}{2} \log \mu',$$

and, therefore, since $\eta \omega' - \eta' \omega = \pm \tfrac{1}{2} i\pi$, we have

$$\left. \begin{aligned} \pm i\pi a &= \quad \omega' \log \mu - \omega \log \mu' \\ \pm i\pi \lambda &= -\eta' \log \mu + \eta \log \mu' \end{aligned} \right\}.$$

Now $\lambda$ may vanish without rendering $G(z)$ a null function. If $a$ vanish (or, what is the same thing, be an integral combination of the periods), then $G(z)$ is an exponential function multiplied by an infinite constant when $\lambda$ does not vanish, and it ceases to be a function when $\lambda$ does vanish. These cases must be taken separately.

First, let $a$ and $\lambda$ vanish[*]; then both $\mu$ and $\mu'$ are unity, the function $F$ is doubly-periodic of the first kind; but the expression for $F$ is not determinate, owing to the form of $G$. To render it determinate, consider $\lambda$ as zero and $a$ as infinitesimal, to be made zero ultimately. Then

$$G(z) = \frac{\sigma(z) + a\sigma'(z) + \dots}{a\sigma(z)} (1 + \text{powers of } a \text{ higher than the first})$$

$$= \frac{1}{a} + \zeta(z) + \text{positive powers of } a.$$

Since $a$ is infinitesimal, $\mu$ and $\mu'$ are very nearly unity. When the function $F$ is given, the coefficients $C_1, C_2, \dots$ may be affected by $a$, so that for any one we have

$$C_k = b_k + a\gamma_k + \text{higher powers of } a,$$

where $\gamma_k$ is finite; and $b_k$ is the actual value for the function which is strictly of the first kind, so that

$$\Sigma b_1 = 0,$$

the summation being extended over the poles of the function. Then retaining only $a^{-1}$ and $a^0$, we have

$$\Sigma \left[ C_1 G(u-c) + C_2 \frac{d}{du} G(u-c) + \dots \dots \dots + C_{n+1} \frac{d^n}{du^n} G(u-c) \right]$$

$$= \Sigma \frac{b_1}{a} + \Sigma \gamma_1 + \Sigma \left[ b_1 \zeta(u-c) + b_2 \frac{d}{du} \zeta(u-c) + \dots + b_{n+1} \frac{d^n}{du^n} \zeta(u-c) \right]$$

$$= C_0 + \Sigma \left[ b_1 \zeta(u-c) + \dots + b_{n+1} \frac{d^n}{du^n} \zeta(u-c) \right],$$

* This case is discussed by Hermite, (l.c., p. 322).

where $C_0$, equal to $\Sigma\gamma_1$, is a constant and the term in $\dfrac{1}{a}$ vanishes. This expression, with the condition $\Sigma b_1 = 0$, is the value of $F(u)$; changing the variables, we have

$$F(z) = C_0 + \Sigma\left[b_1\zeta(z-c) + b_2\frac{d}{dz}\zeta(z-c) + \ldots + b_{n+1}\frac{d^n}{dz^n}\zeta(z-c)\right],$$

with the condition $\Sigma b_1 = 0$, a result agreeing with the one formerly (§ 128) obtained.

When $F$ is not given, but only its infinities are assigned arbitrarily, then $\Sigma C = 0$ because $F$ is to be a doubly-periodic function of the first kind; the term $\dfrac{1}{a}\Sigma C$ vanishes, and we have the same expression for $F(z)$ as before.

Secondly, let $a$ vanish* but not $\lambda$, so that $\mu$ and $\mu'$ have the forms

$$\mu = e^{2\lambda\omega}, \quad \mu' = e^{2\lambda\omega'}.$$

We take a function $\qquad g(z) = e^{\lambda z}\zeta(z);$

then $\qquad\qquad\qquad g(z - 2\omega) = \mu^{-1}e^{\lambda z}\zeta(z - 2\omega)$

$$= \mu^{-1}e^{\lambda z}\{\zeta(z) - 2\eta\}$$

$$= \mu^{-1}\{g(z) - 2\eta e^{\lambda z}\},$$

and $\qquad\qquad\qquad g(z - 2\omega') = \mu'^{-1}\{g(z) - 2\eta'e^{\lambda z}\}.$

Introducing a new function $H(z)$ defined by the equation

$$H(z) = F(z)g(u - z),$$

we have $\qquad\qquad H(z + 2\omega) = H(z) - 2\eta e^{\lambda(u-z)}F(z),$

and $\qquad\qquad\quad H(z + 2\omega') = H(z) - 2\eta'e^{\lambda(u-z)}F(z).$

Consider a parallelogram of periods which contains the point $u$; then, if $\Theta$ be the sum of the residues of $H(z)$ for poles in this parallelogram, we have

$$2\pi i\Theta = \int H(z)\,dz,$$

the integral being taken positively round the parallelogram. But, by § 116, Prop. II. Cor., this integral is

$$4e^{\lambda u}\left\{\omega\eta'\int_0^1 e^{-\lambda(p+2\omega t)}F(p + 2\omega t)\,dt - \omega'\eta\int_0^1 e^{-\lambda(p+2\omega't)}F(p + 2\omega't)\,dt\right\},$$

where $p$ is the corner of the parallelogram and each integral is taken for real values of $t$ from 0 to 1. Each of the integrals is a constant, so far as concerns $u$; and therefore we may take

$$\Theta = -Ae^{\lambda u},$$

the quantity inside the above bracket being denoted by $-\frac{1}{2}i\pi A$.

The residue of $H(z)$ for $z = u$, arising from the simple pole of $g(u - z)$, is $-F(u)$ as in § 137.

If $z = c$ be an accidental singularity of $F(z)$ of order $n + 1$, so that, in the vicinity of $z = c$,

$$F(z) = C_1\frac{1}{z-c} + C_2\frac{d}{dz}\left(\frac{1}{z-c}\right) + \ldots + C_{n+1}\frac{d^n}{dz^n}\left(\frac{1}{z-c}\right) + P(z - c),$$

* This is discussed by Mittag-Leffler, (l.c., p. 322).

then the residue of $H(z)$ for $z = c$ is

$$C_1 g(u-c) + C_2 \frac{d}{du} g(u-c) + \ldots + C_{n+1} \frac{d^n}{du^n} g(u-c);$$

and similarly for all the other accidental singularities of $F(z)$. Hence

$$- F(u) + \Sigma \left\{ C_1 + C_2 \frac{d}{du} + \ldots + C_{n+1} \frac{d^n}{du^n} \right\} g(u-c) = - A e^{\lambda u},$$

or

$$F(z) = A e^{\lambda z} + \Sigma \left\{ C_1 + C_2 \frac{d}{dz} + \ldots + C_{n+1} \frac{d^n}{dz^n} \right\} g(z-c),$$

where the summation extends over all the accidental singularities of $F(z)$ in a parallelogram of periods which contains $z$, and $g(z)$ is the function $e^{\lambda z} \zeta(z)$. This result is due to Mittag-Leffler.

Since $\mu = e^{2\lambda\omega}$ and

$$g(z - c + 2\omega) = \mu g(z-c) + 2\eta\mu e^{\lambda(z-c)},$$

we have

$$\mu F(z) = F(z + 2\omega)$$

$$= \mu A e^{\lambda z} + \Sigma \left\{ C_1 + C_2 \frac{d}{dz} + \ldots + C_{n+1} \frac{d^n}{dz^n} \right\} \mu g(z-c)$$

$$+ 2\eta\mu e^{\lambda z} \Sigma (C_1 + C_2 \lambda + \ldots + C_{n+1} \lambda^n) e^{-\lambda c};$$

and therefore $\quad \Sigma (C_1 + C_2 \lambda + \ldots + C_{n+1} \lambda^n) e^{-\lambda c} = 0,$

the summation extending over all the accidental singularities of $F(z)$. The same equation can be derived through $\mu' F(z) = F(z + 2\omega')$.

Again $\Sigma C_1$ is the sum of the residues in a parallelogram of periods, and therefore

$$2\pi i \, \Sigma C_1 = \int F(z) \, dz,$$

the integral being taken positively round it. If $p$ be one corner, the integral is

$$2\omega (1 - \mu') \int_0^1 F(p + 2\omega t) \, dt - 2\omega' (1 - \mu) \int_0^1 F(p + 2\omega' t) \, dt,$$

each integral being for real variables of $t$.

Hermite's special form can be derived from Mittag-Leffler's by making $\lambda$ vanish.

*Note.* Both Hermite and Mittag-Leffler, in their investigations, have used the notation of the Jacobian theory of elliptic functions, instead of dealing with general periodic functions. The forms of their results are as follows, using as far as possible the notation of the preceding articles.

I. When the function is defined by the equations

$$F(z + 2K) = \mu F(z), \qquad F(z + 2iK') = \mu' F(z),$$

then

$$F(z) = \Sigma \left\{ C_1 + C_2 \frac{d}{dz} + \ldots + C_{n+1} \frac{d^n}{dz^n} \right\} G(z-c),$$

where

$$G(z) = \frac{H'(0) \, H(z + \omega)}{H(z) \, H(\omega)} e^{\lambda z},$$

(the symbol $H$ denoting the Jacobian $H$-function), and the constants $\omega$ and $\lambda$ are determined by the equations

$$\mu = e^{2\lambda K}, \quad \mu' = e^{-\frac{i\pi\omega}{K} + 2\lambda i K'}$$

II. If both $\lambda$ and $a$ be zero, so that $F(z)$ is a doubly-periodic function of the first kind, then

$$F(z) = C_0 + \Sigma \left\{ b_1 + b_2 \frac{d}{dz} + \dots + b_{n+1} \frac{d^n}{dz^n} \right\} \frac{H'(z-c)}{H(z-c)},$$

with the condition $\Sigma b_1 = 0$.

III. If $a$ be zero, but not $\lambda$, then

$$F(z) = A e^{\lambda z} + \Sigma \left\{ C_1 + C_2 \frac{d}{dz} + \dots + C_{n+1} \frac{d^n}{dz^n} \right\} g(z-c),$$

where

$$g(z) = \frac{H'(z)}{H(z)} e^{\lambda z},$$

the constants being subject to the condition

$$\Sigma (C_1 + C_2 \lambda + \dots + C_{n+1} \lambda^n) e^{-\lambda c} = 0,$$

and the summations extending to all the accidental singularities of $F(z)$ in a parallelogram of periods containing the variable $z$.

**139.** Reverting now to the function $F(z)$, we have $G(z)$, defined as

$$\frac{\sigma(z+a)}{\sigma(z)\,\sigma(a)} e^{\lambda z},$$

when $a$ and $\lambda$ are properly determined, satisfying the equations

$$G(z+2\omega) = \mu G(z), \quad G(z+2\omega') = \mu' G(z).$$

Hence $\Omega(z) = F(z)/G(z)$ is a doubly-periodic function of the first kind; and therefore the number of its irreducible zeros is equal to the number of its irreducible infinities, and their sums (proper account being taken of multiplicity) are congruent to one another with moduli $2\omega$ and $2\omega'$.

Let $c_1, c_2, \dots, c_m$ be the set of infinities of $F(z)$ in the parallelogram of periods containing the point $z$; and let $\gamma_1, \dots, \gamma_\mu$ be the set of zeros of $F(z)$ in the same parallelogram, an infinity of order $n$ or a zero of order $n$ occurring $n$ times in the respective sets. The only zero of $G(z)$ in the parallelogram is congruent with $-a$, and its only infinity is congruent with $0$, each being simple. Hence the $m+1$ irreducible infinities of $\Omega(z)$ are congruent with

$$-a, c_1, c_2, \dots, c_m,$$

and its $\mu+1$ irreducible zeros are congruent with

$$0, \gamma_1, \gamma_2, \dots, \gamma_\mu;$$

and therefore

$$m+1 = \mu+1,$$

$$-a + \Sigma c \equiv \Sigma \gamma.$$

From the first it follows* that *the number of infinities of a doubly-periodic function of the second kind in a parallelogram of periods is equal to the number of its zeros, and that the excess of the sum of the former over the sum of the latter is congruent with*

$$\pm \left( \frac{\omega'}{\pi i} \log \mu - \frac{\omega}{\pi i} \log \mu' \right),$$

*the sign being the same as that of* $\Re \left( \dfrac{\omega'}{i\omega} \right)$.

The result just obtained renders it possible to derive another expression for $F(z)$, substantially due to Hermite. Consider a function

$$F_1(z) = \frac{\sigma(z - \gamma_1)\, \sigma(z - \gamma_2) \ldots \sigma(z - \gamma_m)}{\sigma(z - c_1)\, \sigma(z - c_2) \ldots \sigma(z - c_m)}\, e^{\rho z},$$

where $\rho$ is a constant. Evidently $F_1(z)$ has the same zeros and the same infinities, each in the same degree, as $F(z)$. Moreover

$$F_1(z + 2\omega) = F_1(z)\, e^{2\eta(\Sigma c - \Sigma \gamma) + 2\rho\omega},$$
$$F_1(z + 2\omega') = F_1(z)\, e^{2\eta'(\Sigma c - \Sigma \gamma) + 2\rho\omega'}.$$

If, then, we choose points $c$ and $\gamma$, such that

$$\Sigma c - \Sigma \gamma = a,$$

and we take $\rho = \lambda$, where $a$ and $\lambda$ are the constants of $G(z)$, then

$$F_1(z + 2\omega) = \mu F_1(z), \quad F_1(z + 2\omega') = \mu' F_1(z).$$

The function $F_1(z)/F(z)$ is a doubly-periodic function of the first kind, and by the construction of $F_1(z)$ it has no zeros and no infinities in the finite part of the plane: it is therefore a constant. Hence

$$F(z) = A\, \frac{\sigma(z - \gamma_1)\, \sigma(z - \gamma_2) \ldots \sigma(z - \gamma_m)}{\sigma(z - c_1)\, \sigma(z - c_2) \ldots \sigma(z - c_m)}\, e^{\lambda z},$$

where $\Sigma c - \Sigma \gamma = a$, and $a$ and $\lambda$ are determined as for the function $G(z)$.

**140.** One of the most important applications of secondary doubly-periodic functions is that which leads to the solution of Lamé's equation in the cases when it can be integrated by means of uniform functions. This equation is subsidiary to the solution of the general equation, which is characteristic of the potential of an attracting mass at a point in free space; and it can be expressed† either in the form

$$\frac{d^2 w}{dz^2} = (A k^2 \operatorname{sn}^2 z + B)\, w,$$

or in the form

$$\frac{d^2 w}{dz^2} = \{A \wp(z) + B\}\, w,$$

---

* Frobenius, *Crelle*, xciii, pp. 55—68, a memoir which contains developments of the properties of the function $G(z)$. The result appears to have been noticed first by Brioschi, (*Comptes Rendus*, t. xcii, p. 325), in discussing a more limited form.

† The equation arises when the coordinates of any point in space are taken to be the parameters of the three confocal quadrics through the point. For the actual derivation of the equation in either of the forms stated, see my *Theory of Differential Equations*, vol. iv, § 148.

according to the class of elliptic functions used. In order that the integral may be uniform, the constant $A$ must be $n(n+1)$, where $n$ is a positive integer; this value of $A$, moreover, is the value that occurs most naturally in the derivation of the equation. The constant $B$ can be taken arbitrarily.

The foregoing equation is one of a class, the properties of which have been established* by Picard, Floquet, and others. Without entering into their discussion, the following will suffice to connect them with the secondary periodic function.

Let two independent special solutions be $g(z)$ and $h(z)$, uniform functions of $z$; every solution is of the form $\alpha g(z) + \beta h(z)$, where $\alpha$ and $\beta$ are constants. The equation is unaltered when $z + 2\omega$ is substituted for $z$; hence $g(z+2\omega)$ and $h(z+2\omega)$ are solutions, so that we must have

$$g(z+2\omega) = Ag(z) + Bh(z), \quad h(z+2\omega) = Cg(z) + Dh(z),$$

where, as the functions are determinate, $A, B, C, D$ are determinate constants, such that $AD - BC$ is different from zero.

Similarly, we obtain equations of the form

$$g(z+2\omega') = A'g(z) + B'h(z), \quad h(z+2\omega') = C'g(z) + D'h(z).$$

Using both equations to obtain $g(z + 2\omega + 2\omega')$ in the same form, we have

$$BC' = B'C, \quad AB' + BD' = A'B + B'D;$$

and similarly, for $h(z + 2\omega + 2\omega')$, we have

$$CA' + DC' = C'A + D'C, \quad BC' = B'C;$$

therefore $\qquad \dfrac{C}{B} = \dfrac{C'}{B'} = \delta, \quad \dfrac{A-D}{B} = \dfrac{A'-D'}{B'} = \epsilon.$

Let a solution $\qquad F(z) = ag(z) + bh(z)$

be chosen, so as to give

$$F(z+2\omega) = \mu F(z), \quad F(z+2\omega') = \mu' F(z),$$

if possible. The conditions for the first are

$$\frac{aA + bC}{a} = \frac{aB + bD}{b} = \mu,$$

so that $a/b (= \xi)$ must satisfy the equation

$$A - D = \xi B - \frac{C}{\xi};$$

and the conditions for the second are

$$\frac{aA' + bC'}{a} = \frac{aB' + bD'}{b} = \mu',$$

* Picard, *Comptes Rendus*, t. xc, (1880), pp. 128—131, 293—295; *Crelle*, t. xc, (1880), pp. 281—302.

Floquet, *Comptes Rendus*, t. xcviii, (1884), pp. 82—85; *Ann. de l'Éc. Norm. Sup.*, 3me Sér., t. i, (1884), pp. 181—238.

so that $\xi$ must satisfy the equation

$$A' - D' = \xi B' - \frac{C'}{\xi}.$$

These two equations are the same. being

$$\xi^2 - \epsilon\xi - \delta = 0.$$

Let $\xi_1$ and $\xi_2$ be the roots of this equation which, in general, are unequal; and let $\mu_1$, $\mu_1'$ and $\mu_2$, $\mu_2'$ be the corresponding values of $\mu$, $\mu'$. Then two functions, say $F_1(z)$ and $F_2(z)$, are determined: they are independent of one another, so therefore are $g(z)$ and $h(z)$; and therefore every solution can be expressed in terms of them. Hence *a linear differential equation of the second order, having coefficients that are doubly-periodic functions of the first kind, can generally be integrated by means of doubly-periodic functions of the second kind.*

It therefore follows that Lamé's equation, which will be taken in the form

$$\frac{1}{w}\frac{d^2w}{dz^2} = n(n+1)\wp(z) + B,$$

can be integrated by means of secondary doubly-periodic functions.

**141.** Let $z = c$ be an accidental singularity of $w$ of order $m$; then, for points $z$ in the immediate vicinity of $c$, we have

$$w = \frac{A}{(z-c)^m}\{1 + p(z-c) + q(z-c)^2 + \ldots\},$$

and therefore

$$\frac{1}{w}\frac{d^2w}{dz^2} = \frac{m+m^2}{(z-c)^2} - \frac{2mp}{z-c} + \text{positive powers of } z-c.$$

Since this is equal to $\qquad n(n+1)\wp(z) + B$

it follows that $c$ must be congruent to zero and that $m$, a positive integer, must be $n$. Moreover, $p = 0$. Hence *the accidental singularities of $w$ are congruent to zero, and each is of order $n$.*

The secondary periodic function, which has no accidental singularities except those of order $n$ congruent to $z = 0$, has $n$ irreducible zeros. Let them be $-a_1, -a_2, \ldots, -a_n$; then the form of the function is

$$w = \frac{\sigma(z+a_1)\,\sigma(z+a_2)\ldots\sigma(z+a_n)}{\sigma^n(z)}\,e^{\rho z}.$$

Hence

$$\frac{1}{w}\frac{dw}{dz} = \rho - n\zeta(z) + \sum_{r=1}^{n}\zeta(z+a_r),$$

or, taking $\rho = -\Sigma\zeta(a_r)$, we have

$$\frac{1}{w}\frac{dw}{dz} = \sum_{r=1}^{n}\{\zeta(z+a_r) - \zeta(z) - \zeta(a_r)\},$$

and therefore

$$\frac{1}{w}\frac{d^2w}{dz^2} - \frac{1}{w^2}\left(\frac{dw}{dz}\right)^2 = n\wp(z) - \sum_{r=1}^{n}\wp(z+a_r).$$

But, by Ex. 3, § 131, we have

$$\frac{1}{w^2}\left(\frac{dw}{dz}\right)^2 = \frac{1}{4}\left\{\sum_{r=1}^{n}\frac{\wp'(a_r)-\wp'(z)}{\wp(a_r)-\wp(z)}\right\}^2$$

$$= \frac{1}{4}\sum_{r=1}^{n}\left\{\frac{\wp'(a_r)-\wp'(z)}{\wp(a_r)-\wp(z)}\right\}^2 + \frac{1}{2}\sum_{r=1}^{n}\sum_{s=1}^{n}\left\{\frac{\wp'(a_r)-\wp'(z)}{\wp(a_r)-\wp(z)}\cdot\frac{\wp'(a_s)-\wp'(z)}{\wp(a_s)-\wp(z)}\right\}$$

$$= \sum_{r=1}^{n}\{\wp(z+a_r)+\wp(z)+\wp(a_r)\} + \frac{1}{2}\sum_{r=1}^{n}\sum_{s=1}^{n}\left\{\frac{\wp'(a_r)-\wp'(z)}{\wp(a_r)-\wp(z)}\cdot\frac{\wp'(a_s)-\wp'(z)}{\wp(a_s)-\wp(z)}\right\},$$

by Ex. 4, § 131. Thus

$$\frac{1}{w}\frac{d^2w}{dz^2} = 2n\wp(z) + \sum_{r=1}^{n}\wp(a_r) + \frac{1}{2}\sum_{r=1}^{n}\sum_{s=1}^{n}\left\{\frac{\wp'(a_r)-\wp'(z)}{\wp(a_r)-\wp(z)}\cdot\frac{\wp'(a_s)-\wp'(z)}{\wp(a_s)-\wp(z)}\right\}.$$

Now

$$\frac{\wp'(a_r)-\wp'(z)}{\wp(a_r)-\wp(z)}\cdot\frac{\wp'(a_s)-\wp'(z)}{\wp(a_s)-\wp(z)}$$

$$= \frac{4\wp^3(z)-g_2\wp(z)-g_3+\wp'(a_r)\wp'(a_s)-\{\wp'(a_r)+\wp'(a_s)\}\wp'(z)}{\{\wp(z)-\wp(a_r)\}\{\wp(z)-\wp(a_s)\}}$$

$$= 4\{\wp(z)+\wp(a_r)+\wp(a_s)\} + \frac{A\{\wp'(a_r)-\wp'(z)\}}{\wp(z)-\wp(a_r)} + \frac{B\{\wp'(a_s)-\wp'(z)\}}{\wp(z)-\wp(a_s)},$$

where
$$A = \frac{\wp'(a_r)+\wp'(a_s)}{\wp(a_r)-\wp(a_s)} = -B.$$

Let the constants $a$ be such that

$$\left.\begin{aligned}\frac{\wp'(a_1)+\wp'(a_2)}{\wp(a_1)-\wp(a_2)} + \frac{\wp'(a_1)+\wp'(a_3)}{\wp(a_1)-\wp(a_3)} + \ldots = 0\\[2mm]\frac{\wp'(a_2)+\wp'(a_1)}{\wp(a_2)-\wp(a_1)} + \frac{\wp'(a_2)+\wp'(a_3)}{\wp(a_2)-\wp(a_3)} + \ldots = 0\\\vdots\qquad\qquad\vdots\qquad\quad\vdots\qquad\vdots\end{aligned}\right\},$$

$n$ equations of which only $n-1$ are independent, because the sum of the $n$ left-hand sides vanishes. Then in the double summation the coefficient of each of the fractions $\dfrac{\wp'(a_r)-\wp'(z)}{\wp(z)-\wp(a_r)}$ is zero; and so

$$\sum_{r=1}^{n}\sum_{s=1}^{n}\left\{\frac{\wp'(a_r)-\wp'(z)}{\wp(a_r)-\wp(z)}\cdot\frac{\wp'(a_s)-\wp'(z)}{\wp(a_s)-\wp(z)}\right\} = 2n(n-1)\wp(z) + 4(n-1)\sum_{r=1}^{n}\wp(a_r),$$

and therefore
$$\frac{1}{w}\frac{d^2w}{dz^2} = n(n+1)\wp(z) + (2n-1)\sum_{r=1}^{n}\wp(a_r).$$

Hence *it follows that*

$$F(z) = w_1 = \frac{\sigma(z+a_1)\,\sigma(z+a_2)\ldots\sigma(z+a_n)}{\sigma^n(z)}\,e^{-z\sum_{r=1}^{n}\zeta(a_r)}$$

*satisfies Lamé's equation, provided the n constants a be determined by the preceding equations and by the relation*

$$B = (2n-1)\sum_{r=1}^{n}\wp(a_r).$$

Evidently the equation is unaltered when $-z$ is substituted for $z$; and therefore

$$F(-z) = w_2 = \frac{\sigma(z-a_1)\,\sigma(z-a_2)\ldots\sigma(z-a_n)}{\sigma^n(z)}\, e^{z \sum\limits_{r=1}^{n} \zeta(a_r)}$$

is another solution. Every solution is of the form

$$MF(z) + NF(-z),$$

where $M$ and $N$ are arbitrary constants.

COROLLARY. The simplest cases are when $n=1$ and $n=2$.

When $n=1$, the equation is

$$\frac{1}{w}\frac{d^2w}{dz^2} = 2\wp(z) + B;$$

there is only a single constant $a$ determined by the single equation

$$B = \wp(a),$$

and the general solution is

$$w = M\frac{\sigma(z+a)}{\sigma(z)}\, e^{-z\zeta(a)} + N\frac{\sigma(z-a)}{\sigma(z)}\, e^{z\zeta(a)}.$$

When $n=2$, the equation is

$$\frac{1}{w}\frac{d^2w}{dz^2} = 6\wp(z) + B.$$

The general solution is

$$w = M\frac{\sigma(z+a)\,\sigma(z+b)}{\sigma^2(z)}\, e^{-z\zeta(a)-z\zeta(b)} + N\frac{\sigma(z-a)\,\sigma(z-b)}{\sigma^2(z)}\, e^{z\zeta(a)+z\zeta(b)},$$

where $a$ and $b$ are determined by the conditions

$$\frac{\wp'(a)+\wp'(b)}{\wp(a)-\wp(b)} = 0, \qquad \wp(a)+\wp(b) = \tfrac{1}{3}B.$$

Rejecting the solution $a+b \equiv 0$, we have $a$ and $b$ determined by the equations

$$\wp(a) + \dot\wp(b) = \tfrac{1}{3}B, \qquad \wp(a)\,\wp(b) = \tfrac{1}{9}B^2 - \tfrac{1}{4}g_2.$$

For a full discussion of Lamé's equation and for references to the original sources of information, see Halphen, *Traité des fonctions elliptiques*, t. ii, chap. XII., in particular, pp. 495 et seq.

*Ex.* When Lamé's equation has the form

$$\frac{1}{w}\frac{d^2w}{dz^2} = n(n+1)\,k^2\,\mathrm{sn}^2 z - h,$$

obtain the solution for $n=1$, in terms of the Jacobian Theta-Functions,

$$w = A\frac{H(z+\omega)}{\Theta(z)}\, e^{-z\frac{\Theta'(\omega)}{\Theta(\omega)}} + B\frac{H(z-\omega)}{\Theta(z)}\, e^{z\frac{\Theta'(\omega)}{\Theta(\omega)}},$$

where $\omega$ is determined by the equation $\mathrm{dn}^2\,\omega = h - k^2$; and discuss in particular the solution when $h$ has the values $1+k^2$, $1$, $k^2$.

Obtain the solution for $n=2$ in the form

$$w = A\frac{d}{dz}\left[\frac{H(z+\omega)}{\Theta(z)}\, e^{\left\{\lambda - \frac{\Theta'(\omega)}{\Theta(\omega)}\right\} z}\right] + B\frac{d}{dz}\left[\frac{H(z-\omega)}{\Theta(z)}\, e^{-\left\{\lambda - \frac{\Theta'(\omega)}{\Theta(\omega)}\right\} z}\right],$$

where $\lambda$ and $\omega$ are given by the equations

$$\lambda^2 = \frac{(2k^2 \operatorname{sn}^2 a - 1 - k^2)(2k^2 \operatorname{sn}^2 a - 1)(2 \operatorname{sn}^2 a - 1)}{3k^2 \operatorname{sn}^4 a - 2(1+k^2) \operatorname{sn}^2 a + 1},$$

$$\operatorname{sn}^2 \omega = \frac{\operatorname{sn}^4 a\,(2k^2 \operatorname{sn}^2 a - 1 - k^2)}{3k^2 \operatorname{sn}^4 a - 2(1+k^2) \operatorname{sn}^2 a + 1},$$

and $a$ is derived from $h$ by the relation

$$h = 4(1+k^2) - 6k^2 \operatorname{sn}^2 a.$$

Deduce the three solutions that occur when $\lambda$ is zero, and the two solutions that occur when $\lambda$ is infinite.

(Hermite.)

## Doubly-Periodic Functions of the Third Kind.

**142.** The equations characteristic of a doubly-periodic function $\Phi(z)$ of the third kind are

$$\Phi(z + 2\omega) = \Phi(z), \quad \Phi(z + 2\omega') = e^{-\frac{m\pi i}{\omega} z} \Phi(z),$$

where $m$ is an integer different from zero.

Obviously the number of zeros in each parallelogram is invariable, as well as the number of infinities. Let a parallelogram, chosen so that its sides contain no zero and no infinity of $\Phi(z)$, have $p$, $p + 2\omega$, $p + 2\omega'$ for three of its angular points; and let $a_1, a_2, \ldots, a_l$ be the zeros and $c_1, \ldots, c_m$ be the infinities, multiplicity of order being represented by repetitions. Then using $\Psi(z)$ to denote $\frac{d}{dz} \{\log \Phi(z)\}$, we have, as the equations characteristic of $\Psi(z)$,

$$\Psi(z + 2\omega) = \Psi(z), \quad \Psi(z + 2\omega') = \Psi(z) - \frac{m\pi i}{\omega};$$

and for points in the parallelogram

$$\Psi(z) = \sum_{r=1}^{l} \frac{1}{z - a_r} - \sum_{s=1}^{n} \frac{1}{z - c_s} + H(z),$$

where $H(z)$ has no infinity within the parallelogram. Hence

$$2\pi i\,(l - n) = \int \Psi(z)\,dz,$$

the integral being taken round the parallelogram: by using the Corollary to Prop. II. in § 116, we have

$$2\pi i\,(l - n) = -\int_p^{p+2\omega} - \left(\frac{m\pi i}{\omega}\right) dz = 2m\pi i,$$

so that $l = n + m$:

or *the algebraical excess of the number of irreducible zeros over the number of irreducible infinities is equal to* $m$.

Again, since

$$\frac{z}{z - \mu} = 1 + \frac{\mu}{z - \mu},$$

we have

$$\Sigma \frac{a}{z - a} - \Sigma \frac{c}{z - c} + l - n = z\Psi(z) - zH(z),$$

and therefore

$$2\pi i\,(\Sigma a - \Sigma c) = \int z\Psi(z)\,dz,$$

the integral being taken round the parallelogram.  As before, this gives

$$2\pi i \left(\Sigma a - \Sigma c\right) = \int_p^{p+2\omega'} 2\omega \Psi\left(z\right) dz - \int_p^{p+2\omega} \left\{ 2\omega' \Psi\left(z\right) - \frac{m\pi i}{\omega}\left(z + 2\omega'\right)\right\} dz.$$

The former integral is

$$2\omega \int_p^{p+2\omega'} \frac{\Phi'\left(z\right)}{\Phi\left(z\right)} dz$$

$$= 2\omega \left(-\frac{m\pi i}{\omega} p\right) = -2m\pi i p,$$

for the side of the parallelogram contains* no zero and no infinity of $\Phi\left(z\right)$.

The latter integral, with its own sign, is

$$-2\omega' \int_p^{p+2\omega} \frac{\Phi'\left(z\right)}{\Phi\left(z\right)} dz + \frac{m\pi i}{\omega} \int_p^{p+2\omega} \left(z + 2\omega'\right) dz$$

$$= 0 + \frac{m\pi i}{2\omega} \left\{ \left(p + 2\omega + 2\omega'\right)^2 - \left(p + 2\omega'\right)^2 \right\}$$

$$= 2m\pi i \left(p + \omega + 2\omega'\right).$$

Hence                                        $\Sigma a - \Sigma c = m\left(\omega + 2\omega'\right),$

giving *the excess of the sum of the zeros over the sum of the infinities in any parallelogram chosen so as to contain the variable z and to have no one of its sides passing through a zero or an infinity of the function.*

These will be taken as the irreducible zeros and the irreducible infinities: all others are congruent with them.

All these results are obtained through the theorem II. of § 116, which assumes that the argument of $\omega'$ is greater than the argument of $\omega$ or, what is the equivalent assumption (§ 129), that

$$\eta\omega' - \eta'\omega = \tfrac{1}{2}\pi i.$$

**143.**  Taking the function, naturally suggested for the present class by the corresponding function for the former class, we introduce a function

$$\phi\left(z\right) = e^{\lambda z^2 + \mu z} \frac{\sigma\left(z - a_1\right)\sigma\left(z - a_2\right)\ldots\sigma\left(z - a_l\right)}{\sigma\left(z - c_1\right)\sigma\left(z - c_2\right)\ldots\sigma\left(z - c_n\right)},$$

where the $a$'s and the $c$'s are connected by the relations

$$\Sigma a - \Sigma c = m\left(\omega + 2\omega'\right), \quad l - n = m.$$

Then $\phi\left(z\right)$ satisfies the equations characteristic of doubly-periodic functions of the third kind, if

$$\begin{cases} 0 = 4\lambda\omega + 2m\eta, \\ k \,.\, 2\pi i = 4\lambda\omega^2 + 2m\eta\omega + 2\mu\omega + m\pi i - 2m\eta\left(\omega + 2\omega'\right); \end{cases}$$

$$\begin{cases} -\dfrac{m\pi i}{\omega} = 4\lambda\omega' + 2m\eta', \\ k' \,.\, 2\pi i = 4\lambda\omega'^2 + 2m\eta'\omega' + 2\mu\omega' + m\pi i - 2m\eta'\left(\omega + 2\omega'\right), \end{cases}$$

---

* Both in this integral and in the next, which contain parts of the form $\int \frac{dw}{w}$, there is, as in Prop. VII., § 116, properly an additive term of the form $2\kappa\pi i$, where $\kappa$ is an integer.  But, as there, both terms can be removed by modification of the position of the parallelogram; and this modification is supposed, in the proof, to have been made.

$k$ and $k'$ being disposable integers.   These are uniquely satisfied by taking

$$\lambda = -\frac{1}{2}\frac{m\eta}{\omega},$$

$$\mu = \frac{1}{2}\frac{m\pi i}{\omega} + m(\eta + 2\eta'),$$

with                         $k = 0, \quad k' = m.$

Assuming the last two, the values of $\lambda$ and $\mu$ are thus obtained so as to make $\phi(z)$ a doubly-periodic function of the third kind.

Now let $a_1, \ldots, a_l$ be chosen as the irreducible zeros of $\Phi(z)$ and $c_1, \ldots, c_n$ as the irreducible infinities of $\Phi(z)$, which is possible owing to the conditions to which they were subjected.   Then $\Phi(z)/\phi(z)$ is a doubly-periodic function of the first kind; it has no zeros and no infinities in the parallelogram of periods and therefore none in the whole plane; it is therefore a constant, so that

$$\Phi(z) = A e^{-\frac{1}{2}\frac{\eta}{\omega}mz^2 + \left\{\frac{1}{2}\frac{\pi i}{\omega} + (\eta + 2\eta')\right\}mz} \frac{\sigma(z-a_1)\,\sigma(z-a_2)\ldots\sigma(z-a_l)}{\sigma(z-c_1)\,\sigma(z-c_2)\ldots\sigma(z-c_n)},$$

a representation of $\Phi(z)$ in terms of known quantities.

*Ex.*   Had the representation been effected by means of the Jacobian Theta-Functions which would replace $\sigma(z)$ by $H(z)$, then the term in $z^2$ in the exponential would be absent.

**144.**   No limitation on the integral value of $m$, except that it must not vanish, has been made: and the form just obtained holds for all values. Equivalent expressions in the form of sums of functions can be constructed: but there is then a difference between the cases of $m$ positive and $m$ negative.

If $m$ be positive, being the excess of the number of irreducible zeros over the number of irreducible infinities, the function is said to be of positive class $m$; it is evident that there are suitable functions without any irreducible infinities—they are integral functions.

When $m$ is negative $(= -n)$, the function is said to be of negative class $n$; but there are no corresponding integral functions.

**145.**   First, *let $m$ be positive.*

i.   If the function have no accidental singularities, it can be expressed in the form

$$A e^{\lambda z^2 + \mu z}\, \sigma(z-a_1)\, \sigma(z-a_2) \ldots \sigma(z-a_m),$$

with appropriate values of $\lambda$ and $\mu$.

ii.   If the function have $n$ irreducible accidental singularities, then it has $m + n$ irreducible zeros.   We proceed to shew that the function can be expressed by means of similar functions of positive class $m$, with a single accidental singularity.

Using $\lambda$ and $\mu$ to denote

$$-\frac{1}{2}\frac{m\eta}{\omega} \quad \text{and} \quad \frac{1}{2}\frac{m\pi i}{\omega} + m(\eta + 2\eta'),$$

which are the constants in the exponential factor common to all functions of the same class, consider a function, of positive class $m$ with a single accidental singularity, in the form

$$\psi_m(z, u) = e^{\lambda(z^2 - u^2) + \mu(z-u)} \frac{\sigma(z - b_1)\,\sigma(z - b_2)\dots\sigma(z - b_{m+1})}{\sigma(u - b_1)\,\sigma(u - b_2)\dots\sigma(u - b_{m+1})}\frac{1}{\sigma(z - u)},$$

where $b_1, b_2, \dots, b_m$ are arbitrary constants, of sum $s$, and

$$m(\omega + 2\omega') = b_{m+1} + b_1 + b_2 + \dots + b_m - u$$
$$= b_{m+1} + s - u.$$

The function $\psi_m$ satisfies the equations

$$\psi_m(z + 2\omega, u) = \psi_m(z, u), \quad \psi_m(z + 2\omega', u) = e^{-\frac{m\pi z i}{\omega}}\psi_m(z, u);$$

regarded as a function of $z$, it has $u$ for its sole accidental singularity, evidently simple.

The function $\dfrac{1}{\psi_m(z, u)}$ can be expressed in the form

$$e^{\lambda(u^2 - z^2) + \mu(u-z)} \frac{\sigma(u - z)\,\sigma(u - b_1)\dots\sigma(u - b_m)}{\sigma(z - b_1)\dots\dots\dots\sigma(z - b_m)}\frac{\sigma\{s - m(\omega + 2\omega')\}}{\sigma\{u - z - s + m(\omega + 2\omega')\}}.$$

Regarded as a function of $u$, it has $z, b_1, \dots, b_m$ for zeros and $z + s - m(\omega + 2\omega')$ for its sole accidental singularity, evidently simple: also

$$z + b_1 + \dots + b_m - \{z + s - m(\omega + 2\omega')\} = m(\omega + 2\omega').$$

Hence owing to the values of $\lambda$ and $\mu$, it follows that $\dfrac{1}{\psi_m(z, u)}$, when regarded as a function of $u$, satisfies all the conditions that establish a doubly-periodic function of the third kind of positive class $m$, so that

$$\frac{1}{\psi_m(z, u + 2\omega)} = \frac{1}{\psi_m(z, u)},$$
$$\frac{1}{\psi_m(z, u + 2\omega')} = e^{-\frac{m\pi u i}{\omega}}\frac{1}{\psi_m(z, u)};$$

and therefore

$$\psi_m(z, u + 2\omega) = \psi_m(z, u), \quad \psi_m(z, u + 2\omega') = e^{\frac{m\pi u i}{\omega}}\psi_m(z, u).$$

Evidently $\psi_m(z, u)$ regarded as a function of $u$ is of negative class $m$: its infinities and its sole zero can at once be seen from the form

$$\psi_m(z, u) = e^{\lambda(z^2 - u^2) + \mu(z-u)} \frac{\sigma(z - b_1)\dots\sigma(z - b_m)\,\sigma\{u - z - s + m(\omega + 2\omega')\}}{\sigma(u - z)\,\sigma(u - b_1)\dots\sigma(u - b_m)\,\sigma\{s - m(\omega + 2\omega')\}}.$$

Each of the infinities is simple. In the vicinity of $u = z$, the expansion of the function is

$$\frac{-1}{u - z} + \text{positive integral powers of } u - z:$$

and, in the vicinity of $u = b_r$, it is

$$\frac{G_r(z)}{u - b_r} + \text{positive integral powers of } u - b_r,$$

where $G_r(z)$ denotes

$$e^{\lambda(z^2 - b_r^2) + \mu(z - b_r)} \frac{\sigma(z - b_1)\ldots\sigma(z - b_{r-1})\sigma(z - b_{r+1})\ldots\sigma(z - b_m)\sigma\{z + s - b_r - m(\omega + 2\omega')\}}{\sigma(b_r - b_1)\ldots\sigma(b_r - b_{r-1})\sigma(b_r - b_{r+1})\ldots\sigma(b_r - b_m)\sigma\{s - m(\omega + 2\omega')\}},$$

and is therefore an integral function of $z$ of positive class $m$.

Let $\Phi(u)$ be a doubly-periodic function of the third kind, of positive class $m$; and let its irreducible accidental singularities, that is, those which occur in a parallelogram containing the point $u$, be $\alpha_1$ of order $1 + \mu_1$, $\alpha_2$ of order $1 + \mu_2$, and so on. In the immediate vicinity of a point $\alpha_r$, let

$$\Phi(u) = \left(A_r - B_r \frac{d}{du} + C_r \frac{d^2}{du^2} - \ldots \pm M_r \frac{d^{\mu_r}}{dw^{\mu_r}}\right)\frac{1}{u - \alpha_r} + P_r(u - \alpha_r).$$

Then proceeding as in the case of the secondary doubly-periodic functions (§ 137), we construct a function

$$F(u) = \Phi(u)\,\psi_m(z, u).$$

We at once have $\quad F(u + 2\omega) = F(u) = F(u + 2\omega'),$

so that $F(u)$ is a doubly-periodic function of the first kind; hence the sum of its residues for all the poles in a parallelogram of periods is zero.

For the infinities of $F(u)$, which arise through the factor $\psi_m(z, u)$, we have as the residue for $u = z$

$$-\Phi(z),$$

and as the residue for $u = b_r$, where $r = 1, 2, \ldots, m$,

$$\Phi(b_r)\,G_r(z).$$

In the vicinity of $\alpha_r$, we have

$$\psi_m(z, u) = \psi_m(z, \alpha_r) + (u - \alpha_r)\psi_m'(z, \alpha_r) + \frac{(u - \alpha_r)^2}{2!}\psi_m''(z, \alpha_r) + \ldots,$$

where dashes imply differentiation of $\psi_m(z, u)$ with regard to $u$, after which $u$ is made equal to $\alpha_r$; so that in $\Phi(u)\psi_m(z, u)$ the residue for $u = \alpha_r$, where $r = 1, 2, \ldots$, is

$$E_r(z) = A_r\psi_m(z, \alpha_r) + B_r\psi_m'(z, \alpha_r) + C_r\psi_m''(z, \alpha_r) + \ldots + M_r\psi_m^{(\mu_r)}(z, \alpha_r).$$

Hence we have

$$-\Phi(z) + \sum_{r=1}^{m} \Phi(b_r)\,G_r(z) + \sum_{s=1} E_s(z) = 0,$$

and therefore $\quad \Phi(z) = \sum_{s=1} E_s(z) + \sum_{r=1}^{m} \Phi(b_r)\,G_r(z),$

giving *the expression of $\Phi(z)$ by means of doubly-periodic functions of the third kind, which are of positive class $m$ and either have no accidental singularity or have only one and that a simple singularity.*

The $m$ quantities $b_1, \ldots, b_m$ are arbitrary; the simplest case occurs when the $m$ zeros of $\Phi(z)$ are different and are chosen as the values of $b_1, \ldots, b_m$. The value of $\Phi(z)$ is then

$$\Phi(z) = \sum_{s=1} E_s(z),$$

where the summation extends to all the irreducible accidental singularities; while, if there be the further simplification that all the accidental singularities are simple, then

$$\Phi(z) = A_1 \psi_m(z, \alpha_1) + A_2 \psi_m(z, \alpha_2) + \ldots,$$

the summation extending to all the irreducible simple singularities.

*The quantity* $\psi_m(z, \alpha_r)$, *which is equal to*

$$e^{\lambda(z^2 - a_r{}^2) + \mu(z - a_r)} \frac{\sigma(z - b_1) \ldots \sigma(z - b_m)\, \sigma\{z + \Sigma b - m(\omega + 2\omega') - \alpha_r\}}{\sigma(\alpha_r - b_1) \ldots \sigma(\alpha_r - b_m)\, \sigma\{\Sigma b - m(\omega + 2\omega')\}\, \sigma(z - \alpha_r)},$$

and is subsidiary to the construction of the function $E(z)$, *is called the simple element of positive class* $m$.

In the general case, the portion

$$\Sigma\, \Phi(b_r)\, G_r(z)$$

gives an integral function of $z$, and the portion $\sum_{s=1} E_s(z)$ gives a fractional function of $z$.

**146.** Secondly, *let* $m$ *be negative and equal to* $-n$. The equations satisfied by $\Phi(z)$ are

$$\Phi(z + 2\omega) = \Phi(z), \qquad \Phi(z + 2\omega') = e^{\frac{n\pi z i}{\omega}}\, \Phi(z),$$

and the number of irreducible singularities is greater by $n$ than the number of irreducible zeros.

One expression for $\Phi(z)$ is at once obtained by forming its reciprocal, which satisfies the equations

$$\frac{1}{\Phi(z + 2\omega)} = \frac{1}{\Phi(z)}, \qquad \frac{1}{\Phi(z + 2\omega')} = e^{-\frac{n\pi z i}{\omega}} \frac{1}{\Phi(z)},$$

and is therefore of the class just considered: the value of $\dfrac{1}{\Phi(z)}$ is of the form

$$\Sigma\, E_s(z) + \Sigma\, A_r G_r(z).$$

For purposes of expansion, however, this is not a convenient form as it gives only the reciprocal of $\Phi(z)$.

To represent the function, Appell constructed the element

$$\chi_n(z, y) = \frac{\pi}{2\omega} \sum_{s=-\infty}^{s=\infty} e^{\frac{n s \pi i}{\omega}\{y + (s-1)\omega'\}} \cot \frac{\pi(z - y - 2s\omega')}{2\omega},$$

which, since the real part of $\omega'/\omega i$ is positive, converges for all values of $z$ and $y$, except those for which

$$z \equiv y \pmod{2\omega, 2\omega'}.$$

For each of these values one term of the series, and therefore the series itself, becomes infinite of the first order.

Evidently
$$\chi_n(z, y + 2\omega) = \chi_n(z, y),$$
$$\chi_n(z, y + 2\omega') = e^{-\frac{n\pi yi}{\omega}} \chi_n(z, y);$$

therefore in the present case

$$\Omega(y) = \Phi(y) \chi_n(z, y),$$

regarded as a function of $y$, is a doubly-periodic function of the first kind.

Hence the sum of the residues of its irreducible accidental singularities is zero.

Within the parallelogram, which includes $z$, these singularities are :—

(i)   $y = z$, arising through $\chi_n(z, y)$;

(ii)  the singularities of $\Phi(y)$, which are at least $n$ in number, and are $n + l$ in number when $\Phi$ has $l$ irreducible zeros.

The expansion of $\chi_n(z, y)$, in powers of $y - z$, in the vicinity of the point $z$, is

$$\frac{-1}{y - z} + \text{positive integral powers of } y - z;$$

therefore the residue of $\Omega(y)$ is

$$- \Phi(z).$$

Let $\alpha_r$ be any irreducible singularity, and in the vicinity of $\alpha_r$ let $\Phi(y)$ denote

$$\left( A_r - B_r \frac{d}{dy} + C_r \frac{d^2}{dy^2} + \ldots \pm P_r \frac{d^p}{dy^p} \right) \frac{1}{y - \alpha_r}$$

$$+ \text{positive integral powers of } y - \alpha_r,$$

where the series of negative powers is finite because the singularity is accidental; then the residue of $\Omega(y)$ is

$$A_r \chi_n(z, \alpha_r) + B_r \chi_n'(z, \alpha_r) + C_r \chi_n''(z, \alpha_r) + \ldots + P_r \chi_n^{(p)}(z, \alpha_r),$$

where $\chi_n^{(\lambda)}(z, \alpha_r)$ is the value of

$$\frac{d^\lambda \chi_n(z, y)}{dy^\lambda}$$

when $y = \alpha_r$ after differentiation.   Similarly for the residues of other singularities : and so, as their sum is zero, we have

$$\Phi(z) = \Sigma \{ A_r \chi_n(z, \alpha_r) + B_r \chi_n'(z, \alpha_r) + \ldots + P_r \chi_n^{(p)}(z, \alpha_r) \},$$

the summation extending over all the singularities.

The simplest case occurs when all the $N (> n)$ singularities $\alpha$ are accidental and of the first order; the function $\Phi(z)$ can then be expressed in the form

$$A_1\chi_n(z, \alpha_1) + A_2\chi_n(z, \alpha_2) + \ldots + A_N\chi_n(z, \alpha_N).$$

The quantity $\chi_n(z, \alpha)$, which is equal to

$$\frac{\pi}{2\omega} \sum_{s=-\infty}^{s=\infty} e^{\frac{ns\pi i}{\omega}\{(s-1)\omega' + \alpha\}} \cot \frac{\pi(z - \alpha - 2s\omega')}{2\omega},$$

is called the *simple element for the expression of a doubly-periodic function of the third kind of negative class n*.

*Ex.*   Deduce the result

$$\frac{2K}{\pi} \frac{\operatorname{cn} u}{\operatorname{sn} u} = \sum_{s=-\infty}^{s=\infty} (-1)^s \cot \left\{ \frac{\pi(u + 2siK')}{2K} \right\}.$$

**147.**   The function $\chi_n(z, y)$ can be used also as follows.   Since $\chi_m(z, y)$, quà function of $y$, satisfies the equations

$$\chi_m(z, y + 2\omega) = \chi_m(z, y),$$

$$\chi_m(z, y + 2\omega') = e^{-\frac{m\pi y i}{\omega}} \chi_m(z, y),$$

which are the same equations as are satisfied by a function of $y$ of positive class $m$, therefore $\chi_m(\alpha, z)$, which is equal to

$$\frac{\pi}{2\omega} \sum_{s=-\infty}^{s=\infty} e^{\frac{ms\pi i}{\omega}\{z + (s-1)\omega'\}} \cot \frac{\pi(\alpha - z - 2s\omega')}{2\omega},$$

being a function of $z$, satisfies the characteristic equations of § 142; and, in the vicinity of $z = \alpha$,

$$\chi_m(\alpha, z) = \frac{-1}{z - \alpha} + \text{positive integral powers of } z - \alpha.$$

If then we take the function $\Phi(z)$ of § 145, in the case when it has simple singularities at $\alpha_1, \alpha_2, \ldots$ and is of positive class $m$, then

$$\Phi(z) + A_1\chi_m(\alpha_1, z) + A_2\chi_m(\alpha_2, z) + \ldots$$

is a function of positive class $m$ without any singularities: it is therefore equal to an integral function of positive class $m$, say to $G(z)$, where

$$G(z) = A e^{\lambda z^2 + \mu z} \sigma(z - a_1) \ldots \sigma(z - a_m),$$

so that      $$\Phi(z) = G(z) - A_1\chi_m(\alpha_1, z) - A_2\chi_m(\alpha_2, z) - \ldots.$$

*Ex.*   As a single example, consider a function of negative class 2, and let it have no zero within the parallelogram of reference.   Then for the function, in the canonical product-form of § 143, the two irreducible infinities are subject to the relation

$$c_1 + c_2 = 2(\omega + 2\omega'),$$

and the function is      $$\Phi(z) = K e^{\frac{\eta}{\omega} z^2 - \left( \frac{\pi i}{\omega} + 2\eta + 4\eta' \right) z} \frac{1}{\sigma(z - c_1) \sigma(z - c_2)}.$$

The simple elements to express $\Phi(z)$ as a sum are

$$\chi_2(z,\,c_1) = \frac{\pi}{2\omega}\sum_{-\infty}^{\infty} e^{\frac{2s\pi i}{\omega}\{(s-1)\,\omega'+c_1\}}\cot\frac{\pi}{2\omega}(z-c_1-2s\omega'),$$

$$\chi_2(z,\,c_2) = \frac{\pi}{2\omega}\sum_{-\infty}^{\infty} e^{\frac{2s\pi i}{\omega}\{(s-1)\,\omega'+2\omega+4\omega'-c_1\}}\cot\frac{\pi}{2\omega}(z+c_1-2\omega-4\omega'-2s\omega')$$

$$= \frac{\pi}{2\omega}e^{\frac{4\pi i}{\omega}(c_1-\omega')}\sum_{-\infty}^{\infty}e^{\frac{2r\pi i}{\omega}\{(r-1)\,\omega'-c_1\}}\cot\frac{\pi}{2\omega}(z+c_1-2r\omega')$$

after an easy reduction,

$$= e^{\frac{4\pi i}{\omega}(c_1-\omega')}\chi_2(z,\,-c_1).$$

The residue of $\Phi(z)$ for $c_1$, which is a simple singularity, is

$$A_1 = Ke^{\frac{\eta}{\omega}c_1{}^2 - \left(\frac{\pi i}{\omega}+2\eta+4\eta'\right)c_1}\frac{1}{\sigma(c_1-c_2)};$$

and for $c_2$, also a simple singularity, it is

$$A_2 = Ke^{\frac{\eta}{\omega}c_2{}^2 - \left(\frac{\pi i}{\omega}+2\eta+4\eta'\right)c_2}\frac{1}{\sigma(c_2-c_1)},$$

so that

$$\frac{A_1}{A_2} = -e^{\frac{\pi i}{\omega}(c_1-c_2)} = -e^{\frac{2\pi i}{\omega}(c_1-2\omega')}.$$

Hence the expression for $\Phi(z)$ as a sum, which is

$$A_1\chi_2(z,\,c_1)+A_2\chi_2(z,\,c_2),$$

becomes

$$A_1\left\{\chi_2(z,\,c_1)-e^{\frac{2\pi i}{\omega}c_1}\chi_2(z,\,-c_1)\right\};$$

that is, it is a constant multiple of

$$e^{-\frac{\pi i}{\omega}c_1}\chi_2(z,\,c_1)-e^{\frac{\pi i}{\omega}c_1}\chi_2(z,\,-c_1).$$

Again,
$$\Phi(z) = Ke^{\frac{\eta}{\omega}z^2 - \left(\frac{\pi i}{\omega}+2\eta+4\eta'\right)z}\frac{1}{\sigma(z-c_1)\,\sigma(z+c_1-2\omega-4\omega')}$$

$$= -Ke^{\frac{\eta}{\omega}z^2 - \left(\frac{\pi i}{\omega}+2\eta+4\eta'\right)z+2(\eta+2\eta')(z+c_1-\omega-2\omega')}\frac{1}{\sigma(z-c_1)\,\sigma(z+c_1)}$$

$$= Le^{\frac{\eta}{\omega}z^2 - \frac{\pi i z}{\omega}}\frac{\sigma(2c_1)}{\sigma(z-c_1)\,\sigma(z+c_1)},$$

on changing the constant factor. Hence it is possible to determine $L$ so that

$$\Phi(z) = e^{-\frac{\pi i}{\omega}c_1}\chi_2(z,\,c_1)-e^{\frac{\pi i}{\omega}c_1}\chi_2(z,\,-c_1).$$

Taking the residues of the two sides for $z=c_1$, we have

$$Le^{\frac{\eta}{\omega}c_1{}^2 - \frac{\pi i}{\omega}c_1} = e^{-\frac{\pi i}{\omega}c_1},$$

and therefore finally we have

$$e^{\frac{\eta}{\omega}(z^2-c^2)-\frac{\pi i z}{\omega}}\frac{\sigma(2c)}{\sigma(z-c)\,\sigma(z+c)} = e^{-\frac{\pi i c}{\omega}}\chi_2(z,\,c)-e^{\frac{\pi i c}{\omega}}\chi_2(z,\,-c)$$

$$= \frac{\pi}{2\omega}\sum_{-\infty}^{\infty}e^{2s(s-1)\pi i\frac{\omega'}{\omega}}\left\{e^{(2s-1)\frac{\pi i c_1}{\omega}}\cot\frac{\pi}{2\omega}(z-c_1-2s\omega')-e^{-(2s-1)\frac{\pi i c_1}{\omega}}\cot\frac{\pi}{2\omega}(z+c_1-2s\omega')\right\},$$

the right-hand side of which admits of further modification if desired.

Many examples of such developments in trigonometrical series are given by Hermite\*, Biehler†, Halphen‡, Appell§, and Krause‖.

**148**. We shall not further develop the theory of these uniform doubly-periodic functions of the third kind. It will be found in the memoirs of Appell§ to whom it is largely due; and in the treatises of Halphen\*\*, and of Rausenberger††.

It need hardly be remarked that the classes of uniform functions of a single variable which have been discussed form only a small proportion of functions reproducing themselves save as to a factor when the variable is subjected to homographic substitutions, of which a very special example is furnished by linear additive periodicity. Thus there are the various classes of pseudo-automorphic functions, (§ 305) called Thetafuchsian by Poincaré, their characteristic equation being

$$\Theta\left(\frac{\alpha z + \beta}{\gamma z + \delta}\right) = (\gamma z + \delta)^{2m}\,\Theta\,(z),$$

for all the substitutions of the group determining the function: and other classes are investigated in the treatises which have just been quoted.

The following examples relate to particular classes of pseudo-periodic functions.

*Ex.* 1. Shew that, if $F'(z)$ be a uniform function satisfying the equations

$$F'(z+2\omega')=F'(z),$$

$$F\left(z+\frac{2\omega}{m}\right)=bF(z),$$

where $b$ is a primitive $m$th root of unity, then $F(z)$ can be expressed in the form

$$\Sigma\left(A_0+A_1\frac{d}{dz}+\ldots\ldots+A_n\frac{d^n}{dz^n}\right)f(z-a),$$

where $f(z)$ denotes the function

$$\zeta\,(z)+b\zeta\left(z-\frac{2\omega}{m}\right)+b^2\zeta\left(z-\frac{4\omega}{m}\right)+\ldots\ldots+b^{m-1}\zeta\left(z-\frac{2m\omega-2\omega}{m}\right);$$

and prove that $\int F(z)\,dz$ can be expressed in the form of a doubly-periodic function together with a sum of logarithms of doubly-periodic functions with constant coefficients.

(Goursat.)

\* *Comptes Rendus*, t. lv, (1862), pp. 11—18.

† *Sur les développements en séries des fonctions doublement périodiques de troisième espèce*, (Thèse, Paris, Gauthier-Villars, 1879).

‡ *Traité des fonctions elliptiques*, t. i, chap. XIII.

§ *Annales de l'Éc. Norm. Sup.*, 3ᵐᵉ Sér., t. i, pp. 135—164, t. ii, pp. 9—36, t. iii, pp. 9—42.

‖ *Math. Ann.*, t. xxx, (1887), pp. 425—436, 516—534.

\*\* *Traité des fonctions elliptiques*, t. i, chap. XIV.

†† *Lehrbuch der Theorie der periodischen Functionen*, (Leipzig, Teubner, 1884), where further references are given.

*Ex.* 2. Shew that, if a pseudo-periodic function be defined by the equations

$$f(z+2\omega) = f(z)+\lambda,$$
$$f(z+2\omega') = f(z)+\lambda',$$

and if, in the parallelogram of periods containing the point $z$, it have infinities $c, \ldots$ such that in their immediate vicinity

$$f(z) = \left\{ C_1 + C_2 \frac{d}{dz} + \ldots\ldots + C_{n+1} \frac{d^n}{dz^n} \right\} \frac{1}{z-c} + P(z-c),$$

then $f(z)$ can be expressed in the form

$$\frac{\lambda'\eta - \lambda\eta'}{\pm i\pi} z + A + \Sigma \left\{ C_1 + C_2 \frac{d}{dz} + \ldots\ldots + C_{n+1} \frac{d^n}{dz^n} \right\} \zeta(z-c),$$

the summation extending over all the infinities of $f(z)$ in the above parallelogram of periods, and the constants $C_1, \ldots$ being subject to the condition

$$\pm i\pi \Sigma C_1 = \lambda\omega' - \lambda'\omega.$$

Deduce an expression for a doubly-periodic function $\phi(z)$ of the third kind, by assuming

$$f(z) = \frac{\phi'(z)}{\phi(z)}. \tag{Halphen.}$$

*Ex.* 3. If $S(z)$ be a given doubly-periodic function of the first kind, then a pseudo-periodic function $F(z)$, which satisfies the equations

$$F(z+2\omega) = F(z),$$
$$F(z+2\omega') = e^{\frac{n\pi i z}{\omega}} S(z) F(z),$$

where $n$ is an integer, can be expressed in the form

$$F(z) = A e^{\int^z \left\{ \frac{S'(z)}{S(z)} + \frac{n\pi i}{\omega} \right\} \pi(z) dz},$$

where $A$ is a constant and $\pi(z)$ denotes

$$\frac{\eta z}{i\pi} + G + \Sigma \left( B_r + C_r \frac{d}{dz} + D_r \frac{d^2}{dz^2} + \ldots\ldots \right) \zeta(z-b_r),$$

the summation extending over all points $b_r$ and the constants $B_r$ being subject to the relation

$$\Sigma B_r = -\frac{\omega}{i\pi}.$$

Explain how the constants $b$, $G$ and $B$ can be determined. (Picard.)

*Ex.* 4. Shew that the function $F(z)$ defined by the equation

$$F(z) = \sum_{n=-\infty}^{n=\infty} z^{2n+1} (1-z^{2n})^2,$$

for values of $|z|$, which are $<1$, satisfies the equation

$$F(z^2) = F(z);$$

and that the function

$$F_1(x) = \sum_{n=-\infty}^{n=\infty} \frac{\phi_n(x) - a}{\phi_n^2(x)},$$

where $\phi(x) = x^3 - 1$, and $\phi_n(x)$, for positive and negative values of $n$, denotes $\phi[\phi\{\phi \ldots \phi(x)\}]$, $\phi$ being repeated $n$ times, and $a$ is the positive root of $a^3 - a - 1 = 0$; satisfies the equation

$$F_1(x^3 - 1) = F_1(x)$$

for real values of the variable.

Discuss the convergence of the series which defines the function $F_1(x)$. (Appell.)

# CHAPTER XIII.

## FUNCTIONS POSSESSING AN ALGEBRAICAL ADDITION-THEOREM.

**149.** WE may consider at this stage an interesting set\* of important theorems, due to Weierstrass, which are a justification, if any be necessary, for the attention ordinarily (and naturally) paid to functions belonging to the three simplest classes of algebraic, simply-periodic, and doubly-periodic, functions.

*A function* $\phi(u)$ *is said to possess an algebraical addition-theorem*, when among the three values of the function for arguments $u$, $v$, and $u + v$, where $u$ and $v$ are general and not merely special arguments, an algebraical equation exists† having its coefficients independent of $u$ and $v$.

**150.** It is easy to see, from one or two examples, that the function does not need to be a uniform function of the argument. The possibility of multiformity is established in the following proposition:—

*A function defined by an algebraical equation, the coefficients of which are rational functions of the argument, or are uniform simply-periodic functions of the argument, or are uniform doubly-periodic functions of the argument, possesses an algebraical addition-theorem.*

---

\* They are placed in the forefront of Schwarz's account of Weierstrass's theory of elliptic functions, as contained in the *Formeln und Lehrsätze zum Gebrauche der elliptischen Functionen;* but they are there stated (§§ 1—3) without proof. The only proof that has appeared is in a memoir by Phragmén, *Acta Math.*, t. vii, (1885), pp. 33—42 ; and there are some statements (pp. 390—393) in Biermann's *Theorie der analytischen Functionen* relative to the theorems. The proof adopted in the text does not coincide with that given by Phragmén.

† There are functions which possess a kind of algebraical addition-theorem ; thus, for instance, the Jacobian Theta-functions are such that $\Theta_\lambda(u+v)\Theta_\mu(u-v)$ can be rationally expressed in terms of the Theta-functions having $u$ and $v$ for their arguments. Such functions are, however, naturally excluded from the class of functions indicated in the definition.

Such functions, however, possess what may be called a *multiplication-theorem* for multiplication of the argument by an integer, that is, the set of functions $\Theta(mu)$ can be expressed algebraically in terms of the set of functions $\Theta(u)$. This is an extremely special case of a set of transcendental functions having a multiplication-theorem, which are investigated by Poincaré, *Liouville*, $4^{me}$ Sér., t. iv, (1890), pp. 313—365.

First, let the coefficients be rational functions of the argument $u$. If the function defined by the equation be $U$, we have

$$U^m g_0(u) + U^{m-1} g_1(u) + \ldots + g_m(u) = 0,$$

where $g_0(u)$, $g_1(u)$, ..., $g_m(u)$ are rational integral functions of $u$ of degree, say, not higher than $n$. The equation can be transformed into

$$u^n f_0(U) + u^{n-1} f_1(U) + \ldots + f_n(U) = 0,$$

where $f_0(U)$, $f_1(U)$, ..., $f_n(U)$ are rational integral functions of $U$ of degree not higher than $m$.

Let $V$ denote the function when the argument is $v$, and $W$ denote it when the argument is $u + v$; then

$$v^n f_0(V) + v^{n-1} f_1(V) + \ldots + f_n(V) = 0,$$

and
$$(u+v)^n f_0(W) + (u+v)^{n-1} f_1(W) + \ldots + f_n(W) = 0.$$

The algebraical elimination of the two quantities $u$ and $v$ between these three equations leads to an algebraical equation between the quantities $f(U)$, $f(V)$ and $f(W)$, that is, to an algebraical equation between $U$, $V$, $W$, say of the form

$$G(U, V, W) = 0,$$

where $G$ denotes a polynomial function, with coefficients independent of $u$ and $v$. It is easy to prove that $G$ is symmetrical in $U$ and $V$, and that its degree in each of the three quantities $U$, $V$, $W$ is $mn^2$. The equation $G = 0$ implies that the function $U$ possesses an algebraical addition-theorem.

Secondly, let the coefficients* be uniform simply-periodic functions of the argument $u$. Let $\omega$ denote the period: then, by § 113, each of these functions is a rational function of $\tan \dfrac{\pi u}{\omega}$. Let $u'$ denote $\tan \dfrac{\pi u}{\omega}$; then the equation is of the form

$$U^m g_0(u') + U^{m-1} g_1(u') + \ldots + g_m(u') = 0,$$

where the coefficients $g$ are rational (and can be taken as integral) functions of $u'$. If $p$ be the highest degree of $u'$ in any of them, then the equation can be transformed into

$$u'^p f_0(U) + u'^{p-1} f_1(U) + \ldots + f_p(U) = 0,$$

where $f_0(U)$, $f_1(U)$, ..., $f_p(U)$ are rational integral functions of $U$ of degree not higher than $m$.

---

* The limitation to uniformity for the coefficients has been introduced merely to make the illustration simpler; if in any case they were multiform, the equation would be replaced by another which is equivalent to all possible forms of the first arising through the (finite) multiformity of the coefficients: and the new equation would conform to the specified conditions.

Let $v'$ denote $\tan \dfrac{\pi v}{\omega}$, and $w'$ denote $\tan \dfrac{\pi (u + v)}{\omega}$; then the corresponding values of the function are determined by the equations

$$v'^p f_0 (V) + v'^{p-1} f_1 (V) + \dots + f_p (V) = 0,$$

and

$$w'^p f_0 (W) + w'^{p-1} f_1 (W) + \dots + f_p (W) = 0.$$

The relation between $u'$, $v'$, $w'$ is

$$u' v' w' + u' + v' - w' = 0.$$

The elimination of the three quantities $u'$, $v'$, $w'$ among the four equations leads as before to an algebraical equation

$$G (U, V, W) = 0,$$

where $G$ denotes a polynomial function (now of degree $mp^2$) with coefficients independent of $u$ and $v$. The function $U$ therefore possesses an algebraical addition-theorem.

Thirdly, let the coefficients be uniform doubly-periodic functions of the argument $u$. Let $\omega$ and $\omega'$ be the two periods; and let $\wp(u)$, the Weierstrassian elliptic function in those periods, be denoted by $\xi$. Then every coefficient can be expressed in the form

$$\frac{M + N \wp' (u)}{L},$$

where $L$, $M$, $N$ are rational integral functions of $\xi$ of finite degree. Unless each of the quantities $N$ is zero, the form of the equation when these values are substituted for the coefficients is

$$A + B \wp' (u) = 0,$$

so that

$$A^2 = B^2 (4 \xi^3 - g_2 \xi - g_3) ;$$

and this is of the form

$$U^{2m} g_0 (\xi) + U^{2m-1} g_1 (\xi) + \dots + g_{2m} (\xi) = 0,$$

where the coefficients $g$ are rational (and can be taken as integral) functions of $\xi$. If $q$ be the highest degree of $\xi$ in any of them, the equation can be transformed into

$$\xi^q f_0 (U) + \xi^{q-1} f_1 (U) + \dots + f_q (U) = 0,$$

where the coefficients $f$ are rational integral functions of $U$ of degree not higher than $2m$.

Let $\eta$ denote $\wp (v)$ and $\zeta$ denote $\wp (u + v)$; then the corresponding values of the function are determined by the equations

$$\eta^q f_0 (V) + \eta^{q-1} f_1 (V) + \dots \dots + f_q (V) = 0,$$

and

$$\zeta^q f_0 (W) + \zeta^{q-1} f_1 (W) + \dots \dots + f_q (W) = 0.$$

By using Ex. 4, § 131, it is easy to shew that the relation between $\xi$, $\eta$, $\zeta$ is

$$16 (\xi + \eta + \zeta)^2 (\xi - \eta)^2 - 8 (\xi + \eta + \zeta) \{4 (\xi^3 + \eta^3) - g_2 (\xi + \eta) - 2g_3\}$$
$$+ (4 \xi^2 + 4 \xi \eta + 4 \eta^2 - g_2)^2 = 0.$$

The elimination of $\xi$, $\eta$, $\zeta$ from the three equations leads as before to an algebraical equation

$$G\left(U,\,V,\,W\right)=0,$$

of finite degree and with coefficients independent of $u$ and $v$. Therefore in this case also the function $U$ possesses an algebraical addition-theorem.

If, however, all the quantities $N$ be zero, the equation defining $U$ is of the form

$$U^m h_0\left(\xi\right)+U^{m-1}h_1\left(\xi\right)+\ldots+h_m\left(\xi\right)=0\,;$$

and a similar argument then leads to the inference that $U$ possesses an algebraical addition-theorem.

The proposition is thus completely established.

**151.** The generalised converse of the preceding proposition now suggests itself: what are the classes of functions of one variable that possess an algebraical addition-theorem? The solution is contained in Weierstrass's theorem :—

*An analytical function* $\phi\left(u\right)$, *which possesses an algebraical addition-theorem, is either*

(i)  *an algebraic function of* $u$; *or*

(ii)  *an algebraic function of* $e^{\frac{i\pi u}{\omega}}$, *where* $\omega$ *is a suitably chosen constant; or*

(iii)  *an algebraic function of the elliptic function* $\wp\left(u\right)$, *the periods—or the invariants* $g_2$ *and* $g_3$—*being suitably chosen constants.*

Let $U$ denote $\phi\left(u\right)$.

For a given general value of $u$, the function $U$ may have $m$ values where, for functions in general, there is not a necessary limit to the value of $m$; it will be proved that, when the function possesses an algebraical addition-theorem, the integer $m$ must be finite.

For a given general value of $U$, that is, a value of $U$ when its argument is not in the immediate vicinity of a branch-point if there be branch-points, the variable $u$ may have $p$ values, where $p$ may be finite or may be infinite.

Similarly for given general values of $v$ and of $V$, which will be used to denote $\phi\left(v\right)$.

First, let $p$ be finite. Then because $u$ has $p$ values for a given value of $U$ and $v$ has $p$ values for a given value of $V$, and since neither set is affected by the value of the other function, the sum $u+v$ has $p^2$ values because any member of the set $u$ can be combined with any member of the set $v$; and this number $p^2$ of values of $u+v$ is derived for a given value of $U$ and a given value of $V$.

Now in forming the function $\phi\left(u+v\right)$, which will be denoted by $W$, we have $m$ values of $W$ for each value of $u+v$ and therefore we have $mp^2$ values of $W$ for the whole set, that is, for a given value of $U$ and a given value of $V$. Hence the equation between $U$, $V$, $W$ is of degree* $mp^2$ in $W$, necessarily finite when the equation is algebraical; and therefore $m$ is finite.

Because $m$ is finite, $U$ has a finite number $m$ of values for a given value of $u$; and, because $p$ is finite, $u$ has a finite number $p$ of values for a given value of $U$. Hence $U$ is determined in terms of $u$ by an algebraical equation of degree $m$, the coefficients of which are rational integral functions of degree $p$; and *therefore $U$ is an algebraic function of $u$.*

**152.** Next, let $p$ be infinite; then (see *Note*, p. 350) the system of values may be composed of (i) a single simply-infinite series of values or (ii) a finite number of simply-infinite series of values or (iii) a simply-infinite number of simply-infinite series of values, say, a single doubly-infinite series of values or (iv) a finite number of doubly-infinite series of values or (v) an infinite number of doubly-infinite series of values: where, in (v), the infinite number is not restricted to be simply-infinite.

Taking these alternatives in order, we first consider the case where *the $p$ values of $u$ for a given general value of $U$ constitute a single simply-infinite series.* They may be denoted by $f(u, n)$, where $n$ has a simply-infinite series of values and the form of $f$ is such that $f(u, 0) = u$.

Similarly, the $p$ values of $v$ for a given general value of $V$ may be denoted by $f(v, n')$, where $n'$ has a simply-infinite series of values. Then the different values of the argument for the function $W$ are the set of values given by

$$f(u, n) + f(v, n'),$$

for the simply-infinite series of values for $n$ and the similar series of values for $n'$.

The values thus obtained as arguments of $W$ must all be contained in the series $f(u + v, n'')$, where $n''$ has a simply-infinite series of values; and, in the present case, $f(u + v, n'')$ cannot contain other values. Hence for some values of $n$ and some values of $n'$, the total aggregate being not finite, the equation

$$f(u, n) + f(v, n') = f(u + v, n'')$$

must hold, for continuously varying values of $u$ and $v$.

In the first place, an interchange of $u$ and $v$ is equivalent to an interchange of $n$ and $n'$ on the left-hand side; hence $n''$ is symmetrical in $n$ and $n'$. Again, we have

$$\frac{\partial f(u, n)}{\partial u} = \frac{\partial f(u + v, n'')}{\partial (u + v)}$$

$$= \frac{\partial f(v, n')}{\partial v},$$

---

* The degree for special functions may be reduced, as in Cor. 1, Prop. XIII., § 118; but in no case is it increased. Similarly modifications, in the way of finite reductions, may occur in the succeeding cases; but they will not be noticed, as they do not give rise to essential modification in the reasoning.

so that the form of $f(u, n)$ is such that its first derivative with regard to $u$ is independent of $u$. Let $\theta(n)$ be this value, where $\theta(n)$, independent of $u$, may be dependent on $n$; then, since

$$\frac{\partial f(u, n)}{\partial u} = \theta(n),$$

we have

$$f(u, n) = u\theta(n) + \psi(n),$$

$\psi(n)$ being independent of $u$. Substituting this expression in the former equation, we have the equation

$$u\theta(n) + \psi(n) + v\theta(n') + \psi(n') = (u + v)\theta(n'') + \psi(n''),$$

which must be true for all values of $u$ and $v$; hence

$$\theta(n) = \theta(n'') = \theta(n'),$$

so that $\theta(n)$ is a constant and equal to its value when $n = 0$. But when $n$ is zero, $f(u, 0)$ is $u$; so that $\theta(0) = 1$ and $\psi(0) = 0$, and therefore

$$f(u, n) = u + \psi(n),$$

where $\psi$ vanishes with $n$.

The equation defining $\psi$ is

$$\psi(n) + \psi(n') = \psi(n'');$$

for values of $n$ from a singly-infinite series and for values of $n'$ from the same series, that series is reproduced for $n''$. Since $\psi(n)$ vanishes with $n$, we take

$$\psi(n) = n\chi(n),$$

and therefore

$$n\chi(n) + n'\chi(n') = n''\chi(n'').$$

Again, when $n'$ vanishes, the required series of values of $n''$ is given by taking $n'' = n$; and, when $n'$ does not vanish, $n''$ is symmetrical in $n$ and $n'$, so that we have

$$n'' = n + n' + nn'\lambda,$$

where $\lambda$ is not infinite for zero or finite values of $n$ or $n'$. Thus

$$n\chi(n) + n'\chi(n') = (n + n' + nn'\lambda)\chi(n + n' + nn'\lambda).$$

Since the left-hand side is the sum of two functions of distinct and independent magnitudes, the form of the equation shews that it can be satisfied only if

$$\lambda = 0, \text{ so that } n'' = n + n';$$

and

$$\chi(n) = \chi(n'')$$
$$= \chi(n'),$$

so that each is a constant, say $\omega$; then

$$f(u, n) = u + n\omega,$$

which is the form that the series must adopt when the series $f(u + v, n'')$ is obtained by the addition of $f(u, n)$ and $f(v, n')$.

It follows at once that the single series of arguments for $W$ is obtained, as one simply-infinite series, of the form $u + v + n''\omega$. For each of these arguments we have $m$ values of $W$, and the set of $m$ values of $W$ is the same for all the different arguments; that is, $W$ has $m$ values for a given value of $U$ and a given value of $V$. Moreover, $U$ has $m$ values for each argument and likewise $V$; hence, as the equation between $U$, $V$, $W$ is of a degree that is necessarily finite because the equation is algebraical, the integer $m$ is finite.

It thus appears that the function $U$ has a finite number $m$ of values for each value of the argument $u$, and that for a given value of the function the values of the argument form a simply-periodic series represented by $u + n\omega$. But the function $\tan \dfrac{\pi u}{\omega}$ is such that, for a given value, the values of the argument are represented by the series $u + n\omega$; hence for each value of $\tan \dfrac{\pi u}{\omega}$ there are $m$ values of $U$, and for each value of $U$ there is one value of $\tan \dfrac{\pi u}{\omega}$. It therefore follows, by §§ 113, 114, that between $U$ and $\tan \dfrac{\pi u}{\omega}$ there is an algebraical relation which is of the first degree in $\tan \dfrac{\pi u}{\omega}$ and the $m$th degree in $U$, that is, $U$ is an algebraic function of $\tan \dfrac{\pi u}{\omega}$. Hence $U$ is an algebraic function also of $e^{\frac{i\pi u}{\omega}}$.

*Note.* This result is based upon the supposition that the series of arguments, for which a branch of the function has the same value, can be arranged in the form $f(u, n)$, where $n$ has a simply-infinite series of integral values. If, however, there were no possible law of this kind—the foregoing proof shews that, if there be one such law, there is only one such law, with a properly determined constant $\omega$—then the values would be represented by $u_1, u_2, \ldots, u_p$ with $p$ infinite in the limit. In that case, there would be an infinite number of sets of values for $u + v$ of the type $u_\lambda + v_\mu$, where $\lambda$ and $\mu$ might be the same or might be different; each set would give a branch of the function $W$, and then there would be an infinite number of values of $W$ corresponding to one branch of $U$ and one branch of $V$. The equation between $U$, $V$ and $W$ would be of infinite degree in $W$, that is, it would be transcendental and not algebraical. The case is excluded by the hypothesis that the addition-theorem is algebraical, and therefore the equation between $U$, $V$ and $W$ is algebraical.

**153.** Next, let there be a number of simply-infinite series of values of the argument of the function, say $q$, where $q$ is greater than unity and may be either finite or infinite. Let $u_1, u_2, \ldots, u_q$ denote typical members of each series.

Then all the members of the series containing $u_1$ must be of the form $f_1(u_1, n)$, for an infinite series of values of the integer $n$. Otherwise, as in the preceding Note, the sum of the values in the series of arguments $u$ and of those in the same series of arguments $v$ would lead to an infinite number of distinct series of values of the argument $u + v$, with a corresponding infinite number of values $W$; and the relation between $U$, $V$, $W$ would cease to be algebraical.

In the same way, the members of the corresponding series containing $v_1$ must be of the form $f_1(v_1, n')$ for an infinite series of values of the integer $n'$. Among the combinations

$$f_1(u_1, n) + f_1(v_1, n'),$$

the simply-infinite series $f_1(u_1 + v_1, n'')$ must occur for an infinite series of values of $n''$; and therefore, as in the preceding case,

$$f_1(u_1, n) = u_1 + n\omega_1,$$

where $\omega_1$ is an appropriate constant. Further, there is only one series of values for the combination of these two series; it is represented by

$$u_1 + v_1 + n''\omega_1.$$

In the same way, the members of the series containing $u_2$ can be represented in the form $u_2 + n\omega_2$, where $\omega_2$ is an appropriate constant, which may be (but is not necessarily) the same as $\omega_1$; and the series containing $u_2$, when combined with the set containing $v_2$, leads to only a single series represented in the form $u_2 + v_2 + n''\omega_2$. And so on, for all the series in order.

But now, since $u_2 + m_2\omega_2$ where $m_2$ is an integer, is a value of $u$ for a given value of $U$, it follows that $U(u_2 + m_2\omega_2) = U(u_2)$ identically, each being equal to $U$. Hence

$$U(u_1 + m_1\omega_1 + m_2\omega_2) = U(u_1 + m_1\omega_1) = U(u_1) = U,$$

and therefore $u_1 + m_1\omega_1 + m_2\omega_2$ is also a value of $u$ for the given value of $U$, leading to a series of arguments which must be included among the original series or be distributed through them. Similarly $u_1 + \Sigma m_r\omega_r$, where the coefficients $m$ are integers and the constants $\omega$ are properly determined, represents a series of values of the variable $u$, included among the original series or distributed through them. And generally, when account is taken of all the distinct series thus obtained, the aggregate of values of the variable $u$ can be represented in the form $u_\lambda + \Sigma m_r\omega_r$, for $\lambda = 1, 2, \ldots, \kappa$, where $\kappa$ is some finite or infinite integer.

Three cases arise, $(a)$ when the quantities $\omega$ are equal to one another or can be expressed as integral multiples of only one quantity $\omega$, $(b)$ when the quantities $\omega$ are equivalent to two quantities $\Omega_1$ and $\Omega_2$ (the ratio of which is not real), so that each quantity $\omega$ can be expressed in the form

$$\omega_r = p_{1r}\Omega_1 + p_{2r}\Omega_2,$$

the coefficients $p_{1r}$, $p_{2r}$ being finite integers; $(c)$ when the quantities $\omega$ are not equivalent to only two quantities, such as $\Omega_1$ and $\Omega_2$.

For case $(a)$, each of the $\kappa$ infinite series of values $u$ can be expressed in the form $u_\lambda + p\omega$, for $\lambda = 1, 2, ..., \kappa$ and integral values of $p$.

First, let $\kappa$ be finite, so that the original integer $q$ is finite. Then the values of the argument for $W$ are of the type

$$u_\lambda + p\omega + v_\mu + p'\omega,$$

that is,                          $$u_\lambda + v_\mu + p''\omega,$$

for all combinations of $\lambda$ and $\mu$ and for integral values of $p''$. There are thus $\kappa^2$ series of values, each series containing a simply-infinite number of terms of this type.

For each of the arguments in any one of these infinite series, $W$ has $m$ values; and the set of $m$ values is the same for all the arguments in one and the same infinite series. Hence $W$ has $m\kappa^2$ values for all the arguments in all the series taken together, that is, for a given value of $U$ and a given value of $V$. The relation between $U$, $V$, $W$ is therefore of degree $m\kappa^2$, necessarily finite when the equation is algebraical; hence $m$ is finite.

It thus appears that the function $U$ has a finite number $m$ of values for each value of the argument $u$, and that for a given value of the function there are a finite number $\kappa$ of distinct series of values of the argument of the form $u + p\omega$, $\omega$ being the same for all the series. But the function $\tan \dfrac{\pi u}{\omega}$ has one value for each value of $u$, and the series $u + p\omega$ represents the series of values of $u$ for a given value of $\tan \dfrac{\pi u}{\omega}$. It therefore follows that there are $m$ values of $U$ for each value of $\tan \dfrac{\pi u}{\omega}$ and that there are $\kappa$ values of $\tan \dfrac{\pi u}{\omega}$ for each value of $U$; and therefore there is an algebraical relation between $U$ and $\tan \dfrac{\pi u}{\omega}$, which is of degree $\kappa$ in the latter and of degree $m$ in the former. Hence *$U$ is an algebraic function of* $\tan \dfrac{\pi u}{\omega}$ *and therefore also of* $e^{\frac{i\pi u}{\omega}}$.

Next, let $\kappa$ be infinite, so that the original integer $q$ is infinite. Then, as in the Note in § 152, the equation between $U$, $V$, $W$ will cease to be algebraical unless each aggregate of values $u_\lambda + p\omega$, for each particular value of $p$ and for the infinite sequence $\lambda = 1, 2, ..., \kappa$, can be arranged in a system or a set of systems, say $\sigma$ in number, each of the form $f_\rho(u + p\omega, p_\rho)$ for an infinite series of values of $p_\rho$. Each of these implies a series of values $f_\rho(v + p'\omega, p_\rho')$ of the argument of $V$ for the same series of values of $p_\rho'$ as of $p_\rho$, and also a series of values $f_\rho(u + v + p''\omega, p_\rho'')$ of the argument of $W$ for the same series of values of $p_\rho''$. By proceeding as in § 152, it follows that

$$f_\rho(u + p\omega, p_\rho) = u + p\omega + p_\rho\omega_\rho',$$

where $\omega_\rho'$ is an appropriate constant, the ratio of which to $\omega$ can be proved (as in § 106) to be not purely real, and $p_\rho$ has a simply-infinite succession of values. The integer $\sigma$ may be finite or it may be infinite.

When $\omega$ and all the constants $\omega'$ which thus arise are linearly equivalent to two quantities $\Omega_1$ and $\Omega_2$, so that the terms additive to $u$ can be expressed in the form $s_1\Omega_1 + s_2\Omega_2$, then the aggregate of values $u$ can be expressed in the form

$$u_\rho + p_1\Omega_1 + p_2\Omega_2,$$

for a simply-infinite series for $p_1$ and for $p_2$; and $\rho$ has a series of values $1, 2, \ldots, \sigma$. This case is, in effect, the same as case $(b)$.

When $\omega$ and all the constants $\omega'$ are not linearly equivalent to only two quantities, such as $\Omega_1$ and $\Omega_2$, we have a case which, in effect, is the same as case $(c)$.

These two cases must therefore now be considered.

For case $(b)$, either as originally obtained or as derived through part of case $(a)$, each of the (doubly) infinite series of values of $u$ can be expressed in the form

$$u_\lambda + p_1\Omega_1 + p_2\Omega_2,$$

for $\lambda = 1, 2, \ldots, \sigma$, and for integral values of $p_1$ and $p_2$. The integer $\sigma$ may be finite or infinite; the original integer $q$ is infinite.

First, let $\sigma$ be finite. Then the values of the argument for $W$ are of the type

$$u_\lambda + p_1\Omega_1 + p_2\Omega_2 + v_\mu + p_1'\Omega_1 + p_2'\Omega_2,$$

that is,
$$u_\lambda + v_\mu + p_1''\Omega_1 + p_2''\Omega_2,$$

for all combinations of $\lambda$ and $\mu$, and for integral values of $p_1''$ and $p_2''$. There are thus $\sigma^2$ series of values, each series containing a doubly-infinite number of terms of this type.

For every argument there are $m$ values of $W$; and the set of $m$ values is the same for all the arguments in one and the same infinite series. Thus $W$ has $m\sigma^2$ values for all the arguments in all the series, that is, for a given value of $U$ and a given value of $V$; and it follows, as before, from the consideration of the algebraical relation, that $m$ is finite.

The function $U$ thus has $m$ values for each value of the argument $u$; and for a given value of the function there are $\sigma$ series of values of the argument, each series being of the form $u_\lambda + p_1\Omega_1 + p_2\Omega_2$.

Take a doubly-periodic function $\Theta$ having $\Omega_1$ and $\Omega_2$ for its periods, such* that for a given value of $\Theta$ the values of its arguments are of the foregoing form. Whatever be the expression of the function, it is of the order $\sigma$.

---

* All that is necessary for this purpose is to construct, by the use of Prop. XII., § 118, a function having, as its irreducible simple infinities, a series of points $a_1, a_2, \ldots, a_\sigma$—special values of $u_1, u_2, \ldots, u_\sigma$—in the parallelogram of periods, chosen so that no two of the $\sigma$ points $a$ coincide.

Then $U$ has $m$ values for each value of $\Theta$, and $\Theta$ has one value for each value of $U$; hence there is an algebraical equation between $U$ and $\Theta$, of the first degree in the latter and of the $m$th degree in $U$: that is, $U$ is an algebraic function of $\Theta$. But, by Prop. XV. § 119, $\Theta$ can be expressed in the form

$$\frac{M + N\wp'(u)}{L},$$

where $L$, $M$, $N$ are rational integral functions of $\wp(u)$, if $\Omega_1$ and $\Omega_2$ be the periods of $\wp(u)$; and $\wp'(u)$ is a two-valued algebraic function of $\wp(u)$, so that $\Theta$ is an algebraic function of $\wp(u)$. *Hence also $U$ is an algebraic function of $\wp(u)$, the periods of $\wp(u)$ being properly chosen.*

This inference requires that $\sigma$, the order of $\Theta$, be greater than 1. Because $U$ has $m$ values for an argument $u$, the symmetric function $\Sigma U$ has one value for an argument $u$ and it is therefore a uniform function. But each term of the sum has the same value for $u + p_1\Omega_1 + p_2\Omega_2$ as for $u$; and therefore this uniform function is doubly-periodic. The number of independent doubly-infinite series of values of $u$ for a uniform doubly-periodic function is at least two: and therefore there must be at least two doubly-infinite series of values of $u$, so that $\sigma > 1$. Hence a function, that possesses an addition-theorem, cannot have only one doubly-infinite series of values for its argument.

If $\sigma$ be infinite, there is an infinite series of values of $u$ of the form $u_\lambda + p_1\Omega_1 + p_2\Omega_2$; an argument, similar to that in case $(a)$, shews that this is, in effect, the same as case $(c)$.

It is obvious that cases (ii), (iii) and (iv) of § 152 are now completely covered; case (v) of § 152 is covered by case $(c)$ now to be discussed.

**154.** For case $(c)$, we have the series of values $u$ represented by a number of series of the form

$$u_\lambda + \sum_{r=1} m_r\omega_r,$$

where the quantities $\omega$ are not linearly equivalent to two quantities $\Omega_1$ and $\Omega_2$. The original integer $q$ is infinite.

Then, by §§ 108, 110, it follows that integers $m$ can be chosen in an unlimited variety of ways so that the modulus of

$$\sum_{r=1} m_r\omega_r$$

is infinitesimal, and therefore in the immediate vicinity of any point $u_\lambda$ there is an infinitude of points at which the function resumes its value. Such a function would, as in previous instances, degenerate into a mere constant, unless each point were an essential singularity (as is not the case); hence the combination of values which gives rise to this case does not occur.

All the possible cases have been considered: and the truth of Weierstrass's theorem[*] that a function, which has an algebraical addition-theorem, is either an algebraical function of $u$, or of $e^{\frac{i\pi u}{\omega}}$ (where $\omega$ is suitably chosen), or of $\wp(u)$, where the periods of $\wp(u)$ are suitably chosen, is established; and it has incidentally been established—it is, indeed, essential to the derivation of the theorem—that *a function, which has an algebraical addition-theorem, has only a finite number of values for a given argument.*

It is easy to see that *the first derivative has only a finite number of values for a given argument;* for the elimination of $U$ between the algebraical equations

$$G(U, u) = 0, \quad \frac{\partial G}{\partial U} U' + \frac{\partial G}{\partial u} = 0,$$

leads to an equation in $U'$ of the same finite degree as $G$ in $U$.

Further, it is now easy to see that *if the analytical function $\phi(u)$, which possesses an algebraical addition-theorem, be uniform, then it is a rational function either of $u$, or of $e^{\frac{i\pi u}{\omega}}$, or of $\wp(u)$ and $\wp'(u)$;* and that any uniform function, which is transcendental in the sense of § 46 and which possesses an algebraical addition-theorem, is either a simply-periodic function or a doubly-periodic function.

The following examples will illustrate some of the inferences in regard to the number of values of $\phi(u+v)$ arising from series of values for $u$ and $v$.

*Ex.* 1.   Let $\qquad\qquad U = u^{\frac{1}{2}} + (2u+1)^{\frac{1}{2}}.$

Evidently $m$, the number of values of $U$ for a value of $u$, is 4; and, as the rationalised form of the equation is

$$u^2 + 2u(1 - 3U^2) + (U^2 - 1)^2 = 0,$$

the value of $p$, being the number of values of $u$ for a given value of $U$, is 2. Thus the equation in $W$ should be, by § 151, of degree $(4 \cdot 2^2 =) 16$.

This equation is $\qquad \overset{8}{\underset{r=1}{\Pi}} \{3(W^2 - U^2 - V^2) + 1 - 2k_r\} = 0,$

where $k_r$ is any one of the eight values of

$$W(2W^2 - 1)^{\frac{1}{2}} + U(2U^2 - 1)^{\frac{1}{2}} + V(2V^2 - 1)^{\frac{1}{2}};$$

when rationalised, the equation is of the 16th degree in $W$.

*Ex.* 2.   Let $U = \cos u.$

Evidently $m = 1$; the values of $u$ for a given value of $U$ are contained in the double series $u + 2\pi n$, $-u + 2\pi n$, for all values of $n$ from $-\infty$ to $+\infty$. The values of $u + v$ are

$u + 2\pi n + v + 2\pi m$, that is, $u + v + 2\pi p$;   $-u + 2\pi n + v + 2\pi m$, that is, $-u + v + 2\pi p$;

$u + 2\pi n - v + 2\pi m$, that is, $u - v + 2\pi p$;   $-u + 2\pi n - v + 2\pi m$, that is, $-u - v + 2\pi p$,

---

[*] The theorem has been used by Schwarz, *Ges. Werke*, t. ii, pp. 260—268, in determining all the families of plane isothermic curves which are algebraic curves, an 'isothermic' curve being of the form $u = c$, where $u$ is a function satisfying the potential-equation

$$\frac{\partial^2 u}{\partial x^2} + \frac{\partial^2 u}{\partial y^2} = 0.$$

so that the number of series of values of $u+v$ is four, each series being simply-infinite. It might thus be expected that the equation between $U$, $V$, $W$ would be of degree $(1.4=)\,4$ in $W$; but it happens that

$$\cos(u+v)=\cos(-u-v),$$

and so the degree of the equation in $W$ is reduced to half its degree. The equation is

$$W^2-2WUV+U^2+V^2-1=0.$$

*Ex.* 3.   Let $U=\operatorname{sn}u$.

Evidently $m=1$; and there are two doubly-infinite series of values of $u$ determined by a given value of $U$, having the form $u+2m\omega+2m'\omega'$, $\omega-u+2m\omega+2m'\omega'$. Hence the values of $u+v$ are

$$\equiv \quad u+v\ (\mathrm{mod.}\ 2\omega,\ 2\omega')\ ;\qquad \equiv \omega-u+v\ (\mathrm{mod.}\ 2\omega,\ 2\omega')\ ;$$
$$\equiv \omega+u-v\ (\mathrm{mod.}\ 2\omega,\ 2\omega')\ ;\qquad \equiv\ -u-v\ (\mathrm{mod.}\ 2\omega,\ 2\omega')\ ;$$

four in number. The equation may therefore be expected to be of the fourth degree in $W$; it is

$$4\,(1-U^2)\,(1-V^2)\,(1-W^2)=(2-U^2-V^2-W^2+k^2U^2V^2W^2)^2.$$

**155.**   But it must not be supposed that any algebraical equation between $U$, $V$, $W$, which is symmetrical in $U$ and $V$, is one necessarily implying the representation of an algebraical addition-theorem. Without entering into a detailed investigation of the formal characteristics of the equations that are suitable, a latent test is given by implication in the following theorem, also due to Weierstrass :—

*If an analytical function possess an algebraical addition-theorem, an algebraical equation involving the function and its first derivative with regard to its argument exists; and the coefficients in this equation do not involve the argument of the function.*

The proposition might easily be derived by assuming the preceding proposition, and applying the known results relating to the algebraical dependence between those functions, the types of which are suited to the representation of the functions in question, and their derivatives; we shall, however, proceed more directly from the equation expressing the algebraical addition-theorem in the form

$$G\,(U,\ V,\ W)=0,$$

which may be regarded as a rationally irreducible equation.

Differentiating with regard to $u$, we have

$$\frac{\partial G}{\partial U}\,U'+\frac{\partial G}{\partial W}\,W'=0,$$

and similarly, with regard to $v$, we have

$$\frac{\partial G}{\partial V}\,V'+\frac{\partial G}{\partial W}\,W'=0,$$

from which it follows that

$$\frac{\partial G}{\partial U}\,U'-\frac{\partial G}{\partial V}\,V'=0.$$

This equation* will, in general, involve $W$; in order to obtain an equation free from $W$, we eliminate $W$ between

$$G = 0 \quad \text{and} \quad \frac{\partial G}{\partial U} U' = \frac{\partial G}{\partial V} V',$$

the elimination being possible because both equations are of finite degree; and thus in any case we have an algebraical equation independent of $W$ and involving $U$, $U'$, $V$, $V'$.

Not more than one equation can arise by assigning various values to $v$, a quantity that is independent of $u$; for we should have either inconsistent equations or simultaneous equations which, being consistent, determine a limited number of values of $U$ and $U'$ for all values of $u$, that is, only a number of constants. Hence there can be only one equation, obtained by assigning varying values to $v$; and this single equation is the algebraical equation between the function and its first derivative, the coefficients being independent of the argument of the function.

*Note.* A test of suitability of an algebraical equation $G = 0$ between three variables $U$, $V$, $W$ to represent an addition-theorem is given by the condition that the elimination of $W$ between

$$G = 0 \quad \text{and} \quad U' \frac{\partial G}{\partial U} = V' \frac{\partial G}{\partial V}$$

leads to only a single equation between $U$ and $U'$ for different values of $V$ and $V'$.

*Ex.* Consider the equation

$$(2 - U - V - W)^2 - 4 (1 - U)(1 - V)(1 - W) = 0.$$

The deduced equation involving $U'$ and $V'$ is

$$(2VW - V - W + U) U' = (2UW - U - W + V) V',$$

so that

$$W = \frac{(V - U)(V' + U')}{(2V - 1) U' - (2U - 1) V'}.$$

The elimination of $W$ is simple. We have

$$1 - W = \frac{(V + U - 1)(U' - V')}{(2V - 1) U' - (2U - 1) V'},$$

and

$$2 - U - V - W = 2 \frac{(V + U - 1)\{(1 - V) U' - (1 - U) V'\}}{(2V - 1) U' - (2U - 1) V'}.$$

Neglecting $4(V + U - 1) = 0$, which is an irrelevant equation, and multiplying by $(2V - 1) U' - (2U - 1) V'$, we have

$$(V + U - 1)\{(1 - V) U' - (1 - U) V'\}^2 = (1 - U)(1 - V)(U' - V')\{(2V - 1) U' - (2U - 1) V'\},$$

and therefore

$$V(U - V)(1 - V) U'^2 + U(V - U)(1 - U) V'^2 = 0.$$

---

* It is permissible to adopt any subsidiary irrational or non-algebraical form as the equivalent of $G = 0$, provided no special limitation to the subsidiary form be implicitly adopted. Thus, if $W$ can be expressed explicitly in terms of $U$ and $V$, this resoluble (but irrational) equivalent of the equation often leads rapidly to the equation between $U$ and its derivative.

When the irrelevant factor $U - V$ is neglected, this equation gives

$$\frac{U'^2}{U(1-U)} = \frac{V'^2}{V(1-V)},$$

the equation required: and this, indeed, is the necessary form in which the equation involving $U$ and $U'$ arises in general, the variables being combined in associate pairs. Each side is evidently a constant, say $4a^2$; and then we have

$$U'^2 = 4a^2 U(1-U).$$

Then the value of $U$ is $\sin^2(au + \beta)$, the arbitrary additive constant of integration being $\beta$; by substitution in the original equation, $\beta$ is easily proved to be zero.

**156.** Again, if the elimination between

$$G = 0 \text{ and } \frac{\partial G}{\partial U} U' = \frac{\partial G}{\partial V} V'$$

be supposed to be performed by the ordinary algebraical process for finding the greatest common measure of $G$ and $U' \dfrac{\partial G}{\partial U} - V' \dfrac{\partial G}{\partial V}$, regarded as functions of $W$, the final remainder is the eliminant which, equated to zero, is the differential equation involving $U, U', V, V'$; and the greatest common measure, equated to zero, gives the simplest equation in virtue of which the equations $G = 0$ and $\dfrac{\partial G}{\partial U} U' = \dfrac{\partial G}{\partial V} V'$ subsist. It will be of the form

$$f(W, U, V, U', V') = 0.$$

If the function have only one value for each value of the argument, so that it is a uniform function, this last equation can give only one value for $W$; for all the other magnitudes that occur in the equation are uniform functions of their respective arguments. Since it is linear in $W$, the equation can be expressed in the form

$$W = R(U, V, U', V'),$$

where $R$ denotes a rational function. Hence*:—

*A uniform analytical function $\phi(u)$, which possesses an algebraical addition-theorem, is such that $\phi(u + v)$ can be expressed rationally in terms of $\phi(u)$, $\phi'(u)$, $\phi(v)$ and $\phi'(v)$.*

It need hardly be pointed out that this result is not inconsistent with the fact that the algebraical equation between $\phi(u + v)$, $\phi(u)$ and $\phi(v)$ does not, in general, express $\phi(u + v)$ as a rational function of $\phi(u)$ and $\phi(v)$. And it should be noticed that the rationality of the expression of $\phi(u + v)$ in terms of $\phi(u)$, $\phi(v)$, $\phi'(u)$, $\phi'(v)$ is characteristic of functions with an algebraical addition-theorem. Instances do occur of functions such that $\phi(u + v)$ can be expressed, not rationally, in terms of $\phi(u)$, $\phi(v)$, $\phi'(u)$, $\phi'(v)$; they do not possess an algebraical addition-theorem. Such an instance is furnished by $\zeta(u)$; the expression of $\zeta(u + v)$, given in Ex. 3 of § 131, can be modified so as to have the form indicated.

---

* The theorem is due to Weierstrass; see Schwarz, § 2, (l.c. in note to p. 344).

# CHAPTER XIV.

## CONNECTION OF SURFACES.

**157.** In proceeding to the discussion of multiform functions, it was stated (§ 100) that there are two methods of special importance, one of which is the development of Cauchy's general theory of functions of complex variables and the other of which is due to Riemann. The former has been explained in the immediately preceding chapters; we now pass to the consideration of Riemann's method. But, before actually entering upon it, there are some preliminary propositions on the connection of surfaces which must be established; as they do not find a place in treatises on geometry, an outline will be given here, though only to that elementary extent which is necessary for our present purpose.

In the integration of meromorphic functions, it proved to be convenient to exclude the poles from the range of variation of the variable by means of infinitesimal closed simple curves, each of which was thereby constituted a limit of the region: the full boundary of the region was composed of the aggregate of these non-intersecting curves.

Similarly, in dealing with some special cases of multiform functions, it proved convenient to exclude the branch-points by means of infinitesimal curves or by loops. And, in the case of the fundamental lemma of § 16, the region over which integration extended was considered as one which possibly had several distinct curves as its complete boundary.

These are special examples of a general class of regions, at all points within the area of which the functions considered are monogenic, finite, and continuous and, as the case may be, uniform or multiform. But, important as are the classes of functions which have been considered, it is necessary to consider wider classes of multiform functions and to obtain the regions which are appropriate for the representation of the variation of the variable in each case. The most conspicuous examples of such new functions are the algebraic functions, adverted to in §§ 94—99; and it is chiefly in view of their value and of the value of functions dependent upon them, as well as of the kind of surface on which their variable can be simply represented, that we now proceed to establish some of the topological properties of surfaces in general.

**158.** A surface is said to be *connected* when, from any point of it to any other point of it, a continuous line can be drawn without passing out of the surface.　Thus the surface of a circle, that of a plane ring such as arises in Lambert's Theorem, that of a sphere, that of an anchor-ring, are connected surfaces.　Two non-intersecting spheres, not joined or bound together in any manner, are not a connected surface but are two different connected surfaces.　It is often necessary to consider surfaces, which are constituted by an aggregate of several sheets; in order that the surface may be regarded as connected, there must be junctions between the sheets.

One of the simplest connected surfaces is such a plane area as is enclosed and completely bounded by the circumference of a circle.　All lines drawn in it from one internal point to another can be deformed into one another; any simple closed line lying entirely within it can be deformed so as to be evanescent, without in either case passing over the circumference; and any simple line from one point of the circumference to another, when regarded as an impassable barrier, divides the surface into two portions.　Such a surface is called* *simply connected.*

The kind of connected surface next in point of simplicity is such a plane area as is enclosed between and is completely bounded by the circumferences of two concentric circles.　All lines in the surface from one point to another cannot necessarily be deformed into one another, e.g., the lines $z_0az$ and $z_0bz$; a simple closed line cannot necessarily be deformed so as to be evanescent without crossing the boundary, e.g., the line $az_0bza$; and a simple line from a point in one part of the boundary to a point in another and different part of the boundary, such as a line $AB$, does not divide the

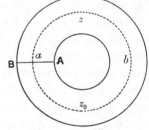

Fig. 35.

surface into two portions but, set as an impassable barrier, it makes the surface simply connected.

Again, on the surface of an anchor-ring, a closed line can be drawn in two essentially distinct ways, $abc$, $ab'c'$, such that neither can be deformed so as to be evanescent or so as to pass continuously into the other. If $abc$ be made the only impassable barrier, a line such as $\alpha\beta\gamma$ cannot be deformed so as to be evanescent; if $ab'c'$ be made the only impassable barrier, the same holds of a line such as $\alpha\beta'\gamma'$. In order to make the surface simply connected, two impassable barriers, such as $abc$ and $ab'c'$, must be set.

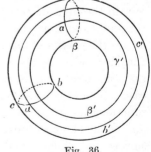

Fig. 36.

Surfaces, like the flat ring or the anchor-ring,

---

\* Sometimes the term *monadelphic* is used.　The German equivalent is *einfach zusammenhängend.*

are called* *multiply connected*; the establishment of barriers has made it possible, in each case, to modify the surface into one which is simply connected.

**159.** It proves to be convenient to arrange surfaces in classes according to the character of their connection; and these few illustrations suggest that the classification may be made to depend, either upon the resolution of the surface, by the establishment of barriers, into one that is simply connected, or upon the number of what may be called independent irreducible circuits. The former mode—that of dependence upon the establishment of barriers— will be adopted, thus following Riemann†; but whichever of the two modes be adopted (and they are not necessarily the only modes), subsequent demands require that the two be brought into relation with one another.

The most effective way of securing the impassability of a barrier is to suppose the surface actually cut along the line of the barrier. Such a section of a surface is either a cross-cut or a loop-cut.

If the section be made through the interior of the surface from one point

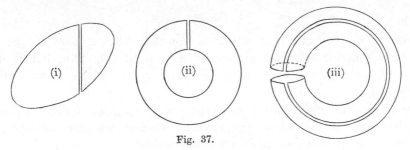

Fig. 37.

of the boundary to another point of the boundary, without intersecting itself or meeting the boundary save at its extremities, it is called a *cross-cut*‡. Every part of it, as it is made, is to be regarded as boundary during the formation of the remainder; and any cross-cut, once made, is to be regarded as boundary during the formation of any cross-cut subsequently made. Illustrations are given in fig. 37.

The definition and explanation imply that the surface has a boundary. Some surfaces, such as a complete sphere and a complete anchor-ring, do not possess a boundary; but, as will be seen later (§§ 163, 168) from the discussion of the evanescence of circuits, it is desirable to assign some boundary in order to avoid merely artificial difficulties as to the numerical

* Sometimes the term *polyadelphic* is used. The German equivalent is *mehrfach zusammen-hängend*.

† " Grundlagen für eine allgemeine Theorie der Functionen einer veränderlichen complexen Grösse," Riemann's *Gesammelte Werke*, pp. 9—12 ; " Theorie der Abel'schen Functionen," ib., pp. 84—89. When reference to either of these memoirs is made, it will be by a citation of the page or pages in the volume of Riemann's Collected Works.

‡ This is the equivalent used for the German word *Querschnitt*; French writers use *Section*, and Italian writers use *Trasversale* or *Taglio trasversale*.

expression of the connection. This assignment usually is made by taking for the boundary of a surface, which otherwise has no boundary, an infinitesimal closed curve, practically a point; thus in the figure of the anchor-ring (fig. 36) the point $a$ is taken as a boundary, and each of the two cross-cuts begins and ends in $a$.

If the section be made through the interior of the surface from a point not on the boundary and, without meeting the boundary or crossing itself, return to the initial point, (so that it has the form of a simple curve lying

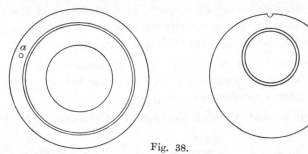

Fig. 38.

entirely in the surface), it is called* a *loop-cut*. Thus a piece can be cut out of a bounded spherical surface by a loop-cut (fig. 38); but it does not necessarily give a separate piece when made in the surface of an anchor-ring.

It is evident that both a cross-cut and a loop-cut furnish a double boundary-edge to the whole aggregate of surface, whether consisting of two pieces or of only one piece after the section.

Moreover, these sections represent the impassable barriers of the preliminary explanations; and no specified form was assigned to those barriers. It is thus possible, within certain limits, to deform a cross-cut or a loop-cut continuously into a closely contiguous and equivalent position. If, for instance, two barriers initially coincide over any finite length, one or other can be slightly deformed so that finally they intersect only in a point; the same modification can therefore be made in the sections.

The definitions of simple connection and of multiple connection will now† be as follows :—

*A surface is simply connected, if it be resolved into two distinct pieces by every cross-cut; but if there be any cross-cut, which does not resolve it into distinct pieces, the surface is multiply connected.*

**160.** Some fundamental propositions, relating to the connection of surfaces, may now be derived.

* This is the equivalent used for the German word *Rückkehrschnitt* ; French writers use the word *Rétrosection*.

† Other definitions will be required, if the classification of surfaces be made to depend on methods other than resolution by sections.

I. *Each of the two distinct pieces, into which a simply connected surface S is resolved by a cross-cut, is itself simply connected.*

If either of the pieces, made by a cross-cut $ab$, be not simply connected, then some cross-cut $cd$ must be possible which will not resolve that piece into distinct portions.

If neither $c$ nor $d$ lie on $ab$, then the obliteration of the cut $ab$ will restore the original surface $S$, which now is not resolved by the cut $cd$ into distinct pieces.

If one of the extremities of $cd$, say $c$, lie on $ab$, then the obliteration of the portion $cb$ will change the two pieces into a single piece which is the original surface $S$; and $S$ now has a cross-cut $acd$, which does not resolve it into distinct pieces.

If both the extremities lie on $ab$, then the obliteration of that part of $ab$ which lies between $c$ and $d$ will change the two pieces into one; this is the original surface $S$, now with a cross-cut $acdb$, which does not resolve it into distinct pieces.

These are all the possible cases should either of the distinct pieces of $S$ not be simply connected; each of them leads to a contradiction of the simple connection of $S$; therefore the hypothesis on which each is based is untenable, that is, the distinct pieces of $S$ in all the cases are simply connected.

COROLLARY 1.  *A simply connected surface is resolved by n cross-cuts into $n+1$ distinct pieces, each simply connected; and an aggregate of m simply connected surfaces is resolved by n cross-cuts into $n+m$ distinct pieces each simply connected.*

COROLLARY 2.  *A surface that is resolved into two distinct simply connected pieces by a cross-cut is simply connected before the resolution.*

COROLLARY 3.  *If a multiply connected surface be resolved into two different pieces by a cross-cut, both of these pieces cannot be simply connected.*

We now come to a theorem* of great importance :—

II.  *If a resolution of a surface by m cross-cuts into n distinct simply connected pieces be possible, and also a different resolution of the same surface by $\mu$ cross-cuts into $\nu$ distinct simply connected pieces, then $m - n = \mu - \nu$.*

Let the aggregate of the $n$ pieces be denoted by $S$ and the aggregate of the $\nu$ pieces by $\Sigma$: and consider the effect on the original surface of a united system of $m + \mu$ simultaneous cross-cuts made up of the two systems of the $m$ and of the $\mu$ cross-cuts respectively. The operation of this system can be carried out in two ways: (i) by effecting the system of $\mu$ cross-cuts on $S$ and

* The following proof of this proposition is substantially due to Neumann, p. 157. Another proof is given by Riemann, pp. 10, 11, and is amplified by Durège, *Elemente der Theorie der Functionen*, pp. 183—190; and another by Lippich, see Durège, pp. 190—197.

(ii) by effecting the system of $m$ cross-cuts on $\Sigma$: with the same result on the original surface.

After the explanation of § 159, we may justifiably assume that the lines of the two systems of cross-cuts meet only in points, if at all: let $\delta$ be the number of points of intersection of these lines. Whenever the direction of a cross-cut meets a boundary line, the cross-cut terminates; and if the direction continue beyond that boundary line, that produced part must be regarded as a new cross-cut.

Hence the new system of $\mu$ cross-cuts applied to $S$ is effectively equivalent to $\mu + \delta$ new cross-cuts. Before these cuts were made, $S$ was composed of $n$ simply connected pieces; hence, after they are applied, the new arrangement of the original surface is made up of $n + (\mu + \delta)$ simply connected pieces.

Similarly, the new system of $m$ cross-cuts applied to $\Sigma$ will give an arrangement of the original surface made up of $\nu + (m + \delta)$ simply connected pieces. These two arrangements are the same: and therefore

$$n + \mu + \delta = \nu + m + \delta,$$

so that
$$m - n = \mu - \nu.$$

It thus appears that, if by any system of $q$ cross-cuts a multiply connected surface be resolved into a number $p$ of pieces distinct from one another and all simply connected, the integer $q - p$ is independent of the particular system of the cross-cuts and of their configuration. The integer $q - p$ is therefore essentially associated with the character of the multiple connection of the surface: and its invariance for a given surface enables us to arrange surfaces according to the value of the integer.

No classification among the multiply connected surfaces has yet been made: they have merely been defined as surfaces in which cross-cuts can be made that do not resolve the surface into distinct pieces.

It is natural to arrange them in classes according to the number of cross-cuts which are necessary to resolve the surface into one of simple connection or a number of pieces each of simple connection.

For a simply connected surface, no such cross-cut is necessary: then $q = 0$, $p = 1$, and in general $q - p = -1$. We shall say that the *connectivity**
is unity. Examples are furnished by the area of a plane circle, and by a spherical surface with one hole†.

A surface is called doubly-connected when, by one appropriate cross-cut, the surface is changed into a single surface of simple connection: then $q = 1$, $p = 1$ for this particular resolution, and therefore in general, $q - p = 0$. We

---

* Sometimes *order of connection*, sometimes *adelphic order*; the German word, that is used, is *Grundzahl*.

† The hole is made to give the surface a boundary (§ 163).

shall say that the connectivity is 2.   Examples are furnished by a plane ring and by a spherical surface with two holes.

A surface is called triply-connected when, by two appropriate cross-cuts, the surface is changed into a single surface of simple connection: then $q = 2$, $p = 1$ for this particular resolution and therefore, in general, $q - p = 1$.   We shall say that the connectivity is 3.   Examples are furnished by the surface of an anchor-ring with one hole in it[*], and by the surfaces[†] in figure 39, the surface in (2) not being in one plane but one part beneath another.

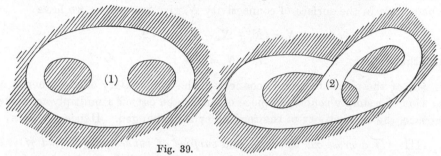

Fig. 39.

And, in general, a surface will be said to be $N$-ply connected or its connectivity will be denoted by $N$, if, by $N-1$ appropriate cross-cuts, it can be changed into a single surface that is simply connected[‡].   For this particular resolution $q = N - 1$, $p = 1$: and therefore in general

$$q - p = N - 2,$$

or
$$N = q - p + 2.$$

Let a cross-cut $l$ be drawn in a surface of connectivity $N$.   There are two cases to be considered, according as it does not or does divide the surface into distinct pieces.

First, let the surface be only one piece after $l$ is drawn: and let its connectivity then be $N'$.   If in the original surface $q$ cross-cuts (one of which can, after the preceding proposition, be taken to be $l$) be drawn dividing the surface into $p$ simply connected pieces, then

$$N = q - p + 2.$$

To obtain these $p$ simply connected pieces from the surface after the cross-cut $l$, it is evidently sufficient to make the $q - 1$ original cross-cuts other than $l$; that is, the modified surface is such that by $q - 1$ cross-cuts it is resolved into $p$ simply connected pieces, and therefore

$$N' = (q - 1) - p + 2.$$

Hence $N' = N - 1$, or the connectivity of the surface is diminished by unity.

* The hole is made to give the surface a boundary (§ 163).

† Riemann, p. 89.

‡ A few writers estimate the connectivity of such a surface as $N-1$, the same as the number of cross-cuts which can change it into a single surface of the simplest rank of connectivity: the estimate in the text seems preferable.

Secondly, let the surface be two pieces after $l$ is drawn, of connectivities $N_1$ and $N_2$ respectively. Let the appropriate $N_1 - 1$ cross-cuts in the former, and the appropriate $N_2 - 1$ in the latter, be drawn so as to make each a simply connected piece. Then, together, there are two simply connected pieces.

To obtain these two pieces from the original surface, it will suffice to make in it the cross-cut $l$, the $N_1 - 1$ cross-cuts, and the $N_2 - 1$ cross-cuts, that is, $1 + (N_1 - 1) + (N_2 - 1)$ or $N_1 + N_2 - 1$ cross-cuts in all. Since these, when made in the surface of connectivity $N$, give two pieces, we have

$$N = (N_1 + N_2 - 1) - 2 + 2,$$

and therefore $\qquad N_1 + N_2 = N + 1.$

If one of the pieces be simply connected, the connectivity of the other is $N$; so that, if a simply connected piece of surface be cut off a multiply connected surface, the connectivity of the remainder is unchanged. Hence :—

III. *If a cross-cut be made in a surface of connectivity $N$ and if it do not divide it into separate pieces, the connectivity of the modified surface is $N - 1$; but if it divide the surface into two separate pieces of connectivities $N_1$ and $N_2$, then $N_1 + N_2 = N + 1$.*

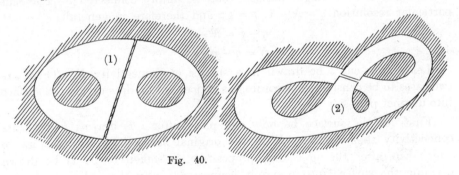

Fig. 40.

Illustrations are shewn, in fig. 40, of the effect of cross-cuts on the two surfaces in fig. 39.

IV. In the same way it may be proved that, *if $s$ cross-cuts be made in a surface of connectivity $N$ and divide it into $r + 1$ separate pieces (where $r \leqslant s$) of connectivities $N_1, N_2, \ldots, N_{r+1}$ respectively, then*

$$N_1 + N_2 + \ldots + N_{r+1} = N + 2r - s,$$

a more general result including both of the foregoing cases.

Thus far we have been considering only cross-cuts: it is now necessary to consider loop-cuts, so far as they affect the connectivity of a surface in which they are made.

A loop-cut is changed into a cross-cut, if from $A$ any point of it a cross-cut be made to any point $C$ in a boundary-curve of the original surface, for $CAbdA$ (fig. 41) is then evidently a cross-cut of the original surface ; and $CA$ is a cross-cut of the surface, which is the modification of the original surface after the loop-cut has been made. Since, by definition, a loop-cut does not meet the boundary, the cross-cut $CA$ does not divide the modified surface into distinct pieces; hence, according as the effect of the loop-cut is, or is not, that of making distinct pieces, so will

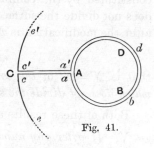

Fig. 41.

the effect of the whole cross-cut be, or not be, that of making distinct pieces.

**161.** Let a loop-cut be drawn in a surface of connectivity $N$; as before for a cross-cut, there are two cases for consideration, according as the loop-cut does or does not divide the surface into distinct pieces.

First, let it divide the surface into two distinct pieces, say of connectivities $N_1$ and $N_2$ respectively. Change the loop-cut into a cross-cut of the original surface by drawing a cross-cut in either of the pieces, say the second, from a point in the course of the loop-cut to some point of the original boundary. This cross-cut, as a section of that piece, does not divide it into distinct pieces : and therefore the connectivity is now $N_2'(= N_2 - 1)$. The effect of the whole section, which is a single cross-cut, of the original surface is to divide it into two pieces, the connectivities of which are $N_1$ and $N_2'$ : hence, by § 160, III.,

$$N_1 + N_2' = N + 1,$$

and therefore

$$N_1 + N_2 = N + 2.$$

If the piece cut out be simply connected, say $N_1 = 1$, then the connectivity of the remainder is $N + 1$. But such a removal of a simply connected piece by a loop-cut is the same as making a hole in a continuous part of the surface : and therefore *the effect of making a simple hole in a continuous part of a surface is to increase by unity the connectivity of the surface.*

If the piece cut out be doubly-connected, say $N_1 = 2$, then the connectivity of the remainder is $N$, the same as the connectivity of the original surface. Such a portion would be obtained by cutting out a piece with a hole in it which, so far as concerns the original surface, would be the same as merely enlarging the hole—an operation that naturally would not affect the connectivity.

Secondly, let the loop-cut not divide the surface into two distinct pieces : and let $N'$ be the connectivity of the modified surface. In this modified surface make a cross-cut $k$ from any point of the loop-cut to a point of the boundary : this does not divide it into distinct pieces and therefore the connectivity after this last modification is $N' - 1$. But the surface thus finally modified is derived from the original surface by the single cross-cut, constituted by the combination of $k$ with the loop-cut; this single cross-cut does not divide the surface into distinct pieces, and therefore the connectivity after the modification is $N-1$.   Hence

$$N'-1 = N-1,$$

that is, $N' = N$, or *the connectivity of a surface is not affected by a loop-cut which does not divide the surface into distinct pieces.*

Both of these results are included in the following theorem :—

V.   *If after any number of loop-cuts made in a surface of connectivity $N$, there be $r+1$ distinct pieces of surface, of connectivities $N_1$, $N_2$, ..., $N_{r+1}$, then*

$$N_1 + N_2 + \ldots + N_{r+1} = N + 2r.$$

Let the number of loop-cuts be $s$.   Each of them can be changed into a cross-cut of the original surface, by drawing in some one of the pieces, as may be convenient, a cross-cut from a point of the loop-cut to a point of a boundary : this new cross-cut does not divide the piece in which it is drawn into distinct pieces.   If $k$ such cross-cuts (where $k$ may be zero) be drawn in the piece of connectivity $N_m$, the connectivity becomes $N_m{}'$, where

$$N_m{}' = N_m - k \,;$$

hence
$$\sum_{m=1}^{r+1} N_m{}' = \sum_{m=1}^{r+1} N_m - \Sigma k = \sum_{m=1}^{r+1} N_m - s.$$

We now have $s$ cross-cuts dividing the surface of connectivity $N$ into $r+1$ distinct pieces, of connectivities $N_1{}'$, $N_2{}'$, ..., $N_r{}'$, $N_{r+1}{}'$; and therefore, by § 160, IV.,
$$N_1{}' + \ldots + N_r{}' + N_{r+1}{}' = N + 2r - s,$$

so that
$$N_1 + N_2 + \ldots + N_{r+1} = N + 2r.$$

This result could have been obtained also by combination and repetition of the two results obtained for a single loop-cut.

Thus a spherical surface with one hole in it is simply connected: when $n-1$ other different holes* are made in it, the edges of the holes being outside one another, the connectivity of the surface is increased by $n-1$, that is, it becomes $n$.   Hence *a spherical surface with $n$ holes in it is $n$-ply connected.*

*Ex.*   Two equal anchor-rings, which are horizontal and have their centres in the same vertical line, are connected together by three vertical right circular cylinders.   Determine the connectivity of the solid so formed.                    (Math. Trip., Part II., 1893.)

**162.**   Occasionally, it is necessary to consider the effect of a slit made in the surface.

---

* These are holes in the surface, not holes bored through the volume of the sphere ; one of the latter would give two holes in the surface.

If the slit have neither of its extremities on a boundary (and therefore no point on a boundary), it can be regarded as the limiting form of a loop-cut which makes a hole in the surface. Such a slit therefore (§ 161) increases the connectivity by unity.

If the slit have one extremity (but no other point) on a boundary, it can be regarded as the limiting form of a cross-cut, which returns on itself as in the figure, and cuts off a single simply connected piece. Such a slit therefore (§ 160, III.) leaves the connectivity unaltered.

If the slit have both extremities on boundaries, it ceases to be merely a slit: it is a cross-cut the effect of which on the connectivity has been obtained. We do not regard such sections as slits.

Fig. 42.

**163**. In the preceding investigations relative to cross-cuts and loop-cuts, reference has continually been made to the boundary of the surface considered.

The *boundary* of a surface consists of a line returning to itself, or of a system of lines each returning to itself. Each part of such a boundary-line as it is drawn is considered a part of the boundary, and thus a boundary-line cannot cut itself and pass beyond its earlier position, for a boundary cannot be crossed: each boundary-line must therefore be a simple curve*.

Most surfaces have boundaries: an exception arises in the case of closed surfaces whatever be their connectivity. It was stated (§ 159) that a boundary is assigned to such a surface by drawing an infinitesimal simple curve in it or, what is the same thing, by making a small hole. The advantage of this can be seen from the simple example of a spherical surface.

When a small hole is made in any surface the connectivity is increased by unity: the connectivity of the spherical surface after the hole is made is unity, and therefore the connectivity of the complete spherical surface must be taken to be zero.

The mere fact that the connectivity is less than unity, being that of the simplest connected surfaces with which we have to deal, is not in itself of importance. But let us return for a moment to the suggested method of determining the connectivity by means of the evanescence of circuits without crossing the boundary. When the surface is the complete spherical surface (fig. 43), there are two essentially distinct ways of making a circuit $C$ evanescent, first, by making it collapse into the point $a$, secondly, by making it expand over the equator and

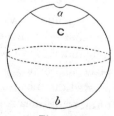

Fig. 43.

* Also a line not returning to itself may be a boundary; it can be regarded as the limit of a simple curve when the area becomes infinitesimal.

then collapse into the point $b$. One of the two is superfluous : it introduces an element of doubt as to the mode of evanescence unless that mode be specified—a specification which in itself is tantamount to an assignment of boundary. And in the case of multiply connected surfaces the absence of boundary, as above, leads to an artificial reduction of the connectivity by unity, arising not from the greater simplicity of the surface but from the possibility of carrying out in two ways the operation of reducing any circuit to given circuits, which is most effective when only one way is permissible. We shall therefore assume a boundary assigned to such closed surfaces as in the first instance are destitute of boundary.

**164.** The relations between the number of boundaries and the connectivity of a surface are given by the following propositions.

I.   *The boundary of a simply connected surface consists of a single line.*

When a boundary consists of separate lines, then a cross-cut can be made from a point of one to a point of another. By proceeding from $P$, a point on one side of the cross-cut, along the boundary $ac...c'a'$ we can by a line lying wholly in the surface reach a point $Q$ on the other side of the cross-cut : hence the parts of the surface on opposite sides of the cross-cut are connected. The surface is therefore not resolved into distinct pieces by the cross-cut.

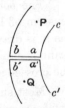

Fig. 44.

A simply connected surface is resolved into distinct pieces by each cross-cut made in it : such a cross-cut as the foregoing is therefore not possible, that is, there are not separate lines which make up its boundary. It has a boundary : the boundary therefore consists of a single line.

II.   *A cross-cut either increases by unity or diminishes by unity the number of distinct boundary-lines of a multiply connected surface.*

A cross-cut is made in one of three ways : either from a point $a$ of one boundary-line $A$ to a point $b$ of another boundary-line $B$; or from a point $a$ of a boundary-line to another point $a$ of the same boundary-line; or from a point of a boundary-line to a point in the cut itself.

If made in the first way, a combination of one edge of the cut, the remainder of the original boundary $A$, the other edge of the cut and the remainder of the original boundary $B$ taken in succession, form a single piece of boundary; this replaces the two boundary-lines $A$ and $B$ which existed distinct from one another before the cross-cut was made. Hence the number of lines is diminished by unity. An example is furnished by a plane ring (ii., fig. 37, p. 361).

If made in the second way, the combination of one edge of the cut with the piece of the boundary on one side of it makes one boundary-line, and the combination of the other edge of the cut with the other piece of the boundary makes another boundary-line. Two boundary-lines, after the cut is made, replace a single boundary-line, which existed before it was made : hence the number of lines is increased by unity. Examples are furnished by the cut surfaces in fig. 40, p. 366.

If made in the third way, the cross-cut may be considered as constituted by a loop-cut and a cut joining the loop-cut to the boundary. The boundary-lines may now be considered as constituted (fig. 41, p. 367) by the closed curve $ABD$ and the closed boundary $abda'c'e'...eca$; that is, there are now two boundary-lines instead of the single boundary-line $ce...e'c'c$ in the uncut surface. Hence the number of distinct boundary-lines is increased by unity.

COROLLARY. *A loop-cut increases the number of distinct boundary-lines by two.*

This result follows at once from the last discussion.

III. *The number of distinct boundary-lines of a surface of connectivity $N$ is $N - 2k$, where $k$ is a positive integer that may be zero.*

Let $m$ be the number of distinct boundary-lines; and let $N - 1$ appropriate cross-cuts be drawn, changing the surface into a simply connected surface. Each of these cross-cuts increases by unity or diminishes by unity the number of boundary-lines; let these units of increase or of decrease be denoted by $\epsilon_1, \epsilon_2, ..., \epsilon_{N-1}$. Each of the quantities $\epsilon$ is $\pm 1$; let $k$ of them be positive, and $N - 1 - k$ negative. The total number of boundary-lines is therefore

$$m + k - (N - 1 - k).$$

The surface now is a single simply connected surface, and there is therefore only one boundary-line ; hence

$$m + k - (N - 1 - k) = 1,$$

so that                                    $$m = N - 2k ;$$

and evidently $k$ is an integer that may be zero.

COROLLARY 1. *A closed surface with a single boundary-line\* is of odd connectivity.*

For example, the surface of an anchor-ring, when bounded, is of connectivity 3 ; the surface, obtained by boring two holes through the volume of a solid sphere, is, when bounded, of connectivity 5.

If the connectivity of a closed surface with a single boundary be $2p + 1$, the surface is often said† to be of *genus p* (§ 178, p. 395).

---

\* See § 159.

† Sometimes *class*. The German word is *Geschlecht* ; French writers use the word *genre*, and Italians *genere*.

COROLLARY 2. *If the number of distinct boundary-lines of a surface of connectivity N be N, any loop-cut divides the surface into two distinct pieces.*

After the loop-cut is made, the number of distinct boundary-lines is $N + 2$; the connectivity of the whole of the cut surface is therefore not less than $N + 2$. It has been proved that a loop-cut, which does not divide the surface into distinct pieces, does not affect the connectivity; hence as the connectivity has been increased, the loop-cut must divide the surface into two distinct pieces. It is easy, by the result of § 161, to see that, after the loop-cut is made, the sum of connectivities of the two pieces is $N + 2$, so that the connectivity of the whole of the cut surface is equal to $N + 2$.

*Note.* Throughout these propositions, a tacit assumption has been made, which is important for this particular proposition when the surface is the means of representing the variable. The assumption is that *the surface is bifacial and not unifacial*; it has existed implicitly throughout all the geometrical representations of variability: it found explicit expression in § 4 when the plane was brought into relation with the sphere: and a cut in a surface has been counted a single cut, occurring on one side, though it would have to be counted as two cuts, one on each side, were the surface unifacial.

The propositions are not necessarily valid, when applied to unifacial surfaces. Consider a surface made out of a long rectangular slip of paper, which is twisted once (or any odd number of times) and then has its ends fastened together. This surface is of double connectivity, because one section can be made across it which does not divide it into separate pieces; it has only a *single* boundary-line, so that Prop. III. just proved does not apply. The surface is unifacial; and it is possible, without meeting the boundary, to pass continuously in the surface from a point $P$ to another point $Q$ which could be reached merely by passing through the material at $P$.

We therefore do not retain unifacial surfaces for consideration.

**165.** The following proposition, substantially due to Lhuilier[*], may be taken in illustration of the general theory.

*If a closed surface of connectivity $2N + 1$ (or of genus $N$) be divided by circuits into any number of simply connected portions, each in the form of a curvilinear polygon, and if F be the number of polygons, E be the number of edges and S the number of angular points, then*

$$2N = 2 + E - F - S.$$

Let the edges $E$ be arranged in systems, a system being such that any line in it can be reached by passage along some other line or lines of the

---

[*] Gergonne, *Ann. de Math.*, t. iii, (1813), pp. 181—186; see also Möbius, *Ges. Werke*, t. ii, p. 468. A *circuit* is defined in § 166.

system; let $k$ be the number of such systems*. To resolve the surface into a number of simply connected pieces composed of the $F$ polygons, the cross-cuts will be made along the edges; and therefore, unless a boundary be assigned to the surface in each system of lines, the first cut for any system will be a loop-cut. We therefore take $k$ points, one in each system as a boundary; the first will be taken as the natural boundary of the surface, and the remaining $k-1$, being the limiting forms of $k-1$ infinitesimal loop-cuts, increase the connectivity of the surface by $k-1$, that is, the connectivity now is $2N+k$.

The result of the cross-cuts is to leave $F$ simply connected pieces: hence $Q$, the number of cross-cuts, is given by

$$Q = 2N + k + F - 2.$$

At every angular point on the uncut surface, three or more polygons are contiguous. Let $S_m$ be the number of angular points, where $m$ polygons are contiguous; then

$$S = S_3 + S_4 + S_5 + \dots$$

Again, the number of edges meeting at each of the $S_3$ points is three, at each of the $S_4$ points is four, at each of the $S_5$ points is five, and so on; hence, in taking the sum $3S_3 + 4S_4 + 5S_5 + \dots$, each edge has been counted twice, once for each extremity. Therefore

$$2E = 3S_3 + 4S_4 + 5S_5 + \dots$$

Consider the composition of the extremities of the cross-cuts; the number of the extremities is $2Q$, twice the number of cross-cuts.

Each of the $k$ points furnishes two extremities; for each such point is a boundary on which the initial cross-cut for each of the systems must begin and must end. These points therefore furnish $2k$ extremities.

The remaining extremities occur in connection with the angular points. In making a cut, the direction passes from a boundary along an edge, past the point along another edge and so on, until a boundary is reached; so that on the first occasion when a cross-cut passes through a point, it is made along two of the edges meeting at the point. Every other cross-cut passing through that point must begin or end there, so that each of the $S_3$ points will furnish one extremity (corresponding to the remaining one cross-cut through the point), each of the $S_4$ points will furnish two extremities (corresponding to the remaining two cross-cuts through the point), and so on. The total number of extremities thus provided is

$$S_3 + 2S_4 + 3S_5 + \dots$$

Hence
$$2Q = 2k + S_3 + 2S_4 + 3S_5 + \dots$$
$$= 2k + 2E - 2S,$$

---

* The value of $k$ is 1 for the proposition and is greater than 1 for the Corollary.

or                                $Q = k + E - S,$

which, combined with              $Q = 2N + k + F - 2,$

leads to the relation             $2N = 2 + E - F - S.$

The simplest case is that of a sphere, when Euler's relation $F + S = E + 2$ is obtained. The case next in simplicity is that of an anchor-ring, for which the relation is $F + S = E$.

COROLLARY. *If the result of making the cross-cuts along the various edges be to give the $F$ polygons, not simply connected areas but areas of connectivities $N_1 + 1$, $N_2 + 1$, ..., $N_F + 1$ respectively, then the connectivity of the original surface is given by*

$$2N = 2 + E - F - S + \sum_{r=1}^{F} N_r.$$

**166.** The method of determining the connectivity of a surface by means of a system of cross-cuts, which resolve it into one or more simply connected pieces, will now be brought into relation with the other method, suggested in § 159, of determining the connectivity by means of irreducible circuits.

A closed line drawn on the surface is called a *circuit*.

A circuit, which can be reduced to a point by continuous deformation without crossing the boundary, is called *reducible*; a circuit, which cannot be so reduced, is called *irreducible*.

An irreducible circuit is either (i) *simple*, when it cannot without crossing the boundary be deformed continuously into repetitions of one or more circuits; or (ii) *multiple*, when it can without crossing the boundary be deformed continuously into repetitions of a single circuit; or (iii) *compound*, when it can without crossing the boundary be deformed continuously into combinations of different circuits, that may be simple or multiple. The distinction between simple circuits and compound circuits, that involve no multiple circuits in their combination, depends upon conventions adopted for each particular case.

A circuit is said to be *reconcileable* with the system of circuits into a combination of which it can be continuously deformed.

If a system of circuits be reconcileable with a reducible circuit, the system is said to be reducible.

Let a simple circuit be denoted by a single letter, say, $A$, $B$, $C$, .... A multiple circuit, composed of $n$ repetitions of a simple circuit $A$, can then be denoted by $A^n$. A compound circuit, composed of a simple circuit $A$ followed by another simple circuit $B$, can be denoted by $AB$: the order of the symbols being of importance. As circuits thus have their symbols associated in the manner of (non-commutative algebraical) factors, the symbol 1 will represent a reducible circuit; for a circuit causing no change must be represented by a factor causing no change.

There are two directions, one positive and the other negative, in which a circuit can be described. Let it be described first in the positive direction and afterwards in the negative direction: the circuit, compounded of the two descriptions, is easily seen to be continuously deformable to a point, and it therefore is reducible. Similarly, if the circuit is described first in the negative direction and afterwards in the positive direction, the compound circuit thus obtained is reducible. Accordingly, if a simple circuit described positively be represented by $A$, the same circuit described negatively can be represented by $A^{-1}$, the symbols of the circuits obeying the associative law.

A compound circuit, reconcileable with a system of simple irreducible circuits $A$, $B$, $C$, ..., would be represented by $A^\alpha B^\beta A^{\alpha'} B^{\beta'} ... C^\gamma A^{\alpha''} ...$, where $\alpha$, $\beta$, $\alpha'$, $\beta'$, ..., $\gamma$, $\alpha''$ are integers positive or negative.

In order to estimate circuits on a multiply connected surface, it is sufficient to know a system of irreducible simple circuits. Such a system is naturally to be considered complete when every other circuit on the surface is reconcileable with the system. It also may be supposed to contain the smallest possible number of simple circuits; for any one, which is reconcileable with the rest, can be omitted without affecting the completeness of the system.

**167.** Such a system is indicated by the following theorems :—

I. *No irreducible simple circuit can be drawn on a simply connected surface*[*].

If possible, let an irreducible circuit $C$ be drawn in a simply connected surface with a boundary $B$. Make a loop-cut along $C$, and change it into a cross-cut by making a cross-cut $A$ from some point of $C$ to a point of $B$; this cross-cut divides the surface into two simply connected pieces, one of which is bounded by $B$, the two edges of $A$, and one edge of the cut along $C$, and the other of which is bounded entirely by the cut along $C$.

The latter surface is smaller than the original surface; it is simply connected and has a single boundary. If an irreducible simple circuit can be drawn on it, we proceed as before, and again obtain a still smaller simply connected surface. In this way, we ultimately obtain an infinitesimal element; for every cut divides the surface, in which it is made, into distinct pieces. Irreducible circuits cannot be drawn in this element; and therefore its boundary is reducible. This boundary is a circuit in a larger portion of the surface: the circuit is reducible so that, in that larger portion, no irreducible circuit is possible and therefore its boundary is reducible. This boundary is a circuit in a still larger portion, and the circuit is

---

[*] All surfaces considered are supposed to be bounded.

reducible : so that in this still larger portion no irreducible circuit is possible and once more the boundary is reducible.

Proceeding in this way, we find that no irreducible simple circuit is possible in the original surface.

COROLLARY.  *No irreducible circuit can be drawn on a simply connected surface.*

II.  *A complete system of irreducible simple circuits for a surface of connectivity $N$ contains $N-1$ simple circuits, so that every other circuit on the surface is reconcileable with that system.*

Let the surface be resolved by cross-cuts into a single simply connected surface:  $N-1$ cross-cuts will be necessary.  Let $CD$ be any one of them : and let $a$ and $b$ be two points on the opposite edges of the cross-cut.  Then since the surface is simply connected, a line can be drawn in the surface from $a$ to $b$ without passing out of the surface or without meeting a part of the boundary, that is, without meeting any other cross-cut.  The cross-cut $CD$ ends either in another cross-cut or in a boundary; the line $ae \dots fb$

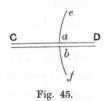

Fig. 45.

surrounds that other cross-cut or that boundary as the case may be : hence, if the cut $CD$ be obliterated, the line $ae \dots fba$ is irreducible on the surface in which the other $N-2$ cross-cuts are made.  But it meets none of those cross-cuts; hence, when they are all obliterated so as to restore the unresolved surface of connectivity $N$, it is an irreducible circuit.  It is evidently not a repeated circuit; hence it is an irreducible simple circuit.  Hence *the line of an irreducible simple circuit on an unresolved surface is given by a line passing from a point on one edge of a cross-cut in the resolved surface to a point on the opposite edge.*

Since there are $N-1$ cross-cuts, it follows that $N-1$ irreducible simple circuits can thus be obtained : one being derived in the foregoing manner from each of the cross-cuts, which are necessary to render the surface simply connected.  It is easy to see that each of the irreducible circuits on an unresolved surface is, by the cross-cuts, rendered impossible as a circuit on the resolved surface.

But every other irreducible circuit $C$ is reconcileable with the $N-1$ circuits, thus obtained.  If there be one not reconcileable with these $N-1$ circuits, then, when all the cross-cuts are made, the circuit $C$ is not rendered impossible, if it be not reconcileable with those which are rendered impossible by the cross-cuts: that is, there is on the resolved surface an irreducible circuit.  But the resolved surface is simply connected, and therefore no irreducible circuit can be drawn on it : hence the hypothesis as to $C$, which leads to this result, is not tenable.

Thus every other circuit is reconcileable with the system of $N-1$ circuits: and therefore *the system is complete\**.

This method of derivation of the circuits at once indicates how far a system is arbitrary. Each system of cross-cuts leads to a complete system of irreducible simple circuits, and *vice versa*; as the one system is not unique, so the other system is not unique.

**168.** It follows that *the number of simple irreducible circuits in any complete system must be the same for the same surface*: this number is $N-1$, where $N$ is the connectivity of the surface. Let $A_1, A_2, ..., A_{N-1}; B_1, B_2, ..., B_{N-1}$; be two distinct complete systems; then we have

$$B_s = \Pi_s (A_1 A_2 ... A_{N-1}),$$

where $\Pi_s$ means the symbolic product representing that circuit compounded of the system $A_1, ..., A_{N-1}$ with which $B_s$ is reconcileable; and

$$A_r = \Pi_{r}' (B_1 B_2 ... B_{N-1})$$

with a similar significance for $\Pi_{r}'$.

Further *any circuit, that is reconcileable with one complete system, is reconcileable with any other complete system*. For if $X$ denote a circuit reconcileable with $A_1, A_2, ..., A_{N-1}$, we have

$$X = \Pi (A_1 A_2 ... A_{N-1}):$$

whence, taking account of the reconcileability of each circuit $A$ with the complete system $B_1, B_2, ..., B_{N-1}$, we have

$$X = \Pi (\Pi_1' \Pi_2' ... \Pi'_{N-1})$$
$$= \Pi'' (B_1 B_2 ... B_{N-1}),$$

thus proving the statement.

For the general question, Jordan's memoir, "Des contours tracés sur les surfaces," *Liouville*, 2$^{me}$ Sér., t. xi, (1866), pp. 110—130, may be consulted.

*Ex.* 1. On a doubly connected surface, one irreducible simple circuit can be drawn. It is easily obtained by first resolving the surface into one that is simply connected—

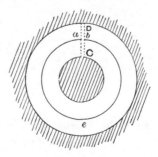

Fig. 46, (i).

* If the number of independent irreducible simple circuits be adopted as a basis for the definition of the connectivity of a surface, the result of the proposition would be taken as the definition: and the resolution of the surface into one, which is simply connected, would then be obtained by developing the preceding theory in the reverse order.

a single cross-cut $CD$ is effective for this purpose—and then by drawing a curve $aeb$ in the surface from one edge of the cross-cut to the other. All other irreducible circuits on the unresolved surface are reconcileable with the circuit $aeba$.

*Ex.* 2. On a triply connected surface, two independent irreducible circuits can be drawn. Thus in the figure $C_1$ and $C_2$ will form a complete system. The circuits $C_3$

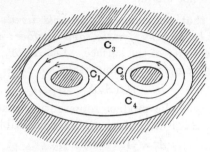

Fig. 46, (ii).

and $C_4$ are also irreducible : they can evidently be deformed into $C_1$ and $C_2$ and reducible circuits by continuous deformation : in the algebraical notation adopted, we have

$$C_3 = C_1 C_2, \quad C_4 = C_1 C_2^{-1}.$$

But $C_3$ and $C_4$ are not simple circuits : hence they are not suited for the construction of a complete system.

*Ex.* 3. Another example of a triply connected surface is given in fig. 47. Two irreducible simple circuits are $C_1$ and $C_2$. Another irreducible circuit is $C_3$; this

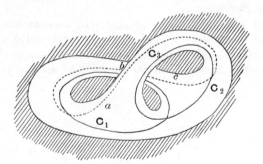

Fig. 47.

can be reconciled with $C_1$ and $C_2$ by drawing the point $a$ into coincidence with the intersection of $C_1$ and $C_2$, and the point $c$ into coincidence with the same point.

*Ex.* 4. As a last example, consider the surface of a solid sphere with $n$ holes bored through it. The connectivity is $2n+1$ : hence $2n$ independent irreducible simple circuits can be drawn on the surface. The simplest complete system is obtained by taking $2n$ curves : made up of a set of $n$, each round one hole, and another set of $n$, each through one hole.

A resolution of this surface is given by taking cross-cuts, one round each hole (making the circuits through the holes no longer possible) and one through each hole (making the circuits round the holes no longer possible).

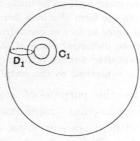

Fig. 48.

The simplest case is that for which $n = 1$; the surface is equivalent to the anchor-ring.

**169.** Surfaces are at present being considered in view of their use as a means of representing the value of a complex variable. The foregoing investigations imply that surfaces can be classed according to their connectivity; and thus, having regard to their designed use, the question arises as to whether all surfaces of the same connectivity are equivalent to one another, so as to be transformable into one another.

Moreover, a surface can be physically deformed and still remain suitable for representation of the variable, provided certain conditions are satisfied. We thus consider geometrical transformation as well as physical deformation; but we are dealing only with the general results and not with the mathematical relations of deformed inextensible surfaces, which are discussed in treatises on Differential Geometry*.

It is evident that continuity is necessary for both: discontinuity would imply discontinuity in the representation of the variable. Points that are contiguous (that is, separated only by small distances measured in the surface) must remain contiguous†: and one point in the unchanged surface must correspond to only one point in the changed surface. Hence *in the continuous deformation of a surface there may be stretching and there may be bending; but there must be no tearing and there must be no joining.*

For instance, a single untwisted ribbon, if cut, comes to be simply connected. If a twist through 180° be then given to one end and that end be then joined to the other, we shall have a once-twisted ribbon, which is a surface with only one face and only one edge; it cannot be looked upon as an equivalent of the former surface.

* See Darboux's *Théorie générale des surfaces*, Books vii and viii, for the fullest discussion. Some account is given in Chapter x of my *Lectures on the differential geometry of curves and surfaces.*

† Distances between points must be measured along the surface, not through space; the distance between two points is a length which one point would traverse before reaching the position of the other, the motion of the point being restricted to take place in the surface. Examples will arise later, in Riemann's surfaces, in which points that are contiguous in space are separated by finite distances on the surface.

A spherical surface with a single hole can have the hole stretched and the surface flattened, so as to be the same as a bounded portion of a plane : the two surfaces are equivalent to one another. Again, in the spherical surface, let a large indentation be made : let both the outer and the inner surfaces be made spherical ; and let the mouth of the indentation be contracted into the form of a long, narrow hole along a part of a great circle. When each point of the inner surface is geometrically moved so that it occupies the position of its reflexion in the diametral plane of the hole, the final form* of the whole surface is that of a two-sheeted surface with a junction along a line : it is a spherical winding-surface, and is equivalent to the simply connected spherical surface.

**170.** It is sufficient, for the purpose of representation, that the two surfaces should have a point-to-point transformation : it is not necessary that physical deformation, without tears or joins, should be actually possible. Thus a ribbon with an even number of twists would be as effective as a limited portion of a cylinder, or (what is the same thing) an untwisted ribbon : but it is not possible to deform the one into the other physically†.

It is easy to see that either deformation or transformation of the kind considered *will change a bifacial surface into a bifacial surface;* that *it will not alter the connectivity,* for it will not change irreducible circuits into reducible circuits, and the number of independent irreducible circuits determines the connectivity : and that *it will not alter the number of boundary curves,* for a boundary will be changed into a boundary. These are necessary relations between the two forms of the surface : it is not difficult to see that they are sufficient for correspondence. For if, on each of two bifacial surfaces with the same number of boundaries and of the same connectivity, a complete system of simple irreducible circuits be drawn, then, when the members of the systems are made to correspond in pairs, the full transformation can be effected by continuous deformation of those corresponding irreducible circuits. It therefore follows that :—

*The necessary and sufficient conditions, that two bifacial surfaces may be equivalent to one another for the representation of a variable, are that the two surfaces should be of the same connectivity and should have the same number of boundaries.*

As already indicated, this equivalence is a geometrical equivalence : deformation may be (but is not of necessity) physically possible.

Similarly, the presence of one or of several knots in a surface makes no essential difference in the use of the surface for representing a variable. Thus a long cylindrical surface is changed into an anchor-ring when its ends are joined together ; but the changed surface would be equally effective for purposes of representation if a knot were tied in the cylindrical surface before the ends are joined.

---

* Clifford, *Coll. Math. Papers*, p. 250.

† The difference between the two cases is that, in physical deformation, the surfaces are the surfaces of continuous matter and are impenetrable ; while, in geometrical transformation, the surfaces may be regarded as penetrable without interference with the continuity.

But it need hardly be pointed out that though surfaces, thus twisted or knotted, are equivalent for the purpose indicated, they are not equivalent for all topological enumerations.

Seeing that bifacial surfaces, with the same connectivity and the same number of boundaries, are equivalent to one another, it is natural to adopt, as the surface of reference, some simple surface with those characteristics; thus for a surface of connectivity $2p + 1$ with a single boundary, the surface of a solid sphere, bounded by a point and pierced through with $p$ holes, could be adopted.

Klein calls* such a surface of reference a *Normal Surface.*

It has been seen that a bounded spherical surface and a bounded simply connected part of a plane are equivalent—they are, moreover, physically deformable into one another.

An untwisted closed ribbon is equivalent to a bounded piece of a plane with one hole in it—they are deformable into one another: but if the ribbon, previous to being closed, have undergone an even number of twists each through 180°, they are still equivalent but are not physically deformable into one another. Each of the bifacial surfaces is doubly connected (for a single cross-cut renders each simply connected) and each of them has two boundaries. If however the ribbon, previous to being closed, have undergone an odd number of twists each through 180°, the surface thus obtained is not equivalent to the single-holed portion of the plane; it is unifacial and has only one boundary.

A spherical surface pierced in $n+1$ holes is equivalent to a bounded portion of the plane with $n$ holes; each is of connectivity $n+1$ and has $n+1$ boundaries. The spherical surface can be deformed into the plane surface by stretching one of its holes into the form of the outside boundary of the plane surface.

*Ex.* Prove that the surface of a bounded anchor-ring can be physically deformed into the surface in fig. 47, p. 378.

For continuation and fuller development of the subjects of the present chapter, the following references, in addition to those which have been given, will be found useful:—

Klein, *Math. Ann.*, t. vii, (1874), pp. 548—557; ib., t. ix, (1876), pp. 476—482.

Lippich, *Math. Ann.*, t. vii, (1874), pp. 212—229; *Wiener Sitzungsb.*, t. lxix, (ii), (1874), pp. 91—99.

Durège, *Wiener Sitzungsb.*, t. lxix, (ii), (1874), pp. 115—120; and section 9 of his treatise, quoted on p. 363, note.

Neumann, chapter vii of his treatise, quoted on p. 5, note.

Dyck, *Math. Ann.*, t. xxxii, (1888), pp. 457—512, ib., t. xxxvii, (1890), pp. 273—316; at the beginning of the first part of this investigation, a valuable series of references is given.

Dingeldey, *Topologische Studien*, (Leipzig, Teubner, 1890).

Mair, *Quart. Journ. of Math.*, vol. xxvii, (1895), pp. 1—35.

* *Ueber Riemann's Theorie der algebraischen Functionen und ihrer Integrale*, (Leipzig, Teubner, 1882), p. 26. This tract has been translated into English by Miss Hardcastle, (Cambridge, Macmillan and Bowes, 1893).

# CHAPTER XV.

## RIEMANN'S SURFACES.

**171.** THE method of representing a variable by assigning to it a position in a plane or on a sphere is effective when properties of uniform functions of that variable are discussed. But when multiform functions, or integrals of uniform functions occur, the method is effective only when certain parts of the plane are excluded, due account being subsequently taken of the effect of such exclusions; and this process, the extension of Cauchy's method, was adopted in Chapter IX.

There is another method, referred to in § 100 as due to Riemann, of an entirely different character. In Riemann's representation, the region, in which the variable $z$ exists, no longer consists of a single plane but of a number of planes; they are distinct from one another in geometrical conception, yet, in order to preserve a representation in which the value of the variable is obvious on inspection, the planes are infinitesimally close to one another. The number of planes, often called *sheets*, is the same as the number of distinct values (or branches) of the function $w$ for a general argument $z$ and, unless otherwise stated, will be assumed finite; each sheet is associated with one branch of the function, and changes from one branch of the function to another are effected by making the $z$-variable change from one sheet to another, so that, to secure the possibility of change of sheet, it is necessary to have means of passage from one sheet to another. The aggregate of all the sheets is a surface, often called a *Riemann's Surface*.

For example, consider the function

$$w = z^{\frac{1}{3}} + (z-1)^{-\frac{1}{3}},$$

the cube roots being independent of one another. It is evidently a nine-valued function; the number of sheets in the appropriate Riemann's surface is therefore nine.

The branch-points are $z=0$, $z=1$, $z=\infty$. Let $\omega$ and $a$ denote a cube-root of unity, independently of one another; then the values of $z^{\frac{1}{3}}$ can be represented in the form

$z^{\frac{1}{3}}$, $\omega z^{\frac{1}{3}}$, $\omega^2 z^{\frac{1}{3}}$; and the values of $(z-1)^{-\frac{1}{3}}$ can be represented in the form $(z-1)^{-\frac{1}{3}}$, $a^2(z-1)^{-\frac{1}{3}}$, $a(z-1)^{-\frac{1}{3}}$. The nine values of $w$ can be symbolically expressed as follows:—

| $w_1$ | 1 | 1 | | $w_4$ | 1 | $a^2$ | | $w_7$ | 1 | $a$ |
|---|---|---|---|---|---|---|---|---|---|---|
| $w_2$ | $\omega$ | 1 | | $w_5$ | $\omega$ | $a^2$ | | $w_8$ | $\omega$ | $a$ |
| $w_3$ | $\omega^2$ | 1 | | $w_6$ | $\omega^2$ | $a^2$ | | $w_9$ | $\omega^2$ | $a$ |

where the symbols opposite to $w$ give the coefficients of $z^{\frac{1}{3}}$ and of $(z-1)^{-\frac{1}{3}}$ respectively.

Now when $z$ describes a small simple circuit positively round the origin, the groups in cyclical order are $w_1$, $w_2$, $w_3$; $w_4$, $w_5$, $w_6$; $w_7$, $w_8$, $w_9$. And therefore, in the immediate vicinity of the origin, there must be means of passage to enable the $z$-point to make the corresponding changes from sheet to sheet. Taking a section of the whole surface near the origin so as to indicate the passages and regarding the right-hand sides as the part from which the $z$-variable moves when it describes a circuit positively, the passages must be in character as indicated in fig. 49. And it is evident that the further description of small simple circuits round the origin will, with these passages, lead to the proper values: thus $w_5$, which after the single description is the value of $w_4$, becomes $w_6$ after another description, and it is evident that a point in the $w_5$ sheet passes into the $w_6$ sheet.

Fig. 49.

When $z$ describes a small simple circuit positively round the point 1, the groups in cyclical order are $w_1$, $w_4$, $w_7$; $w_2$, $w_5$, $w_8$; $w_3$, $w_6$, $w_9$: and therefore, in the immediate vicinity of the point 1, there must be means of passage to render possible the corresponding changes of $z$ from sheet to sheet. Taking a section as before near the point 1 and with similar convention as to the positive direction of the $z$-path, the passages must be in character as indicated in fig. 50.

Fig. 50.

Similarly for infinitely large values of $z$.

If then the sheets can be so joined as to give these possibilities of passage and also give combinations of them corresponding to combinations of the simple paths indicated, then there will be a surface to any point of which will correspond one and only one value of $w$: and when the value of $w$ is given for a point $z$ in an ordinary plane of variation, then that value of $w$ will determine the sheet of the surface in which the point $z$ is to be taken. A surface will then have been constructed such that the function $w$, which is multiform for the single-plane representation of the variable, is uniform for variations in the many-sheeted surface.

Again, for the simple example arising from the two-valued function, defined by the equation

$$w = \{(z-a)(z-b)(z-c)\}^{-\frac{1}{2}},$$

the branch-points are $a$, $b$, $c$, $\infty$; and a small simple circuit round any one of these four points interchanges the two values. The Riemann's surface is two-sheeted and there must be means of passage between the two sheets in the vicinity of $a$, that of $b$, that of $c$, and at the infinite part of the plane.

These examples are sufficient to indicate the main problem. It is the construction of a surface in which the independent variable can move so that, for variations of $z$ in that surface, the multiformity of the function is changed to uniformity. From the nature of the case, the character of the surface will depend on the character of the function: and thus, though all the functions are uniform with their appropriate surfaces, these surfaces are widely various. Evidently for uniform functions of $z$ the appropriate surface on the above method is the single plane already adopted.

**172.** The simplest classes of functions for which a Riemann's surface is useful are (i) those called (§ 94) *algebraic* functions, that is, multiform functions of the independent variable defined by an algebraical equation of the form

$$f(w, z) = 0,$$

which is of finite degree, say $n$, in $w$; and (ii) those usually called *Abelian* functions, which arise through integrals connected with algebraic functions.

Of such an algebraic function there are, in general, $n$ distinct values; but for the special values of $z$, that are the branch-points, two or more of the values coincide. The appropriate Riemann's surface is composed of $n$ sheets; one branch, and only one branch, of $w$ is associated with a sheet. The variable $z$, in its relation to the function, is determined not merely by its modulus and argument but also by its sheet; that is, in the language of the earlier method, we take account of the path by which $z$ acquires a value. The particular sheet in which $z$ lies determines the particular branch of the function. Variations of $z$, which occur within a sheet and do not coincide with points lying in regions of passage between the sheets, lead to variations in the value of the branch of $w$ associated with the sheet; a return to an initial value of $z$, by a path that nowhere lies within a region of passage, leaves the $z$-point in the same sheet as at first and so leads to the initial branch (and to the initial value of the branch) of $w$. But a return to an initial value of $z$ by a path, which, in the former method of representation, would enclose a branch-point, implies a change of the branch of the function according to the definite order prescribed by the branch-point. Hence the final value of the variable $z$ on the Riemann's surface must lie in a sheet that is different from that of the initial (and arithmetically equal) value; and therefore the sheets must be so connected that, in the immediate vicinity of branch-points, there are means of passage from one sheet to another, securing the proper interchanges of the branches of the function as defined by the equation.

**173.** The first necessity is therefore the consideration of the mode in which the sheets of a Riemann's surface are joined: the mode is indicated by the theorem that *sheets of a Riemann's surface are joined along lines.*

The junction might be made either at a point, as with two spheres in contact, or by a common portion of a surface, as with one prism lying on another, or along lines; but whatever the character of the junction be, it must be such that a single passage across it (thereby implying entrance to the junction and exit from it) must change the sheet of the variable.

If the junction were at a point, then the $z$-variable could change from one sheet into another sheet, only if its path passed through that point: any other closed path would leave the $z$-variable in its original sheet. A small closed curve, infinitesimally near the point and enclosing it and no other branch-point, is one which ought to transfer the variable to another sheet because it encloses a branch-point: and this is impossible with a point-junction when the path does not pass through the point. Hence a junction *at a point only* is insufficient to provide the proper means of passage from sheet to sheet.

If the junction were effected by a common portion of surface, then a passage through it (implying an entrance into that portion and an exit from it) ought to change the sheet. But, in such a case, closed contours can be constructed which make such a passage without enclosing the branch-point $a$: thus the junction would cause a change of sheet for certain circuits the description of which ought to leave the $z$-variable in the original sheet. Hence a junction by a *continuous area of surface* does not provide the proper means of passage from sheet to sheet.

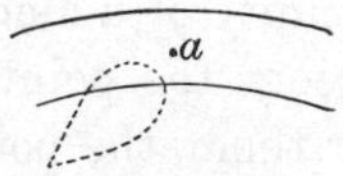

Fig. 51.

The only possible junction which remains is a line. The objection in the last case does not apply to a closed contour which does not contain the branch-point; for the line cuts the curve twice and there are therefore two crossings; the second of them makes the variable return to the sheet which the first crossing compelled it to leave.

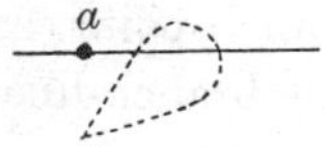

Fig. 52.

Hence the junction between any two sheets takes place along a line.

Such a line is called* a *branch-line*. The branch-points of a multiform function lie on the branch-lines, after the foregoing explanations; and a branch-line can be crossed by the variable only if the variable change its sheet at crossing, in the sequence prescribed by the branch-point of the function which lies on the line. Also, the sequence is reversed when the branch-line is crossed in the reversed direction.

Thus, if two sheets of a surface be connected along a branch-line, a point which crosses the line from the first sheet must pass into the second and a point which crosses the line from the second sheet must pass into the first.

Again, if, along a common direction of branch-line, the first sheet of a surface be connected with the second, the second with the third, and the third with the first,

---

* Sometimes *cross-line*, sometimes *branch-section*. The German title is *Verzweigungschnitt*; the French is *ligne de passage*; see also the note on the equivalents of branch-point, p. 17.

a point which crosses the line from the first sheet in one direction must pass into the second sheet, but if it cross the line in the other direction it must pass into the third sheet.

A branch-point does not necessarily affect all the branches of a function: when it affects only some of them, the corresponding property of the Riemann's surface is in evidence as follows. Let $z = a$ determine a branch-point affecting, say, only $r$ branches. Take $n$ points $a$, one in each of the sheets; and through them draw $n$ lines $cab$, having the same geometrical position in the respective sheets. Then in the vicinity of the point $a$ in each of the $r$ sheets, associated with the $r$ affected branches, there must be means of passage from each one to all the rest of them; and the lines $cab$ can conceivably be the branch-lines with a properly established sequence. The point $a$ does not affect the other $n - r$ branches: there is therefore no necessity for means of passage in the vicinity of $a$ among the remaining $n - r$ sheets. In each of these remaining sheets, the point $a$ and the line $cab$ belong to their respective sheets alone: for them, the point $a$ is not a branch-point and the line $cab$ is not a branch-line.

**174.** Several essential properties of the branch-lines are immediate inferences from these conditions.

I. *A free end of a branch-line in a surface is a branch-point.*

Let a simple circuit be drawn round the free end so small as to enclose no branch-point (except the free end, if it be a branch-point). The circuit meets the branch-line once, and the sheet is changed because the branch-line is crossed; hence the circuit includes a branch-point which therefore can be only the free end of the line.

*Note.* A branch-line may terminate in the boundary of the surface, and then the extremity need not be a branch-point.

II. *When a branch-line extends beyond a branch-point lying in its course, the sequence of interchange is not the same on the two sides of the point.*

If the sequence of interchange be the same on the two sides of the branch-point, a small circuit round the point would first cross one part of the branch-line and therefore involve a change of sheet and then, in its course, would cross the other part of the branch-line in the other direction which, on the supposition of unaltered sequence, would cause a return to the initial sheet. In that case, a circuit round the branch-point would fail to secure the proper change of sheet. Hence the sequence of interchange caused by the branch-line cannot be the same on the two sides of the point.

III. *If two branch-lines with different sequences of interchange have a common extremity, that point is either a branch-point or an extremity of at least one other branch-line.*

If the point be not a branch-point, then a simple curve enclosing it, taken so small as to include no branch-point, must leave the variable in its initial sheet. Let $A$ be such a point, $AB$ and $AC$ be two branch-lines having $A$ for a common extremity; let the sequence be as in the figure, taken for a simple case; and suppose that the variable

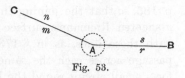

Fig. 53.

initially is in the $r$th sheet. A passage across $AB$ makes the variable pass into the $s$th sheet. If there be no branch-line between $AB$ and $AC$ having an extremity at $A$, and if neither $n$ nor $m$ be $s$, then the passage across $AC$ makes no change in the sheet of the variable and, therefore, in order to restore $r$ before $AB$, at least one branch-line must lie in the angle between $AC$ and $AB$, estimated in the positive trigonometrical sense.

If either $n$ or $m$, say $n$, be $s$, then after passage across $AC$, the point is in the $m$th sheet; then, since the sequences are not the same, $m$ is not $r$ and there must be some branch-line between $AC$ and $AB$ to make the point return to the $r$th sheet on the completion of the circuit.

If then the point $A$ be not a branch-point, there must be at least one other branch-line having its extremity at $A$. This proves the proposition.

COROLLARY 1. *If both of two branch-lines extend beyond a point of inter-section, which is not a branch-point, and if no other branch-line pass through the point, then either no sheet of the surface has both of them for branch-lines, or they are branch-lines for two sheets that are the same.*

COROLLARY 2. *If a change of sequence occur at any point of a branch-line, then either that point is a branch-point or it lies also on some other branch-line.*

COROLLARY 3. *No part of a branch-line with only one branch-point on it can be a closed curve.*

It is evidently superfluous to have a branch-line without any branch-point on it.

**175.** On the basis of these properties, we can obtain a system of branch-lines satisfying the requisite conditions which are :—

(i)   the proper sequences of change from sheet to sheet must be secured by a description of a simple circuit round a branch-point : if this be satisfied for each of the branch-points, it will evidently be satisfied for any combination of simple circuits, that is, for any path whatever enclosing one or more branch-points.

(ii)  the sheet, in which the variable re-assumes its initial value after describing a circuit that encloses no branch-point, must be the initial sheet.

In the $z$-plane of Cauchy's method, let lines be drawn from any point $I$, not a branch-point in the first instance, to each of the branch-points, as in fig. 19, p. 185, so that the joining lines do not meet except at $I$: and suppose the $n$-sheeted Riemann's surface to have branch-lines coinciding geometrically with these lines, as in § 173, and having the sequence of interchange for passage across each the same as the order in the cycle of functional values for a small circuit round the branch-point at its free end. No line (or part of a line) can be a closed curve; the lines need not be straight, but they will be supposed drawn as direct as possible to the points in angular succession.

The first of the above requisite conditions is satisfied by the establishment of the sequence of interchange.

To consider the second of the conditions, it is convenient to divide circuits into two kinds, ($\alpha$) those which exclude $I$, ($\beta$) those which include $I$, no one of either kind (for our present purpose) including a branch-point.

A closed circuit, excluding $I$ and all the branch-points, must intersect a branch-line an even number of times, if it intersect the line in real points. Let the figure (fig. 54) represent such a case: then the crossings at $A$ and $B$ counteract one another and so the part between $A$ and $B$ may without effect be transferred across $IB_3$ so as not to cut the branch-line at all. Similarly for the points $C$ and $D$: and a similar transference of the part now between $C$ and $D$ may be made across the branch-line without effect: that is, the circuit can, without effect, be changed

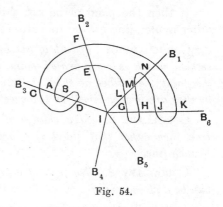

Fig. 54.

so as not to cut the branch-line $IB_3$ at all. A similar change can be made for each of the branch-lines: and so the circuit can, without effect, be changed into one which meets no branch-line and therefore, on its completion, leaves the sheet unchanged.

A closed circuit, including $I$ but no branch-point, must meet each branch-line an odd number of times. A change similar in character to that in the previous case may be made for each branch-line: and without affecting the result, the circuit can be changed so that it meets each branch-line only once. Now the effect produced by a branch-line on the function is the same as the description of a simple loop round the branch-point which with $I$ determines the branch-line: and therefore the effect of the circuit at present contemplated is, after the transformation which does not affect the result, the same as that of a circuit, in the previously adopted mode of representation, enclosing all the branch-points. But, by Cor. III. of § 90, the effect of a circuit which encloses all the branch-points (including $z = \infty$, if it be a branch-point) is to restore the value of the function which it had at the beginning of the circuit: and therefore in the present case the effect is to make the point return to the sheet in which it lay initially.

It follows therefore that, for both kinds of a closed circuit containing no branch-point, the effect is to make the $z$-variable return to its initial sheet on resuming its initial value at the close of the circuit.

Next, let the point $I$ be a branch-point; and let it be joined by lines, as direct* as possible, to each of the other branch-points in angular succession. These lines will be regarded as the branch-lines; and the sequence of interchange for passage across any one is made that of the interchange prescribed by the branch-point at its free extremity.

The proper sequence of change is secured for a description of a simple closed circuit round each of the branch-points other than $I$. Let a small circuit be described round $I$; it meets each of the branch-lines once and therefore its effect is the same as, in the language of the earlier method of representing variation of $z$, that of a circuit enclosing all the branch-points except $I$. Such a circuit, when taken on the Neumann's sphere, as in Cor. III., § 90 and Ex. 2, § 104, may be regarded in two ways, according as one or other of the portions, into which it divides the area of the sphere, is regarded as the included area; in one way, it is a circuit enclosing all the branch-points except $I$, in the other it is a circuit enclosing $I$ alone and no other branch-point. Without making any modification in the final value of $w$, it can (by § 90) be deformed, either into a succession of loops round all the branch-points save one, or into a loop round that one; the effect of these two deformations is therefore the same. Hence the effect of the small closed circuit round $I$ meeting all the branch-lines is the same as, in the other mode of representation, that of a small curve round $I$ enclosing no other branch-point; and therefore the adopted set of branch-lines secures the proper sequence of change of value for description of a circuit round $I$.

The first of the two necessary conditions is therefore satisfied by the present arrangement of branch-lines.

The proof, that the second of the two necessary conditions is also satisfied by the present arrangement of branch-lines, is similar to that in the preceding case, save that only the first kind of circuit of the earlier proof is possible.

It thus appears that a system of branch-lines can be obtained which secures the proper changes of sheet for a multiform function: and therefore Riemann's surfaces can be constructed for such a function, the essential property being that over its appropriate surface an otherwise multiform function of the variable is a uniform function.

* The reason for this will appear in §§ 183, 184.

The multipartite character of the function has its influence preserved by the character of the surface to which the function is referred: the surface, consisting of a number of sheets joined to one another, may be a multiply connected surface.

In thus proving the general existence of appropriate surfaces, there has remained a large arbitrary element in their actual construction: moreover, in particular cases, there are methods of obtaining varied configurations of branch-lines. Thus the assignment of the $n$ branches to the $n$ sheets has been left unspecified, and is therefore so far arbitrary: the point $I$, if not a branch-point, is arbitrarily chosen and so there is a certain arbitrariness of position in the branch-lines. Naturally, what is desired is the simplest appropriate surface: the particularisation of the preceding arbitrary qualities is used to derive a canonical form of the surface.

**176**. The discussion of one or two simple cases will help to illustrate the mode of junction between the sheets, made by branch-lines.

The simplest case of all is that in which the surface has only a single sheet: it does not require discussion.

The case next in simplicity is that in which the surface is two-sheeted: the function is therefore two-valued and is consequently defined by a quadratic equation of the form

$$Lu^2 + 2Mu + N = 0,$$

where $L$, $M$, and $N$ are uniform functions of $z$. When a new variable $w$ is introduced, defined by $Lu + M = w$, so that values of $w$ and of $u$ correspond uniquely, the equation is

$$w^2 = M^2 - LN = P(z).$$

It is evident that every branch-point of $u$ is a branch-point of $w$, and *vice versa;* hence the Riemann's surface is the same for the two equations. Now any root of $P(z)$ of odd degree is a branch-point of $w$. If then

$$P(z) = Q^2(z) R(z),$$

where $R(z)$ is a product of only simple factors, every factor of $R(z)$ leads to a branch-point. If the degree of $R(z)$ be even, the number of branch-points for finite values of the variable is even, and $z = \infty$ is not a branch-point; if the degree of $R(z)$ be odd, the number of branch-points for finite values of the variable is odd, and $z = \infty$ is a branch-point: in either case, the number of branch-points is even.

There are only two values of $w$, and the Riemann's surface is two-sheeted: crossing a branch-line therefore merely causes a change of sheet. The free ends of branch-lines are branch-points; a small circuit round any branch-point causes an interchange of the branches $w$, and a circuit round any two branch-points restores the initial value of $w$ at the end and therefore leaves the variable in the same sheet as at the beginning. These are the essential requirements in the present case; all of them are satisfied by taking *each branch-line as a line connecting two (and only two) of the branch-points.* The ends of all the branch-lines are free: and their number, in this method, is one-half that of the (even) number of branch-points. A small circuit round a branch-point meets a branch-line once and causes a change of sheet; a circuit round two (and not more than two) branch-points causes either no crossing of branch-line or an even number of crossings and therefore restores the variable to the initial sheet.

A branch-line is, in this case, usually drawn in the form of a straight line when the surface is plane: but this form is not essential and all that is desirable is to prevent intersections of the branch-lines.

*Note.* Junction between the sheets along a branch-line is easily secured. The two sheets to be joined are cut along the branch-line. One edge of the cut in the upper sheet, say its right edge looking along the section, is joined to the left edge of the cut in the lower sheet; and the left edge in the upper sheet is joined to the right edge in the lower.

A few simple examples will illustrate these remarks as to the sheets: illustrations of closed circuits will arise later, in the consideration of integrals of multiform functions.

*Ex.* 1. Let $$w^2 = A(z-a)(z-b),$$
so that $a$ and $b$ are the only branch-points. The surface is two-sheeted: the line $ab$ may be made the branch-line. In fig. 55 only part of the upper sheet is shewn[*], as likewise only part of the lower sheet. Continuous lines imply what is visible; and dotted lines what is invisible, on the supposition that the sheets are opaque.

The circuit, closed in the surface and passing round $a$, is made up of the continuous line in the upper sheet from $H$ to $K$: the point crosses the branch-line at $K$ and then passes into the lower sheet, where it describes the dotted line from $K$ to $H$: it then meets and crosses the branch-line at $H$, passes into the upper sheet and in that sheet returns to its initial point. Similarly of the line $ABC$, the part $AB$ lies in the lower sheet, the part $BC$ in the upper: of the line $DG$ the part $DE$ lies in the upper sheet, the part $EFG$ in the lower, the piece $FG$ of this part being there visible beyond the boundary of the retained portion of the upper surface.

*Ex.* 2. Let $$\lambda w^2 = z^3 - a^3.$$
The branch-points (fig. 56) are $A(=a)$, $B(=aa)$, $C(=aa^2)$, where $a$ is a primitive cube root of unity, and $z = \infty$. The branch-lines can be made by $BC$, $A\infty$; and the two-sheeted surface is a surface over which $w$ is uniform. Only a part of each sheet is shewn in the figure; a section also is made at $M$ across the surface, cutting the branch-line $A\infty$.

*Ex.* 3. Let $$w^m = z^n,$$
where $n$ and $m$ are prime to each other. The branch-points are $z = 0$ and $z = \infty$; and the branch-line extends from 0 to $\infty$. There are $m$ sheets; if we associate them in order with the branches $w_s$, where

$$w_s = r^{\frac{n}{m}} e^{\frac{(n\theta + 2s\pi)i}{m}}$$

for $s = 1, 2, \ldots, m$, then the first sheet is connected with the second forwards, the second with the third forwards, and so on; the $m$th being connected with the first forwards.

---

[*] The form of the three figures in the plate opposite p. 392 is suggested by Holzmüller, *Einführung in die Theorie der isogonalen Verwandschaften und der conformen Abbildungen,* (Leipzig, Teubner, 1882), in which several illustrations are given.

The surface is sometimes also called a *winding-surface*; and a branch-point such as $z=0$ on the surface, where a number $m$ of sheets pass into one another in succession, is also called a *winding-point* of order $m-1$ (see p. 17, note). An illustration of the surface for $m=3$ is given in fig. 57, the branch-line being cut so as to shew the branching: what is visible is indicated by continuous lines; what is in the second sheet, but is invisible, is indicated by the thickly dotted line; what is in the third sheet, but is invisible, is indicated by the thinly dotted line.

*Ex.* 4. Consider a three-sheeted surface having four branch-points at $a, b, c, d$; and let each point interchange two branches, say, $w_2, w_3$ at $a$; $w_1, w_3$ at $b$; $w_2, w_3$ at $c$;

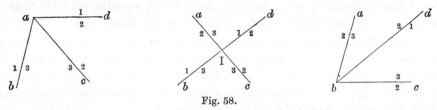

Fig. 58.

$w_1, w_2$ at $d$; the points being as in fig. 58. It is easy to verify that these branch-points satisfy the condition that a circuit, enclosing them all, restores the initial value of $w$.

The branching of the sheets may be made as in the figure, the integers on the two sides of the line indicating the sheets that are to be joined along the line.

A canonical form for such a surface can be derived from the more general case given later (in §§ 186—189).

*Ex.* 5. Shew that, if the equation
$$f(w, z)=0$$
be of degree $n$ in $w$ and be irreducible, all the $n$ sheets of the surface are connected, that is, it is possible by an appropriate path to pass from any sheet to any other sheet.

For if not, let $a$ denote any arbitrary value of $z$, and let $u_1, u_2, ..., u_n$ denote the $n$ values of $w$ when $z=a$. Let $z$ vary, beginning with a value $a$; let the variation be restricted solely by the condition that $z$ does not acquire a value giving rise to a branch-point, and otherwise be perfectly general; and let $z$ return to the value $a$. If it is not possible to pass from any sheet of the Riemann's surface to any other, suppose that the first, second, ..., $m$th sheets are connected with one another, and that no one of them is connected with any one of the rest. Then whatever be the variation of $z$, and whichever of the values $u_1, u_2, ..., u_m$ be chosen as an initial value of $w$, the final value of $w$ (when $z$ resumes its value $a$) will be one of the set $u_1, u_2, ..., u_m$. Hence any rational symmetric function of $u_1, u_2, ..., u_m$ remains unchanged when $z$, after varying quite arbitrarily, resumes an initial value; in other words, that symmetric function of $u_1, u_2, ..., u_m$ is a uniform function of $z$, which (as in § 193) is a rational function of $z$. Consequently, the values $u_1, u_2, ..., u_m$ of $w$ are the roots of an algebraical equation $f_1(w, z)=0$, which is polynomial in $w$ and $z$, and is of degree $m$ in $w$. But these values of $w$ are roots of $f(w, z)=0$; hence $f(w, z)$ is divisible by $f_1(w, z)$, contrary to the given condition that $f(w, z)=0$ is irreducible.

*Corollary I.* When $f=0$ is irreducible, it is possible to make $z$ vary from an initial value, and return to $a$, in such a way that any assigned initial value of $w$ shall lead to any assigned final value of $w$, among the $n$ values which it has for $z=a$.

*Corollary II.* If $z=a$, $w=A$, and $z=\beta$, $w=B$ are any two positions on the Riemann's surface corresponding to an equation $f(w, z)=0$, and if a path exists in the surface

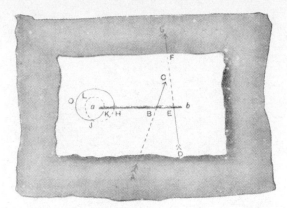

Fig. 55.

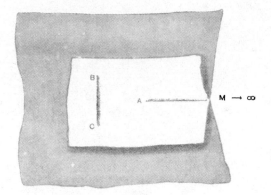

Fig. 56.

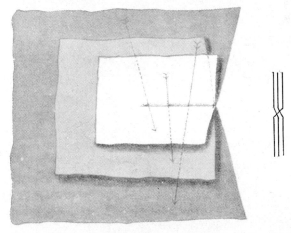

Fig. 57.

joining the one position to the other, then $f$ is either an irreducible polynomial or is some power of an irreducible polynomial.

For if $f$ can be resolved into the product of two different polynomials, each of them equated to zero would give rise to a Riemann's surface ; and the two surfaces would not be connected, so that it would be impossible to pass from any position on one of them to any position on the other. If therefore $f$ is resoluble, its component polynomials must be one and the same: that is, on the given hypothesis, when $f$ is reducible, it is a power of an irreducible polynomial.

**177**. It is not necessary to limit the surface representing the variable to a set of planes; and, indeed, as with uniform functions, there is a convenience in using the sphere for the purpose.

We take $n$ spheres, each of diameter unity, touching the Riemann's plane surface at a point $A$; each sphere is regarded as the stereographic projection of a plane sheet, with regard to the other extremity $A'$ of the spherical diameter through $A$. Then, the sequence of these spherical sheets being the same as the sequence of the plane sheets, branch-points in the plane surface project into branch-points on the spherical surface: branch-lines between the plane sheets project into branch-lines between the spherical sheets and are terminated by corresponding points; and if a branch-line extend in the plane surface to $z = \infty$, the corresponding branch-line in the spherical surface is terminated at $A'$.

A surface will thus be obtained consisting of $n$ spherical sheets; like the plane Riemann's surface, it is one over which the $n$-valued function is a uniform function of the position of the variable point.

But also *the connectivity of the n-sheeted spherical surface is the same as that of the n-sheeted plane surface with which it is associated.*

In fact, the plane surface can be mechanically changed into the spherical surface without tearing, or repairing, or any change except bending and compression: all that needs to be done is that the $n$ plane sheets shall be bent, without making any change in their sequence, each into a spherical form, and that the boundaries at infinity (if any) in the plane sheet shall be compressed into an infinitesimal point, being the South pole of the corresponding spherical sheet or sheets. Any junctions between the plane sheets extending to infinity are junctions terminated at the South pole. As the plane surface has a boundary, which, if at infinity on one of the sheets, is therefore not a branch-line for that sheet, so the spherical surface has a boundary which, if at the South pole, cannot be the extremity of a branch-line.

**178**. We proceed to obtain the connectivity of a Riemann's surface: it is determined by the following theorem :—

*Let the total number of branch-points in a Riemann's n-sheeted surface be r ; and let the number of branches of the function interchanging at the first* *point be $m_1$, the number interchanging at the second be $m_2$, and so on. Then the connectivity of the surface is*

$$\Omega - 2n + 3,$$

*where $\Omega$ denotes $m_1 + m_2 + \ldots + m_r - r$.*

Take * the surface in the bounded spherical form, the connectivity $N$ of which is the same as that of the plane surface: and let the boundary be a small hole $A$ in the outer sheet. By means of cross-cuts and loop-cuts, the surface can be resolved into a number of distinct simply connected pieces.

First, make a slice bodily through the sphere, the edge in the outside sheet meeting $A$ and the direction of the slice through $A$ being chosen so that none of the branch-points lie in any of the pieces cut off. Then $n$ parts, one from each sheet and each simply connected, are taken away. The remainder of the surface has a cup-like form; let the connectivity of this remainder be $M$.

Fig. 59.

This slice has implied a number of cuts.

The cut made in the outside sheet is a cross-cut, because it begins and ends in the boundary $A$. It divides the surface into two distinct pieces, one being the portion of the outside sheet cut off, and this piece is simply connected; hence, by Prop. III. of § 160, the remainder has its connectivity still represented by $N$.

The cuts in all the other sheets, caused by the slice, are all loop-cuts, because they do not anywhere meet the boundary. There are $n - 1$ loop-cuts, and each cuts off a simply connected piece; let the remaining surface be of connectivity $M$. Hence, by Prop. V. of § 161,

$$M + n - 1 = N + 2(n - 1),$$

and therefore $\qquad\qquad M = N + n - 1.$

In this remainder, of connectivity $M$, make $r - 1$ cuts, each of which begins in the rim and returns to the rim, and is to be made through the $n$ sheets together; and choose the directions of these cuts so that each of the $r$ resulting portions of the surface contains one (and only one) of the branch-points.

Consider the portion of the surface which contains the branch-point where $m_1$ sheets of the surface are connected. The $m_1$ connected sheets constitute a piece of a winding-surface round the winding-point of order $m_1 - 1$; the remaining sheets are unaffected by the winding-point, and

* The proof is founded on Neumann's, *Vorlesungen über Riemann's Theorie der Abel'schen Integrale*, pp. 168—172.

therefore the parts of them are $n - m_1$ distinct simply connected pieces. The piece of winding-surface is simply connected; because a circuit, that does not contain the winding-point, is reducible without passing over the winding-point, and a circuit, that does contain the winding-point, is reducible to the winding-point, so that no irreducible circuit can be drawn. Hence the portion of the surface under consideration consists of $n - m_1 + 1$ distinct simply connected pieces.

Similarly for the other portions. Hence the total number of distinct simply connected pieces is

$$\sum_{q=1}^{r} (n - m_q + 1)$$

$$= nr - \sum_{q=1}^{r} m_q + r$$

$$= nr - \Omega.$$

But in the portion of connectivity $M$ each of the $r-1$ cuts causes, in each of the sheets, a cut passing from the boundary and returning to the boundary, that is, a cross-cut. Hence there are $n$ cross-cuts from each of the $r-1$ cuts, and therefore $n(r-1)$ cross-cuts altogether, made in the portion of surface of connectivity $M$.

The effect of these $n(r-1)$ cross-cuts is to resolve the portion of connectivity $M$ into $nr - \Omega$ distinct simply connected pieces; hence, by § 160,

$$M = n(r-1) - (nr - \Omega) + 2,$$

and therefore $\qquad N = M - (n-1) = \Omega - 2n + 3,$

the connectivity of the Riemann's surface.

The quantity $\Omega$, having the value $\sum_{q=1}^{r} (m_q - 1)$, may be called the *ramification* of the surface, as indicating the aggregate sum of the orders of the different branch-points.

*Note.* The surface just considered is a closed surface to which a point has been assigned for boundary; hence, by Cor. 1, Prop. III., § 164, its connectivity is an odd integer. Let it be denoted by $2p + 1$; then

$$2p = \Omega - 2n + 2,$$

and $2p$ is the number of cross-cuts which change the Riemann's surface into one that is simply connected.

The integer $p$ is often called (Cor. 1, Prop. III., § 164) the *genus* of the Riemann's surface; and *the equation*

$$f(w, z) = 0$$

*is said to be of genus $p$, when $p$ is the genus of the associated Riemann's surface.*

The genus of an equation is discussed, partly in association with Abel's Theorem on transcendental integrals, in an interesting paper[*] by Baker, who gives a simple graphical rule to determine the integer when the coefficients are general. This rule is given in the example at the end of § 182.

*Ex.* 1. When the equation is

$$w^2 = \lambda (z - a)(z - b),$$

we have a two-sheeted surface, $n = 2$. There are two branch-points, $z = a$ and $z = b$; but $z = \infty$ is not a branch-point; so that $r = 2$. At each of the branch-points the two values are interchanged, so that $m_1 = 2$, $m_2 = 2$; thus $\Omega = 2$. Hence the connectivity $= 2 - 4 + 3 = 1$, that is, the surface is simply connected.

The surface can be deformed, as in the example in § 169, into a sphere.

*Ex.* 2. When the equation is

$$w^2 = 4z^3 - g_2 z - g_3$$
$$= 4 (z - e_1)(z - e_2)(z - e_3),$$

we have $n = 2$. There are four branch-points, viz., $e_1$, $e_2$, $e_3$, $\infty$, so that $r = 4$; and at each of them the two values of $w$ are interchanged, so that $m_s = 2$ (for $s = 1, 2, 3, 4$), and therefore $\Omega = 8 - 4 = 4$. Hence the connectivity is $4 - 4 + 3$, that is, $3$; and the value of $p$ is unity.

Similarly, the surface associated with the equation

$$w^2 = U(z),$$

where $U(z)$ is a rational integral function of degree $2m - 1$ or of degree $2m$, is of connectivity $2m + 1$; so that $p = m$. The equation

$$w^2 = (1 - z^2)(1 - k^2 z^2)$$

is of genus $p = 1$. The case next in importance is that of the algebraical equation leading to the hyperelliptic functions, when $U$ is either a quintic or a sextic; and then $p = 2$.

*Ex.* 3. Obtain the connectivity of the Riemann's surface associated with the equation

$$w^3 + z^3 - 3awz = 1,$$

where $a$ is a constant, (i) when $a$ is zero, (ii) when $a$ is different from zero.

*Ex.* 4. Shew that, if the surface associated with the equation

$$f(w, z) = 0,$$

have $\mu$ boundary-lines instead of one, and if the equation have the same branch-points as in the foregoing proposition, the connectivity is $\Omega - 2n + \mu + 2$.

*Ex.* 5. Shew that the genus of the equation

$$w^4 - z^2 (z^2 + z + 1) = 0$$

is 1, and that the genus of the equation

$$w^5 + z^5 = 5wz^2$$

is 2.                                                          (Raffy.)

Discuss the genus of the equation

$$w^5 - 5w^3 (z^2 + z + 1) + 5w (z^2 + z + 1)^2 - 2z (z^2 + z + 1)^2 = 0.$$
                                                        . (Raffy : Baker.)

---

[*] "Examples of the application of Newton's polygon to the theory of singular points of algebraic functions," *Camb. Phil. Trans.*, vol. xv, (1894), pp. 403—405.

*Ex.* 6. In the equation

$$w^n = (z - c_1)^{n_1} \ldots (z - c_s)^{n_s},$$

the sum of the positive integers $n_1, \ldots, n_s$ is divisible by $n$. Shew that the genus $p$ of the associated Riemann's surface is given by

$$p = 1 + \tfrac{1}{2} n (s - 2) - \tfrac{1}{2} \sum_{q=1}^{s} \lambda_q,$$

where $\lambda_q$ is the greatest common measure of $n_q$ and $n$.

Shew also that, for surfaces of a given genus $p$, associated with equations of the assigned form, $s$ cannot be greater than $2p - 2$.        (Trinity Fellowship, 1897.)

*Ex.* 7. Shew that the values of $p$ for the equations

    (i)    $w^4 - z^4 + 2wz (w^2 z^2 - 1) = 0$:

    (ii)   $(w^2 - z^2)^2 - 4w^2 z^2 (wz - 1)^2 = 0$:

are 7 and 3 respectively.                                    (Cayley.)

*Ex.* 8. Shew that the genus of the equation

$$w^6 = z^2 (1 - z)^{2n+1},$$

where $n$ is a positive integer or zero, is unity.

*Ex.* 9. Shew that the genus $p$ of the equation

$$w^n = z (1 - z)^2,$$

where $n$ is a positive integer, is given as follows :—

           when $n = 6k - a$, then $p = 3k - a$, for $a = 1, 2, 3$ ;

         ...    $n = 6k + a$,    ...    $p = 3k$    ,   ... $a = 1, 2$ ;

         ...    $n = 6k$      ,    ...    $p = 3k - 1$.

*Ex.* 10. Find the genus of the equation

$$w^n = (1 - z^2) (1 - k^2 z^2),$$

where $n$ is a positive integer $> 2$.

**179.** The consideration of irreducible circuits on the surface at once reveals the multiple connection of the surface, the numerical measure of which has been obtained. In a Riemann's surface, a simple closed *circuit cannot be deformed over a branch-point.* Let $A$ be a branch-point, and let $AE...$ be the branch-line having a free end at $A$. Take a curve $...CED...$ crossing the branch-line at $E$ and passing into a sheet different from that which contains the portion $CE$; and, if possible,

Fig. 60.

let a slight deformation of the curve be made so as to transfer the portion $CE$ across the branch-point $A$. In the deformed position, the curve $...C'E'D'...$ does not meet the branch-line; there is, consequently, no change of sheet in its course near $A$ and therefore $E'D'...$, which is the continuation of $...C'E'$, cannot be regarded as the deformed position of $ED$. The two paths are essentially distinct; and thus the original path cannot be deformed over the branch-point.

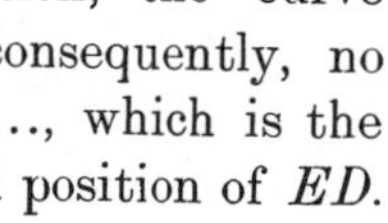

It therefore follows that continuous deformation of a circuit over a branch-point on a Riemann's surface is a geometrical impossibility.

*Ex.* Trace the variation of the curve $CED$, as the point $E$ moves up to $A$ and then returns along the other side of the branch-line.

Hence a circuit containing two or more (but not all) of the branch-points is irreducible; a circuit containing all the branch-points is equivalent to a circuit that contains none of them, and it is therefore reducible.

If a circuit contain only one branch-point, it can be continuously deformed so as to coincide with the point on each sheet and therefore, being deformable into a point, it is a reducible circuit. An illustration has already occurred in the case of a portion of winding-surface containing a single winding-point (Ex. 3, p. 391); all circuits drawn on it are reducible.

It follows from the preceding results that the Riemann's surface associated with a multiform function is generally one of multiple connection; we shall find it convenient to know how it can be resolved, by means of cross-cuts, into a simply connected surface. The representative surface will be supposed a closed surface with a single boundary; its connectivity, necessarily odd, being $2p + 1$, the number of cross-cuts necessary to resolve the surface into one that is simply connected is $2p$; when these cuts have been made, the simply connected surface then obtained will have its boundary composed of a single closed curve.

One or two simple examples of resolution of special Riemann's surfaces will be useful in leading up to the general explanation; in the examples it will be shewn how, in conformity with § 168, the resolving cross-cuts render irreducible circuits impossible.

*Ex.* 1. Let the equation be

$$w^2 = A\,(z - a)(z - b)\,(z - c)\,(z - d),$$

where $a, b, c, d$ are four distinct points, all of finite modulus. The surface is two-sheeted; each of the points $a, b, c, d$ is a branch-point where the two values of $w$ interchange; and so the surface, assumed to have a single boundary, is triply connected, the value of $p$ being unity. The branch-lines are two, each connecting a pair of branch-points; let them be $ab$ and $cd$.

Two cross-cuts are necessary and sufficient to resolve the surface into one that is simply connected. We first make a cross-cut, beginning at the boundary $B$, (say it is in the upper sheet), continuing in that sheet and returning to $B$, so that its course encloses the branch-line $ab$ (but not $cd$) and meets no branch-line. It is a cross-cut, and not a loop-cut, for it begins and ends in the boundary; it is evidently a cut in the upper sheet alone, and does not divide the surface into distinct portions; and, once made, it is to be regarded as boundary for the partially cut surface.

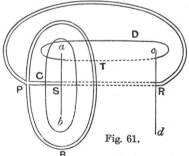

Fig. 61.

The surface in its present condition is connected: and therefore it is possible to pass from one edge to the other of the cut just made. Let $P$ be a point on it; a curve that passes from one edge to the other is indicated by the line $PQR$ in the upper sheet, $RS$ in the lower, and $SP$ in the upper. Along this line make a cut, beginning at $P$ and returning to $P$; it is a cross-cut, partly in the upper sheet and partly in the lower, and it does not divide the surface into distinct portions.

Two cross-cuts in the triply connected surface have now been made; neither of them, as made, divides the surface into distinct portions, and each of them when made reduces the connectivity by one unit; hence the surface is now simply connected. It is easy to see that the boundary consists of a single line not intersecting itself; for beginning at $P$, we have the outer edge of $PBT$, then the inner edge of $PQRSP$, then the inner edge of $PTB$, and then the outer edge of $PSRQP$, returning to $P$.

The required resolution has been effected.

Before the surface was resolved, a number of irreducible circuits could be drawn; a complete system of irreducible circuits is composed of two, by § 168. Such a system may be taken in various ways; let it be composed of a simple curve $C$ lying in the upper sheet and containing the points $a$ and $b$, and a simple curve $D$, lying partly in the upper and partly in the lower sheet and containing the points $a$ and $c$; each of these curves is irreducible, because it encloses two branch-points. Every other irreducible circuit is reconcileable with these two; the actual reconciliation in particular cases is effected most simply when the surface is taken in a spherical form.

The irreducible circuit $C$ on the unresolved surface is impossible on the resolved surface owing to the cross-cut $SPQRS$; and the irreducible circuit $D$ on the unresolved surface is impossible on the resolved surface owing to the cross-cut $PTB$. It is easy to verify that no irreducible circuit can be drawn on the resolved surface.

In practice, it is conveniently effective to select a complete system of irreducible simple circuits and then to make the cross-cuts so that each of them renders one circuit of the system impossible on the resolved surface.

*Ex.* 2.   If the equation be

$$w^2 = 4z^3 - g_2 z - g_3$$
$$= 4 (z - e_1)(z - e_2)(z - e_3),$$

the branch-points are $e_1$, $e_2$, $e_3$ and $\infty$. When the two-sheeted surface is spherical, and the branch-lines are taken to be (i) a line joining $e_1$, $e_2$; and (ii) a line joining $e_3$ to the South pole, the discussion of the surface is similar in detail to that in the preceding example.

*Ex.* 3.   Let the equation be

$$w^2 = Az (1 - z)(\kappa - z)(\lambda - z)(\mu - z),$$

and for simplicity suppose that $\kappa$, $\lambda$, $\mu$ are real quantities subject to the inequalities

$$1 < \kappa < \lambda < \mu < \infty .$$

The associated surface is two-sheeted and has a boundary assigned to it; assuming that its sheets are planes, we shall take some point in the finite part of the upper sheet, not being a branch-point, as the boundary. There are six branch-points, viz., 0, 1, $\kappa$, $\lambda$, $\mu$, $\infty$ at each of which the two values of $w$ interchange; and so the connectivity of the surface is 5, and its genus is 2. The branch-lines can be taken as three, this being the simplest arrangement; let them be the lines joining 0, 1; $\kappa$, $\lambda$; $\mu$, $\infty$.

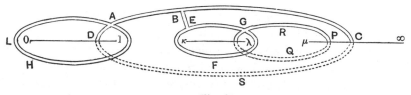

Fig. 62.

Four cross-cuts are necessary to resolve the surface into one that is simply connected and has a single boundary. They may be obtained as follows.

Beginning at the boundary $L$, let a cut $LHA$ be made entirely in the upper sheet along a line which, when complete, encloses the points 0 and 1 but no other branch-points; let the cut return to $L$. This is a cross-cut and it does not divide the surface into distinct pieces; hence, after it is made, the connectivity of the modified surface is 4, and there are two boundary-lines, being the two edges of the cut $LHA$.

Beginning at a point $A$ in $LHA$, make a cut along $ABC$ in the upper sheet until it meets the branch-line $\mu\infty$, then in the lower sheet along $CSD$ until it meets the branch-line 01, and then in the upper sheet from $D$ returning to the initial point $A$. This is a cross-cut and it does not divide the surface into distinct pieces; hence, after it is made, the connectivity of the modified surface is 3, and it is easy to see that there is only one boundary-edge, similar to the single boundary in $Ex.$ 1 when the surface in that example has been completely resolved.

Make a loop-cut $EFG$ along a line, enclosing the points $\kappa$ and $\lambda$ but no other branch-points; and change it into a cross-cut by making a cut from $E$ to some point $B$ of the boundary. This cross-cut can be regarded as $BEFGE$, ending at a point in its own earlier course. As it does not divide the surface into distinct pieces, the connectivity is reduced to 2; and there are two boundary-lines.

Beginning at a point $G$ make another cross-cut $GQPRG$, as in the figure, enclosing the two branch-points $\lambda$ and $\mu$ and lying partly in the upper sheet and partly in the lower. It does not divide the surface into distinct pieces: the connectivity is reduced to unity, and there is a single boundary-line.

Four cross-cuts have been made: and the surface has been resolved into one that is simply connected.

It is easy to verify:—

(i) that neither in the upper sheet, nor in the lower sheet, nor partly in the upper sheet and partly in the lower, can an irreducible circuit be drawn in the resolved surface; and

(ii) that, owing to the cross-cuts, the simplest irreducible circuits in the unresolved surface—viz. those which enclose 0, 1; 1, $\kappa$; $\kappa$, $\lambda$; $\lambda$, $\mu$; respectively—are rendered impossible in the resolved surface.

The equation in the present example, and the Riemann's surface associated with it, lead to the theory of hyperelliptic functions*.

**180.** The last example suggests a method of resolving any two-sheeted surface into a surface that is simply connected.

The number of its branch-points is necessarily even, say $2p+2$. The branch-lines can be made to join these points in pairs, so that there will be $p+1$ of them. To determine the connectivity (§ 178), we have $n=2$ and, since two values are interchanged at every branch-point, $\Omega=2p+2$; so that the connectivity is $2p+1$. Then $2p$ cross-cuts are necessary for the required resolution of the surface.

We make cuts round $p$ of the branch-lines, that is, round all of them but one; each cut is made to enclose two branch-points, and each lies entirely in the upper sheet. These are cuts corresponding to the cuts $LHA$ and $EFG$ in fig. 62; and, as there, the cut round the first branch-line begins and ends

---

* One of the most direct discussions of the theory from this point of view is given by Prym, *Neue Theorie der ultraelliptischen Functionen*, (Berlin, Mayer and Müller, 2nd ed., 1885).

in the boundary, so that it is a cross-cut. All the remaining cuts are loop-cuts at present. This system of $p$ cuts we denote by $a_1, a_2, \ldots, a_p$.

We make other $p$ cuts, one passing from the inner edge of each of the $p$ cuts $a$ already made to the branch-line which it surrounds, then in the lower sheet to the $(p+1)$th branch-line, and then in the upper sheet returning to the point of the outer edge of the cut $a$ at which it began. This system of cuts corresponds to the cuts $ADSCBA$ and $GQPRG$ in fig. 62. Each of them can be taken so as to meet no one of the cuts $a$ except the one in which it begins and ends; and they can be taken so as not to meet one another. This system of $p$ cuts we denote by $b_1, b_2, \ldots, b_p$, where $b_r$ is the cut which begins and ends in $a_r$. All these cuts are cross-cuts, because they begin and end in boundary-lines.

Lastly, we make other $p-1$ cuts from $a_r$ to $b_{r-1}$, for $r = 2, 3, \ldots, p$, all in the upper sheet; no one of them, except at its initial and its final points, meets any of the cuts already made. This system of $p-1$ cuts we denote by $c_2, c_3, \ldots, c_p$.

Because $b_{r-1}$ is a cross-cut, the cross-cut $c_r$ changes $a_r$ (hitherto a loop-cut) into a cross-cut when $c_r$ and $a_r$ are combined into a single cut.

It is evident that no one of these cuts divides the surface into distinct pieces; and thus we have a system of $2p$ cross-cuts resolving the two-sheeted surface of connectivity $2p+1$ into a surface that is simply connected. The cross-cuts in order* are

$$a_1, b_1, c_2 \text{ and } a_2, b_2, c_3 \text{ and } a_3, b_3, \ldots, c_p \text{ and } a_p, b_p.$$

**181.** This resolution of a general two-sheeted surface suggests† Riemann's general resolution of a surface with any (finite) number of sheets.

As before, we assume that the surface is closed and has a single boundary and that its genus is $p$, so that $2p$ cross-cuts are necessary for its resolution into one that is simply connected.

Make a cut in the surface such as not to divide it into distinct pieces; and let it begin and end in the boundary. It is a cross-cut, say $a_1$; it changes the number of boundary-lines to 2, and it reduces the connectivity of the cut surface to $2p$.

Since the surface is connected, we can pass in the surface along a continuous line from one edge of the cut $a_1$ to the opposite edge. Along this line make a cut $b_1$: it is a cross-cut, because it begins and ends in the boundary. It passes from one edge of $a_1$ to the other, that is, from one boundary-line to another. Hence, as in Prop. II. of § 164, it does not divide

---

* See Neumann, pp. 178—182; Prym, *Zur Theorie der Functionen in einer zweiblättrigen Fläche*, (1866).

† Riemann, *Ges. Werke*, pp. 122, 123; Neumann, pp. 182—185.

the surface into distinct pieces; it changes the number of boundaries to 1, and it reduces the connectivity to $2p-1$.

The problem is now the same as at first, except that now only $2p-2$ cross-cuts are necessary for the required resolution. We make a loop-cut $a_2$, not resolving the surface into distinct pieces, and a cross-cut $c_1$ from a point of $a_2$ to a point on the boundary at $b_1$; then $c_1$ and $a_2$, taken together, constitute a cross-cut that does not resolve the surface into distinct pieces. It therefore reduces the connectivity to $2p-2$, and leaves two pieces of boundary.

The surface being connected, we can pass in the surface along a continuous line from one edge of $a_2$ to the opposite edge. Along this line we make a cut $b_2$, evidently a cross-cut, passing, like $b_1$ in the earlier case, from one boundary-line to the other. Hence it does not divide the surface into distinct pieces; it changes the number of boundaries to 1, and it reduces the connectivity to $2p-3$.

Proceeding in $p$ stages, each of two cross-cuts, we ultimately obtain a simply connected surface with a single boundary; and the general effect on the original unresolved surface is to have a system of cross-cuts somewhat of the form

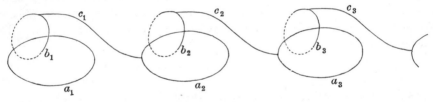

Fig. 63.

The foregoing resolution is called the *canonical resolution* of a Riemann's surface.

*Ex.* 1.  Construct the Riemann's surface for the equation

$$w^3 + z^3 - 3awz = 1,$$

both for $a=0$ and for $a$ different from zero; and resolve it by cross-cuts into a simply connected surface with a single boundary, shewing a complete system of irreducible simple circuits on the unresolved surface.

*Ex.* 2.  Shew that the Riemann's surface for the equation

$$w^3 = \frac{(z-a)(z-b)}{(z-c)(z-d)}$$

is of genus $p=2$; indicate the possible systems of branch-lines, and, for each system, resolve the surface by cross-cuts into a simply connected surface with a single boundary.

(Burnside.)

*Ex.* 3.  Find the connectivity of the surface associated with the equation

$$w^4 z = (z-1)^2 (z+1)^3;$$

draw a possible system of branch-lines, and dissect the surface so as to reduce it to a simply connected one.          (Math. Trip., Part II., 1897.)

**182**. Among algebraical equations with their associated Riemann's surfaces, two general cases of great importance and comparative simplicity distinguish themselves. The first is that in which the surface is two-sheeted; round each branch-point the two branches interchange. The second is that in which, while the surface has a finite number of sheets greater than two, all the branch-points are of the first order, that is, are such that round each of them only two branches of the function interchange. The former has already been considered, in so far as concerns the surface; we now proceed to the consideration of the latter.

The equation is $$f(w, z) = 0,$$

of degree $n$ in $w$; and, for our present purpose, it is convenient to regard $f = 0$ as an equation corresponding to a generalised plane curve of degree $n$, so that no term in $f$ is of dimensions higher than $n$.

The total number of branch-points has been proved, in § 98, to be

$$n (n - 1) - 2\delta - 2\kappa,$$

where $\delta$ is the number of points which are the generalisation of double points on the curve with non-coincident tangents, and $\kappa$ is the number of double points on the curve with coincident tangents. Round each of these branch-points, two branches of $w$ interchange and only two, so that each of the numbers $m_q$ of § 178 is equal to 2; hence the ramification $\Omega$ is

$$2 \{n (n - 1) - 2\delta - 2\kappa\} - \{n (n - 1) - 2\delta - 2\kappa\},$$

that is, $$\Omega = n (n - 1) - 2\delta - 2\kappa.$$

The connectivity of the surface is therefore

$$n (n - 1) - 2\delta - 2\kappa - 2n + 3;$$

and therefore the genus $p$ of the surface is

$$\tfrac{1}{2} (n - 1) (n - 2) - \delta - \kappa.$$

Now this integer is known* as the *deficiency* of the curve; and therefore it appears that *the deficiency of the curve is the same as the genus of the Riemann's surface associated with its equation, and also is the same as the genus of its equation.*

Moreover, the number of branch-points of the original equation is $\Omega$, that is,

$$= 2p + 2n - 2$$
$$= 2 \{p + (n - 1)\}.$$

*Note.* The equality of these numbers, representing the deficiency and the genus, is one among many reasons that lead to the close association of algebraic functions (and

---

* Salmon's *Higher Plane Curves*, §§ 44, 83; Clebsch's *Vorlesungen über Geometrie*, (edited by Lindemann), t. i, pp. 351—429, the German word used instead of deficiency being *Geschlecht*. The name 'deficiency' was introduced by Cayley in 1865: see *Proc. Lond. Math. Soc.*, vol. i, "On the transformation of plane curves."

of functions dependent on them) with the theory of plane algebraic curves, in the investigations of Nöther, Brill, Clebsch and others, referred to in §§ 191, 242; and in the paper by Baker, quoted in § 178. Baker's rule for determining the number is embodied in the following question; and a number of simple examples are given in his paper.

*Ex.* A plane ($A$) of rectangular Cartesian coordinates is ruled with lines parallel to the axes, at unit distances apart, and the angular points of the squares obtained are called unit points. Corresponding to every term $A_{r, s}x^r y^s$ in the equation of an irreducible plane curve (which is referred to rectangular Cartesian axes, the origin being a multiple point of the curve), the point ($r$, $s$) is marked on the plane ($A$) and called a curve point. The outermost of the curve points are joined by finite straight lines so as to form a convex polygon, enclosing the other curve points and having a curve point at each vertex. Considering first the sides of this polygon which are nearest to the origin and limited by the axes of coordinates, and assuming that all the unit points upon these sides are also curve points and that all these sides are inclined to one of the axes at an angle greater than $\frac{1}{4}\pi$, prove that the sum of the number of double points and cusps to which the singularity is equivalent is equal to the number of unit points between these sides and the axes of coordinates together with the number of unit points upon these sides less two. Considering next the complete polygon and assuming the curve to have only three singularities, namely at the origin and at infinity on the two axes of coordinates, and excluding exceptional relations between the coefficients of the terms entering in the equation of the curve, prove that its deficiency is equal to the whole number of unit points actually within the polygon.                    (Math. Trip., Part II., 1893.)

**183.** With a view to the construction of a canonical form of Riemann's surface of genus $p$ for the equation under consideration, it is necessary to consider in some detail the relations between the branches of the functions as they are affected by the branch-points.

The effect produced on any value of the function by the description of a small circuit, enclosing one branch-point (and only one), is known. But when the small circuit is part of a loop, the effect on the value of the function with which the loop begins to be described depends upon the form of the loop; and various results (e.g. Ex. 1, § 104) are obtained by taking different loops. In the first form (§ 175) in which the branch-lines were established as junctions between sheets, what was done was the equivalent of drawing a number of straight loops, which had one extremity common to all and the other free, and of assigning the law of junction according to the law of interchange determined by the description of the loop. As, however, there is no necessary limitation to the forms of branch-lines, we may draw them in other forms, always, of course, having branch-points at their free extremities; and according to the variation in the form of the branch-line, (that is, according to the variation in the form of the corresponding loop or, in other words, according to the deformation of the loop over other branch-points from some form of reference), there will be variation in the law of junction along the branch-lines.

There is thus a large amount of arbitrary character in the forms of the branch-lines, and consequently in the laws of junction along the branch-lines, of the sheets of a Riemann's surface. Moreover, the assignment of the $n$ branches of the function to the $n$ sheets is arbitrary. Hence a considerable amount of arbitrary variation in the configuration of a Riemann's surface is possible within the limits imposed by the invariance of its connectivity. The canonical form will be established by making these arbitrary elements definite.

**184.** After the preceding explanation and always under the hypothesis that the branch-points are simple, we shall revert temporarily to the use of loops and shall ultimately combine them into branch-lines.

When, with an ordinary point as origin, we construct a loop round a branch-point, two and only two of the values of the function are affected by that particular loop; they are interchanged by it; but a different form of loop, from the same origin round the same branch-point, might affect some other pair of values of the function.

To indicate the law of interchange, a symbol will be convenient. If the two values interchanged by a given loop be $w_i$ and $w_m$, the loop will be denoted by $im$; and $i$ and $m$ will be called the numbers of the symbol of that loop.

For the initial configuration of the loops, we shall (as in § 175) take an ordinary point $O$: we shall make loops beginning at $O$, forming them in the sequence of angular succession of the branch-points round $O$ and drawing the double linear part of the loop as direct as possible from $O$ to its branch-point: and, in this configuration, we shall take the law of interchange by a loop to be the law of interchange by the branch-point in the loop.

In any other configuration, the symbol of a loop round any branch-point depends upon its form, that is, depends upon the deformation over other branch-points which the loop has suffered in passing from its initial form. The effect of such deformation must first be obtained: it is determined by the following lemma :—

*When one loop is deformed over another, the symbol of the deformed loop is unaltered, if neither of its numbers or if both of its numbers occur in the symbol of the unmoved loop; but if, before deformation, the symbols have one number common, the new symbol of the deformed loop is obtained from the old symbol by substituting, for the common number, the other number in the symbol of the unmoved loop.*

The sufficient test, to which all such changes must be subject, is that the effect on the values of the function at any point of a contour enclosing both branch-points is the same at that point for all deformations into two loops. Moreover, a complete circuit of all the loops is the same as a contour enclosing all the branch-points; it therefore (Cor. III. § 90) restores the initial value with which the circuit began to be described.

Obviously there are three cases.

First, when the symbols have no number common: let them be $mn$, $rs$. The branch-point in the loop $rs$ does not affect $w_m$ or $w_n$: it is thus effectively not a branch-point for either of the values $w_m$ and $w_n$; and therefore (§ 91) the loop $mn$ can be deformed across the point, that is, it can be deformed across the loop $mn$.

Secondly, when the symbols are the same: the symbol of the deformed loop must be unaltered, in order that the contour embracing only the two branch-points may, as it should, restore after its complete description each of the values affected.

Thirdly, when the symbols have one number common: let $O$ be any point and let the loops be $OA$, $OB$ in any given position such as (i), fig. 64, with symbols $mr$, $nr$ respectively. Then $OB$ may be deformed over $OA$ as in (ii), or $OA$ over $OB$ as in (iii).

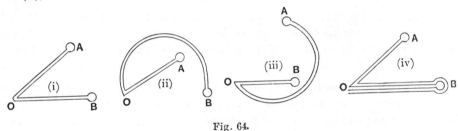

Fig. 64.

The effect at $O$ of a closed circuit, including the points $A$ and $B$ and described positively beginning at $O$, is, in (i) which is the initial configuration, to change $w_m$ into $w_r$, $w_r$ into $w_n$, $w_n$ into $w_m$; this effect on the values at $O$, unaltered, must govern the deformation of the loops.

The two alternative deformations (ii) and (iii) will be considered separately.

When, as in (ii), $OB$ is deformed over $OA$, then $OA$ is unmoved and therefore unaltered: it is still $mr$. Now, beginning at $O$ with $w_m$, the loop $OA$ changes $w_m$ into $w_r$: the whole circuit changes $w_m$ into $w_r$, so that $OB$ must now leave $w_r$ unaltered. Again, beginning with $w_n$, it is unaltered by $OA$, and the whole circuit changes $w_n$ into $w_m$: hence $OB$ must change $w_n$ into $w_m$, that is, the symbol of $OB$ must be $mn$. And, this being so, an initial $w_r$ at $O$ is changed by the whole circuit into $w_n$, as it should be. Hence the new symbol $mn$ of the deformed loop $OB$ in (ii) is obtained from the old symbol by substituting, for the common number $r$, the other number $m$ in the symbol of the unmoved loop $OA$.

We may proceed similarly for the deformation in (iii); or the new symbol may be obtained as follows. The loop $OA$ in (iii) may be deformed to the form in (iv) without crossing any branch-point and therefore without changing its symbol. When this form of the loop is described in the positive direction, $w_n$ initially at $O$ is changed into $w_r$ after the first loop $OB$, for this loop has the position of $OB$ in (i), then it is changed into $w_m$ after the loop $OA$, for this loop has the position of $OA$ in (i), and then $w_m$ is unchanged after the second (and inner) loop $OB$. Thus $w_n$ is changed into $w_m$, so that the symbol is $mn$, a symbol which is easily proved to give the proper results with an initial value $w_m$ or $w_r$ for the whole contour. This change is as stated in the theorem, which is therefore proved.

*Ex.* If the deformation from (i) to (ii) be called superior, and that from (i) to (iii) inferior, then $x$ successive superior deformations give the same loop-configuration, in symbols and relative order for positive description, as $6 - x$ successive inferior deformations.

COROLLARY.   *A loop can be passed unchanged over two loops that have the same symbol.*

Let the common symbol of the unmoved loops be $mn$. If neither number of the deformed loop be $m$ or $n$, passage over each of the loops $mn$ makes no difference, after the lemma; likewise, if its symbol be $mn$. If only one of its numbers, say $n$, be in $mn$, its symbol is $nr$, where $r$ is different from $m$. When the loop $nr$ is deformed over the first loop $mn$, its new symbol is $mr$; when this loop $mr$ is deformed over the second loop $mn$, its new symbol is $nr$, that is, the final symbol is the same as the initial symbol, or the loop is unchanged.

**185.**   The initial configuration of the loops is used by Clebsch and Gordan to establish their simple cycles and thence to deduce the periodicity of the Abelian integrals connected with the equation $f(w, z) = 0$, without reference to the Riemann's surface; and this method of treating the functions that arise through the equation, always supposed to have merely simple branch-points, has been used by Casorati[*] and Lüroth[†].

We can pass from any value of $w$ at the initial point $O$ to any other value by a suitable series of loops; because, were it possible to interchange the values of only some of the branches, an equation could be constructed which had those branches for its roots. The fundamental equation could then be resolved into this equation and an equation having the rest of the branches for its roots: that is, the fundamental equation would cease to be irreducible.

We begin then with any loop, say one connecting $w_1$ with $w_2$. There will be a loop, connecting the value $w_3$ with either $w_1$ or $w_2$; there will be a loop, connecting the value $w_4$ with either $w_1$, $w_2$, or $w_3$; and so on, until we select a loop, connecting the last value $w_n$ with one of the other values. Such a set of loops, $n - 1$ in number, is called *fundamental*.

A passage round the set will not at the end restore the branch with which the description began. When we begin with any value, any other value can be obtained after the description of properly chosen loops of the set.

[*] *Annali di Matematica*, 2$^{da}$ Ser., t. iii, (1870), pp. 1—27.

[†] *Abh. d. K. bay. Akad.*, t. xvi, i Abth., (1887), pp. 199—241.

Any other loop, when combined with a set of fundamental loops, gives a system the description of suitably chosen loops of which restores some initial value; only two values can be restored by the description of loops of the combined system. Thus if the loops in order be 12, 13, 14, …, $1n$ and a loop $qr$ be combined with them, the value $w_q$ is changed into $w_1$ by $1q$, into $w_r$ by $1r$, into $w_q$ by $qr$; and similarly for $w_r$. Such a combination of $n$ loops is called a *simple cycle*.

The total number of branch-points, and therefore of loops, is (§ 182)
$$2\{p+(n-1)\};$$
and therefore the total number of simple cycles is $2p+n-1$. But these simple cycles are not independent of one another.

In the description of any cycle, the loops vary in their operation according to the initial value of $w$: and, for two different initial values of $w$, no loop is operative in the same way. For otherwise all the preceding and all the succeeding loops would operate in the same way and would lead, on reversal, to the same initial value of $w$. Hence a loop of a given cycle can be operative in only two descriptions, once when it changes, say, $w_i$ into $w_j$, and the other when it changes $w_j$ into $w_i$.

Now consider the circuit made up of all the loops. When $w_1$ is taken as the initial value, it is restored at the end: and in the description only a certain number of loops have been operative: the cycle made up of these loops can be resolved into the operative parts of simple cycles, that is, into simple cycles: hence one relation among the simple cycles is given by the consideration of the operative loops when the whole system of the loops is described with an initial value.

Similarly when any other initial value is taken; so that apparently there are $n$ relations, one arising from each initial value. These $n$ relations are not independent: for a simultaneous combination of the operations of all the loops in all the circuits leads to an identically null effect (but no smaller combination would be effective), for each loop is operative twice (and only twice) with opposite effects, shewing that one and only one of the relations is derivable from the remainder. Hence there are $n-1$ independent relations and therefore* the number of independent simple cycles is $2p$.

**186.** We now proceed to obtain a typical form of the Riemann's surface by deforming the initial configuration of the loops into a typical configuration†. The final arrangement of the loops is indicated by the two theorems:—

* Clebsch und Gordan, *Theorie der Abel'schen Functionen*, p. 85.

† The investigation is based upon the following memoirs:—
   Lüroth, "Note über Verzweigungsschnitte und Querschnitte in einer Riemann'schen Fläche," *Math. Ann.*, t. iv, (1871), pp. 181—184; "Ueber die kanonischen Perioden der Abel'schen Integrale," *Abh. d. K. bay. Akad.*, t. xv, ii Abth., (1885), pp. 329—366.
   Clebsch, "Zur Theorie der Riemann'schen Flächen," *Math. Ann.*, t. vi, (1873), pp. 216—230.
   Clifford, "On the canonical form and dissection of a Riemann's Surface," *Lond. Math. Soc. Proc.*, vol. viii, (1877), pp. 292—304.

I. *The loops can be made in pairs in which all loop-symbols are of the form* $(m, m+1)$, *for* $m = 1, 2, \ldots, n-1$. (With this configuration, $w_1$ can be changed by a loop only into $w_2$, $w_2$ by a loop only into $w_3$, and so on in succession, each change being effected by an even number of loops.) This theorem is due to Lüroth.

II. *The loops can be made so that there is only one pair* 12, *only one pair* 23, $\ldots$, *only one pair* $(n-2, n-1)$, *and the remaining* $p+1$ *pairs are* $(n-1, n)$. This theorem is due to Clebsch.

**187.** We proceed to prove Lüroth's theorem, assuming that the loops have the initial configuration of § 184.

Take any loop 12, say $OA$: beginning it with $w_1$, describe loops positively and in succession; then as the value $w_1$ is restored sooner or later, for it must be restored by the circuit of all the loops, let it be restored first by a loop $OB$, the symbol of $OB$ necessarily containing the number 1. Between $OA$ and $OB$ there may be loops whose symbols contain 1 but which have been inoperative. Let each of these in turn be deformed so as to pass back over all the loops between its initial position and $OA$; and then finally over $OA$. Before passing over $OA$ its symbol must contain 1, for there is no loop over which it has passed that, having 1 in its symbol, could make it drop 1 in the passage; but it cannot contain 2, for, if it did, the effect of $OA$ and the deformed loop would be to restore 1, an effect that would have been caused in the original position, contrary to the hypothesis that $OB$ is the first loop that restores 1. Hence after it has passed over $OA$ its symbol no longer contains 1.

Next, pass $OB$ over the loops between its initial position and $OA$ but not over $OA$: its symbol must be 12 in the deformed position since $w_1$ is restored by the loop $OB$. Then $OA$ and the deformed loop $OB$ are each 12; hence each of the loops, between the new position and the old position of $OB$, can be passed over $OA$ and the new loop $OB$ without any change in its symbol. There are therefore, behind $OA$, a series of loops that do not affect $w_1$. Thus the loops are

(a) loops behind $OA$ not affecting $w_1$,     (b) $OA$, $OB$ each 12,

(c) other loops beyond the initial position of $OB$.

Begin now with $w_2$ at the loop $OB$ and again describe loops positively and in succession: then $w_2$ must be restored sooner or later. It may be only after $OA$ is described, so that there has been a complete circuit of all the loops; or it may first be by an intermediate loop, say $OC$.

For the former case, when $OA$ is the first loop by which $w_2$ is restored, we deform as follows. Deform all loops affecting $w_1$, which lie between $OB$ and $OA$, in the positive direction from $OB$ back over other loops and over $OB$. The symbol of each just before its deformation contains 1 but not 2, and therefore after its deformation it does not contain 1. Moreover just after $OB$ is described, $w_2$ is the value, and just before $OA$ is described, $w_1$ is the value; hence the intermediate loops, which have affected $w_1$, must be even in number. Let $OG$ be the first after $OB$ which affects $w_1$, and let the symbol of $OG$ be $1r$. Then beginning $OG$ with $w_1$, the value $w_1$ must be restored by a complete circuit of all the loops, that is, it must be restored by $OB$; and therefore the value must be $w_1$ when beginning $OA$, or $w_1$ must be restored before $OA$. Let $OH$ be the first loop after $OG$ to restore $w_1$; then, by proceeding as above, we can deform all the loops between $OG$ and $OH$ over $OG$, with the result that no such deformed loop affects $w_1$ and that $OG$ and $OH$ are both $1r$. Hence all the loops affecting $w_1$ can be arranged in pairs having the same symbol.

Since $OG$ and $OH$ are a pair with the same symbol, every loop between $OB$ and $OG$ can be passed unchanged over $OG$ and $OH$ together. When this is done, pass $OG$ over $OB$ so that it becomes $2r$, and then $OH$ over $OB$ so that it also is $2r$. Thus these deformed loops $OG$, $OH$ are a pair $2r$; and therefore $OA$ can, without change, be deformed over both so as to be next to $OB$. Let this be done with all the pairs; then, finally, we have

(a)  loops not affecting $w_1$,            (b)  a pair with the symbol 12,

(c)  pairs affecting $w_2$ and not $w_1$,    (d)  loops not affecting $w_1$.

We thus have a pair 12 and loops not affecting $w_1$, so that such a change has been effected as to make all the loops affecting $w_1$ possess the symbol 12.

For the second case, when $OC$ is the first loop to restore $w_2$, the value with which the loop $OB$ whose symbol is 12 began to be described, we treat the loops between $OB$ and $OC$ in a manner similar to that adopted in the former case for loops between $OA$ and $OB$; so that, remembering that now $w_2$ instead of the former $w_1$ is the value dealt with in the recurrence, we can deform these loops into

(a)  loops behind $OB$ which change $w_1$ but not $w_2$,

(b)  $OB$ and $OC$, the symbol of each of which is 12.

Now $OB$ was next to $OA$; hence the set (a) are now next to $OA$. Each of them when passed over $OA$ drops the number 1 from its symbol, and so the whole system now consists of

(a)  loops behind $OA$ not affecting $w_1$,  (b)  $OA$, $OB$, $OC$ each of which is 12,   (c)  other loops.

Begin again with the value $w_1$ before $OA$. Before $OC$ the value is $w_1$; and the whole circuit of the loops must restore $w_1$, which must therefore occur before $OA$. Let $OD$ be the first loop by which $w_1$ is restored. Then treating the loops between $OC$ and $OD$, as formerly those between the initial positions of $OA$ and $OB$ were treated, we shall have

(a) loops behind $OA$ not affecting $w_1$,  (b) $OA$, $OB$ each being 12,
(c) loops between $OB$ and $OC$ not affecting $w_1$,  (d) $OC$, $OD$ each being 12,  (e) other loops.

Except that fewer loops affecting $w_1$ have to be reckoned with, the configuration is now in the same condition as at the end of the first stage. Proceeding therefore as before, we can arrange that all the loops affecting $w_1$ occur in pairs with the symbol 12. Moreover, each of the loops in the set (c) can be passed unchanged over $OA$ and $OB$; so that, finally, we have

(a) pairs of loops with the symbol 12,  (b') loops not affecting $w_1$.

We keep (a) in pairs, so that any desired deformation of loops in (b') over them can be made without causing any change; and we treat the set (b') in the same manner as before, with the result that the set (b') is replaced by

(b) pairs of loops with the symbol 23,  (c') loops not affecting $w_1$ or $w_2$.

And so on, with the ultimate result that *the loops can be made in pairs in which each symbol is of the form $(m, m+1)$ for $m = 1, \ldots, n-1$.*

**188.** We now come to Clebsch's Theorem that the loops thus made can be so deformed that there is only one pair 12, only one pair 23, and so on, until the last symbol $(n-1, n)$, which is the common symbol of $p+1$ pairs.

This can be easily proved after the establishment of the lemma that, *if there be two pairs 12 and one pair 23, the loops can be deformed into one pair 12 and two pairs 23.*

The actual deformation leading to the lemma is shewn in the accompanying scheme: the deformations implied by the continuous lines are those of a loop from the left to the right of the respective lines, and those implied by the dotted lines are those of a loop from the right to the left of the respective lines. It is interesting to draw figures, representing the loops in the various configurations.

| 12 | 12 | 12 | 12 | 23 | 23 |
| 12 | 12 | 12 | 23 | 13 | 23 |
| 12 | 12 | 23 | 13 | 13 | 23 |
| 12 | 12 | 13 | 13 | 23 | 23 |
| 12 | 23 | 12 | 13 | 23 | 23 |
| 12 | 23 | 23 | 12 | 23 | 23 |
| 12 | 12 | 23 | 23 | 23 | 23 |

By the continued use of this lemma we can change all but one of the pairs 12 into pairs 23, all but one of the pairs 23 into pairs 34, and so on, the final configuration being that there are one pair 12, one pair 23, ... and $p+1$ pairs $(n-1, n)$. Thus Clebsch's theorem is proved.

**189.** We now proceed to the construction of the Riemann's surface.

Each loop is associated with a branch-point, and the order of interchange for passage round the branch-point, by means of the loop, is given by the numbers in the symbol of the loop.

Hence, in the configuration which has been obtained, there are two branch-points 12 : we therefore connect them (as in § 176) by a line, not necessarily along the direction of the two loops 12 but necessarily such that it can, without passing over any branch-point, be deformed into the lines of the two loops; and we make this the branch-line between the first and the second sheets. There are two branch-points 23 : we connect them by a line not meeting the former branch-line, and we make it the branch-line between the second and the third sheets. And so on, until we come to the last two sheets. There are $2p+2$ branch-points $n-1, n$: we connect these in pairs (as in § 176) by $p+1$ lines, not meeting one another or any of the former lines, and we make them the $p+1$ branch-lines between the last two sheets.

It thus appears that, *when the winding-points of a Riemann's surface with n sheets of connectivity $2p+1$ are all simple, the surface can be taken in such a form that there is a single branch-line between consecutive sheets except for the last two sheets: and between the last two sheets there are $p+1$ branch-lines.* This form of Riemann's surface may be regarded as the canonical form for a surface, all the branch-points of which are simple.

Further, let $AB$ be a branch-line such as 12. Let two points $P$ and $Q$ be taken in the first sheet on opposite sides of $AB$, so that $PQ$ in space is infinitesimal; and let $P'$ be the point in the second sheet determined by the same value of $z$ as $P$, so that $P'Q$ in the sheet is infinitesimal. Then the value $w_1$ at $P$ is changed by a loop round $A$ (or round $B$) into a value at $Q$ differing only infinitesimally from $w_2$, which is the value at $P'$: that is, the change in the function from $Q$ to $P'$ is infinitesimal. Hence *the value of the function is continuous across a line of passage from one sheet to another.*

**190.** The genus of the foregoing surface is $p$; and it was remarked, in § 170, that a convenient surface of reference of the same genus is that of a solid sphere with $p$ holes bored through it. It is, therefore, proper to indicate the geometrical deformation of a Riemann's surface of this canonical form into a $p$-holed sphere.

The Riemann's surface consists of $n$ sheets connected chainwise each with a single branch-line to the sheet on either side of it, except that the first is connected only with the second and that the last two have $p+1$ branch-lines. We may also consider the whole surface as spherical and the sequence of the sheets from the inside outwards: and the outmost sheet can be considered as bounded.

Let the branch-line between the first and the second sheets be made to lie along part of a great circle. Let the first sheet of the Riemann's surface be reflected in the plane of this great circle: the line becomes a long narrow hole along the great circle, and the reflected sheet becomes a large indentation in the second sheet. Reversing the process of § 169, we can change the new form of the second sheet, so that it is spherical again : it is now the inmost of the $n-1$ sheets of the surface, the connectivity and the ramification of which are unaltered by the operation.

Let this process be applied to each surviving inner sheet in succession. Then, after $n-2$ operations, there will be left a two-sheeted surface; the outer sheet is bounded and the two sheets are joined by $p+1$ branch-lines; so that the connectivity is still $2p+1$. Let these branch-lines be made to lie along a great circle: and let the inner surface be reflected in the plane of this circle. Then, after the reflexion, each of the branch-lines becomes a long narrow hole along the great circle; and there are two spherical surfaces which pass continuously into one another at these holes, the outer of the surfaces being bounded. By stretching one of the holes and flattening the two surfaces, the new form is that of a bifacial flat surface: each of the $p$ holes then becomes a hole through the body bounded by that surface; the stretched hole gives the extreme geometrical limits of the extension of the surface, and the original boundary of the outer surface becomes a boundary hole existing in only one face. The body can now be distended until it takes the form of a sphere, and the final form is that of the surface of a solid sphere with $p$ holes bored through it and having a single boundary.

This is the normal surface of reference (§ 170) of connectivity $2p+1$.

As a last ground of comparison between the Riemann's surface in its canonical form and the surface of the bored sphere, we may consider the system of cross-cuts necessary to transform each of them into a simply connected surface.

We begin with the spherical surface. The simplest irreducible circuits are of two classes, (i) those which go round a hole, (ii) those which go through a hole; the cross-cuts, $2p$ in number, which make the surface simply connected, must be such as to prevent these irreducible circuits.

Round each of the holes we make a cut $a$, the first of them beginning and ending in the boundary: these cuts prevent circuits through the holes. Through each hole we make a cut $b$, beginning and ending at a point in the corresponding cut $a$: we then make from the first $b$ a cut $c_1$ to the second $a$, from the second $b$ a cut $c_2$ to the third $a$, and so on. The surface is then simply connected: $a_1$ is a cross-cut, $b_1$ is a cross-cut, $c_1 + a_2$ is a cross-cut, $b_2$ is a cross-cut, $c_2 + a_3$ is a cross-cut, and so on. The total number is evidently $2p$, the number proper for the reduction; and it is easy to verify that there is a single boundary.

To compare this dissection with the resolution of a Riemann's surface by cross-cuts, say of a two-sheeted surface (the $n$-sheeted surface was transformed into a two-sheeted surface), it must be borne in mind that only $p$ of the $p+1$ branch-lines were changed into holes and the remaining one, which, after the partial deformation, was a hole of the Riemann's surface, was stretched out so as to give the boundary.

It thus appears that the direction of a cut $a$ round a hole in the normal surface of reference is a cut round a branch-line in one sheet, that is, it is a cut $a$ as in the resolution (§ 180) of the Riemann's surface into one that is simply connected.

Again, a cut $b$ is a cut from a point in the boundary across a cut $a$ and through the hole back to the initial point; hence, in the Riemann's surface, it is a cut from some one assigned branch-line across a cut $a_r$, meeting the branch-line surrounded by $a_r$, passing into the second sheet and, without meeting any other cut or branch-line in that surface, returning to the initial point on the assigned branch-line. It is a cut $b$ as in the resolution of the Riemann's surface.

Lastly, a cut $c$ is made from a cut $b$ to a cut $a$. It is the same as in the resolution of the Riemann's surface, and the purpose of each of these cuts is to change each of the loop-cuts $a$ (after the first) into cross-cuts.

A simple illustration arises in the case of a two-sheeted Riemann's surface, of genus $p = 2$. The various forms are :—

(i)  the surface of a two-holed sphere, with the directions of cross-cuts that resolve it into a simply connected surface ; as in (i), fig. 65, $B$, $K$ being at opposite edges of the cut $c_1$ where it meets $a_2$ : $H$, $C$ at opposite edges where it meets $b_1$ : and so on ;

(ii) the spherical surface, resolved into a simply connected surface, bent, stretched, and flattened out ; as in (ii), fig. 65 ;

(iii) the plane Riemann's surface, resolved by the cross-cuts ; as in fig. 63, p. 402.

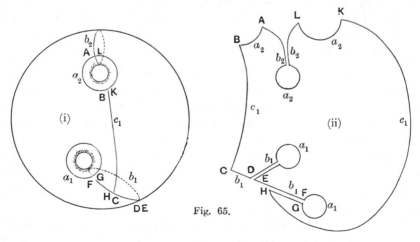

Fig. 65.

Numerous illustrations of transformations of Riemann's surfaces are given by Hofmann, *Methodik der stetigen Deformation von zweiblättrigen Riemann'schen Flächen*, (Halle a. S., Nebert, 1888).

**191.**   We have seen that a bifacial surface with a single boundary can be deformed, at least geometrically, into any other bifacial surface with a single boundary, provided the two surfaces have the same connectivity; and the result is otherwise independent of the constitution of the surface, in regard to sheets and to form or position of branch-lines.   Further, in all the geometrical deformations adopted, the characteristic property is the uniform correspondence of points on the surfaces.

Now with every Riemann's surface, in its initial form, an algebraical equation $f(w, z) = 0$ is associated; but when deformations of the surface are made, the relations that establish uniform correspondence between different forms, practically by means of conformal representation, are often of a transcendental character (Chap. XX.).   Hence, when two surfaces are thus equivalent to one another, and when points on the surfaces are determined solely by the variables in the respective algebraical equations, no relations other than algebraical being taken into consideration, the uniform correspondence of points can only be secured by assigning a new condition that there be uniform transformation between the variables $w$ and $z$ of one surface and the variables $w'$ and $z'$ of the other surface.   And, when this condition is satisfied, the equations are such that the deficiencies of the two (generalised) curves represented by the equations are the same, because they are equal to the common connectivity.   It may therefore be expected that, when the variables in an equation are subjected to uniform transformation, the genus of the equation is unaltered; or in other words, that the deficiency of a curve is an invariant for uniform transformation.

This inference is correct: the actual proof is directly connected with geometry and the theory of Abelian functions, and is given in treatises on those subjects*.   We shall return to the theorem in connection with birational transformation, which will be discussed later: merely remarking now that the result is of importance here, because it justifies the adoption of a simple normal surface of the same genus as the surface of reference.

* Clebsch's *Vorlesungen über Geometrie*, t. i, p. 459, where other references are given; Salmon's *Higher Plane Curves*, pp. 93, 319; Clebsch und Gordan, *Theorie der Abel'schen Functionen*, Section 3; Brill, *Math. Ann.*, t. vi, pp. 33—65.

# CHAPTER XVI.

## ALGEBRAIC FUNCTIONS AND THEIR INTEGRALS.

**192.** IN the preceding chapter sufficient indications have been given as to the character of the Riemann's surface on which the $n$-branched function $w$, determined by the equation

$$f(w, z) = 0,$$

can be represented as a uniform function of the position of the variable. It is unnecessary to consider algebraically multiform functions of position on the surface, for such multiformity would merely lead to another surface of the same kind, on which the algebraically multiform functions would be uniform functions of position; transcendentally multiform functions of position will arise later, through the integrals of algebraic functions. It therefore remains, at the present stage, only to consider the most general uniform function of position on the Riemann's surface.

On the other hand, it is evident that a Riemann's surface of any number of sheets can be constructed, with arbitrary branch-points and assigned sequence of junction; the elements of the surface being subject merely to general laws, which give a necessary relation between the number of sheets, the ramification and the connectivity, and which require the restoration of any value of the function after the description of some properly chosen irreducible circuit. The essential elements of the arbitrary surface, and the merely general laws indicated, are independent of any previous knowledge of an algebraical equation associated with the surface; and a question arises whether, when a Riemann's surface is given, an associated algebraical equation necessarily exists.

Two distinct subjects of investigation, therefore, arise. The first is the most general uniform function of position on a surface associated with a given algebraical equation, and its integral; the second is the discussion of the existence of functions of position on a surface that is given independently of an algebraical equation. Both of them lead, as a matter of fact, to the theory of transcendental (that is, non-algebraical) functions of the most general type, commonly called Abelian transcendents. But the first is, naturally, the more direct, in that the algebraical equation is initially given: whereas, in the second, the prime necessity is the establishment of the so-called Existence-Theorem—that such functions, algebraical and transcendental, exist.

**193.** Taking the subjects of investigation in the assigned order, we suppose the fundamental equation to be irreducible, and rational as regards both the dependent and the independent variable; the general form is therefore

$$w^n G_0(z) + w^{n-1} G_1(z) + \ldots + w G_{n-1}(z) + G_n(z) = 0,$$

the coefficients $G_0(z)$, $G_1(z)$, ..., $G_n(z)$ being rational integral functions of the variable $z$.

The infinities of $w$ are, by § 95, the zeros of $G_0(z)$ and, possibly, $z = \infty$. But, for our present purpose, no special interest attaches to the infinity of a function, as such; we therefore take $wG_0(z)$ as a new dependent variable, and the equation then is

$$f(w, z) = w^n + w^{n-1} g_1(z) + \ldots + w g_{n-1}(z) + g_n(z) = 0,$$

in which the functions $g(z)$ are rational integral functions of $z$.

The distribution of the branches for a value of $z$ which is an ordinary point, and the determination of the branch-points together with the cyclical grouping of the branches round a branch-point, may be supposed known. When the corresponding. $n$-sheeted Riemann's surface (say of connectivity $2p + 1$) is constructed, then $w$ is a uniform function of position on the surface.

Now not merely $w$, but every rational function of $w$ and $z$, is a uniform function of position on the surface; and its branch-points (though not necessarily its infinities) are the same as that of the function $w$.

Conversely, *every uniform function of position on the Riemann's surface, having accidental singularities and infinities only of finite order, is a rational function of $w$ and $z$.* The proof* of this proposition, to which we now proceed, leads to the canonical expression for the most general uniform function of position on the surface, an expression which is used in Abel's Theorem in transcendental integrals.

Let $w'$ denote the general uniform function, and let $w_1'$, $w_2'$, ..., $w_n'$ denote the branches of this function for the points on the $n$ sheets determined by

---

* The proof adopted follows Prym, *Crelle*, t. lxxxiii, (1877), pp. 251—261; see also Klein, *Ueber Riemann's Theorie der algebraischen Functionen und ihrer Integrale*, p. 57.

the arithmetical magnitude $z$; and let $w_1$, $w_2$, ..., $w_n$ be the corresponding branches of $w$ for the magnitude $z$. Then the quantity

$$w_1^s w_1' + w_2^s w_2' + \ldots + w_n^s w_n',$$

where $s$ is any positive integer, is a symmetric function of the possible values of $w^s w'$; it has the same value in whatever sheet $z$ may lie and by whatever path $z$ may have attained its position in that sheet; the said quantity is therefore a uniform function of $z$. Moreover, all its singularities are accidental in character, by the initial hypothesis as to $w'$ and the known properties of $w$; they are finite in number, and therefore the uniform function of $z$ is rational. Let it be denoted by $h_s(z)$, which is an integral function only when all the singularities are for infinite values of $z$; then

$$w_1^s w_1' + w_2^s w_2' + \ldots + w_n^s w_n' = h_s(z),$$

an equation which is valid for any positive integer $s$, there being of course the suitable changes among the rational integral functions $h(z)$ for changes in $s$. It is unnecessary to take $s \geqslant n$, when the equations for the values $0, 1, \ldots, n-1$ of $s$ are retained: for the equations corresponding to values of $s \geqslant n$ can be derived, from the $n$ equations that are retained, by using the fundamental equation determining $w$.

Solving the equations

$$w_1' + w_2' + \ldots + w_n' = h_0(z),$$
$$w_1 w_1' + w_2 w_2' + \ldots + w_n w_n' = h_1(z),$$
$$\ldots \ldots \ldots \ldots \ldots \ldots \quad \vdots \quad \ldots \ldots \ldots$$
$$w_1^{n-1} w_1' + \ldots + w_n^{n-1} w_n' = h_{n-1}(z),$$

to determine $w_1'$, we have

$$w_1' \begin{vmatrix} 1, & 1, \ldots, 1 \\ w_1, & w_2, \ldots, w_n \\ w_1^2, & w_2^2, \ldots, w_n^2 \\ \ldots \ldots \ldots \ldots \\ w_1^{n-1}, & w_2^{n-1}, \ldots, w_n^{n-1} \end{vmatrix} = \begin{vmatrix} h_0(z), & 1, \ldots, 1 \\ h_1(z), & w_2, \ldots, w_n \\ h_2(z), & w_2^2, \ldots, w_n^2 \\ \ldots \ldots \ldots \ldots \\ h_{n-1}(z), & w_2^{n-1}, \ldots, w_n^{n-1} \end{vmatrix}$$

The right-hand side is evidently divisible by the product of the differences of $w_2$, $w_3$, ..., $w_n$; and this product is a factor of the coefficient of $w_1'$. Then, if

$$(w - w_2)(w - w_3) \ldots (w - w_n) = \sum_{r=1}^{n} k_r w^{n-r},$$

where $k_1$ is unity, we have, on removing the common factor,

$$w_1' = \frac{k_n h_0(z) + k_{n-1} h_1(z) + \ldots + k_2 h_{n-2}(z) + h_{n-1}(z)}{(w_1 - w_2)(w_1 - w_3) \ldots (w_1 - w_n)}.$$

But
$$f(w, z) = (w - w_1)(w - w_2) \dots (w - w_n),$$
so that
$$k_2 = w_1 + g_1(z),$$
$$k_3 = w_1{}^2 + w_1 g_1(z) + g_2(z),$$

$$\dots\dots\dots \vdots \dots\dots\dots$$

$$k_n = w_1{}^{n-1} + w_1{}^{n-2} g_1(z) + \dots + g_{n-1}(z).$$

When these expressions for $k$ are substituted in the numerator of the expression for $w_1'$, it takes the form of a rational integral function of $w$ of degree $n-1$ and of $z$, say

$$h_0(z) w_1{}^{n-1} + H_1(z) w_1{}^{n-2} + \dots + H_{n-2}(z) w_1 + H_{n-1}(z).$$

The denominator is evidently $\partial f / \partial w_1$, when $w$ is replaced by $w_1$ after differentiation, so that we now have

$$w_1' = \frac{h_0(z) w_1{}^{n-1} + \dots + H_{n-1}(z)}{\partial f / \partial w_1}.$$

The corresponding form holds for each of the branches of $w'$: and therefore we have

$$w' = \frac{h_0(z) w^{n-1} + H_1(z) w^{n-2} + \dots + H_{n-1}(z)}{\partial f / \partial w}$$

$$= \frac{h_0(z) w^{n-1} + H_1(z) w^{n-2} + \dots + H_{n-1}(z)}{n w^{n-1} + (n-1) w^{n-2} g_1(z) + \dots + g_{n-1}(z)},$$

so that $w'$ is a rational function of $w$ and $z$. The proposition is therefore proved.

By eliminating $w$ between $f(w, z) = 0$ and the equation which expresses $w'$ in terms of $w$ and $z$, or by the use of § 99, it follows that $w'$ satisfies an algebraical equation

$$f_1(w', z) = 0,$$

where $f_1$ is of order $n$ in $w'$. As will be seen later (§ 245), $f_1(w', z)$ either is irreducible, or is an exact power of an irreducible polynomial. When $f_1(w', z)$ is irreducible, the equations $f(w, z) = 0$ and $f_1(w', z) = 0$ have the same Riemann's surface associated with them*.

**194.** It thus appears that there are uniform functions of position on the Riemann's surface just as there are uniform functions of position in a plane. The preceding proposition is limited to the case in which the infinities, whether at branch-points or not, are merely accidental; had the function possessed essential singularities, the general argument would still be valid, but the forms of the uniform functions $h(z)$ would no longer be polynomial. In fact, taking account of the difference in the form of the surface on which the independent variable is represented, we can extend to multiform functions, which are uniform on a Riemann's surface, those propositions for uniform functions which relate to expansion near an ordinary

* Functions related to one another, as $w$ and $w'$ then are, are called *gleichverzweigt*, Riemann, p. 93.

point or a singularity or, by using the substitution of § 93, a branch singularity, those which relate to continuation of functions, and so on; and their validity is not limited, as in Cor. VI., § 90, to a portion of the surface in which there are no branch-points.

Thus we have the theorem that *a uniform rational function of position on the Riemann's surface has as many zeros as it has infinities.*

The number is called * the *degree* of the function.

This theorem may be proved as follows.

The function is a rational function of $w$ and $z$. If it be also integral, let it be $w' = U(w, z)$, where $U$ is integral.

Then the number of the zeros of $w'$ on the surface is the number of simultaneous roots common to the two equations $U(w, z) = 0$, $f(w, z) = 0$. If $u_\lambda$ and $f_\mu$ denote the aggregates of the terms of highest dimensions in these equations—say of dimensions $\lambda$ and $\mu$ respectively—then $\lambda\mu$ is the number of common roots, that is, the number of zeros of $w'$.

The number of points, where $w'$ assumes a value $A$, is the number of simultaneous roots common to the equations $U(w, z) = A$, $f(w, z) = 0$, that is, it is $\lambda\mu$ as before. Hence there are as many points where $w'$ assumes a given value as there are zeros of $w'$; and therefore the number of the infinities is the same as the number of zeros. The number of infinities can also be obtained by considering them as simultaneous roots common to $u_\lambda = 0$, $f_\mu = 0$.

If the function be not integral, it can (§ 193) be expressed in the form $w' = \dfrac{U(w, z)}{V(w, z)}$, where $U$ and $V$ are rational integral functions. The zeros of $w'$ are the zeros of $U$ and the infinities of $V$, the numbers of which, by what precedes, are respectively the same as the infinities of $U$ and the zeros of $V$. The latter are the infinities of $w'$; and therefore $w'$ has as many zeros as it has infinities.

*Note* 1.  When the numerator and the denominator of a uniform fractional function of $z$ have a common zero, we divide both of them by their greatest common measure; and the point is no longer a common zero of their new forms.  But when the numerator $U(w, z)$ and the denominator $V(w, z)$ of a uniform function of position on a Riemann's surface have a common zero, so that there are simultaneous values of $w$ and $z$ for which both vanish, $U$ and $V$ do not necessarily possess a rational common factor; and then the common zero cannot be removed.

It is not difficult to shew that this possibility does not affect the preceding theorem.

*Note* 2.  In estimating the degree of a function through (say) its zeros, it is necessary to have a clear mode of estimating the multiplicity of a zero; likewise of course for its infinities, and for its level points.

Let $w = \alpha$, $z = a$, be a zero of a uniform rational function $U(w, z)$ of position on a Riemann's surface: the multiplicity of the zero is estimated by the expression of $U$ in the immediate vicinity of the position.  For this purpose, let
$$w = \alpha + y, \quad z = a + x.$$

* Sometimes it is called the *order* of the function.

(If $\alpha$ be infinite, we take $w = \dfrac{1}{y}$; if $z$ be infinite, we take $z = \dfrac{1}{x}$; if both be infinite, we use both these substitutions.)

First, let $\alpha$, $a$ be an ordinary point on the Riemann's surface, that is, not a branch-point; then the equation

$$f(\alpha + y,\ a + x) = 0 = f(\alpha,\ a)$$

determines $y$ as a uniform function of $x$ in the immediate vicinity of $\alpha$, $a$, so that we have

$$y = \lambda_1 x + \lambda_2 x^2 + \dots.$$

Now
$$U(w,\ z) = U(\alpha + y,\ a + x)$$
$$= y\,\frac{\partial U}{\partial \alpha} + x\,\frac{\partial U}{\partial a} + \dots;$$

substitute for $y$ on the right-hand side the above value, and suppose that then

$$U(w,\ z) = k_0 x^l + k_1 x^{l+1} + \dots,$$

in the immediate vicinity of the point on the surface. We then say that *the zero $\alpha$, $a$ of $U(w,\ z)$ is of multiplicity $l$.*

Next, let the point $\alpha$, $a$ be a branch-point on the Riemann's surface, so that a number of sheets wind into one another at the point. Then, by § 97, there exists a variable $\zeta$ such that

$$z - a = \zeta^q,$$
$$w - \alpha = \zeta^p (v_1 + v_2 \zeta + \dots),$$

in the immediate vicinity of $\alpha$, $a$: the positive integers $p$ and $q$ having no common factor. If $z = \infty$ give rise to a branch-point, the new variable would be given by $z = t^{-q}$; if $\alpha$ were infinite, the expression for $w$ would be of the form $w = \zeta^{-p}(v_1 + v_2 \zeta + \dots)$; and similarly if both $\alpha$ and $a$ were infinite. As $\alpha$, $a$ is a zero of $U$, we have

$$U(w, z) = (w - \alpha)\frac{\partial U}{\partial \alpha} + (z - c)\frac{\partial U}{\partial a} + \dots.$$

Substitute for both $w - \alpha$ and $z - c$ on the right-hand side: and suppose that then

$$U(w, z) = \kappa_0 \zeta^\lambda + \kappa_1 \zeta^{\lambda+1} + \dots,$$

valid in the immediate vicinity of the point. We then say* that $\zeta$ is an infinitesimal of the first order, and therefore that *the zero $\alpha$, $a$ is of multiplicity $\lambda$.*

---

* Riemann, *Ges. Werke*, p. 96. The justification for regarding $\zeta$ as a small quantity of the first order, that is, the same as $x$ when the point is not a branch-point, is that the value of

$$\frac{1}{2\pi i} \int \frac{dz}{z - a}$$

taken round a simple closed curve enclosing $a$ is $q$, because the curve passes round $a$ in each of the $q$ sheets. Thus $\zeta^q$ counts as having $q$ zeros, and therefore $\zeta$ is of the first order.

**195.** In the case of uniform functions it was seen that, as soon as their integrals were considered, deviations from uniformity occurred. Special investigations indicated the character of the deviations and the limitations to their extent. Incidentally, special classes of functions were introduced, such as many-valued functions, the values differing by multiples of a constant; and thence, by inversion, simply-periodic functions were deduced.

So, too, when multiform functions defined by an algebraical equation are considered, it is necessary to take into special account the deviations from uniformity of value on the Riemann's surface which may be introduced by processes of integration. It is, of course, in connection with the branch-points that difficulties arise; but, as the present method of representing the variation of the variable is distinct from that adopted in the case of uniform functions, it is desirable to indicate how we deal, not merely with branch-points, but also with singularities of functions when the integrals of such functions are under consideration. In order to render the ideas familiar and to avoid prolixity in the explanations relating to general integrals, we shall, after one or two propositions, discuss again some of the instances given in Chapter IX., taking the opportunity of stating general results as occasion may arise.

One or two propositions already proved must be restated: the difference from the earlier forms is solely in the mode of statement, and therefore the reasoning which led to their establishment need not be repeated.

I. *The path of integration between any two points on a Riemann's surface can, without affecting the value of the integral, be deformed in any possible continuous manner that does not make the path pass over any discontinuity of the subject of integration.*

This proposition is established in § 100.

II. *A simple closed curve on a Riemann's surface, which is a path of integration, can, without affecting the value of the integral, be deformed in any possible continuous manner that does not make the curve pass over any discontinuity of the subject of integration.*

Since the curve on the surface is closed, the initial and the final points are the same; the initial branch of the function is therefore restored after the description of the curve. This proposition is established in Corollary II., § 100.

III. *If the path of integration be a curve between two points on different sheets, determined by the same algebraical value of z, the curve is not a closed curve; it must be regarded as a path between the two points;* its deformation is subject to Proposition I.

No restatement, from Chapter IX., of the value of an integral, along a path which encloses a branch-point, is necessary. The method of dealing with the point when that value is infinite will be the same as the method of dealing with other infinities of the function.

**196.** We have already obtained some instances of multiple-valued functions, in the few particular integrals in Chapter IX.; the differences in the values of the functions, arising as integrals, consist solely of multiples of constants. The way in which these constants enter in Riemann's method is as follows.

When the surface is simply connected, there is no substantial difference from the previous theory for uniform functions; we therefore proceed to the consideration of multiply connected surfaces.

On a general surface, of any connectivity, take any two points $z_0$ and $z$. As the surface is one of multiple connection, there will be at least two essentially distinct paths between $z_0$ and $z$, that is, paths which cannot be reduced to one another; one of these paths can be deformed so as to be made equivalent to a combination of the other with some irreducible circuit. Let $z_1$ denote the extremity of the first path, and let $z_2$ denote the same point when regarded as the extremity of the second; then the difference of the two paths is an irreducible circuit passing from $z_1$ to $z_2$. When this circuit is made impossible by a cross-cut $C$ passing through the point $z$, then $z_1$ and $z_2$ may be regarded as points on the opposite edges of the cross-cut: and the irreducible circuit on the unresolved surface becomes a path on the partially resolved surface passing from one edge of the cross-cut to the other.

When the surface is resolved by means of the proper number of cross-cuts into a simply connected surface, there is still a path in the surface from $z_1$ to $z_2$ on opposite edges of the cross-cut $C$: and all paths between $z_1$ and $z_2$ in the resolved surface are reconcileable with one another. One such path will be taken as the canonical path from $z_1$ to $z_2$; it evidently does not meet any of the cross-cuts, so that we consider only those paths which do not intersect any cross-cut.

If then $Z$ be the function of position on the surface to be integrated, the value of the integral for the first path from $z_0$ to $z_1$ is

$$\int_{z_0}^{z_1} Z\,dz \,;$$

and for the second path it is
$$\int_{z_0}^{z_2} Z\,dz,$$

or, by the assigned deformation of the second path, it is

$$\int_{z_0}^{z_1} Z\,dz + \int_{z_1}^{z_2} Z\,dz,$$

the second integral being taken along the canonical path from $z_1$ to $z_2$ in the surface, that is, along the irreducible circuit of canonical form, which would be possible in the otherwise resolved surface were the cross-cut $C$ obliterated.

The difference of the values of the integral is evidently

$$\int_{z_1}^{z_2} Z dz,$$

which is therefore the change made in the value of the integral $\int_{z_0}^{z} Z dz$, when the upper limit passes from one edge of the cross-cut to the other; let it be denoted by $I$. As the curve is, in general, an irreducible circuit, this integral $I$ may not, in general, be supposed zero.

We can arbitrarily assign the positive and the negative edges of some one cross-cut, say $A$. The edges of a cross-cut $B$ that meets $A$ are defined to be positive and negative as follows: when a point moves from one edge of $B$ to the other, by describing the positive edge of $A$ in a direction that is to the right of the negative edge of $A$, the edge of $B$ on which the point initially lies is called its *positive* edge, and the edge of $B$ on which the point finally lies is called its *negative* edge. And so on with the cross-cuts in succession.

The lower limit of the integral determining the modulus for a cross-cut is taken to lie on the negative edge, and the upper on the positive edge.

Regarding a point $\zeta$ on the cross-cut as defining two points $z_1$ and $z_2$ on opposite edges which geometrically are coincident, we now prove that *for all points on the cross-cut which can be reached from $\zeta$ without passing over any other cross-cut, when the surface is resolved into one that is simply connected, the integral $I$ is a constant.* For, if $\zeta'$ be such a point, defining $z_1'$ and $z_2'$ on opposite edges, then $z_1 z_2 z_2' z_1' z_1$ is a circuit on the simply connected surface, which can be made evanescent; and it will be assumed that no infinities of $Z$ lie in the surface within the circuit, an assumption which will be taken into account in §§ 197, 199. Therefore the integral of $Z$, taken round the circuit, is zero. Hence

$$\int_{z_1}^{z_2} Z dz + \int_{z_2}^{z_2'} Z dz + \int_{z_2'}^{z_1'} Z dz + \int_{z_1'}^{z_1} Z dz = 0,$$

that is,

$$\int_{z_1}^{z_2} Z dz - \int_{z_1'}^{z_2'} Z dz = \int_{z_1}^{z_1'} Z dz - \int_{z_2}^{z_2'} Z dz.$$

Along the direction of the cross-cut, the function $Z$ is uniform: and therefore $Z dz$ is the same for each element of the two edges, so long as the cross-cut is not met by any other. Hence the sums of the elements on the two edges are the same for all points on the cross-cut that can be reached from $\zeta$ without meeting a new cross-cut. The two integrals on the right-hand side of the foregoing equation are equal to one another, and therefore also those on the left-hand side, that is,

$$\int_{z_1}^{z_2} Z dz = \int_{z_1'}^{z_2'} Z dz,$$

which shews that *the integral $I$ is constant for different points on a portion of cross-cut that is not met by any other cross-cut.*

If however the cross-cut be met by another cross-cut $C'$, two cases arise according as $C'$ has only one extremity on $C$, or has both extremities on $C$.

First, let $C'$ have only one extremity $O$ on $C$. By what precedes, the integral is constant along $OP$, and it is constant along $OQ$; but we cannot infer that it is the same constant for the two parts. The preceding proof fails in this case; the distance $z_2z_2'$ in the resolved surface is not infinitesimal, and therefore there is no element $Zdz$ for $z_2z_2'$ to be the same as the element for $z_1z_1'$. Let $I_2$ be the constant for $OP$, $I_1$ that for $QO$; and let $QP$ be the negative edge. Then

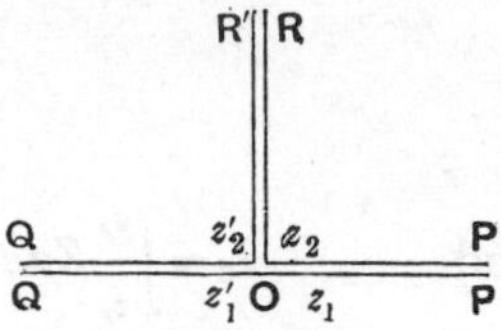

$$I_2 = \int_{z_1}^{z_2} Zdz, \qquad I_1 = \int_{z_1'}^{z_2'} Zdz.$$

Fig. 66.

Let $I'$ be the constant value for the cross-cut $OR$, and let $OR$ be the negative edge; then

$$I' = \int_{z_2}^{z_2'} Zdz.$$

In the completely resolved surface, a possible path from $z_2$ to $z_2'$ is $z_2$ to $z_1$, $z_1$ to $z_1'$, $z_1'$ to $z_2'$; it therefore is the canonical path, so that

$$I' = \int_{z_2}^{z_1} Zdz + \int_{z_1}^{z_1'} Zdz + \int_{z_1'}^{z_2'} Zdz$$

$$= -I_2 + I_1 + \int_{z_1}^{z_1'} Zdz.$$

But $\int_{z_1}^{z_1'} Zdz$ is an integral of a uniform finite function along an infinitesimal arc $z_1 O z_1'$, and it is zero in the limit when we take $z_1$ and $z_1'$ as coincident. Thus

$$I' = I_1 - I_2,$$

or *the constant for the cross-cut $OR$ is the excess of the constant for the part of $PQ$ at the positive edge of $OR$ over the constant for the part of $PQ$ at the negative edge.*

Secondly, let $C'$ have both extremities on $C$, close to one another so that they may be brought together as in the figure: it is effectively the case of the directions of two cross-cuts intersecting one another, say at $O$. Let $I_1, I_2, I_3, I_4$ be the constants for the portions $QO, OP, OR, SO$ of the cross-cuts respectively, and let $z_3z_2$ be the positive edge of $QOP$; then $z_4z_3$ is the positive edge of $SOR$. Then if $\Theta(z)$ denote the value of the integral $\int_{z_0}^{z} Zdz$ at $O$, which is definite because

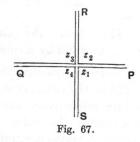

Fig. 67.

the surface is simply connected and no discontinuities of $Z$ lie within the paths of integration, we have

$$I_1 = \int_{z_4}^{z_3} Z dz = \Theta(z_3) - \Theta(z_4),$$

$$I_2 = \int_{z_1}^{z_2} Z dz = \Theta(z_2) - \Theta(z_1);$$

and $$I_3 = \int_{z_2}^{z_3} Z dz = \Theta(z_3) - \Theta(z_2), \quad I_4 = \int_{z_1}^{z_4} Z dz = \Theta(z_4) - \Theta(z_1);$$

so that $$I_1 - I_2 = I_3 - I_4,$$

or *the excess of the constant for the portion of a cross-cut on the positive edge, over the constant for the portion on the negative edge, of another cross-cut is equal to the excess, similarly estimated, for that other cross-cut.*

*Ex.* Consider the constants for the various portions of the cross-cuts in the canonical resolution (§§ 180, 181) of a Riemann's surface. Let the constants for the two portions of $a_r$ be $A_r$, $A_r'$; and the constants for the two portions of $b_r$ be $B_r$, $B_r'$; and let the constant for $c_r$ be $C_r$.

Then, at the junction of $c_r$ and $a_{r+1}$, we have

$$C_r = A_{r+1} \sim A'_{r+1};$$

at the junction of $c_r$ and $b_r$, we have

$$C_r = B_r \sim B_r',$$

and, at the crossing of $a_r$ and $b_r$, we have

$$A_r \sim A_r' = B_r \sim B_r'.$$

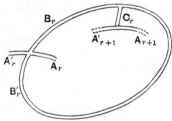

Fig. 68.

Now, because $b_1$ is the only cross-cut which meets $a_1$, we have $A_1 = A_1'$; hence $B_1 = B_1'$, and therefore $C_1 = 0$. Hence $A_2 = A_2'$; therefore $B_2 = B_2'$, and therefore also $C_2 = 0$. And so on.

Hence *the constant for each of the portions of a cross-cut a is the same; the constant for each of the portions of a cross-cut b is the same; and the constant for each cross-cut c is zero.* A single constant may thus be associated with each cross-cut $a$, and a single constant with each cross-cut $b$, in connection with the integral of a given uniform function of position on the Riemann's surface. It has not been proved—and it is not necessarily the fact—that any one of these constants is different from zero; but it is sufficiently evident that, if all the constants be zero, the integral is a uniform function of position on the surface, that is, a uniform function of $w$ and $z$.

**197.** Hence the values of the integral at points on opposite edges of a cross-cut differ by a constant.

Suppose now that the cross-cut is obliterated: the two paths to the point $z$ will be the same as in the case just considered and will furnish the same values respectively, say $U$ and $U + I$. But the irreducible circuit which contributes the value $I$ can be described any number of times; and therefore, taking account solely of this irreducible circuit and of the cross-cuts which render other circuits impossible on the resolved surface, the general value of the integral at the point $z$ is

$$U + kI,$$

where $k$ is an integer and $U$ is the value for some prescribed path.

The constant $I$ is called* a *modulus of periodicity*.

It is important that every modulus of periodicity should be finite; the path which determines the modulus can therefore pass through a point $c$ where $Z = \infty$, or be deformed across it without change in the modulus, only if the limit of $(z-c)Z$ be a uniform zero at the point. If, however, the limit of $(z-c)Z$ at the point be a constant, implying a logarithmic infinity for the integral, or if it be an infinity of finite order (the order not being necessarily an integer), implying an algebraic infinity for the integral, we surround the point $c$ by a simple small curve and exclude the internal area from the range of variation of the independent variable†. This exclusion is secured by making a small loop-cut in the surface round the point; it increases by unity the connectivity of the surface on which the variable is represented.

When the limit of $(z-c)Z$ is a uniform zero at $c$, no such exclusion is necessary: the order of the infinity for $Z$ is easily seen to be a proper fraction and the point to be a branch-point.

Similarly, if the limit of $zZ$ for $z = \infty$ be not zero and the path which determines a modulus can be deformed so as to become infinitely large, it is convenient to exclude the part of the surface at infinity from the range of variation of the variable, proper account being taken of the exclusion. The reason is that the value of the integral for a path entirely at infinity (or for a point-path on Neumann's sphere) is not zero; $z = \infty$ is either a logarithmic or an algebraic infinity of the function. But, if the limit of $zZ$ be zero for $z = \infty$, the exclusion of the part of the surface at infinity is unnecessary.

**198.** When, then, the region of variation of the variable is properly bounded, and the resolution of the surface into one that is simply connected has been made, each cross-cut or each portion of cross-cut, that is marked off either by the natural boundary or by termination in another cross-cut, determines a modulus of periodicity. The various moduli, for a given resolution, are therefore equal, in number, to the various portions of the cross-cuts. Again, a system of cross-cuts is susceptible of great variation, not merely as to the form of individual members of the system (which does not affect the value of the modulus), but in their relations to one another. The total number of cross-cuts, by which the surface can be resolved into one that is simply connected, is a constant for the surface and is independent of

---

* Sometimes the *modulus for the cross-cut*.

† This is the reason for the assumption made on p. 424.

their configuration: but the number of distinct pieces, defined as above, is not independent of the configuration. Now each piece of cross-cut furnishes a modulus of periodicity; a question therefore arises as to the number of independent moduli of periodicity.

Let the connectivity of the surface be $N + 1$, due regard being had to the exclusions, if any, of individual points in the surface: in order that account may be taken of infinite values of the variable, the surface will be assumed spherical. The number of cross-cuts necessary to resolve it into a surface that is simply connected is $N$; whatever be the number of portions of the cross-cuts, the number of these portions is not less than $N$.

When a cross-cut terminates in another, the modulus for the former and the moduli for the two portions of the latter are connected by a relation

$$\omega = \omega_1 \sim \omega_2,$$

so that the modulus for any portion can be expressed linearly in terms of the modulus for the earlier portion and of the modulus for the dividing cross-cut.

Similarly, when the directions of two cross-cuts intersect, the moduli of the four portions are connected by a relation

$$\omega_1 \sim \omega_1' = \omega_2 \sim \omega_2';$$

and by passing along one or other of the cross-cuts, some relation is obtainable between $\omega_1$ and $\omega_1'$ or between $\omega_2$ and $\omega_2'$, so that, again, the modulus of any portion can be expressed linearly in terms of the modulus for the earlier portion and of moduli independent of the intersection.

Hence it appears that a single constant must be associated with each cross-cut as an independent modular constant; and then the constants for the various portions can be linearly expressed in terms of these independent constants. *There are therefore $N$ linearly independent moduli of periodicity:* but no system of moduli is unique, and any system can be modified partially or wholly, if any number of the moduli of the system be replaced by the same number of independent linear combinations of members of the system. These results are the analytical equivalent of geometrical results, which have already been proved, viz., that the number of independent simple irreducible circuits in a complete system is $N$, that no complete system of circuits is unique, and that the circuits can be replaced by independent combinations reconcileable with them.

**199.** If, then, the moduli of periodicity of a function $U$ at the cross-cuts in a resolved surface be $I_1$, $I_2$, ..., $I_N$, all the values of the function at any point on the unresolved surface are included in the form

$$U + m_1 I_1 + m_2 I_2 + \ldots + m_N I_N,$$

where $m_1$, $m_2$, ..., $m_N$ are integers.

Some special examples, treated by the present method, will be useful in leading up to the consideration of integrals of the most general functions of position on a Riemann's surface.

*Ex.* 1. Consider the integral $\int \dfrac{dz}{z}$.

The subject of integration is uniform, so that the surface is one-sheeted. The origin is an accidental singularity and gives a logarithmic infinity for the integral; it is therefore excluded by a small circle round it. Moreover, the value of the integral round a circle of infinitely large radius is not zero: and therefore $z=\infty$ is excluded from the range of variation. The boundary of the single spherical sheet can be taken to be the point $z=\infty$; and the bounded sheet is of connectivity 2, owing to the small circle at the origin. The surface can be resolved into one that is simply connected by a single cross-cut drawn from the boundary at $z=\infty$ to the circumference of the small circle.

If a plane surface be used, this cross-cut is, in effect, a section (§ 103) of the plane made from the origin to the point $z=\infty$.

There is only one modulus of periodicity: its value is evidently $\int \dfrac{dz}{z}$, taken round the origin, that is, the modulus is $2\pi i$. Hence whenever the path of variation from a given point to a point $z$ passes from $A$ to $B$, the value of the integral increases by $2\pi i$; but if the path pass from $B$ to $A$, the value of the integral

Fig. 69.

decreases by $2\pi i$. Thus $A$ is the negative edge, and $B$ the positive edge of the cross-cut.

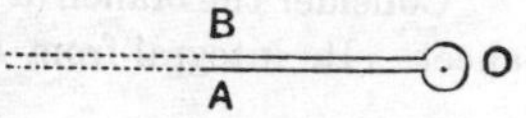

If, then, any one value of $\int_{z_0}^{z} \dfrac{dz}{z}$ be denoted by $w$, all values at the point in the unresolved surface are of the form $w+2m\pi i$, where $m$ is an integer; when $z$ is regarded as a function of $w$, it is a simply-periodic function, having $2\pi i$ for its period.

*Ex.* 2. Consider $\int \dfrac{dz}{z^2-a^2}$. The subject of integration is uniform, so that the surface consists of a single sheet. There are two infinities $\pm a$, each of the first order, because $(z\mp a)Z$ is finite at these two points: they must be excluded by small circles. The limit, when $z=\infty$, of $z/(z^2-a^2)$ is zero, so that the point $z=\infty$ does not need to be excluded. We can thus regard one of the small circles as the boundary of the surface, which is then doubly connected: a single cross-cut from the other circle to the boundary, that is, in effect, a cross-cut joining the two points $a$ and $-a$, resolves the surface into one that is simply connected.

It is easy to see that the modulus of periodicity is $\dfrac{\pi i}{a}$: that $A$ is the negative edge and $B$ the positive edge of the cross-cut: and that, if $w$ be a value of the integral in the unresolved surface at any point, all the values at that point are included in the form

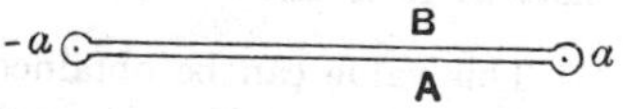

Fig. 70.

$$w+n\frac{\pi i}{a},$$

where $n$ is an integer.

*Ex.* 3. Consider $\int (a^2-z^2)^{-\frac{1}{2}} dz$. The subject of integration is two-valued, so that the surface is two-sheeted. The branch-points are $\pm a$, and $\infty$ is not a branch-point, so that the single branch-line between the sheets may be taken as the straight line joining $a$ and $-a$. The infinities are $\pm a$; but as $(z\mp a)(a^2-z^2)^{-\frac{1}{2}}$ vanishes at the points, they do not need to be excluded. As the limit of $z(a^2-z^2)^{-\frac{1}{2}}$, for $z=\infty$, is not zero, we exclude $z=\infty$ by small curves in each of the sheets.

Taking the surface in the spherical form, we assign as the boundary the small curve round the point $z=\infty$ in one of the sheets. The connectivity of the surface, through its dependence on branch-lines and branch-points, is unity: owing to the exclusion of the point $z=\infty$ by the small curve in the other sheet, the connectivity is increased by one unit: the surface is therefore doubly connected. A single cross-cut will resolve the surface into one that is simply connected: and this cross-cut must pass from the boundary at $z=\infty$ which is in one sheet to the excluded point $z=\infty$.

Since the (single) modulus of periodicity is the value of the integral along a circuit in the resolved surface from one edge of the cross-cut to the other, this circuit can be taken so that in the unresolved surface it includes the two branch-points; and then, by II. of § 195, the circuit can be deformed until it is practically a double straight line in the upper sheet on either side of the branch-line, together with two small circles round $a$ and $-a$ respectively. Let $P$ be the origin, practically the middle point of these straight lines.

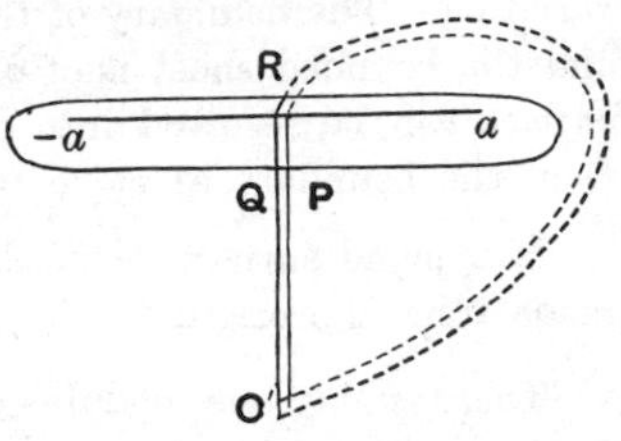

Fig. 71.

Consider the branch $(a^2-z^2)^{-\frac{1}{2}}$ belonging to the upper sheet. Its integral from $P$ to $a$ is

$$\int_0^a (a^2-z^2)^{-\frac{1}{2}}\,dz.$$

From $a$ to $-a$ the branch is $-(a^2-z^2)^{-\frac{1}{2}}$; the point $R$ is contiguous in the surface, not to $P$, but (as in § 189) to the point in the second sheet beneath $P$ at which the branch is $-(a^2-z^2)^{-\frac{1}{2}}$, the other branch having been adopted for the upper sheet. Hence, from $a$ to $-a$ by $R$, the integral is

$$\int_a^{-a} -(a^2-z^2)^{-\frac{1}{2}}\,dz.$$

From $-a$ to $Q$, the branch is $+(a^2-z^2)^{-\frac{1}{2}}$, the same branch as at $P$: hence from $-a$ to $Q$, the integral is

$$\int_{-a}^0 (a^2-z^2)^{-\frac{1}{2}}\,dz.$$

The integral, along the small arcs round $a$ and round $a'$ respectively, vanishes for each. Hence the modulus of periodicity is

$$\int_0^a (a^2-z^2)^{-\frac{1}{2}}\,dz + \int_a^{-a} -(a^2-z^2)^{-\frac{1}{2}}\,dz + \int_{-a}^0 (a^2-z^2)^{-\frac{1}{2}}\,dz,$$

that is, it is $2\pi$.

This value can be obtained otherwise thus. The modulus is the same for all points on the cross-cut; hence its value, taken at $O'$ where $z=\infty$, is

$$\int (a^2-z^2)^{-\frac{1}{2}}\,dz,$$

passing from one edge of the cross-cut at $O'$ to the other, that is, round a curve in the plane everywhere at infinity. This gives

$$2\pi i \operatorname*{Lt}_{z=\infty} z\,(a^2-z^2)^{-\frac{1}{2}} = \frac{2\pi i}{i} = 2\pi,$$

the same value as before.

The latter curve round $O'$, from edge to edge, can easily be deformed into the former curve round $a$ and $-a$ from edge to edge of the cross-cut.

Again, let $w_1$ be a value of the integral for a point $z_1$ in one sheet and $w_2$ be a value for a point $z_2$ in the other sheet with the same algebraical value as $z_1$: take zero as the common lower limit of the integral, being the same zero for the two integrals. As this zero may be taken in either sheet, let it be in that in which $z_1$ lies: and then

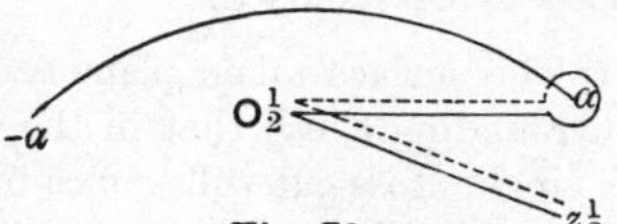

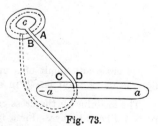

$$w_1 = \int_0^{z_1} (a^2 - z^2)^{-\frac{1}{2}} \, dz.$$

Fig. 72.

To pass from $O$ to $z_2$ for $w_2$, any path can be justifiably deformed into the following: (i) a path round either branch-point, say $a$, so as to return to the point under $O$ in the second sheet, say to $O_2$, (ii) any number $m$ of irreducible circuits round $a$ and $-a$, always returning to $O_2$ in the second sheet, (iii) a path from $O_2$ to $z_2$ lying exactly under the path from $O$ to $z_1$ for $w_1$. The parts contributed by these paths respectively to the integral $w_2$ are seen to be

(i)  a quantity $+\pi$, arising from $\int_0^a (a^2 - z^2)^{-\frac{1}{2}} \, dz + \int_a^0 -(a^2 - z^2)^{-\frac{1}{2}} \, dz$, for reasons similar to those above;

(ii)  a quantity $m2\pi$, where $m$ is an integer positive or negative;

(iii)  a quantity $\int_{O_2}^{z_2} -(a^2 - z^2)^{-\frac{1}{2}} \, dz$.

In the last quantity the minus sign is prefixed, because the subject of integration is everywhere in the second sheet. Now $z_2 = z_1$, and therefore the quantity in (iii) is

$$-\int_0^{z_1} (a^2 - z^2)^{-\frac{1}{2}} \, dz,$$

that is, it is $-w_1$; hence $\qquad w_2 = (2m+1)\pi - w_1.$

If then we take $w = \int_0^z (a^2 - z^2)^{-\frac{1}{2}} \, dz$, the integral extending along some defined curve from an assigned origin, say along a straight line, the values of $w$ belonging to the same algebraical value of $z$ are $2n\pi + w$ or $(2m+1)\pi - w$; and the inversion of the functional relation gives

$$\phi(w) = z = \phi(2n\pi + w)$$
$$= \phi\{(2m+1)\pi - w\},$$

where $m$ and $n$ are any integers.

*Ex.* 4.  Consider $\int \dfrac{dz}{(z-c)(a^2 - z^2)^{\frac{1}{2}}}$, assuming $|c| > |a|$. The surface is two-sheeted, with branch-points at $\pm a$ but not at $\infty$: hence the line joining $a$ and $-a$ is the sole branch-line. The infinities of the subject of integration are $a$, $-a$, and $c$. Of these $a$ and $-a$ need not be excluded, for the same reason that their exclusion was not required in the last example. But $c$ must be excluded; and it must be excluded in both sheets, because $z = c$ makes the subject of integration infinite in both sheets. There are thus two points of accidental singularity of the subject of integration; in the vicinity of these points, the two branches of the subject of integration are

$$\frac{1}{z-c}(a^2 - c^2)^{-\frac{1}{2}} + \ldots, \quad -\frac{1}{z-c}(a^2 - c^2)^{-\frac{1}{2}} - \ldots,$$

Fig. 73.

the relation between the coefficients of $(z-c)^{-1}$ in them being a special case of a more general proposition (§ 210). And since $z/\{(z-c)(a^2-z^2)^{\frac{1}{2}}\}$ when $z=\infty$ is zero, $\infty$ does not need to be excluded.

The surface taken plane is doubly connected, as in the last example, one of the curves surrounding $c$, say that in the upper sheet, being taken as the boundary of the surface. A single cross-cut will suffice to make it simply connected: the direction of the cross-cut must pass from the $c$-curve in the lower sheet to the branch-line and thence to the boundary in the upper sheet.

There is only a single modulus of periodicity, being the constant for the single cross-cut. This modulus can be obtained by means of the curve $AB$ in the first sheet; and, on contraction of the curve (by II. § 195) so as to be infinitesimally near $c$, it is easily seen to be $2\pi i(a^2-c^2)^{-\frac{1}{2}}$, or say $2\pi (c^2-a^2)^{-\frac{1}{2}}$. But the modulus can be obtained also by means of the curve $CD$; and when the curve is contracted, as in the previous example, so as practically to be a loop round $a$ and a loop round $-a$, the value of the integral is

$$2\int_{-a}^{a} \frac{dz}{(z-c)(a^2-z^2)^{\frac{1}{2}}},$$

which is easily proved to be $2\pi (c^2-a^2)^{-\frac{1}{2}}$.

As in Ex. 3, a curve in the upper sheet, which encloses the branch-points and the branch-lines, can be deformed into the curve $AB$.

*Ex.* 5. Consider          $w=\int(4z^3-g_2z-g_3)^{-\frac{1}{2}}\,dz=\int u\,dz.$

The subject of integration is two-valued, and therefore the Riemann's surface is two-sheeted. The branch-points are $z=\infty$, $e_1$, $e_2$, $e_3$, where $e_1$, $e_2$, $e_3$ are the roots of

$$4z^3-g_2z-g_3=0;$$

and no one of them needs to be excluded from the range of variation of the variable.

The connectivity of the surface is 3, so that two cross-cuts are necessary to resolve the surface into one that is simply connected. The configurations of the branch-lines and

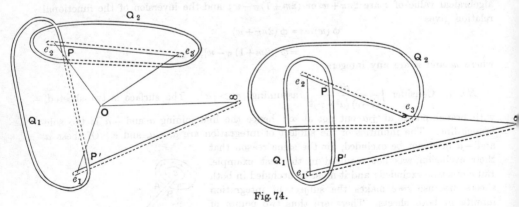

Fig. 74.

of the cross-cuts admit of some variety; two illustrations of branch-lines are given in fig. 74, and a point on $Q_1$ in each diagram is taken as boundary.

The modulus for the cross-cut $Q_1$—say from the inside to the outside—can be obtained in two different ways. First, from $P$, a point on $Q_1$, draw a line to $e_2$ in the first sheet, then across the branch-line, then in the second sheet to $e_3$ and across the branch-line, then in the first sheet round $e_3$ and back to $P$: the circuit is represented by the double line between $e_2$ and $e_3$.   The value of the integral is

$$\int_{e_2}^{e_3} u\,dz + \int_{e_3}^{e_2} (-u)\,dz, \text{ that is, } 2\int_{e_2}^{e_3} u\,dz.$$

Again, it can be obtained by a line from $P'$, another point on $Q_1$, to $\infty$, round the branch-point there and across the branch-line, then in the second sheet to $e_1$ and round $e_1$, then across the branch-line and back to $P'$: the value of the integral is

$$E_1 = 2\int_{e_1}^{\infty} u\,dz.$$

But the modulus is the same for $P$ as for $P'$: hence

$$E_1 = 2\int_{e_1}^{\infty} u\,dz = 2\int_{e_2}^{e_3} u\,dz.$$

This relation can be expressed in a different form.  The path from $e_2$ to $e_3$ can be stretched into another form towards $z=\infty$ in the first sheet, and similarly for the path in the second sheet, without affecting the value of the integral.   Moreover as the integral is zero for $z=\infty$, we can, without affecting the value, add the small part

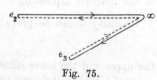

Fig. 75.

necessary to complete the circuits from $e_2$ to $\infty$ and from $e_3$ to $\infty$.   The directions of these circuits being given by the arrows, we have

$$2\int_{e_2}^{e_3} u\,dz = 2\int_{e_2}^{\infty} u\,dz + 2\int_{\infty}^{e_3} u\,dz,$$

or, if

$$E_\lambda = 2\int_{e_\lambda}^{\infty} u\,dz,$$

for $\lambda = 1, 2, 3$, we have*

$$E_1 = 2\int_{e_2}^{e_3} u\,dz = E_2 - E_3,$$

say

$$E_2 = E_1 + E_3;$$

and $E_1$ is the modulus of periodicity for the cross-cut $Q_1$.

In the same way, the modulus of periodicity for $Q_2$ is found to be

$$E_3 = 2\int_{e_3}^{\infty} u\,dz \text{ and to be } 2\int_{e_2}^{e_1} u\,dz,$$

the equivalence of which can be established as before.

Hence it appears that, if $w$ be the value of the integral at any point in the surface, the general value is of the form $w + mE_1 + nE_3$, where $m$ and $n$ are integers.   As the integral is zero at infinity (and for other reasons which have already appeared), it is convenient to take the fixed limit $z_0$ so as to define $w$ by the relation

$$w = \int_z^{\infty} u\,dz.$$

Now corresponding to a given arithmetical value of $z$, there are two points in the surface and two values of $w$: it is important to know the relation to one another of these two values.  Let $z'$ denote the value in the lower sheet: then the path from $z'$ to $\infty$ can be made up of

(i) a path from $z'$ to $\infty'$; (ii) any number of irreducible circuits from $\infty'$ to $\infty'$; and (iii) across the branch-line and round its extremity to $\infty$.

* See Ex. 7, § 104.

These parts respectively contribute to the integral

(i) a quantity $\int_{z'}^{\infty'} (-u)\,dz$, that is, $-\int_z^\infty u\,dz$, or, $-w$; (ii) a quantity $mE_1 + nE_3$, where $m$ and $n$ are integers; (iii) a quantity zero, since the integral vanishes at infinity: so that

$$w' = mE_1 + nE_3 - w.$$

If now we regard $z$ as a function of $w$, say $z = \wp(w)$, we have

$$\wp(w) = z = \wp(mE_1 + nE_3 + w), \qquad \wp(w') = z'.$$

But $z' = z$ arithmetically, so that we have

$$z = \wp(w) = \wp(mE_1 + nE_3 \pm w)$$

as the function expressing $z$ in terms of $w$.

Similarly it can be proved that

$$\wp'(w) = \pm \wp'(mE_1 + nE_3 \pm w),$$

the upper and the lower signs being taken together. Now $\wp(w)$, by itself, determines a value of $z$, that is, it determines two points on the surface: and $\wp'(w)$ has different values for these two points. Hence *a point on the surface is uniquely determined by* $\wp(w)$ *and* $\wp'(w)$.

*Ex.* 6.   Consider $w = \int_0^z \{(1-z^2)(1-k^2z^2)\}^{-\frac{1}{2}}\,dz = \int u\,dz$. The subject of integration is two-valued, so that the surface is two-sheeted. The branch-points are $\pm 1$, $\pm\dfrac{1}{k}$, but not $\infty$; no one of the branch-points need be excluded, nor need infinity.

The connectivity is 3, so that two cross-cuts will render the surface simply connected: let the branch-lines and the cross-cuts be taken as in the figure (fig. 76).

The details of the argument follow the same course as in the previous case.

The modulus of periodicity for $Q_2$ is $2\int_{-1}^1 u\,dz = 4\int_0^1 u\,dz = 4K$, in the ordinary notation.

The modulus of periodicity for $Q_1$ is $2\int_1^{\frac{1}{k}} u\,dz = 2iK'$, as before.

Hence, if $w$ be a value of the integral for a point $z$ in the first sheet, a more general value for that point is

$$w + m4K + n2iK'.$$

Let $w'$ be a value of the integral for a point $z'$ in the second sheet, where $z'$ is arithmetically equal to $z$—the point in the first sheet at which the value of the integral is $w$; then

$$w' = 2K + m4K + n2iK' - w,$$

so that, if we invert the functional relation and take $z = \operatorname{sn} w$, we have

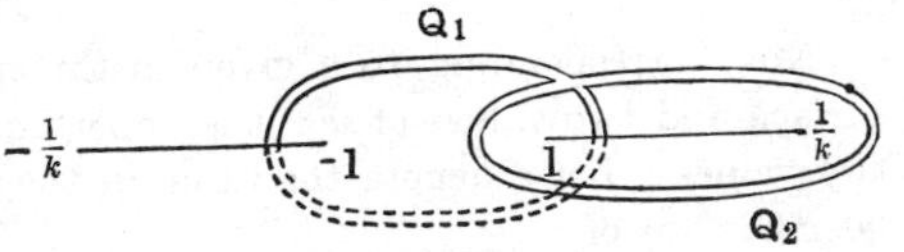

Fig. 76.

$$\operatorname{sn} w = z = \operatorname{sn}(w + 4mK + 2niK')$$

$$= \operatorname{sn}\{(4m+2)K + 2niK' - w\}.$$

*Ex.* 7.   Consider the integral $w = \int \dfrac{dz}{(z-c)\,u}$, where $u = \{(1 - z^2)(1 - k^2 z^2)\}^{\frac{1}{2}}$.

As in the last case, the surface is two-sheeted: the branch-points are $\pm 1$, $\pm \dfrac{1}{k}$; no one of them need be excluded, nor need $z = \infty$. But the point $z = c$ must be excluded in both sheets; for expanding the subject of integration for points in the first sheet in the vicinity of $z = c$, we have

$$\frac{1}{z - c}\{(1 - c^2)(1 - k^2 c^2)\}^{-\frac{1}{2}} + \ldots ,$$

and for points in the second sheet in the vicinity of $z = c$, we have

$$-\frac{1}{z - c}\{(1 - c^2)(1 - k^2 c^2)\}^{-\frac{1}{2}} - \ldots ,$$

in each case giving rise to a logarithmic infinity for $z = c$.

We take the small curves excluding $z = c$ in both sheets as the boundaries of the surface. Then, by Ex. 4, § 178, (or because one of these curves may be regarded as a

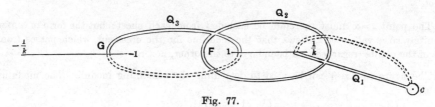

Fig. 77.

boundary of the surface in the last example, and the curve excluding the infinity in the other sheet is the equivalent of a loop-cut which (§ 161) increases the connectivity by unity), the connectivity is 4. The cross-cuts necessary to make the surface simply connected are three. They may be taken as in the figure; $Q_1$ is drawn from the boundary in one sheet to a branch-line and thence round $\dfrac{1}{k}$ to the boundary in the other sheet : $Q_2$ beginning and ending at a point in $Q_1$, and $Q_3$ beginning and ending at a point in $Q_2$.

The moduli of periodicity are:—

for $Q_1$, the quantity $(\Omega_1 =) 2\pi i \{(1 - c^2)(1 - k^2 c^2)\}^{-\frac{1}{2}}$, obtained by taking a small curve round $c$ in the upper sheet :

$Q_2$, the quantity $(\Omega_2 =) 2 \displaystyle\int_{-1}^{1} \dfrac{dz}{(z-c)\,u}$, obtained by taking a circuit round 1 and $\dfrac{1}{k}$, passing from one edge of $Q_2$ to the other at $F$:

$Q_3$, the quantity $(\Omega_3 =) 2 \displaystyle\int_{-1}^{-\frac{1}{k}} \dfrac{dz}{(z-c)\,u}$, obtained by taking a circuit round $-1$ and $-\dfrac{1}{k}$, passing from one edge of $Q_3$ to the other at $G$:

so that, if any value of the integral at a point be $w$, the general value at the point is

$$w + m_1 \Omega_1 + m_2 \Omega_2 + m_3 \Omega_3,$$

where $m_1$, $m_2$, $m_3$ are integers.

Conversely, $z$ is a triply-periodic function of $w$; but the function of $w$ is not uniform (§ 108).

*Ex.* 8.   As a last illustration for the present, consider

$$w = \int_0^z \left(\frac{1 - k^2 z^2}{1 - z^2}\right)^{\frac{1}{2}} dz.$$

The surface is two-sheeted; its connectivity is 3, the branch-points being $\pm 1$, $\pm \dfrac{1}{k}$, but not $z = \infty$.   No one of the branch-points need be excluded, for the integral is finite round each of them.   To consider the integral at infinity, we substitute $z = \dfrac{1}{z'}$, and then

$$w = \int \left(\frac{k^2 - z'^2}{1 - z'^2}\right)^{\frac{1}{2}} \left(-\frac{dz'}{z'^2}\right)$$

$$= - \int \frac{dz'}{z'^2} \left(k - \frac{k'^2}{2k} z'^2 + \dots\right)$$

$$= \frac{k}{z'} + \frac{k'^2}{2k} z' + \dots,$$

giving for the function at infinity an accidental singularity of the first order in each sheet.

The point $z = \infty$ must therefore be excluded from each sheet: but the form of $w$, for infinitely large values of $z$, shews that the modulus for the cross-cut, which passes from one of the points (regarded as a boundary) to the other, is zero.

The figure in Ex. 6 can be used to determine the remaining moduli.   The modulus for $Q_2$ is

$$2 \int_{-1}^{1} \left(\frac{1 - k^2 x^2}{1 - x^2}\right)^{\frac{1}{2}} dx$$

$$= 4 \int_0^1 \frac{1 - k^2 x^2}{\{(1 - x^2)(1 - k^2 x^2)\}^{\frac{1}{2}}} dx$$

$$= 4E,$$

with the notation of Jacobian elliptic functions.   The modulus for $Q_1$ is

$$= 2 \int_1^{\frac{1}{k}} \left(\frac{1 - k^2 x^2}{1 - x^2}\right)^{\frac{1}{2}} dx$$

$$= 2i \int_0^1 \frac{k'^2 y^2}{\{(1 - y^2)(1 - k'^2 y^2)\}^{\frac{1}{2}}} dy,$$

on transforming by the relation $k^2 x^2 + k'^2 y^2 = 1$: the last expression can at once be changed into the form $2i(K' - E')$, with the same notation as before.

If then $w$ be any value of the integral at a point on the surface, the general value there is

$$w + 4mE + 2ni(K' - E'),$$

where $m$ and $n$ are integers.

**200.**   After these illustrations in connection with simple cases, we may proceed with the consideration of the integral of the most general uniform rational function $w'$ of position on a Riemann's surface, constructed in connection with the algebraical equation

$$f(w, z) = w^n + w^{n-1} g_1(z) + \dots + w g_{n-1}(z) + g_n(z) = 0,$$

where the functions $g(z)$ are rational and integral. Subsidiary explanations, which are merely generalised from those inserted in the preceding particular discussions, will now be taken for granted.

Taking $w'$ in the form of § 193, we have

$$w' = \frac{1}{n} h_0(z) + \frac{h_1(z) w^{n-2} + \dots + h_{n-1}(z)}{\dfrac{\partial f}{\partial w}} = \frac{1}{n} h_0(z) + \frac{U(w, z)}{\dfrac{\partial f}{\partial w}},$$

so that in taking the integral of $w'$ we shall have a term $\dfrac{1}{n} \displaystyle\int h_0(z)\, dz$, where $h_0(z)$ is a rational function. This kind of integral has been discussed in Chapter II.; as it has no essential importance for the present investigation, it will be omitted, so that, without loss of generality merely for the present purpose*, we may assume $h_0(z)$ to vanish; and then *the numerator of $w'$ is of degree not higher than $n-2$ in $w$.*

The value of $z$ is insufficient to specify a point on the surface: the values of $w$ and $z$ must be given for this purpose, a requisite that was unnecessary in the preceding examples because the point $z$ was spoken of as being in the upper or the lower of the two sheets of the various surfaces. Corresponding to a value $a$ of $z$, there will be $n$ points: they may be taken in the form $(a_1, \alpha_1), (a_2, \alpha_2), \dots, (a_n, \alpha_n)$, where $a_1, \dots, a_n$ are each arithmetically equal to $a$, and $\alpha_1, \dots, \alpha_n$ are the appropriately arranged roots of the equation

$$f(w, a) = 0.$$

The function $w'$ to be integrated is of the form $\dfrac{U(w, z)}{\dfrac{\partial f}{\partial w}}$, where $U$ is polynomial of degree $n-2$ in $w$, but though rational in $z$ it is not necessarily integral in $z$.

An ordinary point of $w'$, which is neither an infinity nor a branch-point, is evidently an ordinary point of the integral.

The infinities of the subject of integration are of prime importance. They are:—

(i)   the infinities of the numerator,

(ii)   the zeros of the denominator.

The former are constituted by $(\alpha)$, the poles of the coefficients of powers of $w$ in $U(w, z)$, and $(\beta)$, $z = \infty$: this value is included, because the only infinities of $w$, as determined by the fundamental equation, arise for infinite values of $z$, and infinite values of $w$ and of $z$ may make the numerator $U(w, z)$ infinite.

---

* See § 207, where $h_0(z)$ is retained.

So far as concerns the infinities of $w'$ which arise when $z = \infty$ (and therefore $w = \infty$), it is not proposed to investigate the general conditions that the integral should vanish there. The test is of course that the limit, for $z = \infty$, of $\dfrac{z\,U_{\cdot}(w,\,z)}{\dfrac{\partial f}{\partial w}}$ should vanish for each of the $n$ values of $w$.

But the establishment of the general conditions is hardly worth the labour involved; it can easily be made in special cases, and it will be rendered unnecessary for the general case by subsequent investigations.

**201.** The simplest of the instances, less special than the examples already discussed, are two.

The first, which is really that of most frequent occurrence and is of very great functional importance, is that in which $f(w, z) = 0$ has the form

$$w^2 - S(z) = 0,$$

where $S(z)$ is of order $2m - 1$ or $2m$ and all its roots are simple: then $\dfrac{\partial f}{\partial w} = 2w = 2\sqrt{S(z)}$. In order that the limit of $\dfrac{z\,U(w,\,z)}{\dfrac{\partial f}{\partial w}}$ may be zero when $z = \infty$, we see (bearing in mind that $U$, in the present case, is independent of $w$) that the excess of the degree of the numerator of $U$ over its denominator may not be greater than $m - 2$. In particular, if $U$ be an integral function of $z$, a form of $U$ which would leave $\int w'dz$ zero at $z = \infty$ is

$$U = c_0 z^{m-2} + c_1 z^{m-3} + \ldots + c_{m-3}z + c_{m-2}.$$

As regards the other infinities of $U/\sqrt{S(z)}$, they are merely the roots of $S(z) = 0$ or they are the branch-points, each of the first order, of the equation

$$w^2 - S(z) = 0.$$

By the results of § 101, the integral vanishes round each of these points; and each of the points is a branch-point of the integral function. The integral is finite everywhere on the surface: and *the total number of such integrals, essentially different from one another, is the number of arbitrary coefficients in $U$, that is, it is $m - 1$, the same as the genus of the Riemann's surface associated with the equation.*

**202.** The other important instance is that in which the fundamental equation is, so to speak, a generalised equation of a plane curve, so that $g_s(z)$ is a polynomial function of $z$ of degree $s$: then it is easy to see that, at $z = \infty$, each branch $w \propto z$, so that $\dfrac{\partial f}{\partial w} \propto z^{n-1}$: hence $U(w, z)$ can vary only as $z^{n-3}$, in order that the condition may be satisfied. If then $U(w, z)$ be an integral function of $z$, it is evident that it can at most take a form which makes $U = 0$ the generalised equation of a curve of degree $n - 3$; while, if it be $\dfrac{V(w, z)}{z - c}$, then $V(w, z)$, supposed integral in $z$, can at most take a form which makes $V = 0$ the generalised equation of a curve of degree $n - 2$.

Other forms are easily obtainable for accidental singularities of coefficients of $w$ in $U(w, z)$ that are of other orders.

As regards the other possible infinities of the integral, let $c$ be an accidental singularity of a coefficient of some power of $w$ in $U(w, z)$; it may be assumed not to be a zero of $\dfrac{\partial f}{\partial w}$. Denote the $n$ points on the surface by $(c_1, k_1), (c_2, k_2), \ldots, (c_n, k_n)$, where $c_1, c_2, \ldots, c_n$ are arithmetically equal to $c$. In the vicinity of each of these points let $w'$ be expanded: then, neár $(c_r, k_r)$, we have a set of terms of the type

$$\frac{A_{m,r}}{(z - c_r)^m} + \frac{A_{m-1,r}}{(z - c_r)^{m-1}} + \cdots + \frac{A_{2,r}}{(z - c_r)^2} + \frac{A_{1,r}}{z - c_r} + P(z - c_r),$$

where $P(z - c_r)$ is a converging series of positive integral powers of $z - c_r$. A corresponding expansion exists for every one of the $n$ points.

The integral of $w'$ will therefore have a logarithmic infinity at $(c_r, k_r)$, unless $A_{1,r}$ is zero; and it will have an algebraic infinity, unless all the coefficients $A_{2,r}, \ldots\ldots, A_{m,r}$ are zero.

The simplest cases are

(i)   that in which the integral has a logarithmic infinity but no algebraic infinity; and

(ii)  that in which the integral has no logarithmic infinity.

For the former, $w'$ is of the form $\dfrac{W(w, z)}{(z - c)\dfrac{\partial f}{\partial w}}$, and therefore in the vicinity of $c_r$

we have
$$w' = \frac{A_{1,r}}{z - c_r} + P(z - c_r),$$

the value of $A_{1,r}$ being $\dfrac{W(k_r, c_r)}{\dfrac{\partial f}{\partial k_r}}$, and $W$ is an integral function of $k_r$, of degree not higher than $n - 2$. Hence

$$\sum_{r=1}^{n} A_{1,r} = \sum_{r=1}^{n} \frac{W(k_r, c_r)}{\dfrac{\partial f}{\partial k_r}}$$

$$= \sum_{r=1}^{n} \frac{W(k_r, c)}{\dfrac{\partial f}{\partial k_r}},$$

since $c$ is the common arithmetical value of the quantities $c_1$, $c_2$, ..., $c_n$. Now $k_1$, $k_2$, ..., $k_n$ are the roots of

$$f(w, c) = 0,$$

an equation of degree $n$, while $W$ is of degree not higher than $n - 2$; hence, by a known theorem*,

$$\sum_{r=1}^{n} \frac{W(k_r, c)}{\dfrac{\partial f}{\partial k_r}} = 0,$$

so that

$$\sum_{r=1}^{n} A_{1,r} = 0.$$

The validity of the result is not affected if some of the coefficients $A$ vanish. But it is evident that a single coefficient $A$ cannot be the only non-vanishing coefficient; and that, if all but two vanish, those two are equal and opposite.

This result applies to all those accidental singularities of coefficients of powers of $w$ in the numerator of $w'$ which, being of the first order, give rise solely to logarithmic infinities in the integral of $w'$. It is of great importance in regard to moduli of periodicity of the integral.

(ii) The other simple case is that in which each of the coefficients $A_{1,r}$ vanishes, so that the integral of $w'$ has only an algebraic infinity at the point $c_r$, which is then an accidental singularity of order less by unity than its order for $w'$.

In particular, if in the vicinity of $c_r$, the form of $w'$ be

$$\frac{A_{2,r}}{(z - c_r)^2} + P(z - c_r),$$

the integral has an accidental singularity of the first order.

It is easy to prove that

$$\sum_{r=1}^{n} A_{2,r} = 0,$$

so that a single coefficient $A$ cannot be the only non-vanishing coefficient; but the result is of less importance than in the preceding case, for all the moduli of periodicity of the integral at the cross-cuts for these points vanish. And it must be remembered that, in order to obtain the subject of integration in this form, some terms have been removed in § 200, the integral of which would give rise to infinities for either finite or infinite values of $z$.

It may happen that all the coefficients of powers of $w$ in the numerator of $w'$ are integral functions of $z$. Then $z = \infty$ is their only accidental singularity; this value has already been taken into account.

---

* Burnside and Panton, *Theory of Equations*, (7th ed.) vol. i, p. 172.

**203.**  The remaining source of infinities of $w'$, as giving rise to possible infinities of the integral, is constituted by the aggregate of the zeros of $\dfrac{\partial f}{\partial w} = 0$.  Such points are the simultaneous roots of the equations

$$\frac{\partial f}{\partial w} = 0, \quad f(w, z) = 0.$$

In addition to the assumption already made that $f = 0$ is the equation of a generalised curve of the $n$th order, we shall make the further assumptions that all the singular points on it are simple, that is, such that there are only two tangents at the point, either distinct or coincident, and that all the branch-points are simple.

The results of § 98 may now be used.  The total number of the points given as simultaneous roots is $n(n-1)$: the form of the integral in the immediate vicinity of each of the points must be investigated.

Let $(c, \gamma)$ be one of these points on the Riemann's surface, and let $(c + \zeta, \gamma + v)$ be any point in its immediate vicinity.

I.  If $\dfrac{\partial f(w, z)}{\partial z}$ do not vanish at the point, then $(c, \gamma)$ is a branch-point for the function $w$.  We then have

$$f(w, z) = A'\zeta + B'v^2 + \text{quantities of higher dimensions,}$$

for points in the vicinity of $(c, \gamma)$, so that $v \propto \zeta^{\frac{1}{2}}$ when $|\zeta|$ is sufficiently small.  Then

$$\frac{\partial f}{\partial w} = 2B'v + \text{quantities of higher dimensions}$$

$$\propto \zeta^{\frac{1}{2}},$$

when $|\zeta|$ is sufficiently small.  Hence, for such values, the subject of integration is a constant multiple of

$$\frac{U(\gamma, c) + \text{positive integral powers of } v \text{ and } \zeta}{\zeta^{\frac{1}{2}} + \text{powers of } \zeta \text{ with index} > \tfrac{1}{2}},$$

that is, of $\zeta^{-\frac{1}{2}}$, when $|\zeta|$ is sufficiently small.  The integral is therefore a constant multiple of $\zeta^{\frac{1}{2}}$, when $|\zeta|$ is sufficiently small; and its value is therefore zero round the point, which is a branch-point for the function represented by the integral.

II.  If $\dfrac{\partial f(w, z)}{\partial z}$ vanish at the point, we have (with the assumptions of § 98),

$$f(w, z) = A\zeta^2 + 2B\zeta v + Cv^2 + \text{terms of the third and higher degrees;}$$

and there are two cases.

(i)  If $B^2 \gtreqless AC$, the point is not a branch-point, and we have

$$Cv + B\zeta = \zeta(B^2 - AC)^{\frac{1}{2}} + \text{integral powers } \zeta^2, \zeta^3, \ldots$$

as the relation between $v$ and $\zeta$ deduced from $f = 0$.   Then

$$\frac{\partial f}{\partial w} = 2\,(B\zeta + Cv) + \text{terms of second and higher degrees}$$

$$= \lambda\zeta + \text{higher powers of } \zeta.$$

In the vicinity of $(c, \gamma)$, the subject of integration is

$$\frac{U(\gamma, c) + Dv + E\zeta + \text{positive integral powers}}{\lambda\zeta + \text{higher powers of } \zeta}.$$

Hence when it is integrated, the first term is $\dfrac{U(\gamma, c)}{\lambda} \log \zeta$, and the remaining terms are positive integral powers of $\zeta$: that is, such a point is a logarithmic infinity for the integral, unless $U(\gamma, c)$ vanish.

If, then, we seek integrals which have not the point for a logarithmic infinity and we begin with $U$ as the most general function possible, we can prevent the point from being a logarithmic infinity by choosing among the arbitrary constants in $U$ a relation such that

$$U(\gamma, c) = 0.$$

There are $\delta$ such points (§ 98); and therefore $\delta$ relations among the constants in the coefficients of $U$ must be chosen, in order to prevent the integral

$$\int \frac{U(w, z)}{\dfrac{\partial f}{\partial w}}\, dz$$

from having a logarithmic infinity at these points.   When these are chosen, the points become ordinary points of the integral.

(ii)   If $B^2 = AC$, the point is a branch-point; we have

$$B\zeta + Cv = \tfrac{1}{2}L\zeta^{\frac{3}{2}} + M\zeta^2 + N\zeta^{\frac{5}{2}} + \dots$$

as the relation between $\zeta$ and $v$ deduced from $f = 0$.   In that case,

$$\frac{\partial f}{\partial w} = 2\,(B\zeta + Cv) + \text{terms of the second and higher degrees}$$

$$= L\zeta^{\frac{3}{2}} + \text{powers of } \zeta \text{ having indices} > \tfrac{3}{2}.$$

In the vicinity of $(c, \gamma)$, the subject of integration is

$$\frac{U(\gamma, c) + Dv + E\zeta + \text{higher powers}}{L\zeta^{\frac{3}{2}} + \text{higher powers of } \zeta}.$$

Hence when it is integrated, the first term is $-\,2\,\dfrac{U(\gamma, c)}{L}\,\zeta^{-\frac{1}{2}}$, and it can be proved that there is no logarithmic term; the point is an infinity for the integral, unless $U(\gamma, c)$ vanish.

If, however, among the arbitrary constants in $U$ we choose a relation such that

$$U(\gamma, c) = 0,$$

then the numerator of the subject of integration

$$= Dv + E\zeta + \text{higher positive powers}$$
$$= \lambda'\zeta + \mu'\zeta^{\frac{3}{2}} + \text{higher powers of } \zeta,$$

on substituting from the relation between $v$ and $\zeta$ derived from the fundamental equation. The subject of integration then is

$$\frac{\lambda'\zeta + \mu'\zeta^{\frac{3}{2}} + \ldots}{L\zeta^{\frac{3}{2}} + M\zeta^2 + \ldots},$$

that is,

$$\frac{\lambda' + \mu'\zeta^{\frac{1}{2}} + \ldots}{L\zeta^{\frac{1}{2}} + M\zeta + \ldots},$$

the integral of which is

$$2\frac{\lambda'}{L}\zeta^{\frac{1}{2}} + \text{positive powers.}$$

The integral therefore vanishes at the point: and the point is a branch-point for the integral. It therefore follows that we can prevent the point from being an infinity for the function by choosing among the arbitrary constants in $U$ a relation such that

$$U(\gamma, c) = 0.$$

There are $\kappa$ such points (§ 98): and therefore $\kappa$ relations among the constants in the coefficients of $U$ are chosen in order to prevent the integral from becoming infinite at these points. Each of the points is a branch-point of the integral.

**204.** All the possible sources of infinite values of the subject of integration $w', = \dfrac{U(w, z)}{\dfrac{\partial f}{\partial w}}$, have now been considered. A summary of the preceding results leads to the following conclusions relative to $\int w' dz$ :—

(i) an ordinary point of $w'$ is an ordinary point of the integral:

(ii) for infinite values of $z$, the integral vanishes if we assign proper limitations to the form of $U(w, z)$:

(iii) accidental singularities of the coefficients of powers of $w$ in $U(w, z)$ are infinities, either algebraic or logarithmic or both algebraic and logarithmic, of the integral:

(iv) if the coefficients of powers of $w$ in $U(w, z)$ have no accidental singularities except for $z = \infty$, then the integral is finite for infinite values of $z$ (and of $w$) when $U(w, z)$ is the most general rational integral function of $w$ and $z$ of degree $n-3$; but, if the coefficients of powers of $w$ in $U(w, z)$ have an accidental singularity of order $\mu$, then the integral will be finite for infinite values of $z$ (and of $w$) when $U(w, z)$ is the most general rational integral function of $w$ and $z$, the degree in $w$ being not greater than $n-2$ and the dimensions in $w$ and $z$ combined being not greater than $n + \mu - 3$:

(v)　those points, at which $\partial f / \partial w$ vanishes and which are not branch-points of the function, can be made ordinary points of the integral, if we assign proper relations among the constants occurring in $U(w, z)$:

(vi)　those points, at which $\partial f / \partial w$ vanishes and which are branch-points of the function, can, if necessary, be made to furnish zero values of the integral by assigning limitations to the form of $U(w, z)$; each such point is a branch-point of the integral in any case.

These conclusions enable us to select the simplest and most important classes of integrals of uniform functions of position on a Riemann's surface.

**205.** The first class consists of those integrals which do not acquire* an infinite value at any point; they are called integrals of the *first kind*†.

The integrals, considered in the preceding investigations, can give rise to integrals of the first kind, if the numerator $U(w, z)$ of the subject of integration satisfy various conditions. The function $U(w, z)$ must be a polynomial function of dimensions not higher than $n-3$ in $w$ and $z$, in order that the integral may be finite for infinite values of $z$ and for all finite values of $z$ not specially connected with the equation $f(w, z) = 0$; for certain points specially connected with the fundamental equation, being $\delta + \kappa$ in number, the value of $U(w, z)$ must vanish, so that there must be $\delta + \kappa$ relations among its coefficients. But when these conditions are satisfied, then the integral function is everywhere finite, it being remembered that certain limitations on the nature of $f(w, z) = 0$ have been made.

Usually these conditions do not determine $U(w, z)$ uniquely save as to a constant factor; and therefore in the most general integral of the first kind a number of independent arbitrary constants will occur, left undetermined by the conditions to which $U$ is subjected. Each of these constants multiplies an integral which, everywhere finite, is different from the other integrals so multiplied; and therefore the number of different integrals of the first kind

---

* They will be seen to be multiform functions even on the multiply connected Riemann's surface, and they do not therefore give rise to any violation of the theorem of § 40.

† The German title is *erster Gattung*; and similarly for the integrals of the second kind and the third kind.

is equal to the number of arbitrary independent constants, left undetermined in $U$. It is evident that any linear combination of these integrals, with constant coefficients, is also an integral of the first kind; and therefore a certain amount of modification of form among the integrals, after they have been obtained, is possible.

The number of these integrals, linearly independent of one another, is easily found. Because $U$ is a polynomial function of $w$ and $z$ of dimensions $n-3$, it contains $\frac{1}{2}(n-1)(n-2)$ terms in its most general form; but its coefficients satisfy $\delta + \kappa$ relations, and these are all the relations that they need satisfy. Hence the number of undetermined and independent constants which it contains is

$$\tfrac{1}{2}(n-1)(n-2) - \delta - \kappa,$$

which, by § 182, is the genus $p$ of the Riemann's surface; and therefore, for the present case, *the number of integrals, which are finite everywhere on the surface and are linearly independent of one another, is equal to the genus of the Riemann's surface.*

Moreover, the integral of the first kind has the same branch-points as the function $w$. Though the integral is finite everywhere on the surface, yet its derivative $w'$ is not so : the infinities of $w'$ are the branch-points

The result has been obtained on the original suppositions of § 98, which were, that all the singular points of the generalised curve $f(w, z) = 0$ are simple, that is, only two tangents (distinct or coincident) to the curve can be drawn at each such point, and that all the branch-points are simple. Other special cases could be similarly investigated. But it is superfluous to carry out the investigation for a succession of cases, because the result just obtained, and the result of § 201, are merely particular instances of a general theorem which will be proved in Chapter XVIII., viz., that, *associated with a Riemann's surface of connectivity $2p + 1$, there are $p$ linearly independent integrals of the first kind which are finite everywhere on the surface.*

The function $U(w, z)$, which occurs in the subject of integration in an integral of the first kind, is often called an *adjoint* polynomial of order $n-3$; and the generalised curve

$$U(w, z) = 0$$

is called an *adjoint* curve of order $n-3$.

**206.** The functions, which thus arise out of the integral of an algebraic function and are finite everywhere, are not uniform functions of position on the unresolved surface. If the surface be resolved by $2p$ cross-cuts into one that is simply connected, then the function is finite, continuous and uniform everywhere in that resolved surface, which is limited by the cross-cuts as a single boundary. But at any point on a cross-cut, the integral, at the two points on opposite edges, has values that differ by any integer multiple of the modulus of the function for that cross cut (and possibly also by integer multiples of the moduli of the function for the other cross-cuts).

Let the cross-cuts be taken as in § 181; and for an integral of the first kind, say $W$, let the moduli of periodicity for the cross-cuts be

$$\omega_1, \omega_2, \dots, \omega_p, \text{ for } a_1, a_2, \dots, a_p,$$

and

$$\omega_{p+1}, \omega_{p+2}, \dots, \omega_{2p}, \text{ for } b_1, b_2, \dots, b_p,$$

respectively; the moduli for the portions of cross-cuts $c_2, c_3, \dots, c_p$ have been proved to be zero.

Some of these moduli may vanish; but it will be proved later (§ 231) that all the moduli for the cross-cuts $a$, or all the moduli for the cross-cuts $b$, cannot vanish unless the integral is a mere constant. In the general case, with which we are concerned, we may assume that they do not vanish; and so it follows that, *if $W$ be a value of an integral of the first kind at any point on the Riemann's surface, all its values at that point are of the form*

$$W + \sum_{r=1}^{2p} m_r \omega_r,$$

*where the coefficients $m$ are integers.*

The foregoing functions, arising through integrals that are finite everywhere on the surface, will be found the most important from the point of view of Abelian transcendents: but other classes arise, having infinities on the surface, and it is important to indicate their general nature before passing to the proof of the Existence-Theorem.

**207.** First, consider an integral which has algebraic, but not logarithmic, infinities. Taking the subject of integration, as in the preceding case, to be the most general possible so that arbitrary coefficients enter, we can, by assigning suitable relations among these coefficients, prevent any of the points, given as zeros of $\dfrac{\partial f}{\partial w} = 0$, from being infinities of the integral. It follows that then the only infinities of the integral will be the points that are accidental singularities of coefficients of powers of $w$ in the numerator of the general expression for $w'$. These singularities must each be of the second order at least: and, in the expansion of $w'$ in the vicinity of each of them, there must be no term of index $-1$, for it is the index that leads, on integration, to a logarithm.

Such integrals are called integrals of the *second kind*.

The simplest integral of the second kind has an infinity for only a single point on the surface, and the infinity is of the first order only: the integral is then called an *elementary integral of the second kind*. After what has been proved in § 202 (ii), it is evident that an elementary integral of the second kind cannot occur in connection with the equation $f(w, z) = 0$, unless the term $h_0(z)$ of § 200 be retained in the expression for $w'$.

*Ex.* 1.  Adopting the subject of integration obtained in § 200, we have

$$w' - \frac{1}{n} h_0(z) = \frac{U(w, z)}{\frac{\partial f}{\partial w}},$$

where $U$ is of the character considered in the preceding sections, viz., it is of degree $n - 2$ in $w$; various forms of $w'$ lead to various forms of $h_0(z)$ and of $U(w, z)$.

If $\frac{1}{n} h_0(z) = \frac{-1}{(z - c)^2}$, and if $c$ be not a singularity of the coefficient of any power of $w$ in $U$, it is then evident that

$$\int w' dz = \frac{1}{z - c} + \int \frac{U(w, z)}{\frac{\partial f}{\partial w}} dz;$$

and the integral on the right-hand side can by choice among the constants be made an integral of the first kind. The integral is not, however, an elementary integral of the second kind, because $z = c$ is an infinity in each sheet.

*Ex.* 2.  A special integral of the second kind occurs, when we take an accidental singularity, say $z = c$, of the coefficient of some power of $w$ in $U(w, z)$ and we neglect $h_0(z)$; so that, in effect, the subject of integration $w'$ is limited to the form

$$\frac{U(w, z)}{\frac{\partial f}{\partial w}},$$

$U$ being of degree not higher than $n - 2$ in $w$. To the value $z = c$, there correspond $n$ points in the various sheets; if, in the immediate vicinity of any one of the points, $w'$ be of the form

$$\frac{-A_r}{(z - c_r)^2} + P'(z - c_r),$$

in that vicinity the integral is of the form

$$\frac{A_r}{z - c_r} + P(z - c_r).$$

For such an integral the sum of the coefficients $A_r$ is zero: the simplest case arises when all but two, say $A_1$ and $A_2$, of these vanish. The integral is then of the form

$$\frac{A}{z - c_1} + P_1(z - c_1)$$

in the vicinity of $c_1$, and of the form

$$\frac{-A}{z - c_2} + P_2(z - c_2)$$

in the vicinity of $c_2$. But the integral is not an elementary integral of the second kind.

**208.**  To find the general value of an integral of the second kind, all the arithmetically infinite' points would be excluded from the Riemann's surface by small curves: and the surface would be resolved into one that is simply connected. The cross-cuts necessary for this purpose would consist of the set of $2p$ cross-cuts, necessary to resolve the surface as for an integral of the first kind, and of the $k$ additional cross-cuts in relation with the curves excluding the algebraically infinite points.

Let the moduli for the former cross-cuts be

$$\epsilon_1, \epsilon_2, \ldots, \epsilon_p, \text{ for the cuts } a_1, a_2, \ldots, a_p,$$

$$\epsilon_{p+1}, \epsilon_{p+2}, \ldots, \epsilon_{2p} \text{ for the cuts } b_1, b_2, \ldots, b_p, \text{ respectively}:$$

the moduli for the cuts $c$ are zero. It is evident from the form of the integral in the vicinity of any infinite point that, as the integral has only an algebraic infinity, the *modulus for each of the $k$ cross-cuts, obtained by a curve from one edge to the other round the point, is zero*. Hence if one value of the integral of the second kind at a point on the surface be $E(z)$, all its values at that point are included in the form

$$E(z) + \sum_{r=1}^{2p} n_r \epsilon_r,$$

where $n_1, n_2, \ldots, n_{2p}$ are integers.

The importance of the elementary integral of the second kind, independently of its simplicity, is that *it is determined by its infinity, save as to an additive integral of the first kind*.

Let $E_1(z)$ and $E_2(z)$ be two elementary integrals of the second kind, having their single infinity common, and let $a$ be the value of $z$ at this point; then in its vicinity we have

$$E_1(z) = \frac{A_1}{z-a} + P_1(z-a), \qquad E_2(z) = \frac{A_2}{z-a} + P_2(z-a),$$

and therefore $A_1 E_2(z) - A_2 E_1(z)$ is finite at $z = a$. This new function is therefore finite over the whole Riemann's surface: hence it is an integral of the first kind, the moduli of periodicity of which depend upon those of $E_1(z)$ and $E_2(z)$.

*Ex.* It may similarly be proved that for the special case in Ex. 2, § 207, when the integral of the second kind has two simple infinities for the same arithmetical value of $z$ in different sheets, the integral is determinate save as to an additive integral of the first kind.

Let $a_1$ and $a_2$ be the two points for the arithmetical value $a$ of $z$; and let $F(z)$ and $G(z)$ be two integrals of the second kind above indicated having simple infinities at $a_1$ and $a_2$ and nowhere else.

Then in the vicinity of $a_1$ we have

$$F(z) = \frac{A}{z-a_1} + P_1(z-a_1), \qquad G(z) = \frac{B}{z-a_1} + Q_1(z-a_1),$$

so that $BF(z) - AG(z)$ is finite in the vicinity of $a_1$.

Again, in the vicinity of $a_2$, we have, by § 202,

$$F(z) = \frac{-A}{z-a_2} + P_2(z-a_2), \qquad G(z) = \frac{-B}{z-a_2} + Q_2(z-a_2),$$

so that $BF(z) - AG(z)$ is finite in the vicinity of $a_2$ also. Hence $BF(z) - AG(z)$ is finite over the whole surface, and it is therefore an integral of the first kind; which proves the statement.

It therefore appears that, if $F(z)$ be any such integral, every other integral of the same nature at those points is of the form $F(z) + W$, where $W$ is an integral of the first kind. Now there are $p$ linearly independent integrals of the first kind : it therefore follows that there are $p + 1$ linearly independent integrals of the second kind, which have simple infinities with equal and opposite residues at two points, (and at only two points), determined by one algebraical value of $z$.

From the property that an elementary integral of the second kind is determined by its infinity save as to an additive integral of the first kind, we infer that *there are $p + 1$ linearly independent elementary integrals of the second kind with the same single infinity on the Riemann's surface.*

This result can be established in connection with $f(w, z) = 0$ as follows. The subject of integration is

$$\frac{U(w, z)}{(z - a)^2 \dfrac{\partial f}{\partial w}},$$

where for simplicity it is assumed that $a$ is neither a branch-point of the function nor a singular point of the curve $f(w, z) = 0$, and in the present case $U$ is of degree $n - 1$ in $w$. To ensure that the integral vanishes for $z = \infty$, the dimensions of $U(w, z)$ may not be greater than $n - 1$. Hence $U(w, z)$, in its most general form, is a polynomial function of $w$ and $z$ of degree $n - 1$; the total number of terms is therefore $\frac{1}{2} n (n + 1)$, which is also the total number of arbitrary constants.

In order that the integral may not be infinite at each of the $\delta + \kappa$ singularities of the curve $f(w, z) = 0$, a relation $U(\gamma, c) = 0$ must be satisfied at each of them; hence, on this score, there are $\delta + \kappa$ relations among the arbitrary constants.

Let the points on the surface given by the arithmetical value $a$ of $z$ be $(a_1, a_1)$, $(a_2, a_2)$, ..., $(a_n, a_n)$. The integral is to be infinite at only one of them; so that we must have

$$U(a_r, a_r) = 0,$$

for $r = 2, 3, ..., n$; and $n - 1$ is the greatest number of such points for which $U$ can vanish, unless it vanish for all, and then there would be no algebraic infinity. Hence, on this score, there are $n - 1$ relations among the arbitrary constants in $U$.

In the vicinity of $z = a$, $w = a$, let

$$z = a + \zeta, \qquad w = a + v;$$

then we have

$$0 = v \frac{\partial f}{\partial a} + \zeta \frac{\partial f}{\partial a} + \cdots,$$

where $\dfrac{\partial f}{\partial a}$ is the value of $\dfrac{\partial f}{\partial w}$, and $\dfrac{\partial f}{\partial a}$ that of $\dfrac{\partial f}{\partial z}$, for $z = a$ and $w = a$. For sufficiently small values of $|v|$ and $|\zeta|$, we may take

$$0 = v \frac{\partial f}{\partial a} + \zeta \frac{\partial f}{\partial a}.$$

For such points we have

$$U(w, z) = U(a, a) + v \frac{\partial U}{\partial a} + \zeta \frac{\partial U}{\partial a} + \cdots$$

$$= U(a, a) + \frac{\zeta}{\dfrac{\partial f}{\partial a}} \frac{\partial (f, U)}{\partial (a, a)} + \cdots,$$

and

$$\frac{\partial f}{\partial w} = \frac{\partial f}{\partial a} + \frac{\zeta}{\dfrac{\partial f}{\partial a}} \frac{\partial \left( f, \dfrac{\partial f}{\partial a} \right)}{\partial (a, a)} + \cdots.$$

Then unless
$$\frac{1}{U(a, a)} \frac{\partial (f, U)}{\partial (a, a)} = \frac{1}{\frac{\partial f}{\partial a}} \frac{\partial \left(f, \frac{\partial f}{\partial a}\right)}{\partial (a, a)}$$

for $(a_1, a_1)$, and
$$\frac{\partial (f, U)}{\partial (a, a)} = 0$$

for $(a_2, a_2)$, $(a_3, a_3)$, ..., $(a_n, a_n)$, there will be terms in $\frac{1}{\zeta}$ in the expansion of the subject of integration in the vicinity of the respective points, and consequently there will be logarithmic infinities in the integral. Such infinities are to be excluded; and therefore their coefficients, being the residues, must vanish, so that, on this score, there appear to be $n$ relations among the arbitrary constants in $U$. But, as in § 210, the sum of the residues for any point is zero: and therefore, when $n-1$ of them vanish, the remaining residue also vanishes. Hence, from this cause, there are only $n-1$ relations among the arbitrary constants in $U$.

The tale of independent arbitrary constants in $U(w, z)$, remaining after all the conditions are satisfied, is
$$\tfrac{1}{2} n (n+1) - (\delta + \kappa) - (n-1) - (n-1)$$
$$= p + 1.$$

As each constant determines an integral, the inference is that there are $p+1$ linearly independent elementary integrals of the second kind with a common infinity.

**209.** Next, consider integrals which have logarithmic infinities, independently of or as well as algebraic infinities. They are called integrals of the *third kind*. As in the case of integrals of the first kind and the second kind, we take the subject of integration to be as general as possible so that it contains arbitrary coefficients; and we assign suitable relations among the coefficients to prevent any of the points, given as zeros of $\partial f/\partial w$, from becoming infinities of the integral. It follows that the only infinities of the integral are accidental singularities of coefficients of powers of $w$ in the numerator of the general expression for $w'$; and that, when $w'$ is expanded for points in the immediate vicinity of such an expression, the term with index $-1$ must occur.

To find the general value of an integral of the third kind, we should first exclude from the Riemann's surface all the infinite points, say
$$l_1, l_2, \ldots, l_\mu,$$
by small curves; the surface would then have to be resolved into one that is simply connected. The cross-cuts for this purpose would consist of the set of $2p$ cross-cuts, necessary to resolve the surface for an integral of the first kind, and of the additional cross-cuts, $\mu$ in number and drawn from the boundary (taken at some ordinary point of the integral) to the small curves that surround the infinities of the function.

The moduli for the former set may be denoted by
$$\varpi_1, \varpi_2, \ldots, \varpi_p \text{ for the cuts } a_1, a_2, \ldots, a_p,$$
and $\qquad \varpi_{p+1}, \varpi_{p+2}, \ldots, \varpi_{2p}$ for the cuts $b_1, b_2, \ldots, b_p$ respectively;

they are zero for the cuts $c$.   Taking the integral from one edge to the other
of any one of the remaining cross-cuts $l_1, l_2, ..., l_q$, (where $l_q$ is the cross-cut
drawn from the curve surrounding $l_q$ to the boundary), its value is given by
the value of the integral round the small curve and therefore it is $2\pi i \lambda_q$,
where the expansion of the subject of integration in the immediate vicinity
of $z = l_q$ is

$$...... + \frac{A_2}{(z-l_q)^2} + \frac{\lambda_q}{z-l_q} + P(z-l_q).$$

Then, if $\Pi$ be any value of the integral of the third kind at a point on the
unresolved Riemann's surface, all its values at the point are included in the
form

$$\Pi + \sum_{r=1}^{2p} m_r \varpi_r + 2\pi i \sum_{q=1}^{\mu} n_q \lambda_q,$$

where the coefficients $m_1, ..., m_{2p}, n_1, ..., n_\mu$ are integers.

**210.**   It can be proved that *the quantities $\lambda_q$ are subject to the relation*

$$\lambda_1 + \lambda_2 + ... + \lambda_\mu = 0.$$

Let the surface be resolved by the complete system of $2p + \mu$ cross-cuts: the
resolved surface is simply connected and has only a single boundary.   The
subject of integration, $w'$, is uniform and continuous over this resolved surface:
it has no infinities in the surface, for its infinities have been excluded; hence

$$\int w' dz = 0,$$

when the integral is taken round the complete boundary of the resolved
surface.

This boundary consists of the double edges of the cross-cuts $a, b, c, L$,
and the small curves round the $\mu$ points $l$; the two edges of the same cross-
cut being described in opposite directions in every instance.

Since the integral is zero and function is finite everywhere along the
boundary, the parts contributed by the portions of the boundary may be considered separately.

First, for any cross-cut, say $a_q$: let $O$ be the point where it is crossed by $b_q$,
and let the positive direction of description of the whole boundary be indicated
by the arrows (fig. 82, § 230).   Then, for the portion $Ca...E$, the part of the
integral is $\int_C^E w' dz$, or, if $Ca...E$ be the negative edge (as in § 196), the part
of the integral may be denoted by

$$\int_C^E w' dz.$$

The part of the integral for the portion $F...aD$, being the positive
edge of the cross-cut, is $\int_F^D w' dz$, which may be denoted by $-\int_D^F w' dz$.   The

course and the range for the latter part are the same as those for the former, and $w'$ is the same on the two edges of the cross-cut; hence the sum of the two is

$$= \int_C^E (w' - w')\, dz,$$

which evidently vanishes[*]. Hence the part contributed to $\int w'dz$ by the two edges of the cross-cut $a_q$ is zero.

Similarly for each of the other cross-cuts $a$, and for each of the cross-cuts $b$, $c$, $L$.

The part contributed to the integral taken along the small curve enclosing $l_q$ is $2\pi i\lambda_q$, for $q = 1, 2, \ldots, \mu$: hence the sum of the parts contributed to the integral by all these small curves is

$$2\pi i \sum_{q=1}^{\mu} \lambda_q.$$

All the other parts vanish, and the integral itself vanishes; hence

$$2\pi i \sum_{q=1}^{\mu} \lambda_q = 0,$$

establishing the result enunciated.

COROLLARY. *An integral of the third kind, that is, having logarithmic infinities on a Riemann's surface, must have at least two logarithmic infinities.*

If it had only one logarithmic infinity, the result just proved would require that $\lambda_1$ should vanish, and the infinity would then be purely algebraic.

**211.** The simplest instance is that in which there are only two logarithmic infinities; their constants are connected by the equation

$$\lambda_1 + \lambda_2 = 0.$$

If, in addition, the infinities be purely logarithmic, so that there are no algebraically infinite terms in the expansion of the integral in the vicinity of either of the points, the integral is then called an *elementary integral of the third kind*. If two points $C_1$ and $C_2$ on the surface be the two infinities, and if they be denoted by assigning the values $c_1$ and $c_2$ to $z$; and if $\lambda_1 = 1 = -\lambda_2$ (as may be assumed, for the assumption only implies division of the integral by a constant factor), the expansion of the subject of integration for points in the vicinity of $c_1$ is

$$\frac{1}{z - c_1} + P_1(z - c_1),$$

---

[*] It vanishes from two independent causes, first through the factor $w' - w'$, and secondly because $z_E = z_C$, the breadth of any cross-cut being infinitesimal.

The same result holds for each of the cross-cuts $a$ and $b$.

For each of the cross-cuts $c$ and $L$, the sum of the parts contributed by opposite edges vanishes only on account of the factor $w' - w'$; in these cases the variable $z$ is not the same for the upper and the lower limit of the integral.

and for points in the vicinity of $c_2$ the expansion is

$$\frac{-1}{z-c_2} + P_2\,(z-c_2).$$

Such an integral may be denoted by $\Pi_{12}$: its modulus, consequent on the logarithmic infinity, is $2\pi i$.

*Ex.* 1.   Prove that, if $\Pi_{12}$, $\Pi_{23}$, $\Pi_{31}$ be three elementary integrals of the third kind having $c_1$, $c_2$; $c_2$, $c_3$; $c_3$, $c_1$ for their respective pairs of points of logarithmic discontinuity, then $\Pi_{12}+\Pi_{23}+\Pi_{31}$ is either an integral of the first kind or a constant.

Clebsch and Gordan pass from this result to a limit in which the points $c_1$ and $c_2$ coincide and obtain an expression for an elementary integral of the second kind in the form of the derivative of $\Pi_{13}$ with regard to $c_1$.   Klein, following Riemann, passes from an elementary integral of the second kind to an elementary integral of the third kind by integrating the former with regard to its parametric point*.

*Ex.* 2.   Reverting again to the integrals connected with the algebraical equation $f(w, z)=0$, when it can be interpreted as the equation of a generalised curve, an integral of the third kind arises when the subject of integration is

$$w' = \frac{V(w,z)}{(z-c)\dfrac{\partial f}{\partial w}},$$

where $V(w, z)$ is of degree $n-2$ in $w$. If $V(w, z)$ be of degree in $z$ not higher than $n-2$, the integral of $w'$ is not infinite for infinite values of $z$; so that $V(w, z)$ is a general integral function of $w$ of degree $n-2$.

Corresponding to the arithmetical value $c$ of $z$, there are $n$ points on the surface, say $(c_1, k_1), (c_2, k_2), ..., (c_n, k_n)$; and the expansion of $w'$ in the vicinity of $(c_r, k_r)$ is

$$\frac{V(k_r, c_r)}{\dfrac{\partial f}{\partial k_r}}\,\frac{1}{z-c_r}+...$$

the coefficients of the infinite terms being subject to the relation

$$\sum_{r=1}^{n}\frac{V(k_r, c_r)}{\dfrac{\partial f}{\partial k_r}}=0,$$

because $V(w, z)$ is only of degree $n-2$ in $w$. The integral of $w'$ will have a logarithmic infinity at each point, unless the corresponding coefficient vanish.

Not more than $n-2$ of these coefficients can be made to vanish, unless they all vanish; and then the integral has no logarithmic infinity.   Let $n-2$ relations, say

$$V(k_r, c_r)=0,$$

for $r=3, 4, ..., n$, be chosen; and let the $\delta+\kappa$ relations be satisfied which secure that the integral is finite at the singularities of the curve $f(w, z)=0$.   Then the integral is an elementary integral of the third kind, having $(c_1, k_1)$ and $(c_2, k_2)$ for its points of logarithmic discontinuity.

*Ex.* 3.   Prove that there are $p+1$ linearly independent elementary integrals of the third kind, having the same logarithmic infinities on the surface.

---

* Clebsch und Gordan, (l.c., p. 408, note), pp. 28—33; Klein-Fricke, *Vorlesungen über die Theorie der elliptischen Modulfunctionen*, t. i, pp. 518—522; Riemann, p. 100.

*Ex.* 4. Shew that, in connection with the fundamental equation

$$w^3 + z^3 = 1,$$

any integral of the first kind is a constant multiple of

$$\int \frac{dz}{w^2};$$

that an integral of the second kind, of the class considered in Ex. 2, § 207, is given by

$$\int \frac{1-w}{z^2 w^2}\, dz;$$

and that an elementary integral of the third kind is given by

$$\int \frac{1-w}{z w^2}\, dz.$$

*Ex.* 5. An elementary (Jacobian) elliptic integral of the third kind occurs in Ex. 7, p. 435; and a (Jacobian) elliptic integral of the second kind occurs in Ex. 8, p. 436.

Shew that an elementary (elliptic) integral of the second kind, associated with the equation

$$w^2 = 4z^3 - g_2 z - g_3,$$

and having its infinity at $(c_1,\ \gamma_1)$, is

$$\int \frac{\gamma_1(w+\gamma_1) + (6c_1^2 - \frac12 g_2)(z-c_1)}{(z-c_1)^2 w}\, dz;$$

and that an elementary (elliptic) integral of the third kind, associated with the same equation and having its two infinities at $(c_1, \gamma_1)$, $(c_2, \gamma_2)$, is

$$\frac12 \int \left( \frac{w+\gamma_1}{z-c_1} - \frac{w+\gamma_2}{z-c_2} \right) \frac{dz}{w}.$$

*Ex.* 6. Construct an elementary integral of the second kind, which is infinite of the first order at $z=0$, $w=1$, the equation between $w$ and $z$ being

$$w^5 + (z-1)(z^2+1)^2 = 0.$$

(Math. Trip., Part II., 1897.)

A sufficient number of particular examples, and also of examples with a limited generality, have been adduced to indicate some of the properties of functions arising, in the first instance, as integrals of multiform functions of a variable $z$ (or as integrals of uniform functions of position on a Riemann's surface). The succeeding investigation establishes, from the most general point of view, the existence of such functions on a Riemann's surface: they will no longer be regarded as defined solely by integrals of multiform functions.